Madame Bovary
Webster's Spanish Thesaurus Edition

for ESL, EFL, ELP, TOFEL®, TOEIC®, and AP® Test Preparation

Gustave Flaubert
Translated by Eleanor Marx-Aveling

ICON CLASSICS

Published by ICON Group International, Inc.
7404 Trade Street
San Diego, CA 92121 USA

www.icongrouponline.com

Madame Bovary: Webster's Spanish Thesaurus Edition for ESL, EFL, ELP, TOFEL®, TOEIC®, and AP®
Test Preparation

This edition published by ICON Classics in 2005
Printed in the United States of America.

ISBN 0-497-25920-6

Contents

iv

PREFACE FROM THE EDITOR

Webster's paperbacks take advantage of the fact that classics are frequently assigned readings in English courses. By using a running English-to-Spanish thesaurus at the bottom of each page, this edition of *Madame Bovary* by Gustave Flaubert was edited for three audiences. The first includes Spanish-speaking students enrolled in an English Language Program (ELP), an English as a Foreign Language (EFL) program, an English as a Second Language Program (ESL), or in a TOEFL® or TOEIC® preparation program. The second audience includes English-speaking students enrolled in bilingual education programs or Spanish speakers enrolled in English speaking schools. The third audience consists of students who are actively building their vocabularies in Spanish in order to take foreign service, translation certification, Advanced Placement® (AP®)[1] or similar examinations. By using the Rosetta Edition® when assigned for an English course, the reader can enrich their vocabulary in anticipation of an examination in Spanish or English.

Webster's edition of this classic is organized to expose the reader to a maximum number of difficult and potentially ambiguous English words. Rare or idiosyncratic words and expressions are given lower priority compared to "difficult, yet commonly used" words. Rather than supply a single translation, many words are translated for a variety of meanings in Spanish, allowing readers to better grasp the ambiguity of English, and avoid them using the notes as a pure translation crutch. Having the reader decipher a word's meaning within context serves to improve vocabulary retention and understanding. Each page covers words not already highlighted on previous pages. If a difficult word is not translated on a page, chances are that it has been translated on a previous page. A more complete glossary of translations is supplied at the end of the book; translations are extracted from Webster's Online Dictionary.

Definitions of remaining terms as well as translations can be found at www.websters-online-dictionary.org. Please send suggestions to websters@icongroupbooks.com

The Editor
Webster's Online Dictionary
www.websters-online-dictionary.org

[1] TOEFL®, TOEIC®, AP® and Advanced Placement® are trademarks of the Educational Testing Service which has neither reviewed nor endorsed this book. All rights reserved.

DEDICATION

To Marie-Antoine-Jules Senard Member of the Paris Bar, Ex-President of the National Assembly, and Former Minister of the Interior Dear and Illustrious Friend,

Permit me to inscribe your name at the head of this book, and above its dedication; for it is to you, before all, that I owe its publication. Reading over your magnificent defence, my work has acquired for myself, as it were, an unexpected authority.

Accept, then, here, the homage of my gratitude, which, how great soever it is, will never attain the height of your eloquence and your devotion.

Gustave Flaubert
Paris, 12 April 1857

PART ONE

CHAPTER ONE

We were in class when the head-master came in, followed by a "new fellow," not wearing the school **uniform**, and a school **servant** carrying a large desk. Those who had been asleep **woke** up, and every one rose as if just surprised at his work.

The head-master made a sign to us to sit down. Then, turning to the class-master, he said to him in a low voice--

"Monsieur Roger, here is a **pupil** whom I **recommend** to your care; he'll be in the second. If his work and conduct are **satisfactory**, he will go into one of the upper classes, as becomes his age."

The "new fellow," standing in the corner behind the door so that he could hardly be seen, was a country **lad** of about fifteen, and taller than any of us. His hair was cut square on his **forehead** like a village chorister's; he looked **reliable**, but very ill at ease. Although he was not **broad**-shouldered, his short school jacket of green **cloth** with black **buttons** must have been **tight** about the arm-holes, and showed at the opening of the cuffs red wrists **accustomed** to being bare. His legs, in blue **stockings**, looked out from beneath yellow **trousers**, drawn tight by **braces**, He wore **stout**, ill-**cleaned**, hob-nailed boots.

We began **repeating** the **lesson**. He **listened** with all his ears, as **attentive** as if at a **sermon**, not **daring** even to cross his legs or lean on his **elbow**; and when at

Spanish

accustomed: acostumbrado.
attentive: atento.
braces: tirantes.
broad-shouldered: ancho de espaldas.
buttons: botones.
cloth: tela, trapo, paño, la tela, mantel, tejido.
daring: atrevido.
elbow: codo, el codo.
forehead: frente, la frente.
lad: muchacho, chico.
lean: apoyarse, fino, magro, enjuto, apoyar, delgado.
lesson: lección.
listened: Escuchado.
pupil: pupila, alumno, pupilo, a alumno.
recommend: recomendar, recomiende, recomiendo, recomendad, recomendáis, recomendamos, recomienda, recomiendan, recomiendan, recomiendas, encarecer.
reliable: fiable, de confianza, seguro.
repeating: repitiendo, repetidor.
satisfactory: satisfactorio.
sermon: sermón.
servant: criado, criada, sirviente, servidor.
stockings: las medias.
stout: obstinado.
tight: apretado, estanco, hermético, tirante, ajustado, denso, estrecho.
trousers: pantalón, pantalones.
uniform: uniforme.
woke: pret de wake, Despertó.

two o'clock the bell rang, the master was obliged to tell him to fall into line with the rest of us.

When we came back to work, we were in the habit of throwing our **caps** on the ground so as to have our hands more free; we used from the door to **toss** them under the form, so that they hit against the wall and made a lot of dust: it was "the thing."

But, whether he had not noticed the trick, or did not dare to attempt it, the "new fellow," was still holding his cap on his knees even after prayers were over. It was one of those head-gears of **composite** order, in which we can find **traces** of the **bearskin, shako, billycock** hat, **sealskin** cap, and cotton night-cap; one of those poor things, in fine, whose **dumb ugliness** has depths of expression, like an imbecile's face. **Oval, stiffened** with **whalebone**, it began with three round knobs; then came in succession lozenges of **velvet** and rabbit-skin separated by a red band; after that a sort of bag that ended in a **cardboard polygon** covered with complicated **braiding**, from which hung, at the end of a long thin **cord**, small twisted gold **threads** in the manner of a **tassel**. The cap was new; its peak **shone**.

"Rise," said the master.

He stood up; his cap fell. The whole class began to laugh. He **stooped** to pick it up. A **neighbor** knocked it down again with his elbow; he picked it up once more.

"Get rid of your helmet," said the master, who was a bit of a **wag**.

There was a burst of laughter from the boys, which so thoroughly put the poor lad out of **countenance** that he did not know whether to keep his cap in his hand, leave it on the ground, or put it on his head. He sat down again and placed it on his knee.

"Rise," repeated the master, "and tell me your name."

The new boy **articulated** in a **stammering** voice an **unintelligible** name.

"Again!"

The same **sputtering** of syllables was heard, **drowned** by the tittering of the class.

Spanish

articulated: articulado.
bearskin: piel de oso.
billycock: hongo.
braiding: trenzado, trenzando.
caps: mayúsculas.
cardboard: cartón.
composite: compuesto.
cord: cuerda, cordón.
countenance: semblante.
drowned: se ahogado, ahogado.
dumb: mudo.
neighbor: vecino, el vecino, la vecina.

oval: ovalado, óvalo, aovado, elipse.
polygon: polígono.
sealskin: piel de foca.
shako: chacó.
shone: brillado, pret y pp de shine.
sputtering: chisporroteo, farfullando, pulverización en vacío.
stammering: balbuceo, tartamudo, estropajoso, balbuciente, tartamudear, tartamudeo, tartamudez, tartamudeando.
stiffened: atiesado, endurecido, se

agarrotado, anquilosado.
stooped: rebajado.
tassel: borla.
threads: hilos.
toss: arrojar, tirada.
traces: trazas.
ugliness: fealdad.
unintelligible: ininteligible, incomprensible.
velvet: terciopelo, el terciopelo.
wag: menear, meneo, mover.
whalebone: ballena.

"Louder!" cried the master; "louder!"

The "new fellow" then took a supreme resolution, opened an **inordinately** large mouth, and shouted at the top of his voice as if calling someone in the word "Charbovari."

A **hubbub** broke out, rose in **crescendo** with **bursts** of **shrill** voices (they **yelled, barked, stamped**, repeated "Charbovari! Charbovari"), then died away into single notes, growing **quieter** only with great difficulty, and now and again suddenly recommencing along the line of a form **whence** rose here and there, like a damp **cracker** going off, a **stifled** laugh.

However, amid a rain of impositions, order was gradually **re**-established in the class; and the master having succeeded in catching the name of "Charles Bovary," having had it **dictated** to him, **spelt** out, and re-read, at once ordered the poor devil to go and sit down on the punishment form at the foot of the master's desk. He got up, but before going hesitated.

"What are you looking for?" asked the master.

"My c-a-p," **timidly** said the "new fellow," **casting** troubled looks round him.

"Five hundred lines for all the class!" shouted in a furious voice stopped, like the Quos ego, a fresh **outburst**. "Silence!" continued the master **indignantly**, **wiping** his brow with his handkerchief, which he had just taken from his cap. "As to you, 'new boy,' you will **conjugate** 'ridiculus sum' twenty times."

Then, in a gentler tone, "Come, you'll find your cap again; it hasn't been stolen."

Quiet was restored. Heads bent over desks, and the "new fellow" remained for two hours in an **exemplary** attitude, although from time to time some paper **pellet** flipped from the tip of a pen came bang in his face. But he wiped his face with one hand and continued **motionless**, his eyes lowered.

In the evening, at preparation, he pulled out his pens from his desk, arranged his small **belongings**, and carefully ruled his paper. We saw him working **conscientiously**, looking up every word in the dictionary, and taking the greatest pains. Thanks, no doubt, to the willingness he showed, he had not to go down to the class below. But though he knew his rules **passably**, he had little finish in composition. It was the cure of his village who had taught him his first Latin; his parents, from motives of economy, having sent him to school as late as possible.

His father, Monsieur Charles Denis Bartolome Bovary, retired assistant-surgeon-major, **compromised** about 1812 in certain **conscription** scandals, and forced at this time to leave the service, had taken advantage of his fine figure to get hold of a **dowry** of sixty thousand francs that offered in the person of a hosier's daughter who had fallen in love with his good looks. A fine man, a great **talker**, making his spurs ring as he walked, wearing **whiskers** that ran into his moustache, his fingers always **garnished** with rings and dressed in loud colours, he had the dash of a military man with the easy go of a commercial traveller.

Once married, he lived for three or four years on his wife's fortune, dining well, rising late, smoking long **porcelain** pipes, not coming in at night till after the theatre, and **haunting** cafes. The father-in-law died, leaving little; he was **indignant** at this, "went in for the business," lost some money in it, then retired to the country, where he thought he would make money.

But, as he knew no more about farming than **calico**, as he rode his horses instead of sending them to plough, drank his **cider** in bottle instead of selling it in **cask**, ate the finest **poultry** in his **farmyard**, and **greased** his hunting-boots with the fat of his pigs, he was not long in finding out that he would do better to give up all speculation.

For two hundred francs a year he managed to live on the border of the provinces of Caux and Picardy, in a kind of place half farm, half private house; and here, **soured**, eaten up with **regrets**, **cursing** his luck, jealous of everyone, he shut himself up at the age of forty-five, sick of men, he said, and determined to live at peace.

His wife had **adored** him once on a time; she had bored him with a thousand servilities that had only **estranged** him the more. Lively once, **expansive** and **affectionate**, in growing older she had become (after the fashion of wine that, exposed to air, turns to **vinegar**) **ill**-tempered, **grumbling**, **irritable**. She had suffered so much without complaint at first, until she had seem him going after

Spanish

adored: adorado.
affectionate: afectuoso, zalamero, mimoso, cariñoso, amante.
calico: calicó.
cask: tonel, barrica, barril, cofre de plomo.
cider: sidra, la sidra.
compromised: Cedido.
conscription: alistamiento.
cursing: maldecir.
dowry: dote.
estranged: alejado, extrañado,

enajenado.
expansive: expansivo.
farmyard: corral.
garnished: aderezó, con guarnición de.
greased: engrasado.
grumbling: barboteo, quejar, quejumbre, refunfuñadura.
haunting: espantar, frecuentar, guarida, inolvidable, obsesionante, obsesionar, perseguir, persistente, rondar.

ill-tempered: de mal genio, mal genio.
indignant: indignado.
irritable: irritable.
passably: bastante, pasablemente, tolerablemente.
porcelain: porcelana.
poultry: aves, aves de corral, pollería.
regrets: lamenta, excusas.
soured: agrió.
talker: hablador.
vinegar: vinagre, el vinagre.
whiskers: patillas, bigotes.

all the village drabs, and until a score of bad houses sent him back to her at night, weary, **stinking** drunk. Then her pride **revolted**. After that she was silent, **burying** her anger in a dumb **stoicism** that she maintained till her death. She was constantly going about looking after business matters. She called on the lawyers, the president, remembered when bills fell due, got them renewed, and at home **ironed**, **sewed**, washed, looked after the workmen, paid the accounts, while he, **troubling** himself about nothing, **eternally besotted** in sleepy **sulkiness**, whence he only **roused** himself to say **disagreeable** things to her, sat smoking by the fire and **spitting** into the cinders.

When she had a child, it had to be sent out to nurse. When he came home, the lad was **spoilt** as if he were a prince. His mother stuffed him with jam; his father let him run about **barefoot**, and, playing the philosopher, even said he might as well go about quite naked like the young of animals. As opposed to the maternal ideas, he had a certain **virile** idea of childhood on which he sought to mould his son, wishing him to be brought up **hardily**, like a Spartan, to give him a strong constitution. He sent him to bed without any fire, taught him to drink off large **draughts** of rum and to **jeer** at religious processions. But, **peaceable** by nature, the lad answered only poorly to his notions. His mother always kept him near her; she cut out cardboard for him, told him tales, entertained him with endless monologues full of **melancholy gaiety** and charming nonsense. In her life's isolation she **centered** on the child's head all her shattered, broken little vanities. She dreamed of high station; she already saw him, tall, handsome, clever, settled as an engineer or in the law. She taught him to read, and even, on an old piano, she had taught him two or three little songs. But to all this Monsieur Bovary, caring little for letters, said, "It was not worth while. Would they ever have the means to send him to a public school, to buy him a practice, or start him in business? Besides, with cheek a man always gets on in the world." Madame Bovary bit her lips, and the child knocked about the village.

He went after the labourers, drove away with clods of earth the **ravens** that were flying about. He ate **blackberries** along the hedges, **minded** the geese with a long switch, went **haymaking** during harvest, ran about in the woods, played

Spanish

barefoot: descalzo.
besotted: atontado, embriagado, entontecido.
blackberries: zarzamoras.
burying: enterrando.
centered: centrado.
disagreeable: desagradable.
draughts: damas, juego de damas.
eternally: eternamente.
gaiety: alegría.
hardily: apenas, robustamente, audazmente, mal, bravamente,

difícilmente, duramente, fuertemente, intrépidamente, nada de eso, resistentemente.
haymaking: henificación.
ironed: planchado.
jeer: injuriar, burla, insultar, abuchear.
melancholy: melancolía, melancólico.
minded: dispuesto.
peaceable: pacífico.
ravens: cuervos.
revolted: rebelado, rebelde.
roused: espoleado, instigado,

animado.
sewed: pret de sew, cosido.
spitting: escupiendo.
spoilt: nulo, pret y pp de spoil, mimado, estropeado, dañado, consentido.
stinking: hediondo.
stoicism: estoicismo.
sulkiness: capricho, resentimiento.
troubling: molestar, atormentador, preocupante.
virile: viril.

hop-scotch under the church **porch** on **rainy** days, and at great **fetes begged** the **beadle** to let him **toll** the bells, that he might hang all his weight on the long rope and feel himself borne **upward** by it in its swing. Meanwhile he grew like an oak; he was strong on hand, fresh of colour.

When he was twelve years old his mother had her own way; he began lessons. The cure took him in hand; but the lessons were so short and irregular that they could not be of much use. They were given at spare moments in the **sacristy**, standing up, **hurriedly**, between a **baptism** and a burial; or else the cure, if he had not to go out, sent for his pupil after the Angelus. They went up to his room and settled down; the flies and moths **fluttered** round the candle. It was close, the child fell asleep, and the good man, beginning to **doze** with his hands on his stomach, was soon **snoring** with his mouth wide open. On other occasions, when Monsieur le Cure, on his way back after **administering** the **viaticum** to some sick person in the neighbourhood, caught sight of Charles playing about the fields, he called him, lectured him for a quarter of an hour and took advantage of the occasion to make him conjugate his verb at the foot of a tree. The rain interrupted them or an **acquaintance** passed. All the same he was always pleased with him, and even said the "young man" had a very good memory.

Charles could not go on like this. Madame Bovary took strong steps. Ashamed, or rather tired out, Monsieur Bovary gave in without a struggle, and they waited one year longer, so that the lad should take his first **communion**.

Six months more passed, and the year after Charles was finally sent to school at Rouen, where his father took him towards the end of October, at the time of the St. Romain fair.

It would now be impossible for any of us to remember anything about him. He was a youth of even **temperament**, who played in **playtime**, worked in school-hours, was attentive in class, slept well in the **dormitory**, and ate well in the **refectory**. He had in **loco** parentis a **wholesale ironmonger** in the Rue Ganterie, who took him out once a month on Sundays after his shop was shut, sent him for a walk on the **quay** to look at the boats, and then brought him back

Spanish

acquaintance: conocido, conocimiento, notoriedad.
administering: administrando.
baptism: bautismo.
beadle: bedel.
begged: Mendigado.
communion: comunión.
dormitory: dormitorio, la residencia universitaria.
doze: dormitar, dormita, dormitas, dormito, dormiten, dormite, dormitamos, dormitáis, dormitad,
dormitan, echar la siesta.
fetes: fiestas.
fluttered: revoloteado.
hurriedly: precipitadamente, apresuradamente.
ironmonger: ferretero, ferretería, de ferretero.
loco: locomotora, Caracol comestible, Concholepas concholepas.
playtime: hora de recreo.
porch: porche, el porche.
quay: muelle, andén.
rainy: lluvioso.
refectory: comedor universitario, comedor, refectorio.
sacristy: sacristía.
snoring: ronquidos.
temperament: temperamento, genio.
toll: peaje, tañer.
upward: hacia arriba, desde abajo hacia arriba, ascendente.
viaticum: viático.
wholesale: al por mayor, venta al por mayor.

to college at seven o'clock before supper. Every Thursday evening he wrote a long letter to his mother with red **ink** and three **wafers**; then he went over his history note-books, or read an old volume of "Anarchasis" that was **knocking** about the study. When he went for walks he talked to the servant, who, like himself, came from the country.

By **dint** of hard work he kept always about the middle of the class; once even he got a certificate in natural history. But at the end of his third year his parents **withdrew** him from the school to make him study medicine, convinced that he could even take his degree by himself.

His mother chose a room for him on the fourth floor of a dyer's she knew, **overlooking** the Eau-de-Robec. She made arrangements for his board, got him furniture, table and two chairs, sent home for an old **cherry**-tree **bedstead**, and bought besides a small **cast**-iron **stove** with the supply of wood that was to warm the poor child.

Then at the end of a week she **departed**, after a thousand injunctions to be good now that he was going to be left to himself.

The **syllabus** that he read on the notice-board **stunned** him; lectures on **anatomy**, lectures on **pathology**, lectures on **physiology**, lectures on **pharmacy**, lectures on **botany** and clinical medicine, and **therapeutics**, without **counting hygiene** and materia medica--all names of whose etymologies he was **ignorant**, and that were to him as so many doors to sanctuaries filled with magnificent darkness.

He understood nothing of it all; it was all very well to listen-- he did not follow. Still he worked; he had bound note-books, he attended all the courses, never missed a single lecture. He did his little daily task like a mill-horse, who goes round and round with his eyes **bandaged**, not knowing what work he is doing.

To spare him expense his mother sent him every week by the carrier a piece of **veal baked** in the **oven**, with which he **lunched** when he came back from the hospital, while he sat **kicking** his feet against the wall. After this he had to run off to lectures, to the operation-room, to the hospital, and return to his home at

Spanish

anatomy: anatomía.
baked: al horno.
bandaged: vendado, venda.
bedstead: camita, armadura de la cama.
botany: botánica.
cast-iron: hierro colado.
cherry-tree: cerezo.
counting: contar, cuenta.
departed: salido, partido.
dint: esfuerzo grande, abolladura, abollar, abollarse, chichón, golpe,

mellar, mella, fuerza, fuerza de.
hygiene: higiene.
ignorant: ignorante.
ink: tinta, la tinta, entintar.
kicking: patear.
knocking: llamar a la puerta, llamada, golpeteo, golpes, golpeo, golpear, golpe, choque, chocar, aldabonazo, topar.
lunched: Almorzado.
oven: horno, estufa, el horno, orno.
overlooking: con vista a.

pathology: patología.
pharmacy: farmacia.
physiology: fisiología.
stove: estufa, la estufa, hornillo.
stunned: aturdido.
syllabus: plan de estudios.
therapeutics: terapéutica, terapéutico.
veal: ternera, carne de ternera, la ternera.
wafers: los barquillos, galletas.
withdrew: pret de withdraw, secretar, retiró.

the other end of the town. In the evening, after the poor dinner of his landlord, he went back to his room and set to work again in his wet clothes, which **smoked** as he sat in front of the hot stove.

On the fine summer evenings, at the time when the close streets are empty, when the servants are playing shuttle-cock at the doors, he opened his window and leaned out. The river, that makes of this quarter of Rouen a **wretched** little Venice, **flowed** beneath him, between the **bridges** and the **railings**, yellow, **violet**, or blue. Working men, **kneeling** on the banks, washed their bare arms in the water. On poles **projecting** from the attics, skeins of cotton were **drying** in the air. Opposite, beyond the roots spread the pure heaven with the red sun setting. How pleasant it must be at home! How fresh under the beech-tree! And he expanded his nostrils to **breathe** in the sweet odours of the country which did not reach him.

He grew thin, his figure became taller, his face took a **saddened** look that made it nearly interesting. Naturally, through **indifference**, he abandoned all the resolutions he had made. Once he missed a lecture; the next day all the lectures; and, enjoying his **idleness**, little by little, he gave up work altogether. He got into the habit of going to the public-house, and had a passion for **dominoes**. To shut himself up every evening in the dirty public room, to push about on marble tables the small sheep bones with black **dots**, seemed to him a fine proof of his freedom, which raised him in his own **esteem**. It was beginning to see life, the **sweetness** of stolen pleasures; and when he entered, he put his hand on the door-handle with a joy almost **sensual**. Then many things hidden within him came out; he learnt couplets by heart and **sang** them to his **boon** companions, became enthusiastic about Beranger, learnt how to make **punch**, and, finally, how to make love.

Thanks to these **preparatory** labours, he failed completely in his examination for an ordinary degree. He was expected home the same night to celebrate his success. He started on foot, stopped at the beginning of the village, sent for his mother, and told her all. She **excused** him, threw the blame of his failure on the **injustice** of the examiners, encouraged him a little, and took upon herself to set

Spanish

boon: bendición, don.
breathe: respirar, respira, respiren, respiras, respiran, respiramos, respirad, respiráis, respire, respiro.
bridges: puentes.
dominoes: el dominó.
dots: Puntos.
drying: secante, secado, desecación.
esteem: estima, estimar, estimación, considerar, contemplar, aprecio, tomar en consideración, respectar, estimado.

excused: excusado, dispensado.
flowed: fluido.
idleness: ociosidad.
indifference: indiferencia.
injustice: injusticia.
kneeling: arrodillar, arrodillarse, estar de rodillas, arrodillado, de rodillas, arrodillando.
preparatory: preparatorio.
projecting: sobresaliente, saliente, saledizo, proyectar.
punch: ponche, perforar, sacabocados,

punzón, puñetazo.
railings: verja, cancela, reja, Enrejado.
saddened: entristecido.
sang: pret de sing, cantó.
sensual: sensual.
smoked: fumado, ahumado, humeado.
sweetness: dulzura.
violet: violeta, morado.
wretched: miserable, menesteroso, pobre, infeliz, necesitado, desdichado.

matters straight. It was only five years later that Monsieur Bovary knew the truth; it was old then, and he accepted it. Moreover, he could not believe that a man born of him could be a fool.

So Charles set to work again and **crammed** for his examination, **ceaselessly** learning all the old questions by heart. He passed pretty well. What a happy day for his mother! They gave a grand dinner.

Where should he go to practice? To Tostes, where there was only one old doctor. For a long time Madame Bovary had been on the look-out for his death, and the old fellow had barely been packed off when Charles was **installed**, opposite his place, as his **successor**.

But it was not everything to have brought up a son, to have had him taught medicine, and discovered Tostes, where he could practice it; he must have a wife. She found him one--the widow of a **bailiff** at Dieppe--who was **forty**-five and had an income of twelve hundred **francs**. Though she was **ugly**, as dry as a bone, her face with as many **pimples** as the spring has buds, Madame Dubuc had no lack of suitors. To **attain** her ends Madame Bovary had to **oust** them all, and she even succeeded in very **cleverly baffling** the intrigues of a port-butcher backed up by the priests.

Charles had seen in marriage the **advent** of an easier life, thinking he would be more free to do as he liked with himself and his money. But his wife was master; he had to say this and not say that in company, to fast every Friday, dress as she liked, **harass** at her **bidding** those patients who did not pay. She opened his letter, watched his comings and goings, and listened at the partition-wall when women came to **consult** him in his surgery.

She must have her chocolate every morning, attentions without end. She constantly complained of her **nerves**, her chest, her liver. The noise of **footsteps** made her ill; when people left her, **solitude** became **odious** to her; if they came back, it was **doubtless** to see her die. When Charles returned in the evening, she stretched forth two long thin arms from beneath the sheets, put them round his neck, and having made him sit down on the edge of the bed, began to talk to him of her **troubles**: he was **neglecting** her, he loved another. She had been warned

---

Spanish

advent: advenimiento, adviento.
attain: alcanzar, alcanza, alcanzad, alcanzáis, alcanzamos, alcanzan, alcanzas, alcanzo, alcancen, alcance, obtener.
baffling: confundiendo.
bailiff: alguacil, administrador.
bidding: licitación.
ceaselessly: continuamente.
cleverly: hábilmente.
consult: consultar, consultas, consultan, consultamos, consultáis,

consultad, consulto, consulten, consulta, consulte.
crammed: Atracado, hasta los topes.
doubtless: indudable.
footsteps: Huellas.
forty-five: cuarenta y cinco, curenta y cinco.
francs: francos.
harass: acosar, acosa, acosad, acosáis, acosamos, acosan, acosas, acosen, acoso, acose, atormentar.
installed: instalado.

neglecting: Descuidar.
nerves: nervios, nervio.
odious: odioso.
oust: expulsar, expulsas, expulsen, expulsan, expulsamos, expulsáis, expulsad, expulsa, expulso, expulse.
pimples: granos, pústulas.
solitude: soledad.
successor: sucesor, descendiente, causahabiente.
troubles: nubes.
ugly: feo.

she would be **unhappy**; and she **ended** by **asking** him for a **dose** of **medicine** and a little more love.

CHAPTER TWO

One night towards **eleven o'clock** they were **awakened** by the **noise** of a horse **pulling** up outside their door. The servant opened the garret-window and **parleyed** for some time with a man in the street below. He came for the doctor, had a letter for him. Natasie came downstairs **shivering** and **undid** the **bars** and **bolts** one after the other. The man left his horse, and, following the servant, suddenly came in behind her. He **pulled** out from his **wool** cap with grey top-knots a letter **wrapped** up in a **rag** and presented it **gingerly** to Charles, who **rested** on his elbow on the **pillow** to read it. Natasie, standing near the bed, held the light. **Madame** in **modesty** had turned to the wall and showed only her back.

This letter, **sealed** with a small seal in blue **wax**, begged Monsieur Bovary to come immediately to the farm of the Bertaux to set a broken leg. Now from Tostes to the Bertaux was a good **eighteen** miles across country by way of Longueville and Saint-Victor. It was a dark night; Madame Bovary **junior** was afraid of **accidents** for her husband. So it was decided the stable-boy should go on first; Charles would start three hours later when the **moon** rose. A boy was to be sent to meet him, and show him the way to the farm, and open the gates for him.

Towards four o'clock in the morning, Charles, well wrapped up in his **cloak**, set out for the Bertaux. Still **sleepy** from the **warmth** of his bed, he let himself be **lulled** by the quiet **trot** of his horse. When it stopped of its own **accord** in front of

Spanish

accidents: accidentes.
accord: acuerdo, acorde, convenio, arreglo, acordar, concordación, permitir, concordar, otorgar.
awakened: despertado.
bars: cerca, impide.
bolts: pernos.
cloak: abrigo, capa.
eighteen: dieciocho, diez y ocho.
eleven: once.
gingerly: cauteloso, cautelosamente.
junior: hijo, menor.

lulled: Calmó.
madame: señora.
modesty: modestia, pudor.
moon: luna, la luna.
noise: ruido, alboroto, el ruido.
o'clock: hora, en punto.
parleyed: debatió.
pillow: almohada, la almohada.
pulled: tirado, halado.
pulling: tirando, halando, tracción.
rag: trapo, andrajo, harapo.
rested: descansado.

sealed: sellado, hermético, estanco.
shivering: tiritar.
sleepy: soñoliento.
trot: trote, trotar.
undid: Deshizo, pret de undo.
warmth: calor moderado, calor.
wax: cera, crema para zapatos, cerumen, crecer, la cera.
wool: lana, la lana.
wrapped: envuelto, arroparse, chal, cubrir, cubrirse, envoltura, envolver, capa, envolverse, ajustado, manta.

those holes surrounded with **thorns** that are **dug** on the margin of furrows, Charles **awoke** with a start, suddenly remembered the broken leg, and tried to call to mind all the **fractures** he knew. The rain had stopped, day was breaking, and on the branches of the **leafless** trees birds roosted motionless, their little feathers bristling in the cold morning wind. The flat country stretched as far as eye could see, and the **tufts** of trees round the farms at long intervals seemed like dark violet **stains** on the cast grey surface, that on the horizon faded into the **gloom** of the sky.

Charles from time to time opened his eyes, his mind grew **weary**, and, sleep coming upon him, he soon fell into a doze **wherein**, his recent sensations **blending** with memories, he became conscious of a double self, at once student and married man, lying in his bed as but now, and crossing the operation theatre as of old. The warm smell of poultices **mingled** in his brain with the fresh **odour** of **dew**; he heard the iron **rings rattling** along the curtain-rods of the bed and saw his wife sleeping. As he passed Vassonville he came upon a boy sitting on the grass at the edge of a **ditch**.

"Are you the doctor?" asked the child.

And on Charles's answer he took his wooden shoes in his hands and ran on in front of him.

The general **practitioner**, riding along, gathered from his guide's talk that Monsieur Rouault must be one of the **well**-to-do farmers.

He had broken his leg the evening before on his way home from a Twelfth-night **feast** at a neighbour's. His wife had been dead for two years. There was with him only his daughter, who helped him to keep house.

The **ruts** were becoming deeper; they were approaching the Bertaux.

The little lad, **slipping** through a hole in the **hedge**, disappeared; then he came back to the end of a **courtyard** to open the gate. The horse slipped on the wet grass; Charles had to **stoop** to pass under the branches. The watchdogs in their **kennels** barked, **dragging** at their **chains**. As he entered the Bertaux, the horse took **fright** and **stumbled**.

Spanish

awoke: pret y pp de awake.
blending: mezcla.
chains: cadenas.
courtyard: patio, grave.
dew: rocío.
ditch: zanja, cuneta, foso.
dragging: arrastrando, remolcando.
dug: cavado.
feast: banquete, fiesta.
fractures: fracturas, las fracturas.
fright: espanto, susto, miedo, angustia, terror.

gloom: oscuridad, melancolía, tristeza.
hedge: seto vivo, seto, cobertura.
kennels: perrera, residencia canina.
leafless: deshojado.
mingled: mezclado, triscado.
odour: olor.
practitioner: practicante.
rattling: zumbar, muy, rápido, vaivén, realmente, estupendo.
rings: timbres, anillos, anillas.
ruts: carriles.
slipping: corrimiento, resbalar.

stains: manchas.
stoop: inclinar, rebajarse, rebajamiento, pequeña veranda, humillarse, inclinado, pórtico, inclinarse, agachado, agachar, agacharse.
stumbled: tropezado.
thorns: espinas.
tufts: copetes.
weary: cansado, fatigado.
well-to-do: acomodado.
wherein: en qué.

It was a substantial-looking farm. In the stables, over the top of the open doors, one could see great cart-horses quietly feeding from new **racks**. Right along the outbuildings extended a large **dunghill**, from which **manure** liquid **oozed**, while amidst fowls and turkeys, five or six peacocks, a luxury in Chauchois farmyards, were **foraging** on the top of it. The **sheepfold** was long, the barn high, with walls smooth as your hand. Under the cart-shed were two large **carts** and four **ploughs**, with their **whips**, shafts and **harnesses** complete, whose **fleeces** of blue wool were getting **soiled** by the fine dust that fell from the granaries. The courtyard **sloped** upwards, planted with trees set out **symmetrically**, and the **chattering** noise of a flock of geese was heard near the pond.

A young woman in a blue **merino** dress with three **flounces** came to the threshold of the door to receive Monsieur Bovary, whom she led to the kitchen, where a large fire was blazing. The servant's breakfast was boiling beside it in small pots of all sizes. Some damp clothes were drying inside the chimney-corner. The **shovel, tongs**, and the **nozzle** of the **bellows**, all of **colossal** size, shone like polished steel, while along the walls hung many pots and pans in which the clear flame of the hearth, **mingling** with the first rays of the sun coming in through the window, was mirrored **fitfully**.

Charles went up the first floor to see the patient. He found him in his bed, sweating under his **bed**-clothes, having thrown his cotton **nightcap** right away from him. He was a fat little man of fifty, with white skin and blue eyes, the forepart of his head bald, and he wore earrings. By his side on a chair stood a large **decanter** of brandy, whence he poured himself a little from time to time to keep up his spirits; but as soon as he caught sight of the doctor his **elation subsided**, and instead of swearing, as he had been doing for the last twelve hours, began to groan freely.

The fracture was a simple one, without any kind of complication.

Charles could not have hoped for an easier case. Then calling to mind the devices of his masters at the bedsides of patients, he comforted the sufferer with all sorts of kindly remarks, those Caresses of the surgeon that are like the oil they

Spanish

bed-clothes: ropa de la cama.
bellows: fuelle, fuelles.
carts: carretillas.
chattering: parlotear, castañetear los dientes, charlar, parloteo, vibrar, charla, vibración.
colossal: colosal.
decanter: garrafa.
dunghill: muladar.
elation: júbilo.
fitfully: irregularmente, espasmódicamente.

fleeces: vellones.
flounces: sacudidas.
foraging: adentrándose.
harnesses: marcos.
manure: estiércol, abono, abonar, estercolar.
merino: merino.
mingling: mezcladura, entremezclar, mezclar, mezclarse, mezclando, triscando.
nightcap: gorro de dormir, sosiega, bebida.

nozzle: tobera, boquilla.
oozed: rezumado.
ploughs: arados.
racks: cremalleras.
sheepfold: aprisco, majada, redil.
shovel: pala.
sloped: atravesado, inclinado.
soiled: sucio.
subsided: menguado, bajado.
symmetrically: simétricamente.
tongs: tenazas.
whips: zurriagar.

put on bistouries. In order to make some **splints** a **bundle** of laths was brought up from the cart-house. Charles selected one, cut it into two pieces and **planed** it with a fragment of windowpane, while the servant **tore** up sheets to make bandages, and **Mademoiselle** Emma tried to **sew** some **pads**. As she was a long time before she found her work-case, her father grew **impatient**; she did not answer, but as she sewed she **pricked** her fingers, which she then put to her mouth to **suck** them. Charles was surprised at the **whiteness** of her **nails**. They were **shiny**, delicate at the tips, more polished than the ivory of Dieppe, and **almond**-shaped. Yet her hand was not beautiful, perhaps not white enough, and a little hard at the knuckles; besides, it was too long, with no soft inflections in the **outlines**. Her real beauty was in her eyes. Although brown, they seemed black because of the lashes, and her look came at you frankly, with a **candid** boldness.

The **bandaging** over, the doctor was invited by Monsieur Rouault himself to "pick a bit" before he left.

Charles went down into the room on the ground floor. **Knives** and **forks** and silver **goblets** were laid for two on a little table at the foot of a huge bed that had a **canopy** of printed cotton with figures representing Turks. There was an odour of iris-root and damp sheets that escaped from a large oak chest opposite the window. On the floor in corners were sacks of flour stuck upright in rows. These were the **overflow** from the neighbouring **granary**, to which three stone steps led. By way of decoration for the apartment, hanging to a nail in the middle of the wall, whose green paint **scaled** off from the effects of the **saltpetre**, was a **crayon** head of Minerva in gold frame, underneath which was written in Gothic letters "To dear Papa."

First they spoke of the patient, then of the weather, of the great cold, of the wolves that **infested** the fields at night.

Mademoiselle Rouault did not at all like the country, especially now that she had to look after the farm almost alone. As the room was **chilly**, she **shivered** as she ate. This showed something of her full lips, that she had a habit of **biting** when silent.

Spanish

almond-shaped: almendrado.
bandaging: vendaje.
biting: mordaz, punzante, penetrante.
bundle: bulto, manojo, haz, paquete, mazo.
candid: franco, sincero.
canopy: dosel.
chilly: frío, friolero, friolento.
crayon: lápiz de cera.
forks: bifurcarse, horquillas, tenedor.
goblets: copas.
granary: granero.

impatient: impaciente.
infested: infestado.
knives: cuchillo.
mademoiselle: señorita.
nail: clavo, uña, el clavo, clavar, taco, enclavar.
outlines: contornos.
overflow: desbordamiento, inundación, inundar, desbordar, rebosadero.
pads: botón.
planed: planeado.

pricked: pinchado.
saltpetre: salitre.
scaled: escalado, escamoso.
sew: coser, cosa, cosemos, coso, coses, cosen, cosed, cosan, coséis, cose, pegar.
shiny: brillante.
shivered: tiritado.
splints: tablillas.
suck: chupar, mamar, libar, chupas.
tore: pret de tear, rompió.
whiteness: albura.

Her neck stood out from a white **turned**-down **collar**. Her hair, whose two black folds seemed each of a single piece, so smooth were they, was **parted** in the middle by a **delicate** lie that **curved** slightly with the curve of the head; and, just showing the tip of the ear, it was joined behind in a thick **chignon**, with a **wavy** movement at the **temples** that the country doctor saw now for the first time in his life. The upper part of her **cheek** was rose-coloured. She had, like a man, thrust in between two buttons of her **bodice** a **tortoise**-shell eyeglass.

When Charles, after bidding **farewell** to old Rouault, returned to the room before leaving, he found her standing, her forehead against the window, looking into the garden, where the **bean props** had been knocked down by the wind. She turned round. "Are you looking for anything?" she asked.

"My **whip**, if you please," he answered.

He began **rummaging** on the bed, behind the doors, under the chairs. It had fallen to the floor, between the sacks and the wall. Mademoiselle Emma saw it, and **bent** over the **flour** sacks.

Charles out of **politeness** made a **dash** also, and as he **stretched** out his arm, at the same moment felt his **breast brush** against the back of the young girl **bending** beneath him. She drew herself up, **scarlet**, and looked at him over her shoulder as she handed him his whip.

Instead of returning to the Bertaux in three days as he had promised, he went back the very next day, then regularly twice a week, without counting the visits he paid now and then as if by accident.

Everything, moreover, went well; the patient **progressed favourably**; and when, at the end of **forty**-six days, old Rouault was seen trying to walk alone in his "den," Monsieur Bovary began to be looked upon as a man of great capacity. Old Rouault said that he could not have been **cured** better by the first doctor of Yvetot, or even of Rouen.

As to Charles, he did not stop to ask himself why it was a pleasure to him to go to the Bertaux. Had he done so, he would, no doubt, have **attributed** his **zeal** to the importance of the case, or perhaps to the money he hoped to make by it.

Spanish

attributed: adscrito, Atribuido.
bean: haba, judía, alubia.
bending: flexión, torcimiento.
bent: inclinación, torcido.
bodice: corpiño, cuerpo.
breast: pecho, seno, pechuga, mama.
brush: cepillo, cepillar, escobilla, pincel, brocha, el cepillo.
cheek: mejilla, la mejilla, carrillo.
chignon: moño.
collar: cuello, el cuello, collarín.
cured: curado.

curved: curvo, encorvado.
dash: raya, guión, arremetida, corre.
delicate: delicado, fino.
farewell: adiós, despedida.
favourably: favorablemente.
flour: harina, la harina.
forty-six: cuanrenta y seis, cuarenta y seis, quarenta y seis.
parted: despedido.
politeness: cortesía, educación, atenciones.
progressed: adelantado.

props: attrezzo, propiedades, encargado del atrezo, accesorios.
rummaging: registrando.
scarlet: escarlata.
stretched: estirado.
temples: sienes.
tortoise-shell: carey.
turned-down: deterioro.
wavy: ondulado.
whip: látigo, zurriago, azotar, fustigar, fusta, azote.
zeal: celo, ahínco.

Was it for this, however, that his visits to the farm formed a delightful exception to the **meagre** occupations of his life? On these days he rose early, set off at a **gallop**, **urging** on his horse, then got down to wipe his boots in the grass and put on black **gloves** before entering. He liked going into the courtyard, and **noticing** the gate turn against his shoulder, the **cock crow** on the wall, the lads run to meet him. He liked the granary and the **stables**; he liked old Rouault, who pressed his hand and called him his **saviour**; he like the small wooden shoes of Mademoiselle Emma on the **scoured flags** of the kitchen--her high heels made her a little taller; and when she walked in **front** of him, the wooden soles **springing** up quickly struck with a sharp sound against the leather of her boots.

She always accompanied him to the first step of the stairs. When his horse had not yet been brought round she stayed there. They had said "Good-bye"; there was no more talking. The open air wrapped her round, playing with the soft down on the back of her neck, or blew to and fro on her hips the apron-strings, that fluttered like streamers. Once, during a **thaw** the **bark** of the trees in the yard was **oozing**, the snow on the roofs of the outbuildings was **melting**; she stood on the threshold, and went to fetch her **sunshade** and opened it. The sunshade of silk of the colour of pigeons' breasts, through which the sun shone, **lighted** up with **shifting** hues the white skin of her face. She smiled under the tender warmth, and drops of water could be heard falling one by one on the stretched silk.

During the first period of Charles's visits to the Bertaux, Madame Bovary junior never failed to **inquire** after the **invalid**, and she had even chosen in the book that she kept on a system of double entry a clean blank page for Monsieur Rouault. But when she heard he had a daughter, she began to make inquiries, and she learnt the Mademoiselle Rouault, brought up at the Ursuline Convent, had received what is called "a good education"; and so knew dancing, geography, drawing, how to **embroider** and play the piano. That was the last straw.

Spanish

bark: ladrar, corteza, ladrido, barco, cáscara.
cock: gallo, grifo, pene, pija.
crow: el cuervo, corneja, cuervo.
embroider: bordar, bordad, borden, bordas, bordan, bordáis, bordamos, borda, borde, bordo.
flags: banderas.
fro: atrás, allá.
gallop: galope, galopar.
gloves: guantes, los guantes.
inquire: preguntar, inquirís,

inquieran, inquiere, inquieren, inquieres, inquiero, inquirid, inquirimos, inquiera, inquirir.
invalid: inválido, no válido, nulo.
lighted: encendido.
meagre: corvina, exiguo.
melting: deshielo, fusión, derretirse, fundición.
noticing: notando.
oozing: rezumando.
saviour: salvador, redentor.
scoured: fregado, batido, purgado,

restregado, desgrasado, desengrasado.
shifting: cambiar, desplazamiento, movedizo.
springing: saltar.
stables: establos.
sunshade: quitasol, sombrilla.
thaw: deshielo, deshelar, deshelas, deshelo, deshela, deshelad, desheláis, deshelan, deshele, deshelen, deshelamos.
urging: instar.

"So it is for this," she said to herself, "that his face beams when he goes to see her, and that he puts on his new **waistcoat** at the risk of **spoiling** it with the rain. Ah! that woman! That woman!"

And she **detested** her **instinctively**. At first she solaced herself by allusions that Charles did not understand, then by casual observations that he let pass for fear of a storm, finally by open apostrophes to which he knew not what to answer. "Why did he go back to the Bertaux now that Monsieur Rouault was cured and that these **folks hadn't** paid yet? Ah! it was because a young lady was there, some one who know how to talk, to embroider, to be **witty**. That was what he cared about; he wanted town misses." And she went on--

"The daughter of old Rouault a town miss! Get out! Their grandfather was a shepherd, and they have a cousin who was almost had up at the **assizes** for a nasty blow in a **quarrel**. It is not worth while making such a fuss, or showing herself at church on Sundays in a silk **gown** like a **countess**. Besides, the poor old chap, if it hadn't been for the **colza** last year, would have had much **ado** to pay up his arrears."

For very **weariness** Charles left off going to the Bertaux. Heloise made him swear, his hand on the **prayer**-book, that he would go there no more after much **sobbing** and many **kisses**, in a great outburst of love. He **obeyed** then, but the strength of his desire protested against the **servility** of his conduct; and he thought, with a kind of **naive hypocrisy**, that his **interdict** to see her gave him a sort of right to love her. And then the widow was thin; she had long teeth; wore in all weathers a little black **shawl**, the edge of which hung down between her shoulder-blades; her **bony** figure was **sheathed** in her clothes as if they were a **scabbard**; they were too short, and displayed her **ankles** with the **laces** of her large boots crossed over grey stockings.

Charles's mother came to see them from time to time, but after a few days the **daughter**-in-law seemed to put her own edge on her, and then, like two knives, they **scarified** him with their reflections and observations. It was wrong of him to eat so much.

Spanish

ado: ruido.
ankles: los tobillos.
assizes: Tribunal de Justicia en los Condados de Inglaterra, sesión judicial.
bony: óseo, huesudo.
colza: colza.
countess: condesa.
daughter-in-law: nuera.
detested: detestado.
folks: gente.
gown: vestido, toga.

hadn't: no ha.
hypocrisy: hipocresía.
instinctively: instintivamente.
interdict: quitar, vetar, prohibir, prohibición, privar, oponer, obstaculizar, no proponer, interdecir, entredecir, vedar.
kisses: besos.
laces: cintas.
naive: ingenuo.
obeyed: Obedecido, obedeció.
prayer-book: devocionario.

quarrel: disputar, reñir, riña, pelear.
scabbard: vaina.
scarified: escarificada.
servility: servilismo.
shawl: chal.
sheathed: envainado.
sobbing: sollozar.
spoiling: estropear.
waistcoat: chaleco, el chaleco.
weariness: cansancio, aburrimiento, fatiga.
witty: ingenioso.

Why did he always offer a glass of something to everyone who came? What **obstinacy** not to wear **flannels**! In the spring it came about that a **notary** at Ingouville, the **holder** of the widow Dubuc's property, one fine day went off, taking with him all the money in his office. Heloise, it is true, still possessed, besides a share in a boat **valued** at six thousand francs, her house in the Rue St. Francois; and yet, with all this fortune that had been so trumpeted abroad, nothing, **excepting** perhaps a little furniture and a few clothes, had appeared in the household. The matter had to be gone into. The house at Dieppe was found to be eaten up with **mortgages** to its foundations; what she had placed with the notary God only knew, and her share in the boat did not **exceed** one thousand **crowns**. She had **lied**, the good lady! In his **exasperation**, Monsieur Bovary the elder, **smashing** a chair on the flags, accused his wife of having caused **misfortune** to the son by **harnessing** him to such a **harridan**, whose harness wasn't worth her hide. They came to Tostes. Explanations followed. There were scenes. Heloise in tears, throwing her arms about her husband, **implored** him to defend her from his parents.

Charles tried to speak up for her. They grew angry and left the house.

But "the blow had struck home." A week after, as she was hanging up some washing in her yard, she was seized with a spitting of blood, and the next day, while Charles had his back turned to her drawing the window-curtain, she said, "O God!" gave a **sigh** and **fainted**. She was dead! What a surprise! When all was over at the **cemetery** Charles went home. He found no one downstairs; he went up to the first floor to their room; say her dress still hanging at the foot of the **alcove**; then, leaning against the writing-table, he stayed until the evening, buried in a **sorrowful reverie**. She had loved him after all!

Spanish

alcove: alcoba, nicho.
cemetery: cementerio, el cementerio, campo santo.
crowns: coronas.
exasperation: exasperación.
exceed: aventajar, aventajan, aventajen, aventajo, aventajas, aventajáis, aventajad, aventaja, aventaje, aventajamos, exceder.
excepting: excepto.
fainted: pasmado, desfallecido, amortecido, desmayado.

flannels: pantalones de franela.
harness: arnés, arneses, arreos, aparejar, guarniciones.
harnessing: movilización, enjaezar, captación, arreo.
harridan: anciana, bruja, vieja, vieja bruja.
holder: tenedor, titular, soporte, poseedor, portalámpara.
implored: implorado, suplicado.
lied: Mentido.
misfortune: infortunio, desgracia,

desdicha, desventura.
mortgages: hipotecas.
notary: notario, escribano.
obstinacy: obstinación.
reverie: ensueño.
sigh: suspirar, suspiro.
smashing: aplastante.
sorrowful: afligido, pesaroso.
valued: aprecio, estimado, estimación, apreciado, estimable, estimar, valuado, valorar, valorado, cotizado, valor.

CHAPTER THREE

One morning old Rouault brought Charles the money for setting his leg--seventy-five francs in forty-sou pieces, and a **turkey**. He had heard of his loss, and **consoled** him as well as he could.

"I know what it is," said he, **clapping** him on the shoulder; "I've been through it. When I lost my dear departed, I went into the fields to be quite alone. I fell at the foot of a tree; I **cried**; I called on God; I **talked nonsense** to Him. I wanted to be like the **moles** that I saw on the **branches**, their **insides swarming** with **worms**, dead, and an end of it. And when I thought that there were others at that very moment with their nice little wives holding them in their **embrace**, I **struck** great **blows** on the earth with my **stick**. I was pretty well **mad** with not **eating**; the very idea of going to a **cafe disgusted** me--you wouldn't believe it. Well, quite **softly**, one day following another, a spring on a winter, and an autumn after a summer, this **wore** away, piece by piece, **crumb** by crumb; it passed away, it is gone, I should say it has **sunk**; for something always remains at the bottom as one would say--a weight here, at **one's** heart. But since it is the lot of all of us, one must not give way **altogether**, and, because others have died, want to die too. You must pull yourself together, Monsieur Bovary. It will pass away. Come to see us; my daughter thinks of you now and again, d'ye know, and she says you are **forgetting** her. Spring will soon be here. **We'll** have some rabbit-shooting in the warrens to **amuse** you a bit."

Spanish

altogether: todo, en conjunto.
amuse: divertir, diviértete, diviértase, diviértanse, divértidos, me divierto, nos divertimos, os divertís, se divierte, se divierten, te diviertes.
blows: golpes.
branches: ramas.
cafe: café, cafés.
clapping: aplauso, palmada, aplausos, aplaudir, cerrar de golpe.
consoled: Consolado.
cried: Lloró.

crumb: miga, migaja, la miga.
disgusted: inspirado aversión a, asqueado, disgustado, repugnado.
eating: comiendo.
embrace: abrazar, abarcar.
forgetting: olvidando.
insides: tripas.
mad: loco, enojado, chiflado, majara, majareta, demente, enfadado.
moles: lunares.
nonsense: tontería.
one's: uno, propio.

softly: suavemente.
stick: pegar, palo, bastón.
struck: pret y pp de strike, golpeado.
sunk: hundido, pp de sink.
swarming: hormigueo, hormiguilla, enjambrando, ataque de enjambre, piquiña.
talked: Hablado, charlado.
turkey: pavo, Turquía, el pavo.
we'll: Haremos.
wore: falacia, pret de wear, Llevó.
worms: gusanos.

Charles followed his advice. He went back to the Bertaux. He found all as he had left it, that is to say, as it was five months ago. The **pear** trees were already in **blossom**, and Farmer Rouault, on his legs again, came and went, making the farm more full of life.

Thinking it his duty to **heap** the greatest attention upon the doctor because of his sad position, he begged him not to take his hat off, spoke to him in an **undertone** as if he had been ill, and even **pretended** to be angry because nothing rather lighter had been prepared for him than for the others, such as a little **clotted** cream or **stewed** pears. He told stories. Charles found himself laughing, but the **remembrance** of his wife suddenly coming back to him depressed him. Coffee was brought in; he thought no more about her.

He thought less of her as he grew accustomed to living alone. The new delight of independence soon made his **loneliness bearable**. He could now change his meal-times, go in or out without explanation, and when he was very tired stretch himself at full length on his bed. So he **nursed** and **coddled** himself and accepted the consolations that were offered him. On the other hand, the death of his wife had not served him ill in his business, since for a month people had been saying, "The poor young man! what a loss!" His name had been talked about, his practice had increased; and moreover, he could go to the Bertaux just as he liked. He had an **aimless** hope, and was vaguely happy; he thought himself better looking as he **brushed** his whiskers before the **looking**-glass.

One day he got there about three o'clock. Everybody was in the fields. He went into the kitchen, but did not at once catch sight of Emma; the outside **shutters** were closed. Through the chinks of the wood the sun sent across the **flooring** long fine rays that were broken at the corners of the furniture and **trembled** along the ceiling. Some **flies** on the table were **crawling** up the glasses that had been used, and **buzzing** as they drowned themselves in the **dregs** of the cider. The daylight that came in by the **chimney** made velvet of the **soot** at the back of the **fireplace**, and touched with blue the cold **cinders**. Between the window and the **hearth** Emma was **sewing**; she wore no **fichu**; he could see small drops of **perspiration** on her bare shoulders.

Spanish

aimless: sin objeto.
bearable: soportable.
blossom: flor, florecer, lozanía.
brushed: cepillado.
buzzing: zumbido.
chimney: chimenea, la chimenea.
cinders: cenizas.
clotted: grumoso.
coddled: consentido, mimado.
crawling: arrastre.
dregs: heces.
fichu: pañuelo.

fireplace: chimenea, la chimenea, el hogar, hogar.
flies: vuela.
flooring: embaldosar, puesto, enlosar, fondo del mar, material para pisos, pavimentación, embaldosado, enladrillar, revestimiento del suelo, plan, pisos.
heap: montón, grupo, cúmulo, amontonar, pila.
hearth: hogar, chimenea, crisol.
loneliness: soledad, la soledad.

looking-glass: espejo.
nursed: cuidado.
pear: pera, la pera, peral.
perspiration: sudor, transpiración.
pretended: fingido, pretendido.
remembrance: recuerdo.
sewing: cosiendo, pegando, costura.
shutters: obturadores, obturador.
soot: hollín.
stewed: estofado.
trembled: Temblado, tembló.
undertone: voz baja.

After the fashion of country folks she asked him to have something to drink. He said no; she insisted, and at last **laughingly** offered to have a glass of **liqueur** with him. So she went to **fetch** a bottle of curacao from the **cupboard**, reached down two small glasses, filled one to the **brim**, **poured** scarcely anything into the other, and, after having **clinked** glasses, carried hers to her mouth. As it was almost empty she bent back to drink, her head thrown back, her lips **pouting**, her neck on the strain. She laughed at getting none of it, while with the tip of her tongue passing between her small teeth she **licked** drop by drop the bottom of her glass.

She sat down again and took up her work, a white cotton **stocking** she was **darning**. She worked with her head bent down; she did not speak, nor did Charles. The air coming in under the door **blew** a little dust over the flags; he watched it **drift** along, and heard nothing but the **throbbing** in his head and the faint **clucking** of a **hen** that had laid an egg in the yard. **Emma** from time to time **cooled** her cheeks with the palms of her hands, and cooled these again on the knobs of the huge fire-dogs.

She **complained** of suffering since the beginning of the season from **giddiness**; she asked if sea-baths would do her any good; she began talking of her **convent**, Charles of his school; words came to them. They went up into her bedroom. She showed him her old music-books, the little prizes she had won, and the oak-leaf crowns, left at the bottom of a cupboard. She spoke to him, too, of her mother, of the country, and even showed him the bed in the garden where, on the first Friday of every month, she gathered flowers to put on her mother's **tomb**. But the **gardener** they had never knew anything about it; servants are so stupid! She would have **dearly** liked, if only for the winter, to live in town, although the length of the fine days made the country perhaps even more **wearisome** in the summer. And, **according** to what she was saying, her voice was clear, sharp, or, on a sudden all **languor**, drawn out in modulations that ended almost in murmurs as she spoke to herself, now **joyous**, opening big naive eyes, then with her eyelids half closed, her look full of **boredom**, her thoughts **wandering**.

Spanish

according: conforme, de acuerdo con.
blew: pret de blow, Sopló.
boredom: fastidio, aburrimiento.
brim: borde, ala, baranda.
clinked: Tintineado.
clucking: cloqueo, cloquear.
complained: regañado, se quejado, lamentado, demandado, reclamado, se querellado, Quejado.
convent: convento.
cooled: refrescado.
cupboard: armario.
darning: zurcido.
dearly: amorosamente.
drift: deriva, derivar del rumbo, corriente.
emma: Ema.
fetch: traer, traemos, traed, trae, traéis, traes, traigo, traigan, traen, traiga, coger.
gardener: jardinero, el jardinero.
giddiness: mareo.
hen: gallina, la gallina.
joyous: jubiloso, gozoso, de jubiloso, alegre.
languor: languidez.
laughingly: reír, risueñamente.
licked: lamido.
liqueur: licor.
poured: vertido.
pouting: faneca.
stocking: media, la media.
throbbing: palpitante.
tomb: tumba.
wandering: errante, vagando.
wearisome: fatigoso.

Going home at night, Charles went over her words one by one, trying to recall them, to fill out their sense, that he might piece out the life she had lived before he knew her. But he never saw her in his thoughts other than he had seen her the first time, or as he had just left her. Then he asked himself what would become of her--if she would be married, and to whom! **Alas**! Old Rouault was rich, and she!--so beautiful! But Emma's face always rose before his eyes, and a **monotone**, like the **humming** of a top, sounded in his ears, "If you should marry after all! If you should marry!" At night he could not sleep; his throat was **parched**; he was **athirst**. He got up to drink from the **water**-bottle and opened the window. The night was covered with stars, a warm wind **blowing** in the distance; the dogs were **barking**. He turned his head towards the Bertaux.

Thinking that, after all, he should lose nothing, Charles promised himself to ask her in marriage as soon as occasion offered, but each time such occasion did offer the fear of not finding the right words sealed his lips.

Old Rouault would not have been sorry to be rid of his daughter, who was of no use to him in the house. In his heart he excused her, thinking her too clever for **farming**, a calling under the ban of Heaven, since one never saw a **millionaire** in it. Far from having made a fortune by it, the good man was losing every year; for if he was good in **bargaining**, in which he enjoyed the dodges of the trade, on the other hand, agriculture properly so called, and the internal management of the farm, **suited** him less than most people. He did not **willingly** take his hands out of his **pockets**, and did not spare expense in all that concerned himself, **liking** to eat well, to have good **fires**, and to sleep well. He liked old cider, **underdone** legs of **mutton**, glorias well beaten up. He took his meals in the kitchen alone, opposite the fire, on a little table brought to him all ready laid as on the stage.

When, therefore, he perceived that Charles's **cheeks** grew red if near his daughter, which meant that he would **propose** for her one of these days, he **chewed** the **cud** of the matter **beforehand**. He certainly thought him a little meagre, and not quite the **son**-in-law he would have liked, but he was said to be well brought-up, **economical**, very learned, and no doubt would not make too

Spanish

alas: ay, es una lástima.
athirst: sediento.
bargaining: negociación, trato, regateo.
barking: ladrar, ladrido.
beforehand: de antemano.
blowing: soplado, sopladura, soplar, silbido, soplo.
cheeks: mejillas.
chewed: masticado.
cud: rumiada, bolo alimenticio, Rumia.

economical: económico.
farming: labranza, cultivo.
fires: incendios.
humming: zumbador.
liking: afición, gusto.
millionaire: millonario.
monotone: monótono, monotonía.
mutton: carnero, carne de carnero.
parched: se agostado, secado, resecado, abrasado, seco, tostado.
pockets: alvéolos.
propose: proponer, propon, proponed,

propongo, propongan, propones, proponen, proponéis, propone, proponemos, proponga.
son-in-law: yerno.
suited: demanda, conveniente, traje, satisfacer, preparado, pleito, idóneo, ajustarse a, adecuado, acomodado, conjunto.
underdone: poco hecho.
water-bottle: jarra.
willingly: voluntariamente, de buena gana.

many difficulties about the dowry. Now, as old Rouault would soon be forced to sell **twenty**-two acres of "his property," as he **owed** a good deal to the **mason**, to the **harness**-maker, and as the **shaft** of the cider-press wanted **renewing**, "If he **asks** for her," he said to himself, "I'll give her to him."

At Michaelmas Charles went to spend three days at the Bertaux.

The last had passed like the others in **procrastinating** from hour to hour. Old Rouault was seeing him off; they were walking along the road full of ruts; they were about to part. This was the time. Charles gave himself as far as to the corner of the hedge, and at last, when past it--

"Monsieur Rouault," he **murmured**, "I should like to say something to you."

They stopped. Charles was **silent**.

"Well, tell me your story. **Don't** I know all about it?" said old Rouault, **laughing** softly.

"Monsieur Rouault--Monsieur Rouault," **stammered** Charles.

"I ask nothing better", the **farmer** went on. "Although, no doubt, the little one is of my mind, still we must ask her opinion. So you get off--I'll go back home. If it is "yes", you needn't return because of all the people about, and **besides** it would **upset** her too much. But so that you mayn't be eating your heart, I'll open wide the **outer shutter** of the window against the wall; you can see it from the back by **leaning** over the hedge."

And he went off.

Charles **fastened** his horse to a tree; he ran into the road and **waited**. Half an hour passed, then he **counted** nineteen minutes by his watch. Suddenly a noise was heard against the wall; the shutter had been **thrown** back; the **hook** was still **swinging**.

The next day by nine o'clock he was at the farm. Emma **blushed** as he **entered**, and she gave a little forced laugh to keep herself in countenance. Old Rouault **embraced** his future son-in-law. The discussion of money matters was put off; **moreover**, there was plenty of time before them, as the marriage could

---

Spanish

asks: pregunta, pide, solicita.
besides: además, demás, además de, amén de.
blushed: enrojecido.
counted: contado.
don't: no.
embraced: abrazado.
entered: entrado, inscrito, montado.
farmer: campesino, granjero, agricultor, el campesino.
fastened: fijado, sujetado, atado.
harness-maker: guarnicionero.

hook: gancho, anzuelo, garfio, enganchar, enganche.
laugh: reír, reírse, risa, carcajada.
laughing: riendo.
leaning: inclinación.
mason: albañil.
moreover: además, demás.
murmured: Murmurado.
outer: externo, exterior.
owed: adeudado, debido.
procrastinating: aplazando, dilatar.
renewing: renovando.

shaft: eje, árbol, pozo, fuste.
shutter: obturador, contraventana, postigo, persiana.
silent: silencioso, mudo, callado.
stammered: tartamudeó.
swinging: balanceo.
thrown: tirado, pp de throw.
twenty-two: veintidós.
upset: trastornar, indispuesta, trastorno.
waited: Esperado, aguardado, perdado.

not **decently** take place **till** Charles was out of **mourning**, that is to say, about the **spring** of the next year.

The **winter passed waiting** for this. Mademoiselle Rouault was **busy** with her **trousseau**. Part of it was **ordered** at Rouen, and she made herself **chemises** and nightcaps after fashion-plates that she **borrowed**. When Charles **visited** the farmer, the **preparations** for the **wedding** were talked over; they **wondered** in what room they should have **dinner**; they **dreamed** of the number of **dishes** that would be wanted, and what should be entrees.

Emma would, on the **contrary**, have **preferred** to have a **midnight** wedding with **torches**, but old Rouault could not **understand** such an idea. So there was a wedding at which **forty**-three persons were present, at which they **remained** **sixteen** hours at table, began again the next day, and to some **extent** on the days following.

Spanish

borrowed: prestado.
busy: ocupado.
chemises: camisas.
contrary: contrario.
decently: como es debido.
dinner: cena, comida, banquete.
dishes: los platos.
dreamed: soñado.
extent: alcance, magnitud, extensión.
forty-three: cuarenta y tres, curenta y tres.
midnight: medianoche, media noche, la medianoche.
mourning: luto, deplorando, duelo.
ordered: ordenado.
passed: pasado.
preferred: preferido.
preparations: preparativos.
remained: restado, Permanecido.
sixteen: dieciséis, diez y seis.
spring: fuente, muelle, saltar, primavera, resorte, la primavera, manantial, brincar.
till: caja, hasta que, hasta, a que.
torches: antorchas.
trousseau: ajuar.
understand: entender, entiendes, entienda, entiendan, entendemos, entendéis, entended, entienden, entiendo, entiende, comprender.
visited: visitado.
waiting: esperando, espera, aguardando, servicio.
wedding: boda, casándose, la boda.
winter: invierno, el invierno.
wondered: Preguntado.

CHAPTER FOUR

The guests arrived early in carriages, in one-horse **chaises**, two-wheeled cars, old open gigs, waggonettes with **leather** hoods, and the young people from the nearer villages in carts, in which they stood up in rows, holding on to the sides so as not to fall, going at a trot and well **shaken** up. Some came from a distance of thirty miles, from Goderville, from Normanville, and from Cany.

All the relatives of both families had been invited, quarrels between friends arranged, **acquaintances** long since lost sight of written to.

From time to time one heard the **crack** of a whip behind the hedge; then the gates opened, a chaise entered. **Galloping** up to the foot of the steps, it stopped short and **emptied** its load. They got down from all sides, **rubbing knees** and **stretching** arms. The ladies, wearing **bonnets**, had on **dresses** in the town fashion, gold watch chains, pelerines with the ends **tucked** into belts, or little **coloured** fichus fastened down behind with a pin, and that left the back of the neck **bare**. The **lads**, dressed like their papas, seemed **uncomfortable** in their new clothes (many that day hand-sewed their first pair of boots), and by their sides, speaking never a work, wearing the white dress of their first communion **lengthened** for the occasion were some big girls of fourteen or sixteen, cousins or **elder** sisters no doubt, **rubicund**, **bewildered**, their hair **greasy** with rose **pomade**, and very much afraid of **dirtying** their gloves. As there were not enough stable-boys to **unharness** all the carriages, the **gentlemen** turned up their

Spanish

acquaintances: conocidos.
bare: desnudo, pelado, descubierto.
bewildered: descarriado, desconcertado.
bonnets: cabezal, gorras.
chaise: coche postal.
coloured: pintado.
crack: grieta, hendedura, crujido, quebraja, hendidura, crujir, raja.
dirtying: ensuciando.
dresses: los vestidos.
elder: mayor, anciano, saúco.

emptied: desocupado, vaciado.
galloping: galopante, galope, galopando, galopar.
gentlemen: señores.
greasy: grasiento, gordo, grueso, untuoso.
knees: rodillas.
lads: chicos, muchachos.
leather: cuero, duro, el cuero, piel.
lengthened: alargado.
pin: alfiler, patilla, perno, el alfiler, clavija, pasador.

pomade: pomada.
rubbing: frotamiento, fricción, frotación.
rubicund: rubicundo, rubicunda, rubeo.
shaken: sacudido.
stretching: estirar, extensión, estiramiento, estirado, ensanchamiento.
tucked: meta.
uncomfortable: incómodo.
unharness: desenjaezar, desguarnezca.

sleeves and set about it themselves. According to their **different** social positions they wore tail-coats, overcoats, shooting jackets, cutaway-coats; fine tail-coats, **redolent** of family **respectability**, that only came out of the wardrobe on state occasions; overcoats with long **tails flapping** in the wind and round capes and pockets like sacks; shooting jackets of **coarse** cloth, generally worn with a cap with a brass-bound peak; very short cutaway-coats with two small buttons in the back, close together like a pair of eyes, and the tails of which seemed cut out of one piece by a carpenter's **hatchet**. Some, too (but these, you may be sure, would sit at the bottom of the table), wore their best blouses--that is to say, with collars turned down to the shoulders, the back gathered into small **plaits** and the waist fastened very low down with a worked belt.

And the **shirts** stood out from the chests like cuirasses! Everyone had just had his hair cut; ears stood out from the heads; they had been close-shaved; a few, even, who had had to get up before **daybreak**, and not been able to see to **shave**, had **diagonal** gashes under their noses or cuts the size of a three-franc piece along the **jaws**, which the fresh air en route had enflamed, so that the great white **beaming** faces were **mottled** here and there with red **dabs**.

The mairie was a mile and a half from the farm, and they went **thither** on foot, returning in the same way after the ceremony in the church. The procession, first united like one long coloured **scarf** that **undulated** across the fields, along the narrow path **winding** amid the green corn, soon lengthened out, and broke up into different groups that **loitered** to talk. The **fiddler** walked in front with his **violin**, gay with ribbons at its pegs. Then came the married pair, the relations, the friends, all following **pell**-mell; the children stayed behind amusing themselves **plucking** the bell-flowers from oat-ears, or playing amongst themselves **unseen**. Emma's dress, too long, **trailed** a little on the ground; from time to time she stopped to pull it up, and then **delicately**, with her gloved hands, she picked off the coarse grass and the thistledowns, while Charles, empty handed, waited till she had finished. Old Rouault, with a new silk hat and the cuffs of his black coat covering his hands up to the nails, gave his arm to Madame Bovary senior. As to Monsieur Bovary senior, who, **heartily** despising

Spanish

beaming: radiante, brillante.
coarse: áspero, desigual, tosco, grosero, basto.
dabs: manos, verbos dactilares, huellas dactilares.
daybreak: amanecer, alba.
delicately: delicadamente.
diagonal: diagonal.
en: ene, nodo final.
fiddler: violinista.
flapping: batir, aleteo, aleteador.
hatchet: hacha de mano, hacha.

heartily: sinceramente.
jaws: mordazas.
loitered: Holgazaneado.
mottled: moteado.
pell-mell: atropelladamente.
plaits: trenzas.
plucking: punteo, desnudamiento, arrancar.
redolent: fragante.
respectability: respetabilidad.
scarf: bufanda, la bufanda, echarpe, pañuelo.

shave: afeitar, afeitado, afeitarse, rapar.
shirts: camisas.
sleeves: manguitos, mangas.
tails: colas.
thither: allá.
trailed: Arrastrado.
undulated: ondulado.
unseen: no visto.
violin: violín.
winding: devanado, arrollamiento, bobinado.

all these folk, had come simply in a frock-coat of military cut with one row of buttons--he was passing compliments of the bar to a fair young peasant. She bowed, blushed, and did not know what to say. The other wedding guests talked of their business or played tricks behind each **other's** backs, egging one another on in advance to be jolly. Those who listened could always catch the **squeaking** of the fiddler, who went on playing across the fields. When he saw that the rest were far behind he stopped to take breath, slowly rosined his bow, so that the strings should sound more **shrilly**, then set off again, by turns lowering and raising his neck, the better to mark time for himself. The noise of the instrument drove away the little birds from afar.

The table was laid under the cart-shed. On it were four sirloins, six chicken fricassees, stewed veal, three legs of mutton, and in the middle a fine roast **suckling** pig, **flanked** by four **chitterlings** with **sorrel**. At the corners were decanters of brandy. Sweet bottled-cider **frothed** round the corks, and all the glasses had been filled to the brim with wine beforehand. Large dishes of yellow cream, that trembled with the least shake of the table, had designed on their smooth surface the **initials** of the newly **wedded** pair in **nonpareil** arabesques. A **confectioner** of Yvetot had been **intrusted** with the **tarts** and sweets. As he had only just set up on the place, he had taken a lot of trouble, and at **dessert** he himself brought in a set dish that **evoked** loud cries of **wonderment**. To begin with, at its base there was a square of blue cardboard, representing a temple with porticoes, colonnades, and **stucco** statuettes all round, and in the **niches** constellations of **gilt** paper stars; then on the second stage was a **dungeon** of Savoy cake, surrounded by many fortifications in **candied angelica**, **almonds**, **raisins**, and quarters of oranges; and finally, on the upper platform a green field with rocks set in lakes of jam, **nutshell** boats, and a small Cupid balancing himself in a chocolate swing whose two **uprights** ended in real roses for balls at the top.

Until night they ate. When any of them were too tired of sitting, they went out for a stroll in the yard, or for a game with corks in the granary, and then returned to table. Some towards the finish went to sleep and **snored**. But with the

Spanish

almonds: almendras.
angelica: angélica.
candied: confitado, acaramelado.
chitterlings: menudos de cerdo, mondongo.
confectioner: pastelero, confitero, repostero.
dessert: postre, el postre.
dungeon: mazmorra.
evoked: evocado.
flanked: flanqueado.
frothed: espumar.

gilt: dorado.
initials: iniciales.
intrusted: Fiado, se encargado, confiado, encomendado.
niches: nichos.
nonpareil: sin igual, cosa sin par, persona sin pareja, sin par, persona sin par.
nutshell: cáscara de nuez, avellana, cascarón de nuez.
other's: otro.
raisins: las pasas, las pasas de uva,

pasas.
shrilly: chillonamente.
snored: roncado.
sorrel: alazán, acedera.
squeaking: chirriar, rechinamiento.
stucco: estuco.
suckling: amamantando, lactando, lactancia.
tarts: tartas.
uprights: vertical.
wedded: se casado.
wonderment: maravilla, admiración.

coffee everyone woke up. Then they began songs, showed off **tricks**, raised heavy **weights**, performed feats with their fingers, then tried lifting carts on their shoulders, made broad **jokes**, kissed the women. At night when they left, the horses, **stuffed** up to the nostrils with **oats**, could hardly be got into the **shafts**; they kicked, **reared**, the harness broke, their masters laughed or **swore**; and all night in the light of the moon along country roads there were **runaway** carts at full gallop **plunging** into the ditches, **jumping** over yard after yard of stones, **clambering** up the hills, with women leaning out from the **tilt** to catch hold of the reins.

Those who stayed at the Bertaux spent the night drinking in the kitchen. The children had fallen asleep under the seats.

The **bride** had begged her father to be **spared** the usual marriage pleasantries. However, a **fishmonger**, one of their cousins (who had even brought a pair of soles for his wedding present), began to **squirt** water from his mouth through the **keyhole**, when old Rouault came up just in time to stop him, and explain to him that the distinguished position of his son-in-law would not allow of such liberties. The cousin all the same did not give in to these reasons readily. In his heart he accused old Rouault of being proud, and he joined four or five other guests in a corner, who having, through mere chance, been several times running served with the worst helps of meat, also were of opinion they had been badly used, and were **whispering** about their host, and with covered **hints** hoping he would **ruin** himself.

Madame Bovary, senior, had not opened her mouth all day. She had been consulted neither as to the dress of her daughter-in-law nor as to the arrangement of the feast; she went to bed early. Her husband, instead of following her, sent to Saint-Victor for some **cigars**, and smoked till daybreak, drinking kirsch-punch, a mixture unknown to the company. This added greatly to the consideration in which he was held.

Charles, who was not of a **facetious** turn, did not **shine** at the wedding. He answered **feebly** to the puns, **doubles** entendres, compliments, and **chaff** that it was felt a duty to let off at him as soon as the soup appeared.

Spanish

bride: novia, prometida.
chaff: barcia, paja menuda, paja, lo barcia, hollejo, granzas, de barcia, cortar, cascabillo, burlar, bagazo.
cigars: los puros.
clambering: trepando, Gatear, trepanación.
doubles: juego de dobles, dobles.
facetious: jocoso, gracioso, chistoso.
feebly: blandenguemente, enfermizamente, enclenquemente, débilmente.

fishmonger: pescadero.
hints: Información de fuentes -hinting, pistas.
jokes: bromas.
jumping: saltar.
keyhole: ojo de la cerradura.
oats: avena.
plunging: zambullir, hundir, muy bajo, sumergir, zambullida.
reared: criado.
ruin: ruina, arruinar.
runaway: fugitivo.

shafts: ejes.
shine: brillar, brillo, lucir.
spared: libre de, reservado.
squirt: chorro, jeringa.
stuffed: disecado, ahíto, llenó.
swore: pret de swear, Juró.
tilt: inclinación, inclinar.
tricks: engaños.
weights: pesos, pesas, cargas.
whispering: chismes, chismografía, con eco, cuchicheo, de difamación, rumores, susurro, de rumores.

The next day, on the other hand, he seemed another man. It was he who might rather have been taken for the **virgin** of the evening before, whilst the bride gave no sign that revealed anything. The shrewdest did not know what to make of it, and they looked at her when she passed near them with an **unbounded** concentration of mind. But Charles **concealed** nothing. He called her "my wife", tutoyed her, asked for her of everyone, looked for her everywhere, and often he **dragged** her into the yards, where he could be seen from far between the trees, putting his arm around her **waist**, and walking half-bending over her, **ruffling** the **chemisette** of her bodice with his head.

Two days after the wedding the married pair left. Charles, on account of his patients, could not be away longer. Old Rouault had them driven back in his **cart**, and himself accompanied them as far as Vassonville. Here he embraced his daughter for the last time, got down, and went his way. When he had gone about a hundred paces he stopped, and as he saw the cart **disappearing**, its **wheels** turning in the dust, he gave a deep sigh. Then he remembered his wedding, the old times, the first **pregnancy** of his wife; he, too, had been very happy the day when he had taken her from her father to his home, and had carried her off on a **pillion**, **trotting** through the snow, for it was near Christmas-time, and the country was all white. She held him by one arm, her **basket hanging** from the other; the wind blew the long **lace** of her Cauchois **headdress** so that it sometimes **flapped** across his mouth, and when he turned his head he saw near him, on his shoulder, her little **rosy** face, **smiling silently** under the gold **bands** of her cap. To warm her hands she put them from time to time in his breast. How long ago it all was! Their son would have been thirty by now. Then he looked back and saw nothing on the road. He felt **dreary** as an empty house; and **tender** memories mingling with the sad thoughts in his brain, **addled** by the **fumes** of the feast, he felt **inclined** for a moment to take a turn towards the church. As he was afraid, however, that this sight would make him yet more sad, he went right away home.

Monsieur and Madame Charles arrived at Tostes about six o'clock.

The neighbors came to the windows to see their doctor's new wife.

Spanish

addled: podrido, zote.
bands: alzacuello.
basket: cesto, cesta, la cesta, canasta, barquilla, canasto.
cart: carro, carreta, carretilla.
chemisette: camiseta.
concealed: ocultado, disimulado.
disappearing: desapareciendo.
dragged: arrastrado, remolcado.
dreary: triste, lúgubre, árido, horroroso, horrible, afligido.
flapped: batido.

fumes: humos.
hanging: ahorcamiento, pendiente.
headdress: tocado.
inclined: inclinado.
lace: encaje, lazo, cordón, el encaje, la cinta.
pillion: asiento de atrás, asiento trasero, grupera, silla ligera de montar.
pregnancy: embarazo, preñez.
rosy: rosado.
ruffling: erizar.

silently: silenciosamente, silencioso.
smiling: sonriente.
tender: tierno, oferta, dulce, subasta, proposición, ofrecer, destajo, licitación, presentar, reproducir, retratar.
trotting: trote, hacer trotar, trotón, trotador, trotar.
unbounded: ilimitado.
virgin: virgen.
waist: cintura, la cintura, talle.
wheels: ruedas, rueda.

The old **servant presented herself**, curtsied to her, **apologised** for not having **dinner ready**, and **suggested** that **madame**, in the **meantime**, should look over her house.

CHAPTER FIVE

The **brick** front was just in a line with the street, or rather the road. Behind the door hung a cloak with a small collar, a **bridle**, and a black leather cap, and on the floor, in a corner, were a pair of **leggings**, still covered with dry mud. On the right was the one **apartment**, that was both **dining** and sitting room. A **canary** yellow paper, relieved at the top by a **garland** of pale flowers, was **puckered** everywhere over the badly stretched **canvas**; white calico **curtains** with a red border hung crossways at the length of the window; and on the narrow **mantelpiece** a clock with a head of Hippocrates shone **resplendent** between two plate **candlesticks** under oval **shades**. On the other side of the passage was Charles's **consulting** room, a little room about six paces wide, with a table, three chairs, and an office chair. **Volumes** of the "Dictionary of Medical Science," **uncut**, but the binding rather the worse for the successive sales through which they had gone, occupied almost along the six **shelves** of a deal **bookcase**.

The smell of **melted** butter **penetrated** through the walls when he saw patients, just as in the kitchen one could hear the people **coughing** in the consulting room and recounting their histories.

Then, opening on the yard, where the stable was, came a large **dilapidated** room with a stove, now used as a wood-house, **cellar**, and **pantry**, full of old rubbish, of empty **casks**, agricultural **implements** past service, and a mass of **dusty** things whose use it was impossible to guess.

Spanish

apartment: apartamento, piso, cuarto.
bookcase: librería, estante para libros, armario para libros, biblioteca, el estante de libros.
brick: ladrillo, el ladrillo, teja.
bridle: brida, reprimir, contener, malleta, embridar, frenillo.
canary: canario.
candlesticks: candelabros.
canvas: lona, lienzo.
casks: toneles.
cellar: sótano, bodega.

consulting: consultando.
coughing: tos.
curtains: las cortinas.
dilapidated: decrépito, ruinoso.
dining: cenando.
dusty: polvoriento.
garland: guirnalda.
implements: útiles, instrumental, menesteres, implementos, implementa.
leggings: polainas.
mantelpiece: repisa.

melted: derretido, fundido.
pantry: despensa.
penetrated: penetrado.
puckered: arrugado, fruncido.
resplendent: resplandeciente.
shades: averno, matices, sombras, tinieblas.
shelves: estantería.
uncut: sin tallar, no cortado, integral, en bruto, sin abrir, sin cortés, sin cortar, no tallado, sin labrar.
volumes: volúmenes.

The garden, longer than wide, ran between two mud walls with **espaliered** apricots, to a **hawthorn** hedge that separated it from the field. In the middle was a **slate sundial** on a brick **pedestal**; four flower beds with eglantines surrounded symmetrically the more useful kitchen garden bed. Right at the bottom, under the **spruce** bushes, was a cure in **plaster** reading his breviary.

Emma went upstairs. The first room was not **furnished**, but in the second, which was their bedroom, was a **mahogany** bedstead in an alcove with red **drapery**. A shell box **adorned** the chest of **drawers**, and on the secretary near the window a **bouquet** of orange blossoms tied with white **satin** ribbons stood in a bottle. It was a bride's bouquet; it was the other one's. She looked at it. Charles noticed it; he took it and carried it up to the **attic**, while Emma **seated** in an **arm**-chair (they were putting her things down around her) thought of her **bridal** flowers packed up in a **bandbox**, and wondered, **dreaming**, what would be done with them if she were to die.

During the first days she occupied herself in thinking about changes in the house. She took the shades off the candlesticks, had new **wallpaper** put up, the **staircase repainted**, and seats made in the garden round the sundial; she even **inquired** how she could get a basin with a jet **fountain** and fishes. Finally her husband, knowing that she liked to drive out, picked up a second-hand dogcart, which, with new **lamps** and **splashboard** in **striped** leather, looked almost like a tilbury.

He was happy then, and without a care in the world. A meal together, a walk in the evening on the **highroad**, a gesture of her hands over her hair, the sight of her straw hat hanging from the window-fastener, and many another thing in which Charles had never dreamed of pleasure, now made up the endless round of his happiness. In bed, in the morning, by her side, on the pillow, he watched the sunlight **sinking** into the down on her fair cheek, half hidden by the lappets of her night-cap. Seen thus closely, her eyes looked to him **enlarged**, especially when, on **waking** up, she opened and shut them rapidly many times. Black in the shade, dark blue in broad daylight, they had, as it were, depths of different colours, that, darker in the centre, grew paler towards the surface of the eye. His

Spanish

adorned: adornado, decorado.
arm-chair: sillón, butaca.
attic: desván, ático, buhardilla.
bandbox: sombrerera.
bouquet: ramillete.
bridal: nupcial, boda.
drapery: pañería.
drawers: calzoncillos.
dreaming: soñar.
enlarged: ampliado, agrandado.
espaliered: espaldó.
fountain: fuente, la fuente.

furnished: amueblado.
hawthorn: espino, espino blanco, majuelo.
highroad: calle principal, carretera, carretera nacional, carretera principal.
inquired: inquirido, preguntado.
lamps: lámparas.
mahogany: caoba.
pedestal: pedestal.
plaster: esparadrapo, yeso, emplasto, enlucido.

repainted: repintado.
satin: raso, satén.
seated: sentado.
sinking: hundimiento, sumidero.
slate: pizarra.
splashboard: alero, guardabarros.
spruce: abeto, pulcro, picea.
staircase: escalera, la escalera.
striped: rayado, cebrado.
sundial: reloj de sol.
waking: despertar.
wallpaper: papel de empapelar.

own eyes lost themselves in these depths; he saw himself in **miniature** down to the shoulders, with his **handkerchief** round his head and the top of his shirt open. He rose. She came to the window to see him off, and stayed leaning on the **sill** between two **pots** of **geranium**, **clad** in her dressing gown hanging **loosely** about her. Charles, in the street **buckled** his **spurs**, his foot on the **mounting** stone, while she talked to him from above, picking with her mouth some **scrap** of flower or leaf that she blew out at him. Then this, eddying, **floating**, described semicircles in the air like a bird, and was caught before it reached the ground in the ill-groomed **mane** of the old white **mare** standing motionless at the door. Charles from **horseback** threw her a kiss; she answered with a **nod**; she shut the window, and he set off. And then along the highroad, **spreading** out its long **ribbon** of dust, along the deep lanes that the trees bent over as in **arbours**, along paths where the corn reached to the knees, with the sun on his back and the morning air in his nostrils, his heart full of the joys of the past night, his mind at rest, his flesh at ease, he went on, re-chewing his happiness, like those who after dinner taste again the truffles which they are digesting.

Until now what good had he had of his life? His time at school, when he remained shut up within the high walls, alone, in the **midst** of companions **richer** than he or cleverer at their work, who laughed at his accent, who jeered at his clothes, and whose mothers came to the school with **cakes** in their muffs? Later on, when he studied medicine, and never had his **purse** full enough to treat some little work-girl who would have become his mistress? Afterwards, he had lived fourteen months with the widow, whose feet in bed were cold as icicles. But now he had for life this beautiful woman whom he adored. For him the universe did not extend beyond the **circumference** of her **petticoat**, and he **reproached** himself with not **loving** her. He wanted to see her again; he turned back quickly, ran up the stairs with a beating heart. Emma, in her room, was dressing; he came up on **tiptoe**, kissed her back; she gave a cry.

He could not keep from constantly **touching** her **comb**, her ring, her fichu; sometimes he gave her great **sounding** kisses with all his mouth on her cheeks, or else little kisses in a row all along her bare arm from the tip of her fingers up

Spanish

arbours: enramadas.
buckled: Abrochado.
cakes: pasteles, tortas, tarta.
circumference: perímetro, circunferencia, la circunferencia.
clad: vestido, pret y pp de clothe.
comb: peine, peinar, el peine.
floating: flotante, flotación.
geranium: geranio.
handkerchief: pañuelo.
horseback: a caballo.
loosely: flojamente.

loving: cariñoso, amoroso.
mane: melena, crin.
mare: yegua.
midst: medio.
miniature: miniatura.
mounting: montura, montaje.
nod: inclinación, cabecear.
petticoat: enaguas.
pots: servicio telefónico analógico convencional, montones.
purse: portamonedas, monedero, colecta, bolsa, bolso, la bolsa, cartera.

reproached: Reprochado.
ribbon: cinta.
richer: y todos nosotros somos mucho más ricos por ello.
scrap: chatarra, recorte, desechar, sobras, desguazar, de desecho.
sill: umbral, solera.
sounding: sondeo.
spreading: esparcimiento.
spurs: espuelas.
tiptoe: de puntillas, punta del pie.
touching: conmovedor.

to her **shoulder**, and she put him away half-smiling, half-vexed, as you do a child who **hangs** about you.

Before **marriage** she thought **herself** in love; but the **happiness** that should have **followed** this love not having come, she must, she thought, have been **mistaken**. And Emma **tried** to find out what one **meant exactly** in life by the words **felicity, passion, rapture**, that had seemed to her so **beautiful** in **books**.

Spanish

beautiful: bonito, hermoso, bello, precioso.
books: los libros.
exactly: exactamente, justamente, en punto.
felicity: felicidad.
followed: seguido.
hangs: continúa, cuelga.
happiness: felicidad, alegría, dicha.
herself: sí, ella misma, se, sí misma.
marriage: matrimonio, casamiento, enlace.

meant: pret de mean.
mistaken: malo, equivocado.
passion: pasión.
rapture: rapto.
shoulder: hombro, el hombro, espalda, lisera, banquina, reborde, espaldilla.
tried: probado.

CHAPTER SIX

She had read "Paul and Virginia," and she had dreamed of the little bamboo-house, the **nigger** Domingo, the dog Fiddle, but above all of the sweet **friendship** of some dear little brother, who **seeks** red fruit for you on trees taller than steeples, or who runs barefoot over the sand, bringing you a bird's nest.

When she was **thirteen**, her father himself took her to town to place her in the convent. They stopped at an **inn** in the St. Gervais quarter, where, at their **supper**, they used **painted plates** that set **forth** the story of Mademoiselle de la Valliere. The **explanatory legends**, **chipped** here and there by the **scratching** of knives, all **glorified** religion, the tendernesses of the heart, and the pomps of court.

Far from being **bored** at first at the convent, she took pleasure in the society of the good sisters, who, to amuse her, took her to the **chapel**, which one entered from the refectory by a long **corridor**. She played very little during **recreation** hours, knew her **catechism** well, and it was she who always answered Monsieur le Vicaire's difficult questions. Living thus, without every leaving the warm atmosphere of the classrooms, and **amid** these **pale**-faced women wearing rosaries with **brass** crosses, she was softly lulled by the **mystic** languor **exhaled** in the perfumes of the **altar**, the **freshness** of the holy water, and the lights of the tapers. Instead of **attending** to mass, she looked at the **pious** vignettes with their **azure** borders in her book, and she loved the **sick lamb**, the **sacred** heart pierced

Spanish

altar: altar.
amid: en medio de, entre.
attending: asistiendo.
azure: azul celeste, azur.
bored: aburrido.
brass: latón, metal.
catechism: catecismo.
chapel: capilla, iglesia.
chipped: astillado.
corridor: pasillo, corredor.
exhaled: exhalado, espirado.
explanatory: explicativo, aclaratorio.

forth: adelante.
freshness: frescura.
friendship: amistad.
glorified: glorificado.
inn: albergue, fonda, posada, mesón.
lamb: cordero, carne de cordero, el cordero, borrego, oveja.
legends: las leyendas.
mystic: místico.
nigger: negro.
painted: pintado.
pale-faced: caripálido.

pious: piadoso, pío, beato.
plates: placas.
recreation: recreación, recreo.
sacred: sagrado, sacro.
scratching: arañar, arañazo, improvisado, rasguño, rasguñar, raspamiento, rayadura, rascadura, rascar.
seeks: busca.
sick: enfermo.
supper: cena, la cena.
thirteen: trece.

with sharp arrows, or the poor Jesus sinking beneath the cross he carries. She tried, by way of **mortification**, to eat nothing a whole day. She **puzzled** her head to find some **vow** to fulfil.

When she went to **confession**, she **invented** little sins in order that she might stay there longer, kneeling in the shadow, her hands joined, her face against the **grating** beneath the whispering of the priest. The comparisons of **betrothed**, husband, **celestial** lover, and **eternal** marriage, that **recur** in sermons, **stirred** within her soul **depths** of unexpected sweetness.

In the evening, before **prayers**, there was some religious reading in the study. On week-nights it was some abstract of sacred history or the Lectures of the Abbe Frayssinous, and on Sundays passages from the "Genie du Christianisme," as a recreation. How she listened at first to the **sonorous** lamentations of its romantic melancholies reechoing through the world and **eternity**! If her childhood had been spent in the shop-parlour of some business quarter, she might perhaps have opened her heart to those **lyrical** invasions of Nature, which usually come to us only through **translation** in books. But she knew the country too well; she knew the lowing of cattle, the **milking**, the ploughs.

Accustomed to calm aspects of life, she turned, on the contrary, to those of excitement. She loved the sea only for the sake of its storms, and the green fields only when broken up by **ruins**.

She wanted to get some personal profit out of things, and she rejected as **useless** all that did not contribute to the immediate desires of her heart, being of a temperament more **sentimental** than artistic, looking for emotions, not landscapes.

At the convent there was an old **maid** who came for a week each month to **mend** the **linen**. **Patronized** by the **clergy**, because she **belonged** to an ancient family of noblemen **ruined** by the Revolution, she **dined** in the refectory at the table of the good sisters, and after the meal had a bit of **chat** with them before going back to her work. The girls often slipped out from the study to go and see her. She knew by heart the love songs of the last century, and sang them in a low voice as she **stitched** away.

Spanish

belonged: Pertenecido.
betrothed: desposado, prometido.
celestial: celeste, celestial.
chat: charlar, charla, platicar, conversación, plática.
clergy: clero.
confession: confesión, declaración.
depths: lo más hondo.
dined: cenado.
eternal: eterno.
eternity: eternidad.
grating: reja, emparrillado, verja, parrilla, enrejado, irritante.
invented: inventado.
linen: lino, lencería, ropa blanca.
lyrical: lírico.
maid: criada, sirvienta, doncella, la criada.
mend: remendar, enmendar, reparar, zurcir.
milking: ordeñar, Ordeño.
mortification: mortificación.
patronized: fomentado, patrocinado, favorecido, patrocinó.
prayers: ruegos, rezos, oraciones.
puzzled: perplejo, desconcertado.
recur: repetirse.
ruined: arruinado.
ruins: ruinas.
sentimental: sentimental.
sonorous: sonoro.
stirred: batido.
stitched: cosido.
translation: traducción, traslación.
useless: inútil, inservible.
vow: voto.

She told stories, gave them news, went errands in the town, and on the **sly lent** the big girls some novel, that she always carried in the pockets of her **apron**, and of which the good lady herself swallowed long chapters in the intervals of her work. They were all love, lovers, sweethearts, **persecuted** ladies **fainting** in lonely **pavilions**, postilions killed at every stage, horses **ridden** to death on every page, **sombre** forests, **heartaches**, **vows**, **sobs**, tears and kisses, little skiffs by **moonlight**, **nightingales** in **shady** groves, "gentlemen" brave as lions, gentle as **lambs**, **virtuous** as no one ever was, always well dressed, and **weeping** like fountains. For six months, then, Emma, at fifteen years of age, made her hands dirty with books from old **lending** libraries.

Through Walter Scott, later on, she fell in love with historical events, dreamed of old chests, guard-rooms and minstrels. She would have liked to live in some old manor-house, like those long-waisted chatelaines who, in the shade of pointed arches, spent their days leaning on the stone, chin in hand, watching a **cavalier** with white **plume** galloping on his black horse from the distant fields. At this time she had a **cult** for Mary Stuart and enthusiastic **veneration** for **illustrious** or unhappy women. Joan of Arc, Heloise, Agnes Sorel, the beautiful Ferroniere, and Clemence Isaure stood out to her like **comets** in the dark **immensity** of heaven, where also were seen, lost in shadow, and all **unconnected**, St. Louis with his oak, the dying Bayard, some cruelties of Louis XI, a little of St. Bartholomew's Day, the plume of the Bearnais, and always the remembrance of the plates painted in honour of Louis XIV.

In the music class, in the **ballads** she sang, there was nothing but little **angels** with golden wings, **madonnas**, lagunes, gondoliers;-mild compositions that allowed her to catch a glimpse **athwart** the **obscurity** of style and the weakness of the music of the attractive **phantasmagoria** of sentimental realities. Some of her companions brought "keepsakes" given them as new **year's** gifts to the convent. These had to be hidden; it was quite an undertaking; they were read in the dormitory. Delicately handling the beautiful satin **bindings**, Emma looked with **dazzled** eyes at the names of the unknown authors, who had signed their verses for the most part as counts or viscounts.

Spanish

angels: los ángeles.
apron: delantal, el delantal, mandil.
athwart: a través de.
ballads: baladas.
bindings: enlaces, vinculaciones.
cavalier: caballero.
comets: cometas.
cult: culto.
dazzled: deslumbrado.
fainting: desmayo, desvanecimiento.
heartaches: penas.
illustrious: ilustre.

immensity: inmensidad.
lambs: cabezas de turco.
lending: prestando.
lent: prestado, cuaresma.
lions: leones.
madonnas: Madonas.
moonlight: luz de la luna.
nightingales: ruiseñores.
obscurity: oscuridad.
persecuted: perseguido.
phantasmagoria: fantasmagoría.
plume: pluma, penacho.

ridden: pp de ride, cabalgado.
shady: umbrío, sombreado.
sly: furtivo, astuto.
sobs: solloza.
sombre: sombrío.
unconnected: desconecto.
veneration: veneración.
virtuous: virtuoso.
vows: promesas solemnes.
weeping: llorando, lloroso, llanto, llorón.
year's: año.

She trembled as she blew back the tissue paper over the **engraving** and saw it folded in two and fall gently against the page. Here behind the **balustrade** of a balcony was a young man in a short cloak, holding in his arms a young girl in a white dress wearing an alms-bag at her belt; or there were **nameless** portraits of English ladies with fair **curls**, who looked at you from under their round straw hats with their large clear eyes. Some there were **lounging** in their carriages, **gliding** through parks, a **greyhound bounding** along in front of the **equipage** driven at a trot by two **midget** postilions in white **breeches**. Others, dreaming on sofas with an open letter, gazed at the moon through a slightly open window half **draped** by a black curtain. The naive ones, a tear on their cheeks, were **kissing doves** through the bars of a Gothic cage, or, smiling, their heads on one side, were plucking the leaves of a **marguerite** with their **taper** fingers, that curved at the tips like **peaked** shoes. And you, too, were there, Sultans with long pipes **reclining** beneath arbours in the arms of Bayaderes; Djiaours, Turkish sabres, Greek caps; and you especially, pale landscapes of **dithyrambic** lands, that often show us at once palm trees and firs, **tigers** on the right, a lion to the left, Tartar minarets on the horizon; the whole **framed** by a very neat virgin forest, and with a great **perpendicular sunbeam trembling** in the water, where, standing out in relief like white excoriations on a steel-grey ground, swans are swimming about.

And the shade of the argand lamp fastened to the wall above Emma's head lighted up all these pictures of the world, that passed before her one by one in the silence of the dormitory, and to the distant noise of some **belated** carriage rolling over the Boulevards.

When her mother died she cried much the first few days. She had a funeral picture made with the hair of the **deceased**, and, in a letter sent to the Bertaux full of sad reflections on life, she asked to be buried later on in the same grave. The goodman thought she must be ill, and came to see her. Emma was **secretly** pleased that she had reached at a first attempt the rare ideal of pale lives, never **attained** by **mediocre** hearts. She let herself **glide** along with Lamartine **meanderings**, listened to harps on lakes, to all the songs of dying swans, to the

Spanish

attained: alcanzado.
balustrade: balaustrada, barandilla.
belated: tardío.
bounding: saltar.
breeches: calzones, pantalones.
curls: rizos.
deceased: difunto, fallecido.
dithyrambic: ditirámbico.
doves: las palomitas.
draped: cubierto, entapizado, tapizado, drapeado.
engraving: grabado, grabando.

equipage: equipaje, equipo.
framed: encuadrado.
glide: deslizarse, planeo.
gliding: deslizar, planeación.
greyhound: galgo.
kissing: besar.
lounging: repantigar.
marguerite: Margarita.
meanderings: meandros, divagaciones.
mediocre: mediano, mediocre.
midget: enano, en miniatura.

nameless: anónimo.
peaked: cresta, alcanzar el máximo, cima, con visera, cúspide, cumbre, puntiagudo, punta, pico, máximo.
perpendicular: perpendicular.
reclining: reclinando.
secretly: secretamente.
sunbeam: rayo de sol.
taper: manipulador, taladro cónico, conicidad.
tigers: tigres.
trembling: temblar, temblando.

falling of the leaves, the pure virgins **ascending** to heaven, and the voice of the Eternal discoursing down the valleys. She wearied of it, would not **confess** it, continued from habit, and at last was surprised to feel herself **soothed**, and with no more **sadness** at heart than **wrinkles** on her brow.

The good nuns, who had been so sure of her **vocation**, perceived with great **astonishment** that Mademoiselle Rouault seemed to be slipping from them. They had indeed been so **lavish** to her of prayers, retreats, novenas, and sermons, they had so often **preached** the respect due to **saints** and martyrs, and given so much good advice as to the modesty of the body and the **salvation** of her soul, that she did as tightly **reined** horses; she pulled up short and the bit slipped from her teeth. This nature, positive in the midst of its enthusiasms, that had loved the church for the sake of the flowers, and music for the words of the songs, and literature for its **passional stimulus**, **rebelled** against the **mysteries** of faith as it grew **irritated** by discipline, a thing **antipathetic** to her constitution. When her father took her from school, no one was sorry to see her go. The Lady Superior even thought that she had **latterly** been somewhat **irreverent** to the community.

Emma, at home once more, first took pleasure in looking after the servants, then grew disgusted with the country and missed her convent. When Charles came to the Bertaux for the first time, she thought herself quite **disillusioned**, with nothing more to learn, and nothing more to feel.

But the **uneasiness** of her new position, or perhaps the **disturbance** caused by the presence of this man, had **sufficed** to make her believe that she at last felt that **wondrous** passion which, till then, like a great bird with rose-coloured wings, hung in the **splendour** of the **skies** of **poesy**; and now she could not think that the calm in which she lived was the happiness she had dreamed.

Spanish

antipathetic: antagónico, antipático, contrario, opuesto.
ascending: ascendiendo, subiendo, ascendente, escalando.
astonishment: asombro.
confess: confesar, confiesan, confiesen, confieso, confiesas, confesamos, confesad, confesáis, confiesa, confiese, declarar.
disillusioned: desilusionado.
disturbance: molestia, perturbación.
irreverent: irreverente.

irritated: irritado.
latterly: últimamente, en nuestro tiempo, postreramente, en actualidad.
lavish: pródigo.
mysteries: misterios.
passional: pasional, martirologio.
poesy: poesía.
preached: predicado, sermoneado.
rebelled: rebelado.
reined: Contenido.
sadness: tristeza.

saints: santos.
salvation: salvación.
skies: cielo.
soothed: calmado.
splendour: fausto, pomposidad, fulgor, esplendor, lujo.
stimulus: estímulo, excitación.
sufficed: bastado.
uneasiness: malestar.
vocation: vocación.
wondrous: maravilloso.
wrinkles: arugas.

CHAPTER SEVEN

She thought, sometimes, that, after all, this was the **happiest** time of her life--the **honeymoon**, as people called it. To taste the full sweetness of it, it would have been necessary doubtless to fly to those lands with sonorous names where the days after marriage are full of **laziness** most **suave**. In post chaises behind blue **silken** curtains to ride slowly up steep road, listening to the song of the **postilion** re-echoed by the mountains, along with the bells of goats and the **muffled** sound of a **waterfall**; at **sunset** on the shores of gulfs to breathe in the **perfume** of lemon trees; then in the evening on the villa-terraces above, hand in hand to look at the stars, making plans for the future. It seemed to her that certain places on earth must bring happiness, as a plant peculiar to the soil, and that **cannot thrive** elsewhere. Why could not she lean over **balconies** in Swiss chalets, or **enshrine** her melancholy in a Scotch cottage, with a husband dressed in a black velvet coat with long tails, and thin shoes, a pointed hat and **frills**? Perhaps she would have liked to **confide** all these things to someone. But how tell an **undefinable** uneasiness, variable as the clouds, **unstable** as the winds? Words failed her--the opportunity, the courage.

If Charles had but wished it, if he had guessed it, if his look had but once met her thought, it seemed to her that a sudden plenty would have gone out from her heart, as the fruit falls from a tree when shaken by a hand. But as the **intimacy** of

Spanish

balconies: voladizos.
cannot: presente de no poder.
confide: confiar, confiamos, confío, confíen, confían, confiáis, confiad, confía, confías, confíe.
enshrine: encerrar, encierran, encierren, encierre, encierras, encerramos, encerráis, encerrad, encierro, encierra.
frills: adornos, volantes.
happiest: happy.
honeymoon: luna de miel.

intimacy: intimidad.
laziness: flojedad, apoltronamiento, pigricia, poltronería, dejadez, haraganería, flojera, pereza, holgazanería.
muffled: silenciador, sordo, silenciado, mufla, embozar, apagar, apagado, amortiguar, amortiguado.
perfume: perfume, el perfume, perfumar.
postilion: postillón.
silken: de seda, sedoso.

suave: zalamero, fino, cortés, amable, afable.
sunset: puesta del sol, ocaso, puesta de sol.
thrive: prosperar, prospera, prosperen, prosperas, prospero, prosperan, prosperamos, prosperáis, prosperad, prospere.
undefinable: indefinible.
unstable: inestable, inconstante.
waterfall: cascada, la cascada, la catarata.

their life became deeper, the greater became the **gulf** that separated her from him.

Charles's conversation was **commonplace** as a street pavement, and everyone's ideas trooped through it in their everyday **garb**, without exciting emotion, laughter, or thought. He had never had the **curiosity**, he said, while he lived at Rouen, to go to the theatre to see the actors from Paris. He could neither **swim**, nor fence, nor shoot, and one day he could not explain some term of **horsemanship** to her that she had come across in a novel.

A man, on the contrary, should he not know everything, **excel** in **manifold** activities, **initiate** you into the energies of passion, the refinements of life, all mysteries? But this one taught nothing, knew nothing, wished nothing. He thought her happy; and she **resented** this easy calm, this **serene heaviness**, the very happiness she gave him.

Sometimes she would draw; and it was great **amusement** to Charles to stand there **bolt upright** and watch her **bend** over her cardboard, with eyes **half**-closed the better to see her work, or rolling, between her fingers, little bread-pellets. As to the piano, the more quickly her fingers **glided** over it the more he wondered. She struck the notes with **aplomb**, and ran from top to bottom of the **keyboard** without a break. Thus shaken up, the old instrument, whose strings **buzzed**, could be heard at the other end of the village when the window was open, and often the bailiff's clerk, passing along the highroad bare-headed and in list **slippers**, stopped to listen, his sheet of paper in his hand.

Emma, on the other hand, knew how to look after her house. She sent the patients' accounts in well-phrased letters that had no suggestion of a bill. When they had a neighbour to dinner on Sundays, she managed to have some **tasty** dish--piled up pyramids of greengages on vine leaves, served up **preserves** turned out into plates--and even spoke of buying finger-glasses for dessert. From all this much consideration was extended to Bovary.

Charles finished by rising in his own esteem for **possessing** such a wife. He showed with pride in the sitting room two small **pencil sketched** by her that he had had framed in very large **frames**, and hung up against the wallpaper by long

Spanish

amusement: diversión, divertimento, entretenimiento, distracción.
aplomb: aplomo.
bend: curva, doblar, curvar, curvatura, doblegar, codo, inclinar.
bolt: perno, cerrojo, saeta, tornillo, bulón, pestillo, clavija.
buzzed: Zumbado.
commonplace: común, trivial, trivialidad.
curiosity: curiosidad.
excel: sobresalir, aventajar.

frames: cuadros.
garb: vestido.
glided: deslizado.
gulf: golfo, abismo, despeñadero, precipicio.
half-closed: entreabierto.
heaviness: pesadez.
horsemanship: equitación.
initiate: iniciar, instigar, maquinar.
keyboard: teclado, tecla.
manifold: múltiple, colector.
pencil: lápiz.

possessing: poseyendo.
preserves: conservas.
resented: Resentido, notado.
serene: sereno.
sketched: trazado.
slippers: zapatillas.
swim: nadar, nadas, nado, naden, nadad, nadan, nadáis, nadamos, nada, nade.
tasty: sabroso, rico, gustoso.
upright: vertical, montante, derecho.
vine: parra, viña, vid.

green **cords**. People returning from mass saw him at his door in his wool-work slippers.

He came home late--at ten o'clock, at midnight sometimes. Then he asked for something to eat, and as the servant had gone to bed, Emma waited on him. He took off his coat to **dine** more at his ease. He told her, one after the other, the people he had met, the villages where he had been, the **prescriptions** ha had written, and, well pleased with himself, he finished the **remainder** of the **boiled beef** and **onions**, picked pieces off the **cheese**, **munched** an **apple**, emptied his water-bottle, and then went to bed, and lay on his back and snored.

As he had been for a time accustomed to wear nightcaps, his handkerchief would not keep down over his ears, so that his hair in the morning was all **tumbled** pell-mell about his face and **whitened** with the **feathers** of the pillow, whose **strings** came **untied** during the night. He always wore thick boots that had two long creases over the **instep** running **obliquely** towards the **ankle**, while the rest of the upper continued in a straight line as if stretched on a wooden foot. He said that "was quite good enough for the country."

His mother approved of his economy, for she came to see him as **formerly** when there had been some violent row at her place; and yet Madame Bovary senior seemed **prejudiced** against her daughter-in-law. She thought "her ways too fine for their position"; the wood, the sugar, and the candles **disappeared** as "at a grand establishment," and the amount of **firing** in the kitchen would have been enough for **twenty**-five courses. She put her linen in order for her in the **presses**, and taught her to keep an eye on the **butcher** when he brought the meat. Emma put up with these lessons. Madame Bovary was lavish of them; and the words "daughter" and "mother" were **exchanged** all day long, accompanied by little quiverings of the lips, each one **uttering** gentle words in a voice trembling with anger.

In Madame Dubuc's time the old woman felt that she was still the **favorite**; but now the love of Charles for Emma seemed to her a **desertion** from her **tenderness**, an **encroachment** upon what was hers, and she watched her son's happiness in sad silence, as a ruined man looks through the windows at people

Spanish

ankle: tobillo, el tobillo.
apple: manzana, la manzana.
beef: carne de vaca.
boiled: hervido.
butcher: carnicero, matar.
cheese: queso, el queso.
cords: cuerdas.
desertion: deserción.
dine: cenar, cenáis, ceno, cenen, cenas, cenamos, cenad, cenan, cena, cene.
disappeared: desaparecido.
encroachment: invasión, intrusión,

usurpación.
exchanged: cambiada, cambiado.
favorite: favorito, preferido.
firing: encendido.
formerly: anteriormente, antiguamente, delante.
hers: suyo.
instep: empeine.
munched: mascado.
obliquely: oblicuamente.
onions: cebollas.
prejudiced: predispuesto.

prescriptions: las recetas.
presses: Prensas, prensa.
remainder: resto, detrito, desechos, remanente.
strings: instrumentos de cuerda, cuerdas.
tenderness: ternura.
tumbled: Derribado.
twenty-five: veinticinco.
untied: desatado.
uttering: Pronunciar.
whitened: blanqueado.

dining in his old house. She recalled to him as remembrances her troubles and her **sacrifices**, and, **comparing** these with Emma's **negligence**, came to the conclusion that it was not reasonable to **adore** her so exclusively.

Charles knew not what to answer: he **respected** his mother, and he loved his wife **infinitely**; he considered the judgment of the one **infallible**, and yet he thought the conduct of the other **irreproachable**. When Madam Bovary had gone, he tried timidly and in the same terms to **hazard** one or two of the more **anodyne** observations he had heard from his **mamma**. Emma proved to him with a word that he was mistaken, and sent him off to his patients.

And yet, in accord with theories she believed right, she wanted to make herself in love with him. By moonlight in the garden she **recited** all the **passionate** rhymes she knew by heart, and, **sighing**, sang to him many melancholy adagios; but she found herself as calm after as before, and Charles seemed no more **amorous** and no more moved.

When she had thus for a while struck the **flint** on her heart without getting a **spark**, **incapable**, moreover, of understanding what she did not experience as of **believing** anything that did not present itself in conventional forms, she persuaded herself without difficulty that Charles's passion was nothing very **exorbitant**. His outbursts became regular; he embraced her at certain fixed times. It was one habit among other **habits**, and, like a dessert, looked forward to after the **monotony** of dinner.

A **gamekeeper**, cured by the doctor of **inflammation** of the **lungs**, had given madame a little Italian greyhound; she took her out walking, for she went out sometimes in order to be alone for a moment, and not to see before her eyes the eternal garden and the dusty road. She went as far as the beeches of Banneville, near the **deserted pavilion** which forms an angle of the wall on the side of the country. **Amidst** the **vegetation** of the ditch there are long **reeds** with leaves that cut you.

She began by looking round her to see if nothing had changed since last she had been there. She found again in the same places the foxgloves and wallflowers, the beds of **nettles** growing round the big stones, and the **patches** of

Spanish

adore: adorar, adoran, adoren, adore, adoro, adoras, adoramos, adoráis, adora, adorad.
amidst: en medio de, entre.
amorous: amoroso.
anodyne: anodino.
believing: creyendo.
comparing: comparando, cotejando.
deserted: desierto.
exorbitant: exorbitante.
flint: pedernal.
gamekeeper: guardabosque.

habits: hábitos.
hazard: riesgo, arriesgar, peligro, acaso.
incapable: incapaz.
infallible: infalible.
infinitely: infinitamente.
inflammation: inflamación.
irreproachable: irreprochable.
lungs: pulmones, livianos.
mamma: mama.
monotony: monotonía.
negligence: negligencia, descuido.

nettles: molesta, provoca, irrita, Ortigas.
passionate: apasionado.
patches: placas.
pavilion: pabellón.
recited: recitado.
reeds: Peines, totoral.
respected: respetado.
sacrifices: dewayne.
sighing: suspirar.
spark: chispa, echar chispas, chisme.
vegetation: vegetación.

lichen along the three windows, whose shutters, always closed, were **rotting** away on their **rusty** iron bars. Her thoughts, aimless at first, wandered at random, like her greyhound, who ran round and round in the fields, **yelping** after the yellow butterflies, chasing the shrew-mice, or **nibbling** the poppies on the edge of a cornfield.

Then gradually her ideas took definite shape, and, sitting on the grass that she dug up with little **prods** of her sunshade, Emma repeated to herself, "Good heavens! Why did I marry?"

She asked herself if by some other chance combination it would have not been possible to meet another man; and she tried to imagine what would have been these unrealised events, this different life, this unknown husband. All, surely, could not be like this one. He might have been handsome, witty, distinguished, attractive, such as, no doubt, her old companions of the convent had married. What were they doing now? In town, with the noise of the streets, the **buzz** of the theatres and the lights of the **ballroom**, they were living lives where the heart **expands**, the senses bourgeon out. But she--her life was cold as a **garret** whose **dormer** window looks on the north, and **ennui**, the silent spider, was **weaving** its web in the darkness in every corner of her heart.

She recalled the prize days, when she mounted the platform to receive her little crowns, with her hair in long plaits. In her white **frock** and open prunella shoes she had a pretty way, and when she went back to her seat, the gentlemen bent over her to **congratulate** her; the courtyard was full of carriages; **farewells** were called to her through their windows; the music master with his violin case bowed in passing by. How far all of this! How far away! She called Djali, took her between her knees, and **smoothed** the long delicate head, saying, "Come, kiss mistress; you have no troubles."

Then noting the melancholy face of the **graceful** animal, who **yawned** slowly, she **softened**, and comparing her to herself, spoke to her aloud as to somebody in trouble whom one is **consoling**.

Occasionally there came gusts of winds, breezes from the sea rolling in one sweep over the whole **plateau** of the Caux country, which brought even to these

Spanish

ballroom: salón de baile.
buzz: zumbido, zumbar.
congratulate: felicitar, felicita, feliciten, felicitas, felicitáis, felicitamos, felicito, felicitad, felicitan, felicite, congratular.
consoling: confortar, consolador, consolar, despenar, puesto de control, consola.
dormer: claraboya, dormitorio, buhardilla.
ennui: saciedad, tedio, aburrimiento, cansancio, hastío, fastido, desgano.
expands: se expande.
farewells: adiós.
frock: vestido, hábito.
garret: buhardilla, desván.
graceful: gracioso, elegante, airoso, garboso.
lichen: liquen.
nibbling: corte, Mordiscar.
plateau: meseta, altiplano, altiplanicie.
prods: anima, pincha, pica, instiga, estimula.
rotting: pudrir, podrido, podriendo, corrompiendo, pudriendo, envaneciendo, descomponiendo, macándose.
rusty: mohoso, oxidado, herrumbroso.
smoothed: suavizado.
softened: ablandado.
weaving: tejido, textura, tramar, urdir una trama, hilar, tejeduría, tejer.
yawned: Bostezó.
yelping: gañir, gañido, gañendo, gritar.

fields a salt freshness. The **rushes**, close to the ground, **whistled**; the branches trembled in a swift **rustling**, while their summits, ceaselessly **swaying**, kept up a deep **murmur**. Emma drew her shawl round her shoulders and rose.

In the avenue a green light **dimmed** by the leaves lit up the short **moss** that **crackled** softly beneath her feet. The sun was setting; the sky showed red between the branches, and the **trunks** of the trees, uniform, and planted in a straight line, seemed a brown **colonnade** standing out against a background of gold. A fear took hold of her; she called Djali, and hurriedly returned to Tostes by the high road, threw herself into an **armchair**, and for the rest of the evening did not speak.

But towards the end of September something extraordinary fell upon her life; she was invited by the Marquis d'Andervilliers to Vaubyessard.

Secretary of State under the Restoration, the Marquis, anxious to **re**-enter political life, set about preparing for his **candidature** to the Chamber of Deputies long beforehand. In the winter he distributed a great deal of wood, and in the Conseil General always **enthusiastically** demanded new roads for his **arrondissement**. During the **dog**-days he had suffered from an **abscess**, which Charles had cured as if by miracle by giving a **timely** little touch with the **lancet**. The steward sent to Tostes to pay for the operation reported in the evening that he had seen some superb **cherries** in the doctor's little garden. Now cherry trees did not thrive at Vaubyessard; the Marquis asked Bovary for some **slips**; made it his business to thank his personally; saw Emma; thought she had a pretty figure, and that she did not bow like a peasant; so that he did not think he was going beyond the **bounds** of **condescension**, nor, on the other hand, making a mistake, in **inviting** the young couple.

On Wednesday at three o'clock, Monsieur and Madame Bovary, seated in their dog-cart, set out for Vaubyessard, with a great trunk **strapped** on behind and a bonnet-box in front of the apron. Besides these Charles held a bandbox between his knees.

They arrived at **nightfall**, just as the lamps in the park were being lit to show the way for the carriages.

Spanish

abscess: absceso.
armchair: sillón, butaca.
arrondissement: distrito.
bounds: salta, límites.
candidature: candidatura.
cherries: cerezas.
colonnade: columnata.
condescension: condescendencia.
crackled: abertal, crujido.
dimmed: atenuado.
dog-days: canícula.
enthusiastically: entusiásticamente,

entusiasmadamente, calurosamente, entusiastamente, aficionadamente, firmemente.
inviting: invitando.
lancet: lanceta.
moss: musgo.
murmur: murmurar, murmullo.
nightfall: anochecer.
re-enter: reingresar en, reentre, volver a entrar en.
rushes: copiones.
rustling: crujido, crujiente, frufrú,

susurrar, susurro, abigeato.
slips: comprobantes de pago.
strapped: fajó.
swaying: oscilación, oscilar, ladearse, tambalear, vaivén, que balancea, oscilante, mimbrear, influir en, inclinarse, inclinación lateral.
timely: oportuno, a tiempo.
trunks: traje de baño, bañador, mampara encerradora de la escotilla, pantaloneta, pantalón de baño.
whistled: Silbado.

CHAPTER EIGHT

The **chateau**, a modern building in Italian style, with two projecting wings and three **flights** of steps, lay at the foot of an **immense** green-sward, on which some cows were **grazing** among groups of large trees set out at regular **intervals**, while large **beds** of **arbutus**, **rhododendron**, syringas, and **guelder** roses **bulged** out their **irregular** clusters of green along the **curve** of the **gravel** path. A river flowed under a bridge; through the **mist** one could distinguish buildings with **thatched** roofs **scattered** over the field bordered by two gently **sloping**, well timbered hillocks, and in the background amid the trees rose in two **parallel** lines the coach houses and stables, all that was left of the ruined old chateau.

Charles's dog-cart pulled up before the middle flight of steps; servants appeared; the Marquis came forward, and, offering his arm to the doctor's wife, conducted her to the **vestibule**.

It was **paved** with **marble** slabs, was very **lofty**, and the sound of footsteps and that of voices re-echoed through it as in a church.

Opposite rose a straight staircase, and on the left a gallery overlooking the garden led to the **billiard** room, through whose door one could hear the **click** of the **ivory balls**. As she crossed it to go to the drawing room, Emma saw standing round the table men with grave faces, their chins **resting** on high cravats. They all wore orders, and smiled silently as they made their strokes.

Spanish

arbutus: madroño.
balls: bolas, cojones.
beds: las camas.
billiard: billar.
bulged: Sobresalido.
chateau: castillo.
click: clic, hacer clic, chasquido, pulsar, chasquear.
curve: curva, curvo, curvar, la curva, encorvadura.
flights: vuelos.
grave: tumba, grave, crítico, sepulcro.

gravel: grava, arena gruesa, cascajo, gravilla.
grazing: pasto.
guelder: geldre.
immense: inmenso.
intervals: intervalos.
irregular: irregular.
ivory: marfil, de marfil.
lofty: alto, encumbrado.
marble: mármol, canica, jaspear.
mist: niebla, neblina, bruma.
parallel: paralelo.

paved: pavimentado.
resting: anidación, descansar, en reposo.
rhododendron: rododendro.
scattered: disperso, esparcido.
sloping: costanero, inclinado, desarrollo de una curva gráfica, sesgo, inclinación, en pendiente.
thatched: techar con paja, paja, de paja.
timbered: enmaderó.
vestibule: vestíbulo.

On the dark wainscoting of the walls large gold frames **bore** at the bottom names written in black letters. She read: "Jean-Antoine d'Andervilliers d'Yvervonbille, Count de la Vaubyessard and Baron de la Fresnay, killed at the battle of Coutras on the 20th of October, 1857." And on another: "Jean-Antoine-Henry-Guy d'Andervilliers de la Vaubyessard, Admiral of France and Chevalier of the Order of St. Michael, **wounded** at the battle of the Hougue-Saint-Vaast on the 29th of May, 1692; died at Vaubyessard on the 23rd of January 1693." One could hardly make out those that followed, for the light of the lamps **lowered** over the green cloth **threw** a **dim shadow** round the room. **Burnishing** the **horizontal** pictures, it broke up against these in delicate lines where there were cracks in the **varnish**, and from all these great black **squares** framed in with gold stood out here and there some **lighter portion** of the painting--a pale **brow**, two eyes that looked at you, perukes **flowing** over and **powdering** red-coated shoulders, or the **buckle** of a **garter** above a **well**-rounded calf.

The Marquis opened the drawing room door; one of the ladies (the Marchioness herself) came to meet Emma. She made her sit down by her on an **ottoman**, and began talking to her as **amicably** as if she had known her a long time. She was a woman of about forty, with fine shoulders, a hook nose, a drawling voice, and on this evening she wore over her brown hair a simple guipure fichu that fell in a point at the back. A fair young woman sat in a high-backed chair in a corner; and gentlemen with flowers in their buttonholes were talking to ladies round the fire.

At seven dinner was served. The men, who were in the majority, sat down at the first table in the vestibule; the ladies at the second in the dining room with the Marquis and Marchioness.

Emma, on **entering**, felt herself wrapped round by the warm air, a blending of the perfume of flowers and of the fine linen, of the fumes of the **viands**, and the odour of the truffles. The **silver dish covers** reflected the lighted wax candles in the **candelabra**, the cut **crystal** covered with light **steam** reflected from one to the other pale rays; bouquets were placed in a row the whole length of the table; and in the large-bordered plates each **napkin**, **arranged** after the fashion of a

Spanish

amicably: amistosamente, amigablemente.
arranged: arreglado, organizado, dispuesto.
bore: aburrir, barrena, taladrar, calibre, perforar, barrenar, barreno, perforación.
brow: ceja, frente.
buckle: hebilla, abrochar, corchete.
burnishing: bruñido, Bruñir.
candelabra: candelabro.
covers: casquetes.

crystal: cristal.
dim: oscuro, turbio.
dish: plato, el plato, guiso.
entering: entrando, inscribiendo, montando.
flowing: fluido, corriente.
garter: liga.
horizontal: horizontal.
lighter: encendedor, mechero, gabarra.
lowered: bajado, arriado.
napkin: servilleta, la servilleta.
ottoman: otomano.

portion: porción, parte, ración.
powdering: espolvoreado.
shadow: sombra, sombreado.
silver: plata, la plata, plateado.
squares: plaza, cuadrícula, escuadras.
steam: vapor, cocer al vapor, el vapor.
threw: pret de throw, Tiró, tiro.
varnish: barniz, barnizado, barnizar, charol.
viands: vituallas.
well-rounded: polifacético, rotundo.
wounded: herido, herida.

bishop's **mitre**, held between its two **gaping** folds a small oval shaped roll. The red **claws** of **lobsters** hung over the dishes; rich fruit in open **baskets** was **piled** up on moss; there were quails in their **plumage**; smoke was rising; and in silk stockings, knee-breeches, white **cravat**, and **frilled** shirt, the steward, grave as a judge, offering ready carved dishes between the shoulders of the guests, with a touch of the **spoon** gave you the piece chosen. On the large stove of porcelain **inlaid** with copper baguettes the statue of a woman, draped to the chin, gazed motionless on the room full of life.

Madame Bovary noticed that many ladies had not put their gloves in their glasses.

But at the upper end of the table, alone amongst all these women, bent over his full plate, and his napkin tied round his neck like a child, an old man sat eating, letting drops of **gravy drip** from his mouth. His eyes were **bloodshot**, and he wore a little queue tied with black ribbon. He was the Marquis's **father**-in-law, the old Duke de Laverdiere, once on a time favourite of the Count d'Artois, in the days of the Vaudreuil hunting-parties at the Marquis de Conflans', and had been, it was said, the lover of Queen Marie Antoinette, between Monsieur de Coigny and Monsieur de Lauzun. He had lived a life of noisy **debauch**, full of duels, bets, elopements; he had **squandered** his fortune and frightened all his family. A servant behind his chair named aloud to him in his ear the dishes that he pointed to stammering, and constantly Emma's eyes turned **involuntarily** to this old man with hanging lips, as to something extraordinary. He had lived at court and slept in the bed of queens! **Iced** champagne was poured out. Emma shivered all over as she felt it cold in her mouth. She had never seen pomegranates nor **tasted** pineapples. The **powdered** sugar even seemed to her whiter and finer than elsewhere.

The ladies afterwards went to their rooms to prepare for the ball.

Emma made her toilet with the **fastidious** care of an actress on her debut. She did her hair according to the directions of the **hairdresser**, and put on the barege dress spread out upon the bed.

Charles's trousers were tight across the belly.

Spanish

baskets: las cestas.
bloodshot: encarnizado, inyectado en sangre, inyectado de sangre, sanguinolento.
claws: garras.
cravat: corbata.
debauch: distracción, exceso, libertinaje, orgía, seducir, entregarse al vicio, divertirse por completo, corrupción, corromper, corrompa.
drip: gotear, gota, goteo, gota a gota.
fastidious: descontentadizo,

esquilimoso, delicado, exigente, fastidioso, melindroso, de rapidez.
father-in-law: suegro.
frilled: volado.
gaping: abertura, hueco, abrir la boca, abrir boquete en, boquete, vacío, boquiabierto, bostezar, intervalo, abrir brecha en, bostezo.
gravy: salsa, jugo.
iced: escarchado.
inlaid: pret y pp de inlay, incrustado,

embutido.
involuntarily: involuntariamente.
lobsters: las langostas.
mitre: mitra, inglete.
piled: amontonado.
plumage: plumaje.
powdered: empolvar, empolvarse, en polvo, pólvora, polvo, polvorear, pulverizado, pulverizar.
spoon: cuchara, la cuchara.
squandered: malgastado, derrochado.
tasted: gusto, Probado.

"My trouser-straps will be rather awkward for dancing," he said.

"Dancing?" repeated Emma.

"Yes!"

"Why, you must be mad! They would make fun of you; keep your place. Besides, it is more becoming for a doctor," she added.

Charles was silent. He walked up and down waiting for Emma to finish dressing.

He saw her from behind in the glass between two lights. Her black eyes seemed blacker than ever. Her hair, **undulating** towards the ears, shone with a blue **lustre**; a rose in her chignon trembled on its mobile **stalk**, with artificial dewdrops on the tip of the leaves. She wore a gown of pale **saffron trimmed** with three bouquets of **pompon** roses mixed with green.

Charles came and kissed her on her shoulder.

"Let me alone!" she said; "you are **tumbling** me."

One could hear the **flourish** of the violin and the notes of a horn. She went downstairs **restraining** herself from running.

Dancing had begun. Guests were arriving. There was some **crushing**.

She sat down on a form near the door.

The **quadrille** over, the floor was occupied by groups of men standing up and talking and servants in **livery** bearing large **trays**. Along the line of seated women painted fans were **fluttering**, bouquets half hid smiling faces, and gold **stoppered** scent-bottles were turned in partly-closed hands, whose white gloves outlined the nails and **tightened** on the flesh at the wrists. Lace **trimmings**, diamond brooches, **medallion bracelets** trembled on bodices, **gleamed** on breasts, clinked on bare arms.

The hair, well-smoothed over the temples and **knotted** at the **nape**, bore crowns, or **bunches**, or sprays of mytosotis, **jasmine**, **pomegranate** blossoms, ears of corn, and corn-flowers. Calmly seated in their places, mothers with **forbidding** countenances were wearing red turbans.

Spanish

bracelets: esposas.
bunches: coletas.
crushing: aplastante, aplastar, estrujado, trituración.
flourish: florecer, florecemos, florezco, florezcan, florezca, florecen, florecéis, floreced, florece, floreces, prosperar.
fluttering: revolotear.
forbidding: prohibiendo, prohibitivo.
gleamed: brillado.
jasmine: jazmín.
knotted: anudado.

livery: librea.
lustre: brillantez.
medallion: medallón.
nape: nuca, cogote.
pomegranate: granada.
pompon: borla, rosa de pitiminí, variedad de crisantemo.
quadrille: cuadrilla.
restraining: conteniendo, refrenando, reprimiendo.
saffron: azafrán.
stalk: tallo, pedúnculo.

stoppered: tapado.
tightened: apretado.
trays: bandejas.
trimmed: recortado.
trimmings: recortes, arrequives, poda, guarnición, recorte, adorno, accesorios, adornos.
tumbling: pérdida de estabilidad, pérdida de referencia, volteador, volteo, acrobacia, movimiento de rotación, derribar.
undulating: Ondular, ondeo.

Emma's heart beat rather faster when, her partner holding her by the **tips** of the fingers, she took her place in a line with the **dancers**, and waited for the first note to start. But her emotion soon **vanished**, and, swaying to the rhythm of the orchestra, she glided forward with slight movements of the neck. A smile rose to her lips at certain delicate **phrases** of the violin, that sometimes played alone while the other instruments were silent; one could hear the clear **clink** of the louis d'or that were being thrown down upon the card tables in the next room; then all struck again, the cornet-a-piston **uttered** its sonorous note, feet marked time, **skirts swelled** and **rustled**, hands touched and parted; the same eyes falling before you met yours again.

A few men (some fifteen or so), of twenty-five to forty, scattered here and there among the dancers or talking at the doorways, distinguished themselves from the crowd by a certain air of **breeding**, whatever their differences in age, dress, or face.

Their clothes, better made, seemed of finer cloth, and their hair, brought forward in curls towards the temples, **glossy** with more delicate pomades. They had the **complexion** of wealth--that clear complexion that is **heightened** by the **pallor** of porcelain, the **shimmer** of satin, the **veneer** of old furniture, and that an ordered **regimen** of **exquisite nurture maintains** at its best. Their necks moved easily in their low cravats, their long whiskers fell over their turned-down collars, they **wiped** their lips upon handkerchiefs with **embroidered** initials that gave forth a subtle perfume. Those who were beginning to grow old had an air of youth, while there was something mature in the faces of the young. In their **unconcerned** looks was the calm of passions daily **satiated**, and through all their **gentleness** of manner **pierced** that peculiar **brutality**, the result of a command of half-easy things, in which force is exercised and **vanity** amused--the management of **thoroughbred** horses and the society of loose women.

A few steps from Emma a gentleman in a blue coat was talking of Italy with a pale young woman wearing a parure of **pearls**.

They were **praising** the **breadth** of the columns of St. **Peter's**, Tivoly, Vesuvius, Castellamare, and Cassines, the roses of Genoa, the Coliseum by

Spanish

breadth: ancho, amplitud, anchura.
breeding: cría, crianza, reproducción.
brutality: brutalidad.
clink: tintín.
complexion: cutis, tez.
dancers: bailadores, bailarines.
embroidered: bordado.
exquisite: exquisito.
gentleness: apacibilidad, suavidad.
glossy: brillante, lustroso.
heightened: sublimado, levantado,
    elevado.

maintains: mantiene, conserva.
nurture: crianza.
pallor: palidez.
pearls: perlas.
peter's: peter.
phrases: batería libre de
    mantenimiento -- menor tiempo de
    respuesta de servicio.
pierced: agujereado.
praising: alabar.
regimen: régimen.
rustled: susurrado.

satiated: harto, saciada.
shimmer: luz trémula, vibración.
skirts: afueras.
swelled: hinchado.
thoroughbred: animal de casta.
tips: propinas.
unconcerned: indiferente.
uttered: pronunciado.
vanished: desaparecido.
vanity: vanidad.
veneer: chapa.
wiped: limpiado, Enjugado.

moonlight. With her other ear Emma was listening to a conversation full of words she did not understand. A circle gathered round a very young man who the week before had beaten "Miss Arabella" and "Romolus," and won two thousand louis jumping a ditch in England. One complained that his **racehorses** were growing fat; another of the printers' errors that had **disfigured** the name of his horse.

The atmosphere of the ball was heavy; the lamps were growing dim.

Guests were **flocking** to the billiard room. A servant got upon a chair and broke the window-panes. At the crash of the glass Madame Bovary turned her head and saw in the garden the faces of **peasants** pressed against the window looking in at them. Then the memory of the **Bertaux** came back to her. She saw the farm again, the **muddy pond**, her father in a **blouse** under the apple trees, and she saw herself again as formerly, **skimming** with her finger the cream off the milk-pans in the **dairy**. But in the **refulgence** of the present hour her past life, so distinct until then, **faded** away completely, and she almost **doubted** having lived it. She was there; beyond the ball was only shadow overspreading all the rest. She was just eating a **maraschino** ice that she held with her left hand in a silver-gilt cup, her eyes half-closed, and the spoon between her teeth.

A lady near her dropped her **fan**. A gentlemen was passing.

"Would you be so good," said the lady, "as to pick up my fan that has fallen behind the sofa?"

The gentleman **bowed**, and as he moved to stretch out his arm, Emma saw the hand of a young woman throw something white, **folded** in a **triangle**, into his hat. The gentleman, picking up the fan, offered it to the lady **respectfully**; she **thanked** him with an **inclination** of the head, and began **smelling** her bouquet.

After supper, where were plenty of Spanish and Rhine wines, **soups** a la **bisque** and au lait d'amandes, puddings a la Trafalgar, and all sorts of cold meats with jellies that trembled in the dishes, the carriages one after the other began to drive off. Raising the corners of the **muslin curtain**, one could see the light of their lanterns **glimmering** through the darkness. The seats began to empty, some card-players were still left; the musicians were cooling the tips of

Spanish

au: unidad administrativa.
bisque: Biscocho, bizcocho, sopa de mariscos, helado de avellana, ventajas, porcelana blanca.
blouse: blusa, la blusa.
bowed: agobiado, arqueado, cabizbajo, encorvado, inclinado.
curtain: cortina, la cortina.
dairy: lechería.
disfigured: desfigurado.
doubted: dudado.
faded: marchitado, se ajado,

descolorado, despintado, desvaído, descolorirse, descolorido, descolorar, desaparecer, debilitarse, borroso.
fan: ventilador, abanico, animar, entusiasta, incitar, el ventilador, hincha, aficionado, admirador.
flocking: flocado, congregar.
folded: doblado.
glimmering: resplandor, alborear, brillar, luz ténue, vislumbre.
inclination: inclinación, tentación.
maraschino: marrasquino.

muddy: embarrado, fangoso, lodoso.
muslin: muselina.
peasants: campesinado.
pond: estanque, charca, el estanque.
racehorses: caballos de carreras.
refulgence: refulgencia, brillantez.
respectfully: respetuosamente.
skimming: desnatando.
smelling: oler.
soups: sopas.
thanked: agradecido.
triangle: triángulo, triangulo.

their fingers on their **tongues**. Charles was half **asleep**, his back **propped** against a door.

At three o'clock the **cotillion** began. Emma did not know how to **waltz**. Everyone was waltzing, Mademoiselle d'Andervilliers herself and the Marquis; only the guests **staying** at the castle were still there, about a **dozen** persons.

One of the waltzers, however, who was **familiarly** called Viscount, and whose low cut waistcoat seemed **moulded** to his chest, came a second time to ask Madame Bovary to **dance**, **assuring** her that he would guide her, and that she would get through it very well.

They began slowly, then went more **rapidly**. They turned; all around them was turning--the lamps, the furniture, the wainscoting, the floor, like a **disc** on a **pivot**. On passing near the doors the bottom of Emma's dress caught against his trousers.

Their legs **commingled**; he looked down at her; she raised her eyes to his. A **torpor seized** her; she stopped. They started again, and with a more rapid movement; the Viscount, dragging her along disappeared with her to the end of the gallery, where **panting**, she almost fell, and for a moment rested her head upon his breast. And then, still turning, but more slowly, he **guided** her back to her seat. She **leaned** back against the wall and covered her eyes with her hands.

When she opened them again, in the middle of the drawing room three waltzers were kneeling before a lady sitting on a **stool**.

She **chose** the Viscount, and the violin struck up once more.

Everyone looked at them. They passed and re-passed, she with **rigid** body, her **chin** bent down, and he always in the same **pose**, his figure curved, his elbow **rounded**, his chin thrown forward. That woman knew how to waltz! They kept up a long time, and **tired** out all the others.

Then they talked a few moments longer, and after the goodnights, or rather good mornings, the guests of the chateau **retired** to bed.

Charles dragged himself up by the **balusters**. His "knees were going up into his body." He had spent five **consecutive** hours standing bolt upright at the card

Spanish

asleep: dormido.
assuring: asegurando.
balusters: barandilla.
chin: barba, barbilla, la barbilla, mentón.
chose: escoger.
commingled: Mezclada.
consecutive: consecutivo, sucesivo.
cotillion: cotillón.
dance: bailar, baile, danza, danzar, el baile.
disc: disco.

dozen: docena, la docena.
familiarly: conocidamente, con demasiada confianza, familiarmente.
guided: dirigido, guiado, indicado, teledirigido.
leaned: inclinado, ladeado.
moulded: amoldado, modelado, Moldeado.
panting: jadeante, palpitación.
pivot: pivote.
pose: darse tono, ser presuntuoso, ponerse, postura, plantear, posar.

propped: sostenido.
rapid: rápido.
retired: jubilado, retirado, pensionado.
rigid: rígido.
rounded: redondeado.
seized: agarrado, asido.
staying: quedando, permaneciendo.
stool: taburete.
tired: cansado.
tongues: lenguas.
torpor: estupor.
waltz: vals.

tables, watching them play whist, without understanding anything about it, and it was with a deep sigh of relief that he pulled off his boots.

Emma threw a shawl over her shoulders, opened the window, and **leant** out.

The night was dark; some drops of rain were falling. She **breathed** in the **damp** wind that **refreshed** her eyelids. The music of the ball was still **murmuring** in her ears. And she tried to keep herself **awake** in order to **prolong** the **illusion** that this **luxurious** life that she would soon have to give up.

Day began to break. She looked long at the windows of the chateau, trying to guess which were the rooms of all those she had noticed the evening before. She would **fain** have known their lives, have penetrated, **blended** with them. But she was shivering with cold. She **undressed**, and **cowered** down between the sheets against Charles, who was asleep.

There were a great many people to **luncheon**. The **repast lasted** ten minutes; no **liqueurs** were served, which **astonished** the doctor.

Next, Mademoiselle d'Andervilliers collected some pieces of roll in a small basket to take them to the swans on the **ornamental** waters, and they went to walk in the hot-houses, where strange plants, bristling with hairs, rose in pyramids under hanging vases, whence, as from **over**-filled nests of **serpents**, fell long green cords **interlacing**. The **orangery**, which was at the other end, led by a covered way to the outhouses of the chateau. The Marquis, to amuse the young woman, took her to see the stables.

Above the basket-shaped racks porcelain slabs bore the names of the horses in black letters. Each animal in its **stall** whisked its tail when anyone went near and said "Tchk! tchk!" The boards of the harness room shone like the flooring of a drawing room. The carriage harness was piled up in the middle against two **twisted columns**, and the bits, the whips, the spurs, the **curbs**, were **ranged** in a line all along the wall.

Charles, meanwhile, went to ask a **groom** to put his horse to. The dog-cart was brought to the foot of the steps, and, all the parcels being crammed in, the

---

Spanish

astonished: asombrado, sorprendido, estupefacto.
awake: despierto, despertar, despertarse.
blended: mezclado.
breathed: respirado.
columns: columnas.
cowered: se acurrucado, se agachado.
curbs: limita.
damp: húmedo, mojar, humedad.
fain: dispuesto.
groom: novio.

illusion: ilusión, espejismo.
interlacing: enlazamiento, entrelazado, enlace, encruzamiento, entrelazando, concatenando.
lasted: Durado.
leant: pret y pp de lean.
liqueurs: licores.
luncheon: almuerzo.
luxurious: lujoso, suntuoso.
murmuring: murmurar.
orangery: invernadero de naranjos.
ornamental: decorativo, ornamental.

over-filled: sature.
prolong: prolongar, prolongáis, prolonguen, prolongo, prolongas, prolongamos, prolongad, prolonga, prolongan, prolongue.
ranged: recorrido.
refreshed: refrescado.
repast: comida.
serpents: serpientes.
stall: establo, cuadra, puesto, casilla.
twisted: retorcido, torcido.
undressed: sin curtir.

Bovarys paid their **respects** to the Marquis and Marchioness and set out again for Tostes.

Emma watched the turning wheels in silence. Charles, on the **extreme** edge of the seat, held the **reins** with his two arms wide **apart**, and the little horse **ambled** along in the shafts that were too big for him. The **loose** reins hanging over his **crupper** were **wet** with **foam**, and the box fastened on behind the chaise gave great regular **bumps** against it.

They were on the heights of Thibourville when suddenly some horsemen with cigars between their lips passed laughing. Emma thought she **recognized** the Viscount, turned back, and caught on the **horizon** only the movement of the heads **rising** or falling with the **unequal cadence** of the trot or gallop.

A **mile farther** on they had to stop to mend with some **string** the traces that had broken.

But Charles, giving a last look to the harness, saw something on the ground between his horse's legs, and he **picked** up a **cigar**-case with a green **silk** border and beblazoned in the centre like the door of a **carriage**.

"There are even two cigars in it," said he; "they'll do for this evening after dinner."

"Why, do you smoke?" she asked.

"Sometimes, when I get a chance."

He put his find in his pocket and **whipped** up the **nag**.

When they reached home the dinner was not ready. Madame lost her **temper**. Nastasie **answered rudely**.

"Leave the room!" said Emma. "You are forgetting yourself. I give you warning."

For dinner there was **onion soup** and a piece of veal with sorrel.

Charles, seated opposite Emma, **rubbed** his hands **gleefully**.

"How good it is to be at home again!"

Spanish

ambled: Andado.
answered: contesta, Contestado.
apart: aparte, por separado, particular, separado.
bumps: badén, irregularidades.
cadence: cadencia.
carriage: coche, carro, cureña.
cigar-case: cigarrera.
crupper: baticola, grupa.
extreme: extremo.
farther: más lejos.
foam: espuma, la espuma.

gleefully: gozosamente, alegremente.
horizon: horizonte.
loose: suelto, flojo.
mile: legua, milla, la milla.
nag: rocín, jaca.
onion: cebolla, la cebolla.
picked: picado.
recognized: reconocido.
reins: riñones, rienda, riendas.
respects: rispetti, saludos, recuerdos.
rising: creciente, subida, alcista.
rubbed: frotado.

rudely: grosero, groseramente, bastamente, rudamente.
silk: seda, la seda.
soup: sopa, la sopa.
string: cuerda, cadena, mondar habas, cordón.
temper: humor, genio, templar, temperamento.
unequal: desigual.
wet: mojado, húmedo, mojar, humedecer.
whipped: batido, Azotado.

Nastasie could be heard crying. He was rather **fond** of the poor girl. She had formerly, during the wearisome time of his **widowhood**, kept him company many an evening. She had been his first patient, his **oldest** acquaintance in the place.

"Have you given her warning for good?" he asked at last.

"Yes. Who is to prevent me?" she replied.

Then they **warmed** themselves in the kitchen while their room was being made ready. Charles began to smoke. He smoked with lips **protruding**, spitting every moment, **recoiling** at every **puff**.

"You'll make yourself ill," she said **scornfully**.

He put down his **cigar** and ran to **swallow** a glass of cold water at the **pump**. Emma **seizing** hold of the cigar case threw it quickly to the back of the cupboard.

The next day was a long one. She walked about her little garden, up and down the same **walks, stopping** before the beds, before the **espalier**, before the plaster **curate**, looking with **amazement** at all these things of once-on-a-time that she knew so well. How far off the ball seemed already! What was it that thus set so far **asunder** the morning of the day before yesterday and the evening of **to-**day? Her journey to Vaubyessard had made a hole in her life, like one of those great **crevices** that a storm will sometimes make in one night in mountains. Still she was resigned. She **devoutly** put away in her drawers her beautiful dress, down to the satin shoes whose soles were **yellowed** with the **slippery** wax of the **dancing** floor. Her heart was like these. In its **friction** against wealth something had come over it that could not be **effaced**.

The memory of this ball, then, became an occupation for Emma.

Whenever the Wednesday came round she said to herself as she awoke, "Ah! I was there a week--a fortnight--three weeks ago."

And little by little the faces grew confused in her remembrance.

She forgot the tune of the quadrilles; she no longer saw the **liveries** and appointments so **distinctly**; some details escaped her, but the **regret** remained with her.

Spanish

amazement: asombro, pasmo.
asunder: separadamente.
cigar: cigarro, puro, el puro, el cigarro, cigarro puro.
crevices: grieta.
curate: coadjutor, cura.
dancing: bailando, baile.
devoutly: devotamente, beatamente.
distinctly: distintamente.
effaced: borrado.
espalier: espaldera.
fond: aficionado.

friction: fricción, rozamiento, frotación.
liveries: Libreas.
oldest: mayor.
protruding: sobresaliendo, sobresaliente.
puff: bollo esponjado, bocanada, soplo.
pump: bomba, bombear, dar a la bomba.
recoiling: retráctil.
regret: sentir, lamentar, deplorar,

arrepentirse, pesar.
scornfully: desdeñosamente.
seizing: agarrando, asiendo.
slippery: resbaladizo, escurridizo.
stopping: parando, deteniendo.
swallow: golondrina, tragar, golondrina común, deglutir.
to-day: hoy.
walks: anda, camina.
warmed: entibiado.
widowhood: viudez.
yellowed: amarillo.

CHAPTER NINE

Often when Charles was out she took from the cupboard, between the folds of the linen where she had left it, the green silk cigar case. She looked at it, opened it, and even **smelt** the odour of the lining--a **mixture** of **verbena** and **tobacco**. Whose was it? The Viscount's? Perhaps it was a present from his **mistress**. It had been embroidered on some **rosewood frame**, a pretty little thing, **hidden** from all eyes, that had **occupied** many hours, and over which had fallen the soft curls of the **pensive worker**. A breath of love had passed over the **stitches** on the canvas; each **prick** of the **needle** had fixed there a hope or a memory, and all those **interwoven** threads of silk were but the **continuity** of the same silent passion. And then one morning the Viscount had taken it away with him. Of what had they **spoken** when it lay upon the wide-mantelled **chimneys** between flower-vases and Pompadour clocks? She was at Tostes; he was at Paris now, far away! What was this Paris like? What a **vague** name! She **repeated** it in a low voice, for the **mere** pleasure of it; it **rang** in her **ears** like a great **cathedral bell**; it shone before her eyes, even on the **labels** of her pomade-pots.

At night, when the **carriers** passed under her windows in their carts **singing** the "Marjolaine," she awoke, and listened to the noise of the iron-bound wheels, which, as they **gained** the country road, was soon **deadened** by the soil. "They will be there to-morrow!" she said to herself.

Spanish

bell: timbre, campana, campanilla, la campana.
carriers: operadores, aseguradoras.
cathedral: catedral.
chimneys: chimeneas.
continuity: continuidad.
deadened: amortiguado, amortizado.
ears: orejas, las orejas, oídos.
frame: marco, trama, bastidor, chasis, armadura, armazón, cuadro, estructura, enmarcar.
gained: ganado.

hidden: ocultado, oculto, escondido, secreto.
interwoven: entretejido.
labels: etiquetas.
mere: mero.
mistress: señora.
mixture: mezcla, la mezcla.
needle: aguja, alfiler, la aguja.
occupied: ocupado, desempeñado.
pensive: pensativo.
prick: pinchar, punzada, polla.
rang: sonó, pret de ring.

repeated: repetido.
rosewood: palisandro, palosanto, palo de rosa.
singing: cantando, canto.
smelt: eperlano.
spoken: hablado.
stitches: puntos de sutura, los puntos de sutura.
tobacco: tabaco.
vague: vago.
verbena: verbena.
worker: trabajador, obrero, laborante.

And she followed them in thought up and down the hills, **traversing** villages, gliding along the highroads by the light of the stars. At the end of some **indefinite** distance there was always a **confused** spot, into which her dream died.

She bought a plan of Paris, and with the tip of her finger on the map she walked about the capital. She went up the boulevards, stopping at every turning, between the lines of the streets, in front of the white squares that represented the houses. At last she would close the **lids** of her weary eyes, and see in the darkness the gas **jets flaring** in the wind and the steps of carriages lowered with much noise before the peristyles of theatres.

She took in "La Corbeille," a lady's journal, and the "Sylphe des Salons." She **devoured**, without **skipping** a work, all the accounts of first nights, **races**, and soirees, took interest in the **debut** of a **singer**, in the opening of a new shop. She knew the **latest fashions**, the **addresses** of the best **tailors**, the days of the Bois and the Opera. In Eugene Sue she studied descriptions of furniture; she read Balzac and George Sand, seeking in them **imaginary** satisfaction for her own desires. Even at table she had her book by her, and turned over the pages while Charles **ate** and talked to her. The memory of the Viscount always returned as she read. Between him and the imaginary personages she made comparisons. But the circle of which he was the centre gradually **widened** round him, and the **aureole** that he bore, **fading** from his form, **broadened** out beyond, **lighting** up her other **dreams**.

Paris, more vague than the **ocean**, glimmered before Emma's eyes in an atmosphere of **vermilion**. The many lives that stirred amid this **tumult** were, however, divided into parts, classed as distinct pictures. Emma **perceived** only two or three that **hid** from her all the rest, and in themselves represented all **humanity**. The world of ambassadors moved over **polished floors** in drawing rooms **lined** with mirrors, round oval tables covered with velvet and gold-fringed cloths. There were dresses with **trains**, deep mysteries, **anguish** hidden beneath smiles. Then came the society of the duchesses; all were pale; all got up at four o'clock; the women, poor angels, wore English point on their petticoats;

Spanish

addresses: direcciones.
anguish: angustia, miedo, angustiar.
ate: comí.
aureole: aureola.
broadened: Ensanchado.
confused: confuso, confundido.
debut: debú, debut, debutar, estreno, noche primera, presentación, primera vez.
devoured: devorado.
dreams: sueños.
fading: desvanecimiento.

fashions: modas.
flaring: abocinado.
floors: Suelo, solados - forjados.
hid: escondió, pret de hide.
humanity: humanidad.
imaginary: imaginario.
indefinite: indefinido.
jets: azabaches, chorros.
lids: cubiertas.
lighting: iluminación, alumbrado.
lined: rayado.
ocean: océano.

perceived: percibido.
polished: fino, pulido, esmerado.
races: carreras.
singer: cantor, cantora, cantante, el cantor.
skipping: saltar, salto a la comba.
tailors: sastres.
trains: trenes.
traversing: Atravesar.
tumult: tumulto, ruido.
vermilion: bermellón.
widened: Ensanchado.

and the men, **unappreciated** geniuses under a **frivolous outward seeming**, rode horses to death at pleasure parties, spent the summer season at Baden, and towards the **forties** married **heiresses**. In the private rooms of restaurants, where one **sups** after midnight by the light of wax candles, laughed the **motley** crowd of men of letters and **actresses**. They were **prodigal** as kings, full of ideal, ambitious, fantastic **frenzy**. This was an existence outside that of all others, between heaven and earth, in the midst of storms, having something of the **sublime**. For the rest of the world it was lost, with no particular place and as if non-existent. The nearer things were, moreover, the more her thoughts turned away from them. All her immediate surroundings, the wearisome country, the middle-class **imbeciles**, the **mediocrity** of existence, seemed to her exceptional, a peculiar chance that had caught hold of her, while beyond stretched, as far as eye could see, an immense land of joys and passions. She confused in her desire the sensualities of luxury with the delights of the heart, **elegance** of manners with **delicacy** of sentiment. Did not love, like Indian plants, need a special soil, a particular temperature? Signs by moonlight, long embraces, tears flowing over **yielded** hands, all the fevers of the flesh and the languors of tenderness could not be separated from the balconies of great **castles** full of **indolence**, from boudoirs with silken curtains and thick carpets, well-filled flower-stands, a bed on a raised dias, nor from the **flashing** of precious stones and the shoulder-knots of liveries.

The lad from the **posting** house who came to groom the mare every morning passed through the passage with his heavy wooden shoes; there were holes in his blouse; his feet were bare in list slippers. And this was the groom in knee-britches with whom she had to be content! His work done, he did not come back again all day, for Charles on his return put up his horse himself, **unsaddled** him and put on the **halter**, while the servant-girl brought a bundle of straw and threw it as best she could into the **manger**.

To replace Nastasie (who left Tostes **shedding torrents** of tears) Emma took into her service a young girl of fourteen, an **orphan** with a sweet face. She **forbade** her wearing cotton caps, taught her to address her in the third person, to bring a glass of water on a plate, to knock before coming into a room, to iron,

Spanish

actresses: actrices.
castles: castillos.
delicacy: manjar, dulce, delicadeza.
elegance: elegancia.
flashing: destello.
forbade: pret de forbid, entredicho, prohibió.
forties: años cuarenta.
frenzy: frenesí.
frivolous: frívolo, hueco.
halter: cabestro.
heiresses: herederas.

imbeciles: imbéciles.
indolence: indolencia.
manger: pesebre.
mediocrity: mediocridad.
motley: abigarramiento, abigarrado, multicolor.
orphan: huérfano.
outward: exterior.
posting: puesto, expedición, remitir, mostrar, poste, destino, pase de asientos, anunciar, mandar por correo, mandar, fijar.

prodigal: pródigo.
seeming: pareciendo.
shedding: derramamiento.
sublime: sublimas, sublima, sublimen, sublimo, sublime, sublimamos, sublimad, sublimáis, subliman, admirable, bello.
sups: cena, sorbos.
torrents: torrentes.
unappreciated: no apreciado.
unsaddled: desazonado, desensillado.
yielded: cedido, Rendido, rentado.

starch, and to dress her--wanted to make a lady's-maid of her. The new servant obeyed without a murmur, so as not to be sent away; and as madame usually left the key in the **sideboard**, Felicite every evening took a small supply of sugar that she ate alone in her bed after she had said her prayers.

Sometimes in the afternoon she went to chat with the postilions.

Madame was in her room upstairs. She wore an open **dressing** gown that showed between the shawl **facings** of her bodice a **pleated** chamisette with three gold buttons. Her belt was a **corded girdle** with great tassels, and her small **garnet** coloured slippers had a large **knot** of ribbon that fell over her instep. She had bought herself a **blotting** book, writing case, pen-holder, and envelopes, although she had no one to write to; she dusted her what-not, looked at herself in the glass, picked up a book, and then, dreaming between the lines, let it drop on her knees. She longed to travel or to go back to her convent. She wished at the same time to die and to live in Paris.

Charles in snow and rain **trotted** across country. He ate omelettes on **farmhouse** tables, **poked** his arm into damp beds, received the **tepid spurt** of blood-lettings in his face, listened to death-rattles, examined basins, turned over a good deal of dirty linen; but every evening he found a **blazing** fire, his dinner ready, easy-chairs, and a **well**-dressed woman, charming with an odour of freshness, though no one could say whence the perfume came, or if it were not her skin that made **odorous** her **chemise**.

She **charmed** him by numerous attentions; now it was some new way of **arranging** paper **sconces** for the candles, a **flounce** that she altered on her gown, or an extraordinary name for some very simple dish that the servant had spoilt, but that Charles swallowed with pleasure to the last **mouthful**. At Rouen she saw some ladies who wore a **bunch** of **charms** on the watch-chains; she bought some charms. She wanted for her mantelpiece two large blue glass vases, and some time after an ivory necessaire with a silver-gilt **thimble**. The less Charles understood these refinements the more they **seduced** him. They added something to the pleasure of the **senses** and to the comfort of his **fireside**. It was like a golden dust **sanding** all along the narrow path of his life.

Spanish

arranging: arreglando, organizando, disponiendo.
blazing: llameante.
blotting: oreo, secar.
bunch: manojo, racimo.
charmed: encantado.
charms: amuletos.
chemise: camisa.
corded: cortado, con cuerda.
dressing: abono, preparación, aliño, apósito.
facings: vueltas, paramentos.

farmhouse: masía, masada, granja, cortijo, casa de labor, alquería.
fireside: hogar, chimenea.
flounce: salir enfadado, volante, moverse torpemente, sacudida.
garnet: granate.
girdle: cinto, cinturón, pretina, faja.
knot: nudo, correlimos gordo, lazo.
mouthful: bocado.
odorous: oloroso.
pleated: plisado.
poked: metido.

sanding: lijado, smerigliatura.
sconces: fortines.
seduced: seducido.
senses: juicio, los sentidos, sentido.
sideboard: armario, aparador.
spurt: borbotón.
starch: almidón, fécula, almidonar.
tepid: tibio.
thimble: dedal.
trotted: Trotado.
well-dressed: acicalado, bien entrazado, bien vestido.

He was well, looked well; his reputation was firmly established.

The country-folk loved him because he was not proud. He **petted** the children, never went to the public house, and, moreover, his **morals inspired** confidence. He was **specially** successful with catarrhs and chest complaints. Being much afraid of **killing** his patients, Charles, in fact only **prescribed** sedatives, from time to time and **emetic**, a **footbath**, or **leeches**. It was not that he was afraid of surgery; he **bled** people **copiously** like horses, and for the taking out of teeth he had the "devil's own wrist."

Finally, to keep up with the times, he took in "La Ruche Medicale," a new **journal** whose **prospectus** had been sent him. He read it a little after dinner, but in about five minutes the warmth of the room added to the effect of his dinner sent him to sleep; and he sat there, his chin on his two hands and his hair spreading like a mane to the foot of the **lamp**. Emma looked at him and shrugged her shoulders. Why, at least, was not her husband one of those men of **taciturn** passions who work at their books all night, and at last, when about sixty, the age of **rheumatism** sets in, wear a string of orders on their ill-fitting black coat? She could have wished this name of Bovary, which was hers, had been illustrious, to see it displayed at the booksellers', repeated in the newspapers, known to all France. But Charles had no **ambition**.

An Yvetot doctor whom he had **lately** met in consultation had somewhat **humiliated** him at the very **bedside** of the patient, before the **assembled** relatives. When, in the evening, Charles told her this **anecdote**, Emma **inveighed** **loudly** against his **colleague**. Charles was much touched. He **kissed** her forehead with a **tear** in his eyes. But she was **angered** with shame; she felt a wild desire to strike him; she went to open the window in the passage and breathed in the fresh air to **calm** herself.

"What a man! What a man!" she said in a low voice, biting her lips.

Besides, she was becoming more irritated with him. As he grew older his manner grew heavier; at dessert he cut the corks of the empty **bottles**; after eating he **cleaned** his teeth with his tongue; in taking soup he made a gurgling

Spanish

ambition: ambición, aspiración.
anecdote: anécdota.
angered: enojado.
assembled: ensamblado, congregado.
bedside: lado de la cama, cabecera.
bled: Sangrado.
bottles: las botellas.
calm: tranquilo, calma, calmar, quieto, silencio, sosegado, sosegar, aquietar, sereno.
cleaned: limpiado.
colleague: colega, compañero.

copiously: copiosamente.
emetic: emético, vomitivo.
footbath: baño de pies.
humiliated: humillado.
inspired: inspirado.
inveighed: vituperado.
journal: diario, periódico, gorrón, revista, muñón, libro diario.
killing: matanza.
kissed: Besado.
lamp: lámpara, la lámpara.
lately: últimamente.

leeches: sanguijelas.
loudly: en alta voz, ruidosamente.
morals: moral, moralidad.
petted: acariciado.
prescribed: prescrito, recetado.
prospectus: prospecto, prospecto de emisión.
rheumatism: reumatismo, reuma.
specially: especialmente.
taciturn: taciturno, taciturna.
tear: lágrima, desgarrar, rajar, romper, rasgar, desgarro.

noise with every **spoonful**; and, as he was getting **fatter**, the puffed-out cheeks seemed to push the eyes, always small, up to the temples.

Sometimes Emma tucked the red borders of his under-vest **unto** his waistcoat, **rearranged** his cravat, and threw away the dirty gloves he was going to put on; and this was not, as he **fancied**, for himself; it was for herself, by a **diffusion** of **egotism**, of nervous **irritation**. Sometimes, too, she told him of what she had read, such as a passage in a novel, of a new play, or an anecdote of the "upper ten" that she had seen in a **feuilleton**; for, after all, Charles was something, an ever-open ear, and ever-ready **approbation**. She **confided** many a thing to her greyhound. She would have done so to the **logs** in the fireplace or to the **pendulum** of the clock.

At the bottom of her heart, however, she was waiting for something to happen. Like **shipwrecked sailors**, she turned **despairing** eyes upon the solitude of her life, seeking **afar** off some white sail in the mists of the horizon. She did not know what this chance would be, what wind would bring it her, towards what shore it would drive her, if it would be a **shallop** or a three-decker, **laden** with anguish or full of **bliss** to the portholes. But each morning, as she awoke, she hoped it would come that day; she listened to every sound, **sprang** up with a start, wondered that it did not come; then at sunset, always more saddened, she longed for the **morrow**.

Spring came round. With the first warm weather, when the pear trees began to blossom, she suffered from **dyspnoea**.

From the beginning of July she counted how many weeks there were to October, thinking that perhaps the Marquis d'Andervilliers would give another ball at Vaubyessard. But all September passed without letters or visits.

After the ennui of this **disappointment** her heart once more remained empty, and then the same series of days recommenced. So now they would thus follow one another, always the same, **immovable**, and bringing nothing. Other lives, however flat, had at least the chance of some event. One **adventure** sometimes brought with it **infinite** consequences and the scene changed. But nothing

Spanish

adventure: aventura.
afar: lejos.
approbation: aprobación.
bliss: beatitud.
confided: Confiado.
despairing: sin esperanza, desesperación, desesperado, desesperanza, desesperanzarse, desesperar.
diffusion: difusión.
disappointment: desilusión, decepción.

dyspnoea: disnea.
egotism: egotismo.
fancied: preferido, imaginario.
fatter: más gordo.
feuilleton: folletín.
immovable: inconmovible, inamovible, que no se puede mover, inmovible, inmoble, inmobiliario, inmóvil, fijo, inalterable.
infinite: infinito.
irritation: irritación.
laden: cargado, abrumado.

logs: bloques, libros de control, troncos.
morrow: día siguiente.
pendulum: péndulo.
rearranged: reorganizado.
sail: vela, navegar, la vela.
sailors: marinería.
shallop: chalupa.
shipwrecked: náufrago.
spoonful: cucharada.
sprang: pret de spring, saltó.
unto: hacia.

happened to her; God had **willed** it so! The future was a dark corridor, with its door at the end shut fast.

She gave up music. What was the good of playing? Who would hear her? Since she could never, in a velvet gown with short sleeves, striking with her light fingers the ivory keys of an Erard at a concert, feel the murmur of **ecstasy envelop** her like a **breeze**, it was not worth while boring herself with **practicing**. Her drawing cardboard and her **embroidery** she left in the cupboard. What was the good? What was the good? Sewing irritated her. "I have read everything," she said to herself. And she sat there making the tongs **red**-hot, or looked at the rain falling.

How sad she was on Sundays when **vespers** sounded! She listened with dull attention to each **stroke** of the **cracked** bell. A cat slowly walking over some roof put up his back in the pale rays of the sum. The wind on the highroad blew up clouds of dust. Afar off a dog sometimes **howled**; and the bell, keeping time, continued its **monotonous ringing** that died away over the fields.

But the people came out from church. The women in **waxed clogs**, the peasants in new **blouses**, the little bare-headed children skipping along in front of them, all were going home. And till nightfall, five or six men, always the same, stayed playing at corks in front of the large door of the inn.

The winter was severe. The windows every morning were covered with **rime**, and the light **shining** through them, dim as through ground-glass, sometimes did not change the whole day long. At four o'clock the lamp had to be lighted.

On fine days she went down into the garden. The dew had left on the **cabbages** a silver lace with long **transparent** threads spreading from one to the other. No birds were to be heard; everything seemed asleep, the espalier covered with **straw**, and the vine, like a great sick **serpent** under the **coping** of the wall, along which, on drawing hear, one saw the many-footed woodlice crawling. Under the spruce by the **hedgerow**, the **curie** in the three-cornered hat reading his **breviary** had lost his right foot, and the very plaster, **scaling** off with the **frost**, had left white scabs on his face.

Spanish

blouses: blusas.
breeze: brisa, la brisa.
breviary: breviario.
cabbages: coles.
clogs: atasca.
coping: albardilla.
cracked: agrietado.
curie: curio.
ecstasy: éxtasis.
embroidery: bordado.
envelop: enrollar, enrollad, enrolle, enrollas, enrollo, enrollan,

enrollamos, enrolláis, enrolla, enrollen, envolver.
frost: helada, escarcha, la escarcha.
hedgerow: seto, seto vivo.
howled: Rugido.
monotonous: monótono.
practicing: que ejerce, practicante, ejercicio, práctica, entrenamiento, ejercicios.
red-hot: candente, salchicha, vigoroso.
rime: escarcha, rima.
ringing: zumbido, sonando,

sobreoscilación.
scaling: escala, escalada.
serpent: serpiente.
shining: brillante, luminoso.
straw: paja, pajita, la paja.
stroke: acariciar, caricia, apoplejía, carrera, golpe, derrame cerebral, recorrido.
transparent: transparente.
vespers: vísperas.
waxed: encerado, parafinado.
willed: Hizo.

Then she went up again, shut her door, put on coals, and fainting with the heat of the hearth, felt her boredom **weigh** more heavily than ever. She would have like to go down and talk to the servant, but a sense of shame **restrained** her.

Every day at the same time the **schoolmaster** in a black **skullcap** opened the shutters of his house, and the rural policeman, wearing his **sabre** over his blouse, passed by. Night and morning the post-horses, three by three, crossed the street to water at the pond. From time to time the bell of a public house door rang, and when it was **windy** one could hear the little brass basins that served as signs for the hairdresser's shop **creaking** on their two **rods**. This shop had as **decoration** an old engraving of a **fashion**-plate stuck against a windowpane and the wax **bust** of a woman with yellow hair. He, too, the hairdresser, **lamented** his **wasted** calling, his **hopeless** future, and dreaming of some shop in a big town--at Rouen, for example, overlooking the harbour, near the theatre--he walked up and down all day from the mairie to the church, sombre and waiting for customers. When Madame Bovary looked up, she always saw him there, like a **sentinel** on duty, with his skullcap over his ears and his **vest** of **lasting**.

Sometimes in the afternoon outside the window of her room, the head of a man appeared, a **swarthy** head with black whiskers, smiling slowly, with a broad, gentle smile that showed his white teeth. A waltz immediately began and on the **organ**, in a little drawing room, dancers the size of a finger, women in pink turbans, Tyrolians in jackets, monkeys in frock **coats**, gentlemen in knee-breeches, turned and turned between the sofas, the consoles, **multiplied** in the bits of looking glass held together at their corners by a piece of gold paper. The man turned his handle, looking to the right and left, and up at the windows. Now and again, while he shot out a long squirt of brown **saliva** against the **milestone**, with his knee raised his instrument, whose hard **straps** tired his shoulder; and now, **doleful** and drawling, or gay and hurried, the music **escaped** from the box, **droning** through a curtain of pink **taffeta** under a brass **claw** in **arabesque**. They were **airs** played in other places at the theatres, **sung** in drawing rooms, **danced** to at night under lighted lustres, echoes of the world

Spanish

airs: aires.
arabesque: arabesco.
bust: busto.
claw: garra, arañar.
coats: membranas.
creaking: crujido, chirriando.
danced: bailo.
decoration: alhaja, decoración, adorno.
doleful: triste.
droning: zumbando.
escaped: escapado.
fashion-plate: figurín.

hopeless: desesperado.
lamented: lamentado.
lasting: continuo, duradero.
milestone: hito.
multiplied: multiplicado.
organ: órgano.
restrained: contenido, refrenado, dueño de sí mismo, reprimido.
rods: bastones.
sabre: sable.
saliva: saliva.
schoolmaster: maestro de escuela.

sentinel: centinela.
skullcap: solideo, casquete, gorro.
straps: abrazaderas, cintas.
sung: cantado.
swarthy: moreno.
taffeta: tafetán, tafeta.
vest: chaleco, el chaleco, camiseta.
wasted: gastado, acabado.
weigh: pesar, pese, pesa, pesad, pesáis, pesamos, pesan, pesas, peso, pesen, ponderar.
windy: ventoso.

that reached even to Emma. Endless sarabands ran through her head, and, like an Indian dancing girl on the flowers of a carpet, her thoughts **leapt** with the notes, **swung** from dream to dream, from sadness to sadness. When the man had caught some coppers in his cap, he drew down an old cover of blue cloth, **hitched** his organ on to his back, and went off with a heavy **tread**. She watched him going.

But it was above all the meal-times that were **unbearable** to her, in this small room on the ground floor, with its smoking stove, its creaking door, the walls that **sweated**, the damp flags; all the **bitterness** in life seemed served up on her plate, and with smoke of the boiled beef there rose from her secret soul **whiffs** of **sickliness**. Charles was a slow **eater**; she played with a few **nuts**, or, leaning on her elbow, **amused** herself with drawing lines along the **oilcloth** table cover with the point of her knife.

She now let everything in her household take care of itself, and Madame Bovary senior, when she came to spend part of Lent at Tostes, was much surprised at the change. She who was formerly so careful, so **dainty**, now passed whole days without dressing, wore grey cotton stockings, and **burnt tallow** candles. She kept saying they must be economical since they were not rich, adding that she was very **contented**, very happy, that Tostes pleased her very much, with other speeches that closed the mouth of her **mother**-in-law. Besides, Emma no longer seemed inclined to follow her advice; once even, Madame Bovary having thought fit to maintain that mistresses ought to keep an eye on the religion of their servants, she had answered with so angry a look and so cold a smile that the good woman did not **interfere** again.

Emma was growing difficult, **capricious**. She ordered dishes for herself, then she did not touch them; one day **drank** only pure milk, the next **cups** of tea by the dozen. Often she **persisted** in not going out, then, **stifling**, threw open the windows and put on light dresses. After she had well **scolded** her servant she gave her **presents** or sent her out to see neighbours, just as she sometimes threw beggars all the silver in her purse, although she was by no means **tender**-hearted or easily accessible to the feelings of others, like most country-bred people, who

Spanish

amused: se divirtió, entretenido.
bitterness: amargura, rencor, amargor.
burnt: quemado.
capricious: caprichoso.
contented: contento, satisfecho.
cups: taza.
dainty: fino, amable, delicado, poquita.
drank: pret de drink, bebió.
eater: tener siempre buen apetito, comedero, comedor, manzana, agua.
hitched: Atado.

interfere: interponer, injerir, inmiscuirse, interferirse, entrometido, interponerse, interpuesto, intervenga, introducir, interferir, obstruir.
leapt: pret y pp de leap, bañado, brincado, saltado.
mother-in-law: suegra.
nuts: chiflado, nuez.
oilcloth: hule.
persisted: persistido.
presents: presenta, la presente.
scolded: regañado.

sickliness: palidez, mala salud, lo empalagoso.
stifling: sofocante, ahogante.
sweated: Sudado.
swung: Columpiado, pret y pp de swing.
tallow: sebo.
tender-hearted: tierno de corazón, bondadoso.
tread: banda de rodadura, pisar.
unbearable: insufrible, insoportable.
whiffs: huele.

always retain in their souls something of the **horny hardness** of the **paternal** hands.

Towards the end of February old Rouault, in memory of his cure, himself brought his son-in-law a superb turkey, and stayed three days at Tostes. Charles being with his patients, Emma kept him company. He smoked in the room, **spat** on the firedogs, talked farming, **calves**, cows, poultry, and municipal council, so that when he left she closed the door on him with a feeling of satisfaction that surprised even herself. Moreover she no longer concealed her contempt for anything or anybody, and at times she set herself to express **singular** opinions, finding fault with that which others approved, and **approving** things **perverse** and **immoral**, all of which made her husband open his eyes widely.

Would this misery last for ever? Would she never issue from it? Yet she was as good as all the women who were living happily. She had seen duchesses at Vaubyessard with clumsier waists and **commoner** ways, and she **execrated** the injustice of God. She leant her head against the walls to **weep**; she **envied** lives of stir; longed for **masked** balls, for violent pleasures, with all the **wildness** that she did not know, but that these must surely yield.

She grew pale and suffered from **palpitations** of the heart.

Charles prescribed **valerian** and **camphor** baths. Everything that was tried only seemed to **irritate** her the more.

On certain days she **chatted** with **feverish rapidity**, and this over-excitement was suddenly followed by a state of torpor, in which she remained without speaking, without moving. What then **revived** her was pouring a bottle of eau-de-cologne over her arms.

As she was constantly complaining about Tostes, Charles fancied that her illness was no doubt due to some local cause, and **fixing** on this idea, began to think seriously of setting up elsewhere.

From that moment she drank vinegar, **contracted** a sharp little **cough**, and completely lost her appetite.

Spanish

approving: aprobando, aprobar, aprobatorio.
calves: pare, Pantorillas, terneros.
camphor: alcanfor.
chatted: charlo.
commoner: plebeyo.
contracted: contraído, contratado.
cough: toser, tos, la tos.
envied: envidiado.
execrated: execrado.
feverish: febril, afiebrado.
fixing: fijando, reparando, fijación,

accesorios.
hardness: dureza.
horny: córneo, corneo.
immoral: inmoral.
irritate: irritar, irrite, irrito, irrita, irritad, irritáis, irritamos, irritan, irritas, irriten.
masked: enmascarado.
palpitations: palpitaciones.
paternal: paterno, paternal.
perverse: perverso.
rapidity: rapidez.

revived: reavivado.
singular: original, excepcional, único, individual, raro, singularísimo, solo, extraño.
spat: reñir.
valerian: valeriana.
weep: llorar, llore, lloren, llora, lloro, lloras, lloran, lloramos, lloráis, llorad.
wildness: locura, furia, turbulencia, rusticidad, páramo, lo salvaje, lo estrafalario, lo disparatado, lo difícil, lo alborotado, lo fantástico.

It cost Charles much to give up Tostes after living there four years and "when he was beginning to get on there." Yet if it must be! He took her to Rouen to see his old master. It was a **nervous complaint**: change of air was needed.

After looking about him on this side and on that, Charles **learnt** that in the Neufchatel arrondissement there was a considerable market town called Yonville-l'Abbaye, whose doctor, a Polish **refugee**, had **decamped** a week before. Then he wrote to the **chemist** of the place to ask the number of the population, the distance from the **nearest** doctor, what his **predecessor** had made a year, and so forth; and the answer being satisfactory, he made up his mind to move towards the spring, if Emma's health did not improve.

One day when, in view of her **departure**, she was **tidying** a **drawer**, something pricked her finger. It was a **wire** of her wedding bouquet. The **orange** blossoms were yellow with dust and the silver bordered satin ribbons **frayed** at the **edges**. She threw it into the fire. It **flared** up more quickly than dry straw. Then it was, like a red bush in the cinders, slowly devoured. She watched it **burn**.

The little **pasteboard berries burst**, the wire twisted, the gold lace melted; and the **shriveled** paper corollas, fluttering like black butterflies at the back of the stove, at least **flew** up the chimney.

When they left Tostes at the month of March, Madame Bovary was **pregnant**.

Spanish

berries: bayas.
burn: arder, quemar, quemadura, quemarse, encender, la quemadura, abrasar.
burst: ráfaga, reventar, estallar, salva, reventón, resquebrajarse, quebraja, grieta, hendidura, henderse, ráfaga de impulsos.
chemist: químico, farmacéutico, boticario.
complaint: queja, reclamación, cargo, demanda, querella, pleito, denuncia, acusación.
decamped: decampado.
departure: salida, partida, desviación.
drawer: cajón, librador, la gaveta, gaveta.
edges: cantos, Conmutador de Sólo aristas.
flared: acampanado.
flew: voló, pret de fly.
frayed: raído.
learnt: pret de learn.
nearest: más cercano.
nervous: nervioso.
orange: naranja, anaranjado, la naranja, naranjo.
pasteboard: cartón.
predecessor: predecesor.
pregnant: embarazada, en estado, encinta, preñada.
refugee: refugiado.
shriveled: aborrajado, quemado, encogido, arrugado, secado.
tidying: Ordenar.
wire: alambre, hilo.

PART TWO

CHAPTER ONE

Yonville-l'Abbaye (so called from an old Capuchin **abbey** of which not even the ruins remain) is a market-town **twenty**-four miles from Rouen, between the Abbeville and Beauvais roads, at the foot of a valley **watered** by the Rieule, a little river that **runs** into the Andelle after turning three water-mills near its mouth, where there are a few **trout** that the lads amuse themselves by **fishing** for on Sundays.

We leave the highroad at La Boissiere and keep straight on to the top of the Leux hill, whence the valley is seen. The river that runs through it makes of it, as it were, two regions with **distinct** physiognomies--all on the left is **pasture** land, all of the right **arable**. The **meadow stretches** under a **bulge** of low hills to join at the back with the pasture land of the Bray country, while on the eastern side, the **plain**, gently rising, **broadens** out, showing as far as eye can follow its **blond** cornfields. The water, flowing by the grass, **divides** with a white line the colour of the roads and of the **plains**, and the country is like a great **unfolded mantle** with a green velvet **cape** bordered with a **fringe** of silver.

Before us, on the **verge** of the horizon, lie the **oaks** of the forest of Argueil, with the **steeps** of the Saint-Jean hills **scarred** from top to bottom with red irregular lines; they are rain tracks, and these brick-tones standing out in narrow **streaks** against the grey colour of the mountain are due to the **quantity** of iron **springs** that flow beyond in the **neighboring** country.

Spanish

abbey: abadía.
arable: cultivable.
blond: rubio.
broadens: ensancha.
bulge: protuberancia.
cape: capa, capotillo, cabo, esclavina.
distinct: claro, distinto, evidente.
divides: divide, separa, aparta, comparte, segrega.
fishing: pesca, pesquero.
fringe: borde, fleco, franja, baranda.
mantle: abrigo, manto.

meadow: prado, pradera.
neighboring: vecino.
oaks: robles.
pasture: pasto, pacer, pastura, pastizal, pastar.
plain: llanura, llano, claro, evidente, liso, plano.
plains: llanos.
quantity: cantidad, la cantidad, magnitud, cuantidad.
runs: corre.
scarred: marcar con cicatriz,

cicatrizado, con cicatrices, marcado, que tiene cicatrices, rasguño, cicatriz.
springs: muelle, ballestas, muelles, resorte, ballesta.
steeps: remoja, empapa, escarpado.
streaks: mechones.
stretches: estira.
trout: trucha.
twenty-four: veinticuatro.
unfolded: desplegado.
verge: lisera, borde.
watered: regado, inflado.

Here we are on the **confines** of Normandy, Picardy, and the Ile-de-France, a bastard land whose language is without accent and its landscape is without character. It is there that they make the worst Neufchatel cheeses of all the arrondissement; and, on the other hand, farming is costly because so much manure is needed to **enrich** this **friable** soil full of sand and flints.

Up to 1835 there was no **practicable** road for getting to Yonville, but about this time a cross-road was made which joins that of Abbeville to that of Amiens, and is occasionally used by the Rouen wagoners on their way to Flanders. Yonville-l'Abbaye has remained **stationary** in **spite** of its "new outlet." Instead of improving the soil, they persist in keeping up the pasture lands, however **depreciated** they may be in value, and the lazy borough, growing away from the plain, has naturally spread riverwards. It is seem from afar **sprawling** along the banks like a **cowherd** taking a **siesta** by the **water**-side.

At the foot of the hill beyond the bridge begins a **roadway**, planted with young aspens, that leads in a straight line to the first houses in the place. These, **fenced** in by hedges, are in the middle of courtyards full of **straggling** buildings, wine-presses, cart-sheds and distilleries scattered under thick trees, with **ladders**, poles, or **scythes** hung on to the branches. The thatched roofs, like fur caps drawn over eyes, reach down over about a third of the low windows, whose coarse **convex** glasses have **knots** in the middle like the **bottoms** of bottles. Against the plaster wall **diagonally** crossed by black **joists**, a meagre pear-tree sometimes **leans** and the ground-floors have at their door a small swing-gate to keep out the **chicks** that come **pilfering** crumbs of bread **steeped** in cider on the threshold. But the courtyards grow narrower, the houses closer together, and the fences disappear; a bundle of ferns swings under a window from the end of a **broomstick**; there is a blacksmith's **forge** and then a wheelwright's, with two or three new carts outside that partly block the way. Then across an open space appears a white house beyond a grass **mound** ornamented by a Cupid, his finger on his lips; two brass vases are at each end of a flight of steps; scutcheons blaze upon the door. It is the notary's house, and the finest in the place.

Spanish

bottoms: producto de fondo.
broomstick: palo de escoba.
chicks: pollito.
confines: fronteras.
convex: convexo.
cowherd: vaquero.
depreciated: desvalorado, depreciado.
diagonally: diagonalmente, diagonal.
enrich: enriquecer, enriquecen, enriquezco, enriqueces, enriquecemos, enriquecéis, enriqueced, enriquece, enriquezcan,

enriquecerse, enriquezca.
fenced: cercado.
forge: forjar, falsificar, forja, fraguar, inventar.
friable: friable.
joists: mordazas, eclisas.
knots: pulsos, nudos.
ladders: las escaleras, escalas.
leans: inclinación ficticia.
mound: montón de tierra, montículo.
pilfering: ratería.
practicable: transitable, factible,

practicable.
roadway: calzada.
scythes: guadañas.
siesta: sesteo.
spite: rencor.
sprawling: yaciendo, desmadejado, extender.
stationary: estacionario.
steeped: remojado, empapado.
straggling: vagando, disperso, retraso, extendido, fluctuación de trayecto.
water-side: ribera.

The Church is on the other side of the street, twenty paces farther down, at the entrance of the square. The little cemetery that **surrounds** it, closed in by a wall breast high, is so full of graves that the old stones, level with the ground, form a continuous pavement, on which the grass of itself has marked out regular green squares. The church was **rebuilt** during the last years of the reign of Charles X. The wooden roof is beginning to **rot** from the top, and here and there has black **hollows** in its blue colour. Over the door, where the organ should be, is a **loft** for the men, with a **spiral** staircase that **reverberates** under their wooden shoes.

The **daylight** coming through the plain glass windows falls obliquely upon the pews ranged along the walls, which are adorned here and there with a straw **mat** bearing beneath it the words in large letters, "Mr. So-and-so's pew." Farther on, at a spot where the building **narrows**, the **confessional** forms a **pendant** to a **statuette** of the Virgin, **clothed** in a satin **robe**, coifed with a **tulle veil sprinkled** with silver stars, and with red cheeks, like an **idol** of the Sandwich Islands; and, finally, a copy of the "Holy Family, presented by the Minister of the Interior," overlooking the high altar, between four candlesticks, **closes** in the perspective. The **choir stalls**, of deal wood, have been left unpainted.

The market, that is to say, a **tiled** roof supported by some twenty posts, **occupies** of itself about half the public square of Yonville. The town hall, constructed "from the designs of a Paris architect," is a sort of Greek temple that forms the corner next to the chemist's shop. On the **ground**-floor are three Ionic columns and on the first floor a **semicircular** gallery, while the **dome** that crowns it is occupied by a Gallic cock, resting one foot upon the "Charte" and holding in the other the scales of Justice.

But that which most **attracts** the eye is opposite the Lion d'Or inn, the chemist's shop of Monsieur Homais. In the evening especially its argand lamp is lit up and the red and green **jars** that **embellish** his shop-front throw far across the street their two streams of colour; then across them as if in Bengal lights is seen the shadow of the chemist leaning over his desk. His house from top to bottom is **placarded** with inscriptions written in large hand, round hand, printed hand: "Vichy, Seltzer, Barege waters, blood purifiers, Raspail patent medicine, Arabian racahout, Darcet lozenges, Regnault **paste**, **trusses**, baths, **hygienic** chocolate," etc. And the **signboard**, which takes up all the breadth of the shop, bears in gold letters, "Homais, Chemist." Then at the back of the shop, behind the great scales fixed to the counter, the word "Laboratory" appears on a **scroll** above a glass door, which about half-way up once more **repeats** "Homais" in gold letters on a black ground.

Beyond this there is nothing to see at Yonville. The street (the only one) a **gunshot** in length and flanked by a few shops on either side stops short at the turn of the highroad. If it is left on the right hand and the foot of the Saint-Jean hills followed the cemetery is soon reached.

At the time of the **cholera**, in order to **enlarge** this, a piece of wall was pulled down, and three acres of land by its side purchased; but all the new portion is almost **tenantless**; the **tombs**, as **heretofore**, continue to crowd together towards the gate. The keeper, who is at once **gravedigger** and church beadle (thus making a double profit out of the parish corpses), has taken advantage of the **unused** plot of ground to plant potatoes there. From year to year, however, his small field grows smaller, and when there is an **epidemic**, he does not know whether to **rejoice** at the deaths or regret the burials.

"You live on the dead, Lestiboudois!" the curie at last said to him one day. This grim remark made him reflect; it checked him for some time; but to this day he carries on the **cultivation** of his little tubers, and even maintains **stoutly** that they grow naturally.

Since the events about to be **narrated**, nothing in fact has changed at Yonville. The tin **tricolour** flag still swings at the top of the church-steeple; the two **chintz** streamers still **flutter** in the wind from the linen-draper's; the chemist's **fetuses**, like **lumps** of white **amadou**, rot more and more in their **turbid** alcohol, and above the big door of the inn the old golden lion, faded by rain, still shows passers-by its **poodle** mane.

On the evening when the Bovarys were to arrive at Yonville, Widow Lefrancois, the **landlady** of this inn, was so very busy that she sweated great

Spanish

amadou: yesca.
chintz: zaraza.
cholera: cólera.
cultivation: cultivo.
enlarge: ampliar, amplíe, amplía, amplíen, amplías, amplían, ampliamos, ampliáis, ampliad, amplío, agrandar.
epidemic: epidemia, epidémico.
fetuses: fetos.
flutter: aletear, vibración, centelleo.
gravedigger: sepulturero, enterrador.

gunshot: disparo.
heretofore: hasta aquí, hasta ahora.
hygienic: higiénico.
landlady: arrendadora, casera, dueña, patrona, propietaria, propietaria de una vivienda, ama.
lumps: amontona.
narrated: narrado.
paste: pegar, masa, pasta, engrudo.
poodle: perro de lanas.
rejoice: alegrarse, regocijarse, alegrar.
repeats: repite.

scroll: desplazar, voluta, desfilar, rollo de papel, pergamino.
signboard: letrero.
stoutly: corpulentamente, fuerte, reciamente, resueltamente, robustamente.
tenantless: sin arrendatario.
tombs: tumbas.
tricolour: tricolor.
trusses: bragueros.
turbid: turbio.
unused: sin usar, no usado.

drops as she moved her **saucepans**. **To**-morrow was market-day. The meat had to be cut beforehand, the fowls drawn, the soup and coffee made. Moreover, she had the boarders' meal to see to, and that of the doctor, his wife, and their servant; the billiard-room was **echoing** with bursts of laughter; three millers in a small **parlour** were calling for **brandy**; the wood was blazing, the **brazen** pan was **hissing**, and on the long kitchen table, amid the quarters of raw mutton, rose **piles** of plates that **rattled** with the shaking of the block on which **spinach** was being chopped.

From the poultry-yard was heard the **screaming** of the fowls whom the servant was **chasing** in order to **wring** their necks.

A man slightly marked with small-pox, in green leather slippers, and wearing a velvet cap with a gold tassel, was **warming** his back at the chimney. His face expressed nothing but self-satisfaction, and he appeared to take life as **calmly** as the **goldfinch** suspended over his head in its **wicker cage**: this was the chemist.

"Artemise!" shouted the landlady, "chop some wood, fill the water bottles, bring some brandy, look sharp! If only I knew what dessert to offer the guests you are expecting! Good **heavens**! Those furniture-movers are beginning their **racket** in the billiard-room again; and their van has been left before the front door! The 'Hirondelle' might run into it when it draws up. Call Polyte and tell him to put it up. Only think, Monsieur Homais, that since morning they have had about fifteen games, and drunk eight jars of cider! Why, they'll tear my cloth for me," she went on, looking at them from a distance, her **strainer** in her hand.

"That wouldn't be much of a loss," replied Monsieur Homais. "You would buy another."

"Another billiard-table!" **exclaimed** the widow.

"Since that one is coming to pieces, Madame Lefrancois. I tell you again you are doing yourself harm, much harm! And besides, players now want narrow pockets and heavy cues. Hazards aren't played now; everything is changed! One must keep pace with the times! Just look at Tellier!"

The **hostess reddened** with **vexation**. The chemist went on--

Spanish

brandy: coñac, aguardiente.
brazen: de latón, descarado.
cage: jaula, la jaula.
calmly: calmadamente, serenamente.
chasing: cazar, rama, perseguir, cincelar, cazador, caza, caña, persecución.
echoing: resonar.
exclaimed: exclamado.
goldfinch: jilguero.
heavens: cielo, cielos.
hissing: silbar, silbido, sisteo.

hostess: anfitriona, azafata.
parlour: salón, locutorio, parlanatorio, Sala, sala de recibir.
piles: hemorroides.
racket: raqueta.
rattled: zumbado.
reddened: enrojecido.
saucepans: cacerolas.
screaming: llamativo, chillón, chillar, estridente, grito, gritar.
spinach: espinaca, espinacas, la espinaca.

strainer: colador, filtro, cedazo.
to-morrow: mañana.
vexation: vejación, zaherimiento, molestia, sinsabor, disgusto, atufamiento, animosidad, mal trato.
warming: caldeamiento, calentamiento, entibiar.
wicker: mimbre.
wring: arrancar, retorcer, arrancáis, arrancas, arranquen, arranco, arrancan, arrancamos, arranca, arrancad, arranque.

"You may say what you like; his table is better than yours; and if one were to think, for example, of getting up a **patriotic** pool for Poland or the sufferers from the Lyons floods--"

"It isn't beggars like him that'll **frighten** us," **interrupted** the landlady, shrugging her **fat** shoulders. "Come, come, Monsieur Homais; as long as the 'Lion d'Or' exists people will come to it. We've **feathered** our **nest**; while one of these days you'll find the 'Cafe Francais' closed with a big **placard** on the shutters. Change my billiard-table!" she went on, speaking to herself, "the table that comes in so **handy** for **folding** the **washing**, and on which, in the **hunting** season, I have **slept** six visitors! But that **dawdler**, Hivert, doesn't come!"

"Are you waiting for him for your gentlemen's dinner?"

"Wait for him! And what about Monsieur Binet? As the clock **strikes** six you'll see him come in, for he hasn't his equal under the sun for **punctuality**. He must always have his seat in the small parlour. He'd rather die than dine anywhere else. And so **squeamish** as he is, and so particular about the cider! Not like Monsieur Leon; he sometimes comes at seven, or even half-past, and he doesn't so much as look at what he **eats**. Such a nice young man! Never **speaks** a rough word!"

"Well, you see, there's a great difference between an **educated** man and an old **carabineer** who is now a tax-collector."

Six o'clock struck. Binet came in.

He wore a blue frock-coat falling in a straight line round his thin body, and his leather **cap**, with its lappets knotted over the top of his head with string, showed under the turned-up peak a **bald** forehead, **flattened** by the constant wearing of a **helmet**. He wore a black cloth waistcoat, a hair collar, grey trousers, and, all the year round, well-blacked boots, that had two parallel swellings due to the **sticking** out of his big-toes. Not a hair stood out from the regular line of fair whiskers, which, **encircling** his jaws, framed, after the fashion of a garden border, his long, wan face, whose eyes were small and the nose **hooked**. Clever at all games of cards, a good **hunter**, and writing a fine hand, he had at home a

Spanish

bald: calvo, pelado.
cap: gorro, gorra, birrete, el gorro, tapa, tapón, zuncho, tapar, casquillo, bonete.
carabineer: carabinero, soldado de fusil, soldado con fusil.
dawdler: ocioso.
eats: come.
educated: educado, instruido.
encircling: rodeando.
fat: gordo, grasa, grueso, manteca.
feathered: emplumado.

flattened: aplanado.
folding: plegable.
frighten: espantar, espantad, espanta, espantáis, espantamos, espantan, espantas, espanten, asustar, espante, espanto.
handy: hábil, manuable.
helmet: casco.
hooked: encorvado, enganchado, ganchudo.
hunter: cazador.
hunting: cazando, caza, penduleo,

cacería.
interrupted: interrumpido.
nest: nido, el nido, anidar.
patriotic: patriótico.
placard: cartel.
punctuality: puntualidad.
slept: dormido.
speaks: habla.
squeamish: delicado, aprensivo.
sticking: pegajoso.
strikes: golpea.
washing: lavado, lavava.

lathe, and amused himself by turning napkin rings, with which he filled up his house, with the **jealousy** of an **artist** and the egotism of a bourgeois.

He went to the small parlour, but the three millers had to be got out first, and during the whole time necessary for **laying** the cloth, Binet remained silent in his place near the stove. Then he **shut** the door and took off his cap in his usual way.

"It isn't with saying civil things that he'll wear out his tongue," said the chemist, as soon as he was along with the landlady.

"He never talks more," she replied. "Last week two **travelers** in the cloth line were here--such **clever chaps** who told such jokes in the evening, that I fairly cried with laughing; and he stood there like a **dab** fish and never said a word."

"Yes," **observed** the chemist; "no **imagination**, no sallies, nothing that makes the society-man."

"Yet they say he has parts," **objected** the landlady.

"Parts!" replied Monsieur Homais; "he, parts! In his own line it is possible," he added in a calmer tone. And he went on--

"Ah! That a **merchant**, who has large **connections**, a **jurisconsult**, a doctor, a chemist, should be thus **absent**-minded, that the should become **whimsical** or even **peevish**, I can understand; such cases are **cited** in history. But at least it is because they are thinking of something. Myself, for example, how often has it **happened** to me to look on the **bureau** for my pen to write a **label**, and to find, after all, that I had put it behind my ear!"

Madame Lefrancois just then went to the door to see if the "Hirondelle" were not coming. She started. A man **dressed** in black suddenly came into the kitchen. By the last **gleam** of the **twilight** one could see that his face was rubicund and his form **athletic**.

"What can I do for you, Monsieur le Curie?" asked the landlady, as she reached down from the chimney one of the **copper** candlesticks placed with their candles in a row. "Will you take something? A thimbleful of Cassis? A glass of wine?"

Spanish

absent-minded: distraído.
artist: artista.
athletic: atlético.
bureau: oficina, mesa, escritorio, agencia.
chaps: rajar, resquebrajar, quijada, muchacho, grieta, carrillo, agrietar, zajones.
cited: Citado, mencionado.
clever: hábil, diestro, experto, ágil, listo, inteligente.
connections: conexiones.

copper: cobre, el cobre, cobrizo, caldera.
dab: lenguado, untar, palmada, toba, dar palmadas, golpecito.
dressed: vestido, con guarnición de.
gleam: destello.
imagination: imaginación.
jealousy: celos.
jurisconsult: jurisconsulto.
label: etiqueta, rótulo, rotular, etiquetar, el marbete.
lathe: torno.

laying: colocando, poniendo.
merchant: comerciante, negociante, mercader.
objected: objetado.
observed: observado.
peevish: malhumorado.
pen: pluma, la pluma, corral, un bolígrafo.
shut: cerrar, cerrado.
travelers: viajantes.
twilight: crepúsculo, anochecer.
whimsical: caprichoso, antojadizo.

The priest **declined** very **politely**. He had come for his **umbrella**, that he had forgotten the other day at the Ernemont convent, and after asking Madame Lefrancois to have it sent to him at the **presbytery** in the evening, he left for the church, from which the Angelus was ringing.

When the chemist no longer heard the noise of his boots along the square, he thought the priest's behaviour just now very **unbecoming**. This refusal to take any **refreshment** seemed to him the most odious hypocrisy; all priests tippled on the sly, and were trying to bring back the days of the **tithe**.

The landlady took up the defence of her curie.

"Besides, he could double up four men like you over his knee. Last year he helped our people to bring in the straw; he carried as many as six trusses at once, he is so strong."

"Bravo!" said the chemist. "Now just send your daughters to confess to fellows which such a temperament! I, if I were the Government, I'd have the priests bled once a month. Yes, Madame Lefrancois, every month--a good **phlebotomy**, in the interests of the police and morals."

"Be quiet, Monsieur Homais. You are an **infidel**; you've no religion."

The chemist answered: "I have a religion, my religion, and I even have more than all these others with their **mummeries** and their **juggling**. I adore God, on the contrary. I believe in the Supreme Being, in a Creator, whatever he may be. I care little who has placed us here below to **fulfil** our duties as citizens and fathers of families; but I don't need to go to church to kiss silver plates, and **fatten**, out of my pocket, a lot of good-for-nothings who live better than we do. For one can know Him as well in a wood, in a field, or even **contemplating** the eternal **vault** like the **ancients**. My God! Mine is the God of Socrates, of Franklin, of Voltaire, and of Beranger! I am for the profession of faith of the 'Savoyard Vicar,' and the **immortal** principles of '89! And I **can't** admit of an old boy of a God who takes walks in his garden with a **cane** in his hand, who **lodges** his friends in the **belly** of **whales**, **dies** uttering a cry, and rises again at the end of three days; things **absurd** in themselves, and completely **opposed**, moreover, to all physical laws, which prove to us, by the way, that priests have always

Spanish

absurd: absurdo.
ancients: antiguo.
belly: vientre, barriga, panza.
cane: palo, bastón, junco, caña.
can't: no puede.
contemplating: contemplando, meditando.
declined: rechazado.
dies: muere.
fatten: engordar, engordan, engordo, engorden, engordas, engordamos, engordáis, engordad, engorda, engorde.

fulfil: cumplir, realizar, cumpla, efectuar.
immortal: inmortal, imperecedero.
infidel: infiel.
juggling: hacer malabares, hacer malabarismos, juglaria, malabar, malabarismo, malabares.
lodges: cabañas.
mummeries: Pantomimas.
opposed: opuesto.
phlebotomy: flebotomía.

politely: comedidamente, cortésmente, educadamente, refinadamente.
presbytery: presbiterio, casa del cura.
refreshment: refresco.
tithe: diezmar.
umbrella: paraguas, el paraguas, sombrilla.
unbecoming: impropio.
vault: bóveda, sótano, cámara acorazada, caja fuerte.
whales: ballenas.

wallowed in turpid **ignorance**, in which they would fain **engulf** the people with them."

He **ceased**, looking round for an audience, for in his **bubbling** over the chemist had for a moment fancied himself in the midst of the town council. But the landlady no longer heeded him; she was listening to a **distant rolling**. One could **distinguish** the noise of a carriage mingled with the clattering of loose horseshoes that beat against the ground, and at last the "Hirondelle" stopped at the door.

It was a yellow box on two large wheels, that, **reaching** to the tilt, **prevented** travelers from seeing the road and dirtied their shoulders. The small panes of the narrow windows rattled in their sashes when the coach was closed, and **retained** here and there patches of **mud** amid the old layers of dust, that not even storms of rain had altogether **washed** away. It was drawn by three horses, the first a leader, and when it came down-hill its bottom **jolted** against the ground.

Some of the inhabitants of Yonville came out into the square; they all spoke at once, asking for news, for explanations, for hampers. Hivert did not know whom to answer. It was he who did the errands of the place in town. He went to the shops and brought back **rolls** of leather for the **shoemaker**, old iron for the **farrier**, a **barrel** of **herrings** for his mistress, caps from the milliner's, **locks** from the hair-dresser's and all along the road on his return journey he **distributed** his parcels, which he threw, standing upright on his seat and **shouting** at the top of his voice, over the enclosures of the yards.

An accident had **delayed** him. Madame Bovary's greyhound had run across the field. They had whistled for him a quarter of an hour; Hivert had even gone back a mile and a half **expecting** every moment to catch sight of her; but it had been necessary to go on.

Emma had **wept**, grown angry; she had accused Charles of this misfortune. Monsieur Lheureux, a **draper**, who happened to be in the coach with her, had tried to **console** her by a number of examples of lost dogs **recognizing** their masters at the end of long years. One, he said had been told of, who had come back to Paris from Constantinople. Another had gone one hundred and fifty

Spanish

barrel: barril, tonel, cañón.
bubbling: burbujeo.
ceased: ceso, Cesado.
console: consolar, consola.
delayed: retrasado, retardado, demorado, demora de proceso.
distant: lejano, distante.
distinguish: distinguir, distinguís, distinguid, distingues, distinguen, distingue, distingo, distinga, distinguimos, distingan.
distributed: distribuido, repartido.

draper: lencero, pañero.
engulf: tragar, traguen, tragad, tragáis, tragamos, tragan, tragas, trague, traga, trago, tomar.
expecting: esperando.
farrier: herrador.
herrings: arenque.
ignorance: ignorancia.
jolted: sacudido.
locks: Bloqueos, pelo, cerradura, cabellos, bloquear.
mud: barro, lodo, fango, el barro, el

lodo.
prevented: impedido, prevenido.
reaching: alcanzar.
recognizing: reconociendo.
retained: retenido.
rolling: rodante.
rolls: en gabardina.
shoemaker: zapatero.
shouting: griterío.
wallowed: se encenagado.
washed: lavado, lavo.
wept: Llorado.

miles in a **straight** line, and **swum** four rivers; and his own father had **possessed** a **poodle**, which, after **twelve** years of **absence**, had all of a **sudden jumped** on his back in the **street** as he was going to **dine** in town.

Spanish

absence: ausencia, falta.
dine: cenar, cenáis, ceno, cenen, cenas, cenamos, cenad, cenan, cena, cene.
jumped: Saltado.
poodle: perro de lanas.
possessed: poseído.
straight: derecho, recto, directamente, recta.
street: calle, la calle.
sudden: repentino, brusco, súbito.
swum: pp de swim.
twelve: doce.

CHAPTER TWO

Emma got out first, then Felicite, Monsieur Lheureux, and a **nurse**, and they had to **wake** up Charles in his corner, where he had slept **soundly** since night set in.

Homais introduced himself; he offered his **homages** to madame and his respects to monsieur; said he was charmed to have been able to **render** them some **slight** service, and added with a **cordial** air that he had **ventured** to **invite** himself, his wife being away.

When Madame Bovary was in the kitchen she went up to the chimney.

With the tips of her fingers she caught her dress at the **knee**, and having thus pulled it up to her ankle, held out her foot in its black **boot** to the fire above the **revolving** leg of mutton. The **flame lit** up the whole of her, **penetrating** with a **crude** light the **woof** of her gowns, the fine **pores** of her fair skin, and even her eyelids, which she **blinked** now and again. A great red **glow** passed over her with the blowing of the wind through the **half**-open door.

On the other side of the chimney a young man with fair hair watched her silently.

As he was a good deal bored at Yonville, where he was a **clerk** at the notary's, Monsieur Guillaumin, Monsieur Leon Dupuis (it was he who was the second **habitue** of the "Lion d'Or") frequently put back his dinner-hour in hope that

Spanish

blinked: Parpadeado.
boot: bota, maletero, arranque.
clerk: empleado, dependiente, oficinista, secretario, el dependiente.
cordial: cordial.
crude: crudo, basto.
flame: llama, flamear, la flama.
glow: resplandecer, resplandor.
habitue: asiduo, parroquiano.
half-open: entreabran, entreabro, entreabrís, entreabrimos, entreabrid, entreabres, entreabre, entreabra,

entreabren, entreabierto, a medio abrir.
homages: homenajes.
invite: invitar, invitas, invita, invite, invitan, invitamos, invitáis, invitad, invito, inviten.
knee: rodilla, la rodilla.
lit: encendido, pret y pp de light, alumbrado, iluminado.
nurse: enfermera, cuidar, comadrona, enfermero, la enfermera, niñera, nodriza, amamantar.

penetrating: penetrando, penetrante.
pores: poro, los poros.
render: devolver.
revolving: rotativo, girando.
slight: leve, desaire.
soundly: sanamente, solventemente, sólidamente, razonablemente, profundamente, firmemente, vigorosamente.
ventured: Aventurado.
wake: estela, despertar.
woof: trama.

some **traveler** might come to the inn, with whom he could chat in the evening. On the days when his work was done early, he had, for want of something else to do, to come **punctually**, and **endure** from soup to cheese a tete-a-tete with Binet. It was therefore with **delight** that he accepted the landlady's suggestion that he should dine in company with the newcomers, and they passed into the large parlour where Madame Lefrancois, for the purpose of showing off, had had the table laid for four.

Homais asked to be allowed to keep on his skull-cap, for fear of **coryza**; then, turning to his neighbour--

"Madame is no doubt a little **fatigued**; one gets jolted so **abominably** in our 'Hirondelle.'"

"That is true," replied Emma; "but moving about always **amuses** me. I like change of place."

"It is so tedious," **sighed** the clerk, "to be always **riveted** to the same places."

"If you were like me," said Charles, "constantly **obliged** to be in the saddle"--

"But," Leon went on, **addressing** himself to Madame Bovary, "nothing, it seems to me, is more pleasant--when one can," he added.

"Moreover," said the **druggist**, "the practice of medicine is not very hard work in our part of the world, for the state of our roads allows us the use of gigs, and generally, as the farmers are **prosperous**, they pay pretty well. We have, **medically** speaking, besides the ordinary cases of enteritis, **bronchitis**, **bilious** affections, etc., now and then a few **intermittent** fevers at harvest-time; but on the whole, little of a serious nature, nothing special to note, unless it be a great deal of **scrofula**, due, no doubt, to the **deplorable** hygienic conditions of our **peasant dwellings**. Ah! you will find many prejudices to **combat**, Monsieur Bovary, much obstinacy of **routine**, with which all the efforts of your science will daily come into **collision**; for people still have **recourse** to novenas, to relics, to the **priest**, rather than come straight to the doctor of the chemist. The **climate**, however, is not, truth to tell, bad, and we even have a few nonagenarians in our **parish**. The **thermometer** (I have made some **observations**) falls in winter to 4

Spanish

abominably: abominablemente.
addressing: direccionamiento.
amuses: se divierte, entretiene.
bilious: bilioso.
bronchitis: bronquitis.
climate: clima, el clima.
collision: colisión, choque, abordaje, atropellamiento.
combat: combate, combatir.
coryza: rinitis.
delight: deleitar, delicia, encantar.
deplorable: lamentable, lastimoso.

druggist: droguero.
dwellings: vivienda.
endure: durar, duráis, duro, duren, dure, duras, duran, duramos, dura, durad, tolerar.
falls: se cae, decrece, derriba.
fatigued: fatigado, rendido.
intermittent: intermitente.
medically: médicamente, médico, facultativamente.
obliged: obligado.
observations: observaciones.

parish: parroquia.
peasant: campesino.
priest: sacerdote, cura, preste.
prosperous: próspero.
punctually: puntualmente.
recourse: recurso.
riveted: remachado.
routine: rutina.
scrofula: escrófula.
sighed: suspirado.
thermometer: termómetro.
traveler: viajero, viajante.

degrees Centigrade at the outside, which gives us 24 degrees Reaumur as the maximum, or otherwise 54 degrees Fahrenheit (English scale), not more. And, as a matter of fact, we are **sheltered** from the north winds by the forest of Argueil on the one side, from the west winds by the St. Jean range on the other; and this heat, moreover, which, on account of the **aqueous** vapours given off by the river and the considerable number of cattle in the fields, which, as you know, **exhale** much **ammonia**, that is to say, nitrogen, hydrogen and oxygen (no, nitrogen and hydrogen alone), and which **sucking** up into itself the **humus** from the ground, **mixing** together all those different emanations, **unites** them into a **stack**, so to say, and combining with the electricity **diffused** through the atmosphere, when there is any, might in the long run, as in tropical countries, **engender insalubrious** miasmata--this heat, I say, finds itself perfectly **tempered** on the side whence it comes, or rather whence it should come--that is to say, the southern side-- by the **south**-eastern winds, which, having cooled themselves passing over the Seine, reach us sometimes all at once like breezes from Russia."

"At any rate, you have some walks in the neighbourhood?" continued Madame Bovary, speaking to the young man.

"Oh, very few," he answered. "There is a place they call La Pature, on the top of the hill, on the edge of the forest. Sometimes, on Sundays, I go and stay there with a book, watching the sunset."

"I think there is nothing so **admirable** as sunsets," she resumed; "but especially by the side of the sea."

"Oh, I adore the sea!" said Monsieur Leon.

"And then, does it not seem to you," continued Madame Bovary, "that the mind **travels** more freely on this **limitless expanse**, the **contemplation** of which **elevates** the soul, gives ideas of the infinite, the ideal?"

"It is the same with **mountainous** landscapes," continued Leon. "A cousin of mine who travelled in Switzerland last year told me that one could not picture to **oneself** the poetry of the lakes, the charm of the waterfalls, the **gigantic** effect of the glaciers. One sees **pines** of incredible size across torrents, cottages suspended over **precipices**, and, a thousand feet below one, whole valleys when the clouds

Spanish

admirable: admirable, estupendo.
ammonia: amoníaco, amoniaco.
aqueous: acuoso.
contemplation: contemplación.
diffused: difundido, EXTENSIVO.
elevates: eleva.
engender: engendrar, engendran,
engendramos, engendráis,
engendrad, engendras, engendra,
engendren, engendro, engendre,
criar.
exhale: exhalar, exhala, exhalen,

exhale, exhalas, exhalan, exhalamos,
exhalo, exhalad, exhaláis, respirar.
expanse: extensión.
gigantic: gigantesco.
humus: humus.
insalubrious: insalubre.
limitless: ilimitado.
mixing: mezcla.
mountainous: montañoso.
oneself: uno mismo.
pines: los pinos.
precipices: precipicios.

sheltered: albergue, refugiarse,
refugiado, protegido, asilo, amparar,
abrigo, abrigado, proteger,
resguardo, albergar.
south-eastern: del sudeste.
stack: pila, apilar, montón.
sucking: succión, lechal, mamar,
mamada, chupadura, chupante,
chupar, chupada, chupón, absorber.
tempered: templado.
travels: viaja, viajes.
unites: reúne, une.

open. Such **spectacles** must **stir** to enthusiasm, **incline** to **prayer**, to ecstasy; and I no longer **marvel** at that **celebrated musician** who, the better to **inspire** his imagination, was in the **habit** of playing the **piano** before some **imposing** site."

"You play?" she asked.

"No, but I am very fond of music," he replied.

"Ah! don't you listen to him, Madame Bovary," interrupted Homais, bending over his plate. "That's **sheer** modesty. Why, my dear fellow, the other day in your room you were singing 'L'Ange Gardien' **ravishingly**. I heard you from the laboratory. You gave it like an actor."

Leon, in fact, **lodged** at the chemist's where he had a small room on the second floor, overlooking the Place. He blushed at the **compliment** of his **landlord**, who had already turned to the doctor, and was **enumerating** to him, one after the other, all the principal inhabitants of Yonville. He was telling anecdotes, giving information; the **fortune** of the notary was not known exactly, and "there was the Tuvache household," who made a good deal of show.

Emma continued, "And what music do you prefer?"

"Oh, German music; that which makes you dream."

"Have you been to the opera?"

"Not yet; but I shall go next year, when I am living at Paris to finish reading for the bar."

"As I had the honour of putting it to your husband," said the chemist, "with regard to this poor Yanoda who has run away, you will find yourself, thanks to his **extravagance**, in the possession of one of the most comfortable houses of Yonville. Its greatest **convenience** for a doctor is a door giving on the Walk, where one can go in and out unseen. Moreover, it contains everything that is **agreeable** in a household--a **laundry**, kitchen with offices, sitting-room, fruit-room, and so on. He was a **gay** dog, who didn't care what he spent. At the end of the garden, by the side of the water, he had an **arbour** built just for the purpose of **drinking** beer in summer; and if madame is fond of **gardening** she will be able--"

Spanish

agreeable: agradable, conforme, grato.
arbour: cenador, emparrado.
celebrated: celebrado, festejado, célebre, famoso.
compliment: cumplimiento, cumplido.
convenience: conveniencia, comodidad.
drinking: potable, el beber, bebida, beber.
enumerating: enumerando.
extravagance: extravagancia, derroche.
fortune: suerte, fortuna.

gardening: jardinería.
gay: alegre, homosexual.
habit: costumbre, hábito, resabio, mala costumbre.
imposing: imponente, imponiendo.
incline: inclinar, propender, cuesta.
inspire: inspirar, animar, inspiráis, inspiro, inspiren, inspire, inspiras, inspiramos, inspirad, inspira, inspiran.
landlord: casero, propietario.
laundry: lavadero, lavandería, colada,

lavado.
lodged: encamado, Habitado.
marvel: maravilla, asombrarse.
musician: músico, el músico.
piano: el piano, piano.
prayer: oración, rezo, ruego, plegaria, súplica.
ravishingly: encantar.
sheer: puro.
spectacles: gafas, lentes, anteojos.
stir: conmover, revolver, remover, agitar.

Madame Bovary

"My wife doesn't care about it," said Charles; "although she has been **advised** to take exercise, she **prefers** always sitting in her room reading."

"Like me," replied Leon. "And indeed, what is better than to sit by one's fireside in the evening with a book, while the wind beats against the window and the lamp is burning?"

"What, indeed?" she said, fixing her large black eyes wide open upon him.

"One **thinks** of nothing," he continued; "the hours **slip** by. Motionless we **traverse** countries we **fancy** we see, and your thought, **blinding** with the **fiction**, playing with the details, follows the **outline** of the adventures. It **mingles** with the characters, and it seems as if it were yourself **palpitating** beneath their costumes."

"That is true! That is true?" she said.

"Has it ever happened to you," Leon went on, "to come across some vague idea of one's own in a book, some dim image that comes back to you from afar, and as the completest expression of your own slightest sentiment?"

"I have experienced it," she replied.

"That is why," he said, "I especially love the poets. I think verse more tender than **prose**, and that it **moves** far more easily to tears."

"Still in the long run it is tiring," continued Emma. Now I, on the contrary, adore stories that **rush breathlessly** along, that frighten one. I **detest** commonplace heroes and **moderate** sentiments, such as there are in nature."

"In fact," observed the clerk, "these works, not touching the heart, miss, it seems to me, the true end of art. It is so **sweet**, amid all the disenchantments of life, to be able to **dwell** in thought upon **noble** characters, **pure** affections, and pictures of happiness. For myself, living here far from the world, this is my one **distraction**; but Yonville **affords** so few resources."

"Like Tostes, no doubt," replied Emma; "and so I always **subscribed** to a lending library."

Spanish

advised: aconsejado.
affords: produce.
blinding: deslumbrante, deslumbrando, deslumbramiento, esparcido de gravilla.
breathlessly: jadeantemente.
detest: detestar, detesto, detesta, detestad, detestáis, detestamos, detestan, detestas, detesten, deteste, aborrecer.
distraction: distracción.
dwell: morar, morad, moren, moras,

moráis, moran, moramos, mora, more, moro, habitar.
fancy: figurarse, de fantasía, imaginación.
fiction: ficción.
mingles: mezcla, trisca.
moderate: moderado, módico, moderar.
moves: mueve.
noble: hidalgo, noble.
outline: esquema, esbozo, perfil, contorno, bosquejo, boceto.

palpitating: palpitando.
prefers: prefiere.
prose: prosa.
pure: puro, limpio.
rush: apresurarse, junco, prisa.
slip: deslizamiento, resbalar, desliz, deslizar, combinación.
subscribed: se suscrito, subscrito.
sweet: dulce, caramelo, postre.
thinks: piensa, reflexiona.
traverse: travesaño.
verse: verso, estrofa, copla, versículo.

"If madame will do me the **honour** of making use of it", said the chemist, who had just caught the last words, "I have at her **disposal** a library **composed** of the best authors, Voltaire, Rousseau, Delille, Walter Scott, the 'Echo des Feuilletons'; and in **addition** I receive various **periodicals**, among them the 'Fanal de Rouen' daily, having the advantage to be its **correspondent** for the districts of Buchy, Forges, Neufchatel, Yonville, and vicinity."

For two hours and a half they had been at table; for the servant Artemis, **carelessly** dragging her old list slippers over the flags, brought one **plate** after the other, **forgot** everything, and **constantly** left the door of the billiard-room half open, so that it beat against the wall with its hooks.

Unconsciously, Leon, while talking, had placed his foot on one of the bars of the chair on which Madame Bovary was sitting. She wore a small blue silk **necktie**, that kept up like a **ruff** a gauffered **cambric** collar, and with the **movements** of her head the lower part of her face **gently** sunk into the linen or came out from it. Thus side by side, while Charles and the chemist chatted, they entered into one of those vague conversations where the hazard of all that is said **brings** you back to the **fixed** centre of a common **sympathy**. The Paris theatres, titles of novels, new quadrilles, and the world they did not know; Tostes, where she had lived, and Yonville, where they were; they **examined** all, talked of everything till to the end of dinner.

When coffee was **served** Felicite went away to get ready the room in the new house, and the guests soon raised the **siege**. Madame Lefrancois was asleep near the cinders, while the stable-boy, **lantern** in hand, was waiting to show Monsieur and Madame Bovary the way home. **Bits** of straw **stuck** in his red hair, and he **limped** with his left leg. When he had taken in his other hand the cure's umbrella, they started.

The town was asleep; the **pillars** of the market threw great **shadows**; the earth was all **grey** as on a summer's night. But as the doctor's house was only some fifty paces from the inn, they had to say good-night almost immediately, and the company **dispersed**.

Spanish

addition: adición, suma, apéndice, añadidura.
bits: los bits.
brings: trae.
cambric: batista.
carelessly: descuidadamente, sin cuidado.
composed: dueño de sí mismo, compuesto, sosegado.
constantly: constantemente, siempre, continuamente.
correspondent: corresponsal, correspondiente.
dispersed: disperso, dispersado.
disposal: tentación, disposición, eliminación.
examined: examinado, registrado.
fixed: fijo, fijado, reparado.
forgot: olvidado, pret de forget.
gently: suavemente.
grey: gris, pardo.
honour: honor, homenaje.
lantern: farol, linterna.
limped: Cojeado.
movements: los movimientos.
necktie: corbata, la corbata.
periodicals: publicaciones periódicas.
pillars: pilar.
plate: plato, placa, lámina, libra, el plato, plancha, chapa, chapar.
ruff: combatiente.
served: servido.
shadows: oscuridad.
siege: sitio, asedio.
stuck: punzar, picar, atrancarse.
sympathy: simpatía.

As soon as she entered the **passage**, Emma felt the **cold** of the plaster **fall** about her **shoulders** like damp linen. The walls were new and the **wooden stairs creaked**. In their **bedroom**, on the first floor, a **whitish** light passed through the curtain less windows.

She could **catch** glimpses of **tree** tops, and beyond, the **fields**, half-drowned in the **fog** that **lay reeking** in the moonlight along the course of the **river**. In the middle of the room, pell-mell, were scattered drawers, bottles, curtain-rods, gilt poles, with mattresses on the **chairs** and basins on the ground--the two men who had brought the **furniture** had left everything about carelessly.

This was the **fourth** time that she had slept in a **strange** place.

The first was the day of her going to the convent; the second, of her **arrival** at Tostes; the third, at Vaubyessard; and this was the fourth. And each one had **marked**, as it were, the **inauguration** of a new **phase** in her life. She did not believe that things could present themselves in the same way in different places, and since the portion of her life **lived** had been bad, no **doubt** that which remained to be lived would be better.

Spanish

arrival: llegada, aprovisionamiento, arribo, venida.
bedroom: dormitorio, alcoba, el dormitorio.
catch: coger, cogéis, cojan, coged, cogemos, cogen, coges, coja, coge, cojo, asir.
chairs: las sillas.
cold: frío, resfriado, catarro, constipado.
creaked: chirriado.
doubt: dudar, duda.

fall: caer, os caéis, cáedos, se caen, se cae, te caes, caígase, cáete, caíganse, me caigo, nos caemos.
fields: campos.
fog: niebla, bruma, neblina, la neblina.
fourth: cuarto, el cuarto.
furniture: mobiliario, muebles, mueblaje, ajuar, mueble.
inauguration: inauguración.
lay: poner, colocar, coloque, colocamos, pongan, ponga, pones, ponen, ponemos, ponéis, poned.

lived: vivido, habitado.
marked: marcado.
passage: paso, pasillo, pasaje.
phase: fase.
reeking: apestando, oliendo.
river: río.
shoulders: espalda, hombros.
stairs: escalera, escaleras.
strange: extraño, raro, ajeno.
tree: árbol.
whitish: blanquecino.
wooden: de madera.

CHAPTER THREE

The next day, as she was getting up, she saw the clerk on the Place. She had on a **dressing**-gown. He looked up and bowed. She **nodded quickly** and **recluse** the window.

Leon waited all day for six o'clock in the evening to come, but on going to the inn, he found no one but Monsieur Binet, already at table. The dinner of the evening before had been a **considerable event** for him; he had never till then talked for two hours **consecutively** to a "lady." How then had he been able to **explain**, and in such language, the number of things that he could not have said so well before? He was usually **shy**, and **maintained** that **reserve** which **partakes** at once of modesty and **dissimulation**.

At Yonville he was **considered** "well-bred." He listened to the **arguments** of the **older** people, and did not seem **hot** about politics--a **remarkable** thing for a young man. Then he had some **accomplishments**; he painted in water-colours, could read the **key** of G, and **readily** talked **literature** after dinner when he did not play **cards**. Monsieur Homais respected him for his education; Madame Homais **liked** him for his good-nature, for he often took the little Homais into the garden--little brats who were always **dirty**, very much spoilt, and **somewhat lymphatic**, like their mother. Besides the servant to look after them, they had Justin, the chemist's **apprentice**, a second **cousin** of Monsieur Homais, who had

Spanish

accomplishments: triunfos.
apprentice: aprendiz.
arguments: argumentos.
cards: la baraja, tarjetas, los naipes.
consecutively: sucesivamente, consecutivamente.
considerable: notable, considerable.
considered: considerado.
cousin: primo, prima, el primo.
dirty: sucio, ensuciar, verde, manchar.
dissimulation: disimulación.
dressing-gown: camarera.

event: acontecimiento, evento, suceso, acaecimiento, ocurrencia.
explain: explicar, explica, explico, explicas, explican, explicamos, explicáis, explicad, expliquen, explique, aclarar.
hot: caliente, picante, caluroso.
key: llave, tecla, clave, la llave, teclear, chaveta.
literature: literatura, la literatura.
lymphatic: linfático.

maintained: mantenido, conservado.
nodded: Cabeceado.
older: mayor.
partakes: comparte.
quickly: rápidamente, de prisa, aprisa, pronto.
readily: de buena gana.
recluse: recluso.
remarkable: notable.
reserve: reservar, reserva, pedir.
shy: tímido, vergonzoso.
somewhat: algo, poco, bastante.

been taken into the house from charity, and who was useful at the same time as a servant.

The druggist proved the best of neighbours. He gave Madame Bovary information as to the trades-people, sent **expressly** for his own cider merchant, tasted the drink himself, and saw that the casks were properly placed in the cellar; he explained how to set about getting in a supply of butter cheap, and made an arrangement with Lestiboudois, the **sacristan**, who, besides his **sacerdotal** and **funeral** functions, looked after the principal gardens at Yonville by the hour or the year, according to the taste of the customers.

The need of looking after others was not the only thing that urged the chemist to such **obsequious cordiality**; there was a plan **underneath** it all.

He had **infringed** the law of the 19th Ventose, year xi., article I, which forbade all persons not having a **diploma** to **practise** medicine; so that, after certain **anonymous denunciations**, Homais had been **summoned** to Rouen to see the **procurer** of the king in his own private room; the **magistrate** receiving him standing up, **ermine** on shoulder and cap on head. It was in the morning, before the court opened. In the corridors one heard the heavy boots of the gendarmes walking past, and like a **far**-off noise great locks that were shut. The druggist's ears tingled as if he were about to have an **apoplectic** stroke; he saw the depths of dungeons, his family in tears, his shop sold, all the jars dispersed; and he was obliged to enter a cafe and take a glass of **rum** and seltzer to recover his spirits.

Little by little the memory of this **reprimand** grew fainter, and he continued, as heretofore, to give anodyne consultations in his back-parlour. But the mayor resented it, his colleagues were **jealous**, everything was to be **feared**; **gaining** over Monsieur Bovary by his attentions was to **earn** his **gratitude**, and prevent his speaking out later on, should he notice anything. So every morning Homais brought him "the paper," and often in the afternoon left his shop for a few moments to have a chat with the Doctor.

Charles was **dull**: patients did not come. He remained seated for hours without speaking, went into his consulting room to sleep, or watched his wife sewing. Then for **diversion** he employed himself at home as a **workman**; he even

Spanish

anonymous: anónimo.
apoplectic: apoplético.
cordiality: cordialidad.
denunciations: denuncias de convenios.
diploma: acta, certificado, diploma.
diversion: distracción, desviación, desvío, diversión.
dull: embotado, obtuso, mate, aburrido, soso.
earn: ganar, ganan, ganamos, ganáis, ganad, gano, ganen, gana, gane,

ganas, obtener.
ermine: armiño.
expressly: expresamente.
far-off: remoto.
feared: temido.
funeral: entierro, funeral, fúnebre, enterramiento.
gaining: ganar.
gratitude: gratitud, gracias, reconocimiento.
infringed: infringido.
jealous: celoso.

magistrate: magistrado.
obsequious: obsequioso.
practise: practicar.
procurer: alcahuete.
reprimand: reprimenda, reprender.
rum: ron, el ron.
sacerdotal: sacerdotal.
sacristan: sacristán.
summoned: convocado.
underneath: abajo, debajo, debajo de, en el fondo.
workman: obrero, trabajador.

tried to do up the attic with some paint which had been left behind by the **painters**. But money matters worried him. He had spent so much for **repairs** at Tostes, for madame's **toilette**, and for the moving, that the whole dowry, over three thousand crowns, had slipped away in two years.

Then how many things had been spoilt or lost during their carriage from Tostes to Yonville, without counting the plaster **cure**, who falling out of the coach at an over-severe **jolt**, had been **dashed** into a thousand fragments on the pavements of Quincampoix! A pleasanter trouble came to **distract** him, namely, the pregnancy of his wife. As the time of her **confinement** approached he **cherished** her the more. It was another bond of the flesh establishing itself, and, as it were, a continued **sentiment** of a more complex union. When from afar he saw her **languid** walk, and her figure without **stays** turning softly on her **hips**; when opposite one another he looked at her at his ease, while she took tired **poses** in her armchair, then his happiness knew no bounds; he got up, embraced her, passed his hands over her face, called her little mamma, wanted to make her dance, and half-laughing, half-crying, uttered all kinds of **caressing** pleasantries that came into his head. The idea of having **begotten** a child delighted him. Now he wanted nothing. He knew human life from end to end, and he sat down to it with **serenity**.

Emma at first felt a great astonishment; then was anxious to be delivered that she might know what it was to be a mother. But not being able to spend as much as she would have liked, to have a swing-bassinette with rose silk curtains, and embroidered caps, in a fit of bitterness she gave up looking after the trousseau, and ordered the whole of it from a village **needlewoman**, without **choosing** or **discussing** anything. Thus she did not amuse herself with those preparations that **stimulate** the tenderness of mothers, and so her **affection** was from the very **outset**, perhaps, to some extent **attenuated**.

As Charles, however, spoke of the boy at every meal, she soon began to think of him more consecutively.

She hoped for a son; he would be strong and dark; she would call him George; and this idea of having a male child was like an expected **revenge** for all

Spanish

affection: afecto, cariño, afectuosidad, amor.
attenuated: se atenuado.
begotten: engendrado.
caressing: mimoso, zalamero.
cherished: querido.
choosing: escogiendo, elegiendo.
confinement: encierro.
cure: curar, curación, cura, sanar.
dashed: quebrado.
discussing: discutiendo, debatiendo.
distract: distraer, distrae, distraed,

distraéis, distraemos, distraen, distraes, distraigan, distraigo, distraiga, confundir.
hips: las caderas.
jolt: traqueteo, empujar, sacudir.
languid: lánguido.
needlewoman: costurera.
outset: principio.
painters: pintores.
poses: plantea, posa.
repairs: reparaciones, reparación.
revenge: venganza, revancha.

sentiment: sentimiento, opinión, sensibilidad, parecer, sentimentalismo.
serenity: serenidad.
stays: queda, permanece.
stimulate: estimular, estimulamos, estimulen, estimulan, estimulo, estimuláis, estimulad, estimula, estimulas, estimule, instigar.
toilette: wáter, de tocador, inodoro, lavabo, retrete, sanitario, servicios, tocado, vestido, atavío, baño.

her **impotence** in the past. A man, at least, is free; he may travel over passions and over countries, overcome **obstacles**, taste of the most **far**-away pleasures. But a woman is always **hampered**. At once **inert** and flexible, she has against her the **weakness** of the flesh and legal **dependence**. Her will, like the veil of her **bonnet**, held by a string, flutters in every wind; there is always some desire that **draws** her, some **conventionality** that restrains.

She was **confined** on a Sunday at about six o'clock, as the sun was rising.

"It is a girl!" said Charles.

She turned her head away and fainted.

Madame Homais, as well as Madame Lefrancois of the Lion d'Or, almost immediately came running in to embrace her. The chemist, as man of **discretion**, only offered a few **provincial** felicitations through the **half**-opened door. He wished to see the child and thought it well made.

Whilst she was getting well she occupied herself much in seeking a name for her daughter. First she went over all those that have Italian endings, such as Clara, Louisa, Amanda, Atala; she liked Galsuinde pretty well, and Yseult or Leocadie still better.

Charles wanted the child to be called after her mother; Emma opposed this. They ran over the **calendar** from end to end, and then **consulted outsiders**.

"Monsieur Leon," said the chemist, "with whom I was talking about it the other day, wonders you do not chose Madeleine. It is very much in fashion just now."

But Madame Bovary, senior, cried out loudly against this name of a **sinner**. As to Monsieur Homais, he had a preference for all those that **recalled** some great man, an illustrious fact, or a generous idea, and it was on this system that he had **baptized** his four children. Thus Napoleon represented **glory** and Franklin **liberty**; Irma was perhaps a **concession** to **romanticism**, but Athalie was a **homage** to the greatest **masterpiece** of the French stage. For his **philosophical** convictions did not interfere with his **artistic tastes**; in him the **thinker** did not **stifle** the man of sentiment; he could make distinctions, make

Spanish

artistic: artístico.
baptized: bautizado.
bonnet: capot, capó, gorro, capota.
calendar: calendario, almanaque, el calendario.
concession: concesión.
confined: limitado.
consulted: consultado.
conventionality: convencionalismo.
dependence: dependencia.
discretion: discreción.
draws: dibuja, traza, encanta.

far-away: lejano.
glory: gloria.
half-opened: entreabierto.
hampered: estorbado.
homage: homenaje.
impotence: impotencia.
inert: inerte.
liberty: libertad, la libertad.
masterpiece: obra maestra.
obstacles: obstáculos.
outsiders: trabajadores periféricos.
philosophical: filosófico.

provincial: provinciano.
recalled: hacer volver, desmarcado, recordar, recordado, llamar de nuevo, recuperar, llamada, desmarcar, recuperado, revocar, revocación.
romanticism: romanticismo.
sinner: pecador.
stifle: babilla.
tastes: gustos.
thinker: pensador.
weakness: debilidad.

allowances for imagination and **fanaticism**. In this tragedy, for example, he found fault **with** the ideas, but **admired** the style; he detested the conception, but **applauded** all the details, and **loathed** the characters while he grew enthusiastic over their dialogue. When he read the fine passages he was **transported**, but when he thought that mummers would get something out of them for their show, he was **disconsolate**; and in this confusion of sentiments in which he was involved he would have like at once to crown Racine with both his hands and discuss with him for a good quarter of an hour.

At last Emma remembered that at the chateau of Vaubyessard she had heard the Marchioness call a young lady Berthe; from that moment this name was chosen; and as old Rouault could not come, Monsieur Homais was requested to stand **godfather**. His gifts were all products from his establishment, to wit: six boxes of **jujubes**, a whole **jar** of racahout, three cakes of **marshmallow** paste, and six **sticks** of **sugar**-candy into the **bargain** that he had come across in a cupboard. On the evening of the ceremony there was a grand dinner; the cure was present; there was much excitement. Monsieur Homais towards liqueur-time began singing "Le Dieu des **bonnes** gens." Monsieur Leon sang a **barcarolle**, and Madame Bovary, senior, who was **godmother**, a **romance** of the time of the Empire; finally, M. Bovary, senior, insisted on having the child brought down, and began **baptizing** it with a glass of champagne that he poured over its head. This **mockery** of the first of the **sacraments** made the Abbe Bournisien angry; old Bovary replied by a **quotation** from "La Guerre des Dieux"; the cure wanted to leave; the ladies implored, Homais **interfered**; and they succeeded in making the priest sit down again, and he quietly went on with the **half**-finished coffee in his **saucer**.

Monsieur Bovary, senior, stayed at Yonville a month, **dazzling** the native by a superb policeman's cap with silver tassels that he wore in the morning when he smoked his pipe in the square. Being also in the habit of drinking a good deal of brandy, he often sent the servant to the Lion d'Or to buy him a bottle, which was put down to his son's account, and to perfume his handkerchiefs he used up his daughter-in-law's whole supply of eau-de-cologne.

Spanish

admired: admirado.
applauded: Aplaudido.
baptizing: bautizando.
barcarolle: barcarola.
bargain: trato, negociar, ganga, regatear, convenio.
bonnes: niñeras.
dazzling: deslumbrante.
disconsolate: desconsolado.
fanaticism: fanatismo, el fanaticismo.
godfather: padrino, compadre.
godmother: madrina.

half-finished: semi-acabado.
interfered: intervenido, interpuesto, obstruido, perturbado, introducido, entrometido, injerido, entremetido, inmiscuido, interferido.
jar: tarro, jarra, la jarra.
jujubes: jinjoles.
loathed: detestado.
marshmallow: malvavisco.
mockery: burla.
quotation: cotización, cita, citación.
romance: amorío, cuento,

enamoramiento, fantasear, libro de caballerías, lo romántico, neolatino, románico, exagerar, romance, romanza.
sacraments: sacramentos.
saucer: platillo, el platillo.
sticks: leño, vara, palillo, adherir, batuta, palo, pegar, ramitas, punzar, picar.
sugar-candy: azúcar cande.
transported: Transportado.
wit: ingenio.

The latter did not at all **dislike** his company. He had **knocked** about the world, he talked about Berlin, Vienna, and Strasbourg, of his **soldier** times, of the mistresses he had had, the grand luncheons of which he had **partaken**; then he was **amiable**, and sometimes even, either on the stairs, or in the garden, would **seize** hold of her waist, **crying**, "Charles, look out for yourself."

Then Madame Bovary, senior, became **alarmed** for her son's happiness, and **fearing** that her husband might in the long-run have an immoral influence upon the ideas of the young woman, took care to **hurry** their departure. Perhaps she had more serious reasons for uneasiness. Monsieur Bovary was not the man to respect anything.

One day Emma was suddenly seized with the desire to see her little girl, who had been put to nurse with the carpenter's wife, and, without looking at the calendar to see whether the six weeks of the Virgin were yet passed, she set out for the Rollets' house, **situated** at the extreme end of the village, between the highroad and the fields.

It was mid-day, the shutters of the houses were closed and the slate roofs that **glittered** beneath the **fierce** light of the blue sky seemed to strike **sparks** from the **crest** of the gables. A heavy wind was blowing; Emma felt weak as she walked; the stones of the **pavement** hurt her; she was **doubtful** whether she would not go home again, or go in somewhere to rest.

At this moment Monsieur Leon came out from a **neighbouring** door with a bundle of papers under his arm. He came to **greet** her, and stood in the **shade** in front of the Lheureux's shop under the projecting grey **awning**.

Madame Bovary said she was going to see her baby, but that she was beginning to grow tired.

"If--" said Leon, not daring to go on.

"Have you any business to attend to?" she asked.

And on the clerk's answer, she begged him to **accompany** her. That same evening this was known in Yonville, and Madame Tuvache, the mayor's wife,

Spanish

accompany: acompañar, acompañen, acompaña, acompaño, acompañas, acompañan, acompañamos, acompañáis, acompañad, acompañe.
alarmed: alarmado.
amiable: amistoso, amable.
awning: toldo.
crest: cresta, penacho.
crying: llorando.
dislike: aversión, repugnancia, detestar, detesto, detesten, deteste, detestas, detestan, detesta,

detestamos, detestáis.
doubtful: dudoso.
fearing: por miedo a, por temor a, temer.
fierce: feroz.
glittered: brillado.
greet: saludar, saludad, saludáis, saludamos, saludan, saludas, saluda, saluden, salude, saludo, acoger.
hurry: apresurarse, prisa.
knocked: Golpeado.
neighbouring: vecino, contiguo,

adyacente.
partaken: compartido.
pavement: acera, pavimento.
seize: agarrar, coger, agarro, agarre, agarras, agarra, agarren, agarran, agarramos, agarráis, agarrad.
shade: sombra, sombrear, pantalla, matizar, tono, matiz.
situated: situado.
soldier: soldado, el soldado.
sparks: telegrafista, moscas, iluminista.

declared in the presence of her servant that "Madame Bovary was **compromising** herself."

To get to the nurse's it was necessary to turn to the left on leaving the street, as if making for the cemetery, and to follow between little houses and yards a small path bordered with **privet** hedges. They were in **bloom**, and so were the speedwells, eglantines, thistles, and the sweetbriar that sprang up from the thickets. Through **openings** in the hedges one could see into the huts, some pigs on a dung-heap, or **tethered** cows rubbing their **horns** against the **trunk** of trees. The two, side by side walked slowly, she leaning upon him, and he restraining his pace, which he **regulated** by hers; in front of them a **swarm** of midges fluttered, buzzing in the warm air.

The recognized the house by an old walnut-tree which **shaded** it.

Low and covered with brown tiles, there hung outside it, beneath the **dormer**-window of the garret, a string of onions. Faggots upright against a **thorn** fence surrounded a bed of **lettuce**, a few square feet of **lavender**, and sweet **peas stung** on sticks. Dirty water was running here and there on the grass, and all round were several indefinite **rags**, **knitted** stockings, a red calico jacket, and a large sheet of coarse linen spread over the hedge. At the noise of the gate the nurse appeared with a baby she was suckling on one arm. With her other hand she was pulling along a poor **puny** little fellow, his face covered with scrofula, the son of a Rouen **hosier**, whom his parents, too taken up with their business, left in the country.

"Go in," she said; "your little one is there asleep."

The room on the ground-floor, the only one in the **dwelling**, had at its farther end, against the wall, a large bed without curtains, while a **kneading**-trough took up the side by the window, one **pane** of which was **mended** with a piece of blue paper. In the corner behind the door, shining hob-nailed shoes stood in a row under the **slab** of the **washstand**, near a bottle of oil with a **feather** stuck in its mouth; a Matthieu Laensberg lay on the dusty mantelpiece amid gunflints, candle-ends, and bits of amadou.

Spanish

bloom: flor, florecer, veladura, floración, florecimiento.
compromising: comprometido, comprometedor.
dormer-window: buharda.
dwelling: morando, vivienda, morada.
feather: pluma, la pluma.
horns: herramienta, cornamenta, cuernos, cuerna.
hosier: calcetero.
kneading-trough: amasadera.
knitted: de punto.
lavender: lavanda, espliego.
lettuce: lechuga, la lechuga.
mended: Mejorado.
openings: oportunidad.
pane: hoja de vidrio, panel, cristal.
peas: guisantes.
privet: alheña.
puny: endeble.
rags: los trapos.
regulated: regulado.
shaded: matizado, obscurecido, matiz, matizar, obscurecer, Sombread, sombreado, sombrear, degradado, tono, sombra.
slab: libra, lámina, losa, placa, plancha, costero.
stung: picado, pret y pp de sting.
swarm: enjambre, pulular, hormiguear.
tethered: atado.
thorn: espina.
trunk: tronco, baúl, maleta, trompa, portaequipajes.
washstand: lavabo, lavamanos.

Finally, the last **luxury** in the apartment was a "Fame" blowing her trumpets, a picture cut out, no doubt, from some perfumer's prospectus and **nailed** to the wall with six wooden shoe-pegs.

Emma's child was asleep in a wicker-cradle. She took it up in the **wrapping** that **enveloped** it and began singing softly as she **rocked** herself to and fro.

Leon **walked** up and down the room; it seemed strange to him to see this beautiful woman in her **nankeen dress** in the midst of all this **poverty**. Madam Bovary reddened; he turned away, thinking perhaps there had been an **impertinent** look in his eyes. Then she put back the little girl, who had just been sick over her collar.

The nurse at once came to **dry** her, **protesting** that it wouldn't show.

"She gives me other doses," she said: "I am always a-washing of her. If you would have the **goodness** to order Camus, the **grocer**, to let me have a little **soap**, it would really be more **convenient** for you, as I needn't trouble you then."

"Very well! very well!" said Emma. "Good morning, Madame Rollet," and she went out, wiping her **shoes** at the door.

The good woman **accompanied** her to the end of the **garden**, talking all the time of the trouble she had getting up of nights.

"**I'm** that **worn** out sometimes as I **drop** asleep on my chair. I'm sure you might at **least** give me just a **pound** of ground **coffee**; that'd last me a month, and I'd take it of a morning with some milk."

After having **submitted** to her **thanks**, Madam Bovary left. She had gone a little way down the **path** when, at the sound of wooden shoes, she turned round. It was the nurse.

"What is it?"

Then the peasant woman, taking her **aside** behind an **elm** tree, began talking to her of her husband, who with his trade and six francs a year that the captain--

"Oh, be quick!" said Emma.

Spanish

accompanied: acompañado.
aside: aparte, al lado.
coffee: café.
convenient: conveniente.
dress: vestido, vestir, vendar, vestirse, el vestido, ponerse, revestir.
drop: gota, caer, disminuir, amainar, decrecer, menguar, caída, descenso, dejar caer.
dry: seco, secar, enjugar.
elm: olmo.
enveloped: enrollado, envuelto.

garden: jardín, el jardín.
goodness: bondad.
grocer: tendero, almacenero, bodeguero, abacero.
i'm: soy.
impertinent: impertinente.
least: menos, mínimo, menor.
luxury: lujo, el lujo.
nailed: clavado, remachado.
nankeen: nanquín, mahón.
path: sendero, camino, ruta, senda, trayectoria, vía, ruta de acceso,

trayecto, recorrido, la senda.
pound: libra, la libra.
poverty: pobreza, indigencia.
protesting: protestar, protestador.
rocked: Mecido.
shoes: los zapatos.
soap: jabón, enjabonar.
submitted: sometido.
thanks: gracias, agradece.
walked: andado, Caminado.
worn: gastado, usado.
wrapping: envoltura, envoltorio.

"Well," the nurse went on, **heaving** sighs between each word, "I'm afraid he'll be put out seeing me have coffee along, you know men--"

"But you are to have some," Emma repeated; "I will give you some. You bother me!"

"Oh, dear! my poor, dear lady! you see in consequence of his **wounds** he has terrible **cramps** in the chest. He even says that cider **weakens** him."

"Do make **haste**, Mere Rollet!"

"Well," the latter continued, making a **curtsey**, "if it weren't asking too much," and she curtsied once more, "if you would"--and her eyes begged--"a jar of brandy," she said at last, "and I'd **rub** your little one's feet with it; they're as tender as one's tongue."

Once rid of the nurse, Emma again took Monsieur Leon's arm. She walked fast for some time, then more slowly, and looking straight in front of her, her eyes rested on the shoulder of the young man, whose frock-coat had a black-velvety collar. His brown hair fell over it, straight and carefully arranged. She noticed his **nails** which were longer than one wore them at Yonville. It was one of the clerk's chief **occupations** to **trim** them, and for this purpose he kept a special knife in his writing desk.

They returned to Yonville by the water-side. In the warm season the bank, wider than at other times, showed to their foot the garden walls whence a few steps led to the river. It flowed **noiselessly, swift**, and cold to the eye; long, thin grasses **huddled** together in it as the current drove them, and spread themselves upon the **limpid** water like **streaming** hair; sometimes at the **tip** of the reeds or on the **leaf** of a water-lily an **insect** with fine legs **crawled** or rested. The sun pierced with a **ray** the small blue **bubbles** of the waves that, breaking, followed each other; **branchless** old willows **mirrored** their grey **backs** in the water; beyond, all around, the meadows seemed empty. It was the dinner-hour at the farms, and the young woman and her **companion** heard nothing as they walked but the fall of their steps on the earth of the path, the words they spoke, and the sound of Emma's dress rustling round her.

Spanish

backs: espaldas.
branchless: sin ramas.
bubbles: burbuja, porosidad, burbujas.
companion: acompañante, compañero.
cramps: grampillones, obstáculo.
crawled: Arrastrado, Repelado.
curtsey: bravura, cortesía, reverencia, hacer con cortesía.
haste: prisa, precipitación.
heaving: tirar, movimiento vertical del

buque, dislocación.
huddled: apiñado.
insect: insecto, el insecto.
leaf: hoja, la hoja.
limpid: límpido.
mirrored: reflejado.
nails: clavos.
noiselessly: calladamente, silenciosamente, tranquilamente.
occupations: ocupaciones.
ray: rayo, raya, radio, irradiar.
rub: frotar, refregar, friccionar.

streaming: flujo, difusión de video digital en tiempo real, efecto de canalización, correr, transferencia de datos desde el disco duro.
swift: rápido, veloz, ligero, vencejo común.
tip: punta, propina, basurero, consejo, escombrera.
trim: en buen estado, recortar, adornar, guarnecer.
weakens: debilita.
wounds: las heridas, heridas.

The walls of the gardens with pieces of bottle on their coping were hot as the glass windows of a **conservatory**. Wallflowers had **sprung** up between the **bricks**, and with the tip of her open sunshade Madame Bovary, as she passed, made some of their faded flowers **crumble** into a yellow dust, or a **spray** of **overhanging honeysuckle** and **clematis** caught in its fringe and **dangled** for a moment over the silk.

They were talking of a **troupe** of Spanish dancers who were expected shortly at the Rouen theatre.

"Are you going?" she asked.

"If I can," he answered.

Had they nothing else to say to one another? Yet their eyes were full of more serious speech, and while they forced themselves to find **trivial** phrases, they felt the same languor **stealing** over them both. It was the **whisper** of the soul, deep, **continuous**, **dominating** that of their voices. Surprised with wonder at this strange sweetness, they did not think of speaking of the **sensation** or of seeking its cause. Coming joys, like **tropical** shores, throw over the immensity before them their **inborn softness**, an odorous wind, and we are lulled by this **intoxication** without a thought of the horizon that we do not even know.

In one place the ground had been **trodden** down by the **cattle**; they had to step on large green stones put here and there in the mud.

She often stopped a moment to look where to place her foot, and **tottering** on a stone that shook, her arms **outspread**, her form bent forward with a look of **indecision**, she would laugh, afraid of falling into the **puddles** of water.

When they arrived in front of her garden, Madame Bovary opened the little gate, ran up the steps and disappeared.

Leon returned to his office. His chief was away; he just **glanced** at the **briefs**, then cut himself a pen, and at last took up his hat and went out.

He went to La Pature at the top of the Argueil hills at the beginning of the forest; he threw himself upon the ground under the pines and watched the sky through his fingers.

Spanish

bricks: ladrillos.
briefs: braguitas.
cattle: ganado, ganado vacuno.
clematis: clemátide.
conservatory: conservatorio.
continuous: continuo.
crumble: desmoronarse, desmenuzar, derruirse.
dangled: balanceado, pendido, se bamboleado, colgado.
dominating: dominando.
glanced: mirado.

honeysuckle: madreselva.
inborn: innato.
indecision: indecisión.
intoxication: intoxicación, embriaguez, envenenamiento.
outspread: desplegado, extendido, extensión.
overhanging: saliente.
puddles: charcos.
sensation: sensación, sentimiento.
softness: blandura, suavidad.
spray: rociar, rocío, atomizador,

aerosol, pulverización.
sprung: pp de spring, de muelles, brotado, saltado.
stealing: hurto, taking, robando.
tottering: tambaleante, tambalear, tambaleando.
trivial: trivial.
trodden: pisado, pp de tread.
tropical: tropical.
troupe: compañía teatral.
whisper: cuchichear, cuchicheo, susurrar, susurro, murmurar.

"How bored I am!" he said to himself, "how bored I am!"

He thought he was to be **pitied** for living in this village, with Homais for a friend and Monsieru Guillaumin for master. The latter, entirely **absorbed** by his business, **wearing** gold-rimmed spectacles and red whiskers over a white cravat, **understood** nothing of mental refinements, although he **affected** a **stiff** English manner, which in the beginning had **impressed** the clerk.

As to the chemist's **spouse**, she was the best wife in Normandy, **gentle** as a **sheep**, loving her children, her father, her mother, her cousins, weeping for other's **woes**, **letting** everything go in her **household**, and **detesting** corsets; but so **slow** of movement, such a bore to listen to, so common in appearance, and of such **restricted** conversation, that although she was thirty, he only twenty, although they slept in rooms next each other and he spoke to her daily, he never thought that she might be a woman for another, or that she possessed anything else of her sex than the gown.

And what else was there? Binet, a few **shopkeepers**, two or three publicans, the cure, and finally, Monsieur Tuvache, the **mayor**, with his two sons, rich, **crabbed**, **obtuse** persons, who **farmed** their own lands and had feasts among themselves, **bigoted** to boot, and quite unbearable companions.

But from the general background of all these human **faces** Emma's stood out **isolated** and yet **farthest** off; for between her and him he seemed to see a vague **abyss**.

In the beginning he had called on her several times along with the druggist. Charles had not **appeared** particularly **anxious** to see him again, and Leon did not know what to do between his fear of being **indiscreet** and the desire for an intimacy that seemed almost impossible.

Spanish

absorbed: absorbido, absorto.
abyss: abismo, despeñadero, precipicio.
affected: afectado, conmovido.
anxious: inquieto, ansioso.
appeared: Aparecido, comparecido.
bigoted: intolerante.
crabbed: malhumorado, indescifrable, apretado.
detesting: detestando.
faces: Caras.
farmed: cultivado.

farthest: más lejanamente, a distancia, a lo lejos, a lo más, lejano, lejos, a la mayor distancia, más, más lejano, más lejos, remotamente.
gentle: dulce, suave, manso, apacible.
household: hogar, casa.
impressed: impresionado.
indiscreet: indiscreto.
isolated: aislado.
letting: alquilando, dejando.
mayor: alcalde.
obtuse: obtuso, embotado.

pitied: compadecido.
restricted: limitado, restringido.
sheep: oveja, la oveja.
shopkeepers: tenderos.
slow: lento.
spouse: cónyuge, esposo, esposa.
stiff: rígido, tieso, espeso.
understood: entendido, comprendido.
wearing: llevando, llevar puesto, usar, uso, desgastado, usando.
woes: dolencia.

CHAPTER FOUR

When the first cold days set in Emma left her bedroom for the sitting-room, a long apartment with a low **ceiling**, in which there was on the mantelpiece a large bunch of **coral spread** out against the looking-glass. Seated in her **arm chair** near the window, she could see the villagers **pass** along the pavement.

Twice a day Leon went from his office to the Lion d'Or. Emma could hear him coming from afar; she leant forward **listening**, and the young man glided past the curtain, always dressed in the same way, and without **turning** his head. But in the twilight, when, her chin resting on her left hand, she let the embroidery she had **begun** fall on her knees, she often **shuddered** at the **apparition** of this shadow suddenly gliding past. She would get up and order the table to be **laid**.

Monsieur Homais called at dinner-time. Skull-cap in hand, he came in on tiptoe, in order to **disturb** no one, always repeating the same **phrase**, "Good evening, everybody." Then, when he had taken his **seat** at the table between the **pair**, he asked the **doctor** about his patients, and the **latter** consulted his as to the **probability** of their **payment**. Next they talked of "what was in the paper."

Homais by this hour knew it almost by heart, and he repeated it from end to end, with the reflections of the penny-a-liners, and all the stories of individual catastrophes that had **occurred** in France or **abroad**. But the subject becoming

Spanish

abroad: en el extranjero, fuera, en el la extranjero, al extranjero.
apparition: aparición.
arm: brazo, armar, el brazo, arma.
begun: empezado, principiado.
ceiling: techo, el techo, tope, cielo raso.
chair: silla, la silla, presidencia, cátedra.
coral: coral.
disturb: molestar, moleste, molestad, molestáis, molestamos, molestan, molestas, molesta, molesto, molesten, incomodar.
doctor: médico, doctor.
laid: puesto, colocado, recostado, acostado.
latter: último.
listening: escuchando.
occurred: ocurrido.
pair: par, pareja, emparejar.
pass: pasar, adelantar, paso, pase, desfiladero, entregar, pasada, aprobar, alargar, paso de montaña, llegar.
payment: pago, retribución, abono.
phrase: frase, expresar, expresión.
probability: probabilidad, apariencia.
seat: asiento, el asiento, sitio, sede, asentar, sentar.
shuddered: estremecido.
spread: propagar, extender, difundir, extensión, untar, diferencial, extenderse, cobertor.
turning: girando, volviendo, trastornando.

exhausted, he was not slow in **throwing** out some **remarks** on the dishes before him.

Sometimes even, half-rising, he delicately **pointed** out to madame the **tenderest morsel**, or turning to the servant, gave her some advice on the **manipulation** of stews and the hygiene of **seasoning**.

He talked **aroma**, osmazome, juices, and **gelatine** in a **bewildering** manner. Moreover, Homais, with his head **fuller** of recipes than his shop of jars, **excelled** in making all kinds of preserves, vinegars, and sweet liqueurs; he knew also all the latest inventions in economic **stoves**, together with the art of **preserving** cheese and of **curing** sick wines.

At eight o'clock Justin came to fetch him to shut up the shop.

Then Monsieur Homais gave him a sly look, especially if Felicite was there, for he half **noticed** that his apprentice was fond of the doctor's house.

"The young dog," he said, "is beginning to have ideas, and the **devil** take me if I don't believe he's in love with your servant!"

But a more serious **fault** with which he reproached Justin was his constantly listening to conversation. On Sunday, for example, one could not get him out of the **drawing**-room, **whither** Madame Homais had called him to fetch the children, who were **falling** asleep in the arm-chairs, and dragging down with their backs calico chair-covers that were too large.

Not many people came to these soirees at the chemist's, his scandal-mongering and political opinions having **successfully alienated** various **respectable** persons from him. The clerk never failed to be there. As soon as he heard the bell he ran to meet Madame Bovary, took her shawl, and put away under the shop-counter the **thick** list shoes that she wore over her **boots** when there was **snow**.

First they played some hands at trente-et-un; next Monsieur Homais played ecarte with Emma; Leon behind her gave her advice.

Standing up with his hands on the back of her chair he saw the **teeth** of her comb that bit into her chignon. With every movement that she made to throw her

Spanish

alienated: alienado, enajenado.
aroma: olor, aroma.
bewildering: desconcertando, desconcierto.
boots: botas.
curing: curación, curado.
devil: diablo, el diablo.
drawing-room: estrado.
excelled: sobrevenido, aventajado, descollado, sobresalido.
exhausted: agotado, exhausto.
falling: cayéndose, decreciendo,

derribando, caída.
fault: culpa, defecto, avería, falla, falta, fallo, error, imperfección.
fuller: abatanador, batán.
gelatine: gelatina.
manipulation: manipulación.
morsel: pedacito, bocado.
noticed: advertido.
pointed: puntiagudo.
preserving: conservación, preservar.
remarks: observaciones.
respectable: respetable, honorable.

seasoning: condimento, secado, sazonar, sazón.
snow: nevar, nieve, la nieve.
stoves: estufas.
successfully: con éxito.
teeth: dientes, dentadura.
tenderest: ofrezca.
thick: grueso, espeso, gordo, denso.
throw: lanzar, echar, tirar, tirada, arrojar, lanzamiento.
throwing: lanzamiento.
whither: adónde, adonde.

cards the right side of her dress was drawn up. From her turned-up hair a dark colour fell over her back, and growing **gradually** paler, lost itself little by little in the shade. Then her dress fell on both sides of her chair, **puffing** out full of folds, and reached the ground. When Leon **occasionally** felt the **sole** of his boot resting on it, he drew back as if he had trodden upon some one.

When the game of cards was over, the druggist and the Doctor played dominoes, and Emma, **changing** her place, leant her elbow on the table, turning over the leaves of "L'Illustration". She had brought her **ladies'** journal with her. Leon sat down near her; they looked at the engravings together, and waited for one another at the bottom of the **pages**. She often begged him to read her the verses; Leon **declaimed** them in a languid voice, to which he carefully gave a **dying** fall in the love passages. But the noise of the dominoes **annoyed** him. Monsieur Homais was strong at the game; he could beat Charles and give him a double-six. Then the three hundred finished, they both stretched themselves out in front of the fire, and were soon asleep. The fire was dying out in the cinders; the **teapot** was empty, Leon was still reading.

Emma listened to him, **mechanically** turning around the **lampshade**, on the **gauze** of which were painted clowns in carriages, and tight-rope **dances** with their balancing-poles. Leon stopped, **pointing** with a **gesture** to his **sleeping** audience; then they talked in low **tones**, and their conversation seemed the more sweet to them because it was **unheard**.

Thus a kind of **bond** was established between them, a **constant commerce** of books and of romances. Monsieur Bovary, little given to jealousy, did not trouble himself about it.

On his **birthday** he received a beautiful phrenological head, all marked with figures to the **thorax** and painted blue. This was an attention of the clerk's. He showed him many others, even to doing errands for him at Rouen; and the book of a **novelist** having made the **mania** for **cactuses fashionable**, Leon bought some for Madame Bovary, bringing them back on his knees in the "Hirondelle," **pricking** his fingers on their hard hairs.

Spanish

annoyed: fastidiado, molestado, enojado, enfadado.
birthday: cumpleaños.
bond: lazo, bono, obligación, fianza, cinta, adherencia, enlace.
cactuses: cactos.
changing: cambiando.
commerce: comercio.
constant: constante, continuo.
dances: baila.
declaimed: declamado, proclamado.
dying: muriendo, agonizante.
fashionable: de moda.
gauze: gasa.
gesture: gesto, ademán, acción.
gradually: gradualmente, poco a poco.
ladies: damas, señoras.
lampshade: pantalla.
mania: manía.
mechanically: mecánicamente.
novelist: novelista.
occasionally: de vez en cuando, a veces, ocasionalmente.
pages: páginas.
pointing: rejuntado.
pricking: pinchar, picor, punción, punzada, hormigueo, que pincha, el pinchazo, punzante.
puffing: reclamo excesivo, soplar.
sleeping: durmiendo, durmiente.
sole: lenguado, suela, único, solo, planta.
teapot: tetera, la tetera.
thorax: tórax.
tones: tonos.
unheard: inaudito.

She had a board with a balustrade fixed against her window to hold the pots. The clerk, too, had his small hanging garden; they saw each other **tending** their flowers at their windows.

Of the windows of the village there was one yet more often occupied; for on Sundays from morning to night, and every morning when the weather was bright, one could see at the dormer-window of the garret the **profile** of Monsieur Binet bending over his lathe, whose monotonous humming could be heard at the Lion d'Or.

One evening on coming home Leon found in his room a **rug** in velvet and wool with leaves on a pale ground. He called Madame Homais, Monsieur Homais, Justin, the children, the cook; he spoke of it to his chief; every one wanted to see this rug. Why did the doctor's wife give the clerk presents? It looked **queer**. They decided that she must be his **lover**.

He made this seem likely, so ceaselessly did he talk of her charms and of her wit; so much so, that Binet once **roughly** answered him--

"What does it matter to me since I'm not in her set?"

He **tortured** himself to find out how he could make his **declaration** to her, and always **halting** between the fear of **displeasing** her and the **shame** of being such a **coward**, he wept with **discouragement** and desire. Then he took **energetic** resolutions, wrote letters that he tore up, put it off to times that he again **deferred**.

Often he set out with the determination to **dare** all; but this resolution soon deserted him in Emma's presence, and when Charles, **dropping** in, invited him to **jump** into his chaise to go with him to see some patient in the **neighbourhood**, he at once accepted, bowed to madame, and went out. Her husband, was he not something **belonging** to her? As to Emma, she did not ask herself whether she loved. Love, she thought, must come suddenly, with great outbursts and lightnings--a **hurricane** of the skies, which falls upon life, **revolutionises** it, **roots** up the will like a leaf, and **sweeps** the whole heart into the abyss. She did not know that on the **terrace** of houses it makes **lakes** when the **pipes** are **choked**,

Spanish

belonging: perteneciendo.
choked: estrangulado.
coward: cobarde, el cobarde.
dare: atreverse, reto, cariño.
declaration: declaración.
deferred: diferido.
discouragement: desaliento.
displeasing: desagradando, desagradable.
dropping: goteante.
energetic: enérgico, energético.
halting: parar, detenerse, hacer alto,

renqueante, parada, interrupción, interrumpir, claudicante, vacilante, alto, detener.
hurricane: huracán.
jump: saltar, salto, brinco, brincar.
lakes: lagos.
lover: querido, amante, novio.
neighbourhood: barrio, vecindad, vecindario.
pipes: tubos para tuberías, tubería, gaita.
profile: perfil, perfilar.

queer: raro.
revolutionises: revoluciona.
roots: raíz, raigambre, raíces.
roughly: ásperamente, aproximadamente, bruscamente.
rug: alfombra, tapete.
shame: vergüenza, verguenza, pudor, oprobio, avergonzar.
sweeps: barre.
tending: cuidando, tendiendo.
terrace: terraza, terraplén, la terraza.
tortured: torturado.

and she would thus have **remained** in her **security** when she **suddenly**
discovered a **rent** in the **wall** of it.

Spanish

discovered: descubierto.
remained: restado, Permanecido.
rent: alquiler, renta, alquilar, arrendar,
  el alquiler.
security: seguridad, garantía, dinero
  del embase, recaudo.
suddenly: de repente, de golpe,
  repentinamente, de sopetón.
wall: pared, muro, tabique, la pared,
  mural, muralla.

CHAPTER FIVE

It was a Sunday in February, an afternoon when the snow was falling.

They had all, Monsieur and Madame Bovary, Homais, and Monsieur Leon, gone to see a yarn-mill that was being built in the **valley** a mile and a half from Yonville. The druggist had taken Napoleon and Athalie to give them some exercise, and Justin accompanied them, **carrying** the umbrellas on his shoulder.

Nothing, however, could be less **curious** than this curiosity. A great piece of **waste** ground, on which pell-mell, amid a **mass** of **sand** and stones, were a few break-wheels, already rusty, **surrounded** by a **quadrangular** building pierced by a number of little windows. The building was **unfinished**; the **sky** could be seen through the joists of the **roofing**. **Attached** to the stop-plank of the **gable** a bunch of straw **mixed** with corn-ears fluttered its tricoloured ribbons in the wind.

Homais was talking. He **explained** to the company the future importance of this **establishment**, **computed** the **strength** of the floorings, the **thickness** of the walls, and **regretted extremely** not having a yard-stick such as Monsieur Binet possessed for his own special use.

Emma, who had taken his arm, bent **lightly** against his shoulder, and she looked at the sun's disc shedding afar through the mist his **pale** splendour. She turned. Charles was there. His cap was drawn down over his **eyebrows**, and his two thick **lips** were trembling, which added a look of **stupidity** to his face; his

Spanish

attached: fijado, adjuntado, adjunto, sujetado.
carrying: llevando, transportando, cargando.
computed: estimado, calculado, computado.
curious: curioso.
establishment: establecimiento.
explained: explicado.
extremely: extremamente, extremadamente, sumamente.
eyebrows: las cejas.

gable: aguilón, gablete.
lightly: ligeramente.
lips: labios, los labios.
mass: masa, misa, en masa.
mixed: mixto, mezclado.
pale: pálido, palidecer, descolorido.
quadrangular: cuadrangular.
regretted: Lamentado.
roofing: cobertizo, material para techado, techador, techumbre.
sand: arena, la arena, lijar.
sky: cielo, el cielo.

strength: fuerza, resistencia, virtud, potencia, fortaleza.
stupidity: estupidez.
surrounded: rodeado, circundado.
thickness: espesor, grosor, espesura, grueso.
unfinished: inacabado.
valley: valle.
waste: desechos, desperdicio, residuo, residuos, detrito, gastar, acabar, desperdicios, derrochar, gasto, desecho.

very back, his calm back, was **irritating** to **behold**, and she saw written upon his **coat** all the **platitude** of the **bearer**.

While she was **considering** him thus, **tasting** in her irritation a sort of **depraved** pleasure, Leon made a step forward. The cold that made him pale seemed to add a more gentle languor to his face; between his cravat and his neck the somewhat loose collar of his **shirt** showed the skin; the **lobe** of his ear looked out from beneath a **lock** of hair, and his large blue eyes, raised to the **clouds**, seemed to Emma more limpid and more beautiful than those mountain-lakes where the heavens are mirrored.

"Wretched boy!" suddenly cried the chemist.

And he ran to his son, who had just **precipitated** himself into a heap of **lime** in order to **whiten** his boots. At the reproaches with which he was being **overwhelmed** Napoleon began to **roar**, while Justin **dried** his shoes with a **wisp** of straw. But a **knife** was wanted; Charles offered his.

"Ah!" she said to herself, "he carried a knife in his pocket like a peasant."

The **hoar**-frost was falling, and they turned back to Yonville.

In the evening Madame Bovary did not go to her neighbour's, and when Charles had left and she felt herself alone, the **comparison** re-began with the **clearness** of a sensation almost actual, and with that **lengthening** of **perspective** which memory gives to things. Looking from her bed at the clean fire that was **burning**, she still saw, as she had down there, Leon standing up with one hand behind his cane, and with the other holding Athalie, who was quietly sucking a piece of ice. She thought him **charming**; she could not tear herself away from him; she recalled his other attitudes on other days, the words he had spoken, the sound of his voice, his whole person; and she repeated, pouting out her lips as if for a kiss--

"Yes, charming! charming! Is he not in love?" she asked herself; "but with whom? With me?"

Spanish

behold: tenga.
burning: quemadura, ardiente.
charming: encantador, simpático, lindo, bonito, coquetón, amable.
clearness: claridad.
clouds: las nubes, nubes.
coat: abrigo, chaqueta, capa.
comparison: comparación, cotejo.
considering: considerando.
depraved: depravado.
dried: seco.
ear: oreja, espiga, la oreja, oído.

hoar-frost: escarcha.
irritating: irritante, irritando, enojoso.
knife: cuchillo, el cuchillo, cuchilla, la navaja, acuchillar.
lengthening: alargando, alargamiento.
lime: cal, lima, la lima, uni.
lobe: lóbulo.
lock: cerradura, esclusa, cerrar, la cerradura, cerrojo, bloquear, la esclusa, bucle, mechón, bloqueo, cerrar con llave.
overwhelmed: enterrado.

perspective: perspectiva.
platitude: tópico.
precipitated: precipitado.
roar: rugido, bramar, rugir, estruendo.
shirt: camisa, camiseta, la camisa.
tasting: cata, degustación, gustando.
whiten: blanquear, blanqueo, blanqueáis, blanqueen, blanquee, blanqueas, blanqueamos, blanquead, blanquea, blanquean.
wisp: agudeza, fragmento, ingenio, jirón, manojito, rastro.

All the **proofs arose** before her at once; her heart leapt. The flame of the fire threw a joyous light upon the ceiling; she turned on her back, stretching out her arms.

Then began the eternal **lamentation**: "Oh, if Heaven had out willed it! And why not? What prevented it?"

When Charles came home at midnight, she seemed to have just awakened, and as he made a noise **undressing**, she complained of a **headache**, then asked carelessly what had happened that evening.

"Monsieur Leon," he said, "went to his room early."

She could not help smiling, and she fell asleep, her soul filled with a new delight.

The next day, at **dusk**, she received a visit from Monsieur Lherueux, the draper. He was a man of ability, was this **shopkeeper**. Born a Gascon but **bred** a Norman, he **grafted** upon his southern **volubility** the **cunning** of the Cauchois. His fat, **flabby**, **beardless** face seemed **dyed** by a **decoction** of **liquorice**, and his white hair made even more **vivid** the keen **brilliance** of his small black eyes. No one knew what he had been formerly; a **pedlar** said some, a **banker** at Routot according to others. What was certain was that he made complex calculations in his head that would have **frightened** Binet himself. **Polite** to **obsequiousness**, he always held himself with his back bent in the position of one who bows or who **invites**.

After leaving at the door his hat surrounded with **crape**, he put down a green bandbox on the table, and began by **complaining** to madame, with many civilities, that he should have remained till that day without gaining her confidence. A poor shop like his was not made to attract a "fashionable lady"; he **emphasized** the words; yet she had only to command, and he would undertake to provide her with anything she might wish, either in **haberdashery** or linen, **millinery** or fancy goods, for he went to town regularly four times a month. He was **connected** with the best houses. You could speak of him at the "Trois Freres," at the "Barbe d'Or," or at the "Grand Sauvage"; all these gentlemen knew him as well as the insides of their pockets. To-day, then he had come to show

Spanish

arose: pret de arise, Surgió.
banker: banquero, el banquero.
beardless: imberbe.
bred: pret y pp de breed, Criado.
brilliance: brillo, brillantez.
complaining: regañando, demandando, lamentando, quejándose, querellándose, reclamando, quejumbroso, quejar.
connected: conectado, conexo.
crape: crespón.
cunning: astucia, astuto, hábil.

decoction: decocción.
dusk: anochecer, crepúsculo.
dyed: colorado, teñido.
emphasized: subrayado, enfatizado.
flabby: flojo, flácido, fláccido.
frightened: espantado, asustado.
grafted: injertó.
haberdashery: mercería, camisería.
headache: dolor de cabeza, jaqueca, cefalea.
invites: invita.
lamentation: lamento, lamentación.

liquorice: regaliz.
millinery: sombrerería.
obsequiousness: sumisión.
pedlar: vendedor ambulante, vendedor al detalle, buhonero.
polite: cortés, educado.
proofs: testigos.
shopkeeper: tendero.
undressing: desnudar, desnudando, desvistiendo.
vivid: vívido, gráfico.
volubility: volubilidad.

madame, in **passing**, various **articles** he happened to have, thanks to the most rare opportunity. And he pulled out **half**-a-dozen embroidered collars from the box.

Madame Bovary examined them. "I do not require anything," she said.

Then Monsieur Lheureux delicately **exhibited** three Algerian **scarves**, several **packet** of English **needles**, a pair of straw slippers, and finally, four eggcups in **cocoanut** wood, **carved** in open work by convicts. Then, with both hands on the table, his neck stretched out, his figure bent forward, **open**-mouthed, he watched Emma's look, who was walking up and down **undecided** amid these goods. From time to time, as if to remove some **dust**, he filliped with his nail the silk of the scarves spread out at full length, and they rustled with a little noise, making in the green twilight the gold spangles of their **tissue scintillate** like little stars.

"How much are they?"

"A mere nothing," he replied, "a mere nothing. But there's no hurry; **whenever** it's convenient. We are not Jews."

She **reflected** for a few moments, and ended by again **declining** Monsieur Lheureux's offer. He replied quite unconcernedly--

"Very well. We shall understand one another by and by. I have always got on with ladies--if I didn't with my own!"

Emma smiled.

"I wanted to tell you," he went on **good**-naturedly, after his **joke**, "that it isn't the money I should trouble about. Why, I could give you some, if need be."

She made a gesture of surprise.

"Ah!" said he quickly and in a low voice, "I **shouldn't** have to go far to find you some, **rely** on that."

And he began asking after Pere Tellier, the **proprietor** of the "Cafe Francais," whom Monsieur Bovary was then attending.

"What's the matter with Pere Tellier? He coughs so that he **shakes** his whole house, and I'm afraid he'll soon want a deal **covering** rather than a **flannel** vest.

Spanish

articles: constitución, estatutos, articulado, artículos, estipulaciones.
carved: tallado, labrado.
cocoanut: coco, fruta de coco, de coco.
covering: envoltura, cobertura, revestimiento, cubrir, cubierta.
declining: declinante, decadente.
dust: polvo, quitar el polvo, quitar el polvo a.
exhibited: exhibido.
flannel: franela, la franela.
good-naturedly: amablemente,

bondadosamente.
half-a-dozen: media docena.
joke: bromear, broma, burla, chanza, chiste, la broma, chasco, chancear.
needles: agujas, aguja.
open-mouthed: boquiabierto.
packet: paquete.
passing: paso.
proprietor: propietario.
reflected: reflejado.
rely: confiar, confíe, confías, confían, confíen, confiáis, confío, confiad,

confía, confiamos.
scarves: cáscara.
scintillate: chispear, centellear, chispee, chispead, chispéis, chispeamos, chispea, chispeas, chispeen, chispeo, chispean.
shakes: sacude.
shouldn't: contracción de should not.
tissue: tejido.
undecided: indeciso.
whenever: cada vez que, cuando quiera que, cuando.

He was such a **rake** as a young man! Those sort of people, madame, have not the least **regularity**; he's burnt up with brandy. Still it's **sad**, all the same, to see an acquaintance go off."

And while he fastened up his box he discoursed about the doctor's patients.

"It's the **weather**, no doubt," he said, looking **frowningly** at the floor, "that causes these illnesses. I, too, don't feel the thing. One of these days I shall even have to consult the doctor for a pain I have in my back. Well, **good**-bye, Madame Bovary. At your service; your very **humble** servant." And he **closed** the door gently.

Emma had her dinner served in her bedroom on a **tray** by the fireside; she was a long time over it; everything was well with her.

"How good I was!" she said to herself, thinking of the scarves.

She heard some **steps** on the stairs. It was Leon. She got up and took from the **chest** of drawers the first **pile** of dusters to be **hemmed**. When he came in she seemed very busy.

The **conversation languished**; Madame Bovary gave it up every few minutes, **whilst** he himself seemed quite **embarrassed**. Seated on a low chair near the fire, he turned round in his **fingers** the ivory thimble-case. She **stitched** on, or from time to time turned down the hem of the cloth with her nail. She did not speak; he was silent, **captivated** by her **silence**, as he would have been by her speech.

"Poor fellow!" she thought.

"How have I **displeased** her?" he asked himself.

At last, however, Leon said that he should have, one of these days, to go to Rouen on some office business.

"Your music **subscription** is out; am I to **renew** it?"

"No," she **replied**.

"Why?"

"Because--"

And **pursing** her lips she slowly drew a long stitch of grey **thread**.

Spanish

captivated: cautivado.
chest: pecho, arca, aparador, el pecho, caja.
closed: cerrado.
conversation: conversación.
displeased: desagradado, disgustado.
embarrassed: avergonzado, desconcertado.
fingers: los dedos.
frowningly: ceñudamente.
good-bye: despedida, adiós.
hem: dobladillo.

humble: humilde, humillar.
languished: Languidecido.
pile: montón, pilote, pila, pelo, amontonar, estaca.
pursing: cierre de la jareta, embolsamiento, embolsar.
rake: rastrillo, rastro, rastrear.
regularity: regularidad.
renew: renovar, renueve, renueven, renuevas, renuevan, renueva, renovamos, renovad, renuevo, renováis, reanudar.

replied: Contestado.
sad: triste, afligido.
silence: silencio, acallar, hacer callar, el silencio.
steps: pasos.
stitch: puntada, coser.
subscription: suscripción, abono, cuota.
thread: hilo, rosca, hebra, el hilo.
tray: bandeja.
weather: tiempo, el tiempo, clima.
whilst: mientras.

This work irritated Leon. It seemed to **roughen** the ends of her fingers. A **gallant** phrase came into his head, but he did not risk it.

"Then you are giving it up?" he went on.

"What?" she asked hurriedly. "Music? Ah! yes! Have I not my house to look after, my husband to **attend** to, a thousand things, in fact, many duties that must be considered first?"

She looked at the **clock**. Charles was late. Then, she affected **anxiety**. Two or three times she even repeated, "He is so good!"

The clerk was fond of Monsieur Bovary. But this tenderness on his **behalf** astonished him **unpleasantly**; nevertheless he took up on his praises, which he said everyone was singing, especially the chemist.

"Ah! he is a good fellow," **continued** Emma.

"Certainly," replied the clerk.

And he began talking of Madame Homais, whose very **untidy appearance** generally made them laugh.

"What does it matter?" interrupted Emma. "A good **housewife** does not trouble about her appearance."

Then she **relapsed** into silence.

It was the same on the following days; her **talks**, her **manners**, everything changed. She took interest in the **housework**, went to church **regularly**, and looked after her servant with more **severity**.

She took Berthe from nurse. When **visitors** called, Felicite brought her in, and Madame Bovary undressed her to show off her **limbs**. She **declared** she adored children; this was her **consolation**, her **joy**, her passion, and she accompanied her **caresses** with lyrical outburst which would have **reminded** anyone but the Yonville people of Sachette in "Notre Dame de Paris."

When Charles came home he found his slippers put to **warm** near the fire. His waistcoat now never wanted **lining**, nor his shirt buttons, and it was quite a **pleasure** to see in the cupboard the night-caps arranged in piles of the same

Spanish

anxiety: ansiedad.
appearance: aspecto, apariencia, aparición, comparecencia, vista, apersonamiento.
attend: asistir, asistan, asisto, asistís, asistimos, asistid, asistes, asisten, asiste, asista, visitar.
behalf: nombre.
caresses: caricias.
clock: reloj, el reloj, ceas.
consolation: consuelo.
continued: continuado, durado.

declared: declarado.
gallant: galante, galán, valeroso.
housewife: ama de casa.
housework: tareas de la casa, quehaceres domésticos, labores domésticas, trabajo casero.
joy: alegría.
limbs: extremidades.
lining: forro, revestimiento.
manners: modales, educación.
pleasure: placer, agrado, gusto, complacencia, el gusto.

regularly: regularmente, a menudo.
relapsed: reincidido.
reminded: recordado.
roughen: poner áspero.
severity: severidad, gravedad.
talks: habla, charla.
unpleasantly: desagradablemente, ingratamente, molestamente.
untidy: desaliñado.
visitors: turistas, visitantes.
warm: caliente, caluroso, calentar, cálido.

height. She no longer **grumbled** as formerly at taking a turn in the garden; what he proposed was always done, although she did not understand the wishes to which she submitted without a murmur; and when Leon saw him by his fireside after dinner, his two hands on his stomach, his two feet on the **fender**, his two cheeks red with feeding, his eyes **moist** with happiness, the child crawling along the carpet, and this woman with the **slender** waist who came behind his armchair to kiss his forehead: "What madness!" he said to himself. "And how to reach her!"

And thus she seemed so virtuous and **inaccessible** to him that he lost all hope, even the faintest. But by this **renunciation** he placed her on an extraordinary **pinnacle**. To him she stood outside those **fleshly attributes** from which he had nothing to obtain, and in his heart she rose ever, and became farther removed from him after the magnificent manner of an **apotheosis** that is taking wing. It was one of those pure feelings that do not interfere with life, that are **cultivated** because they are rare, and whose loss would **afflict** more than their passion rejoices.

Emma grew **thinner**, her cheeks paler, her face longer. With her black hair, her large eyes, her **aquiline** nose, her **birdlike** walk, and always silent now, did she not seem to be passing through life scarcely touching it, and to bear on her brow the vague **impress** of some **divine destiny**? She was so sad and so calm, at once so gentle and so **reserved**, that near her one felt oneself seized by an **icy charm**, as we **shudder** in churches at the perfume of the flowers mingling with the cold of the marble. The others even did not escape from this **seduction**. The chemist said--

"She is a woman of great parts, who wouldn't be **misplaced** in a sub-prefecture."

The housewives admired her economy, the patients her politeness, the poor her charity.

But she was **eaten** up with desires, with **rage**, with hate. That dress with the narrow folds hid a **distracted** fear, of whose **torment** those **chaste** lips said nothing. She was in love with Leon, and sought solitude that she might with the

Spanish

afflict: afligir, afligís, aflijan, afligimos, afligid, afliges, afligen, aflige, aflijo, aflija, entristecer.
apotheosis: apoteosis.
aquiline: aquilino, aguileño.
attributes: atributos.
birdlike: como un pajarito, pajaril.
charm: encanto, hechizar, encantar, gracia, embelesar, amuleto.
chaste: casto.
cultivated: cultivado, culto.
destiny: destino, suerte.

distracted: distraído.
divine: divino.
eaten: comido.
fender: guardabarros, parachoques.
fleshly: carnudo, carna, carnal, carnoso.
grumbled: quejado.
icy: helado, álgido.
impress: impresionar, imprimir, estampar, huella.
inaccessible: inaccesible.
misplaced: extraviado.

moist: húmedo.
pinnacle: pináculo, pico.
rage: rabia, furia, furor, ira.
renunciation: renuncia.
reserved: reservado, reservada.
seduction: seducción.
shudder: estremecerse.
slender: fino, esbelto.
thinner: escaso, fino, flaco, ligero, ralo, enrarecerse, tenue, diluyente, aguarrás, débil, solvente.
torment: tormento.

more ease delight in his image. The sight of his form **troubled** the **voluptuousness** of this **mediation**. Emma **thrilled** at the sound of his step; then in his presence the **emotion** subsided, and afterwards there remained to her only an immense astonishment that ended in sorrow.

Leon did not know that when he left her in **despair** she rose after he had gone to see him in the street. She concerned herself about his comings and goings; she watched his face; she invented quite a history to find an excuse for going to his room. The chemist's wife seemed happy to her to sleep under the same roof, and her thoughts constantly centered upon this house, like the "Lion d'Or" pigeons, who came there to **dip** their red feet and white wings in its gutters. But the more Emma recognised her love, the more she **crushed** it down, that it might not be evident, that she might make it less. She would have liked Leon to guess it, and she imagined chances, catastrophes that should **facilitate** this.

What restrained her was, no doubt, idleness and fear, and a sense of shame also. She thought she had **repulsed** him too much, that the time was past, that all was lost. Then, pride, and joy of being able to say to herself, "I am virtuous," and to look at herself in the glass taking resigned poses, consoled her a little for the **sacrifice** she believed she was making.

Then the lusts of the flesh, the **longing** for money, and the melancholy of passion all blended themselves into one suffering, and instead of turning her thoughts from it, she clave to it the more, urging herself to pain, and seeking everywhere occasion for it. She was irritated by an ill-served dish or by a half-open door; **bewailed** the velvets she had not, the happiness she had missed, her too **exalted** dreams, her narrow home.

What **exasperated** her was that Charles did not seem to notice her anguish. His conviction that he was making her happy seemed to her an **imbecile insult**, and his **sureness** on this point **ingratitude**. For whose sake, then was she virtuous? Was it not for him, the **obstacle** to all felicity, the cause of all **misery**, and, as it were, the sharp **clasp** of that complex **strap** that **bucked** her in on all sides.

Spanish

bewailed: Lamentado.
bucked: corcoveado.
clasp: broche.
crushed: aplastado.
despair: desesperación.
dip: buzamiento, zambullida, pendiente.
emotion: emoción.
exalted: exaltado.
exasperated: exasperado.
facilitate: facilitar, facilitan, faciliten, facilito, facilitas, facilitamos, facilitáis,
facilita, facilitad, facilite.
imbecile: imbécil.
ingratitude: ingratitud.
insult: insultar, insulto, injuria, injuriar, ofender, ofensa, ultrajar, ultraje, improperio, el insulto, denuesto.
longing: anhelo, anhelante.
mediation: mediación.
misery: pobreza, miseria, indigencia.
obstacle: obstáculo, impedimento.
repulsed: Repeló.
sacrifice: sacrificio, sacrificar, ofrecer, presentar.
strap: correa.
sureness: confianza, seguridad, firmeza, certidumbre, certeza, lo certero.
thrilled: estremecido.
troubled: molestar, de enfermedad, agitado, problema, desventurado, apurado, molestarse, dificultad, no sabroso, pasado difícilmente, pena.
voluptuousness: voluptuosidad.

On him alone, then, she **concentrated** all the various hatreds that **resulted** from her boredom, and every effort to **diminish** only **augmented** it; for this useless trouble was added to the other reasons for despair, and **contributed** still more to the **separation** between them. Her own gentleness to herself made her **rebel** against him. Domestic mediocrity drove her to **lewd fancies**, marriage tenderness to **adulterous** desires. She would have like Charles to beat her, that she might have a better right to **hate** him, to revenge herself upon him. She was surprised sometimes at the **atrocious conjectures** that came into her thoughts, and she had to go on smiling, to hear repeated to her at all hours that she was happy, to **pretend** to be happy, to let it be believed.

Yet she had **loathing** of this hypocrisy. She was seized with the **temptation** to **flee** somewhere with Leon to try a new life; but at once a vague **chasm** full of darkness opened within her **soul**.

"Besides, he no longer **loves** me," she thought. "What is to become of me? What help is to be hoped for, what consolation, what solace?"

She was left broken, **breathless**, inert, sobbing in a low voice, with flowing tears.

"Why don't you tell master?" the servant asked her when she came in during these crises.

"It is the nerves," said Emma. "Do not speak to him of it; it would worry him."

"Ah! yes," Felicite went on, "you are just like La Guerine, Pere Guerin's daughter, the **fisherman** at Pollet, that I used to know at Dieppe before I came to you. She was so sad, so sad, to see her standing upright on the **threshold** of her house, she seemed to you like a winding-sheet spread out before the door. Her illness, it appears, was a kind of fog that she had in her head, and the doctors could not do anything, nor the priest either. When she was taken too bad she went off quite alone to the sea-shore, so that the **customs** officer, going his **rounds**, often found her lying flat on her face, crying on the **shingle**. Then, after her marriage, it went off, they say."

"But with me," replied Emma, "it was after marriage that it began."

Spanish

adulterous: adúltero.
atrocious: atroz.
augmented: aumentado.
breathless: jadeante, sin aliento.
chasm: abismo, precipicio, despeñadero.
concentrated: concentrado.
conjectures: supone.
contributed: Contribuido.
customs: aduana, costumbres.
diminish: disminuir, disminuyes, disminuid, disminuyo, disminuyen,

disminuye, disminuyan, disminuís, disminuimos, disminuya, menguar.
fancies: extravagante.
fisherman: pescador, el pescador.
flee: huir, huyes, huyen, huís, huyan, huyo, huid, huye, huimos, huya, escapar.
hate: odiar, odio, aborrecer, detestar.
lewd: lujurioso, obsceno, lascivo.
loathing: detestando, aversión, aborrecimiento.
loves: amor.

pretend: fingir, fingimos, finjo, fingís, fingid, finges, fingen, finge, finjan, finja, pretender.
rebel: rebelde, rebelarse.
resulted: Resultado.
rounds: cartuchería, redondea.
separation: separación, retiro, aislamiento.
shingle: tablilla.
soul: alma, espíritu, ánimo.
temptation: tentación.
threshold: umbral.

CHAPTER SIX

One evening when the window was open, and she, sitting by it, had been **watching** Lestiboudois, the beadle, **trimming** the box, she suddenly heard the Angelus ringing.

It was the beginning of April, when the primroses are in bloom, and a warm wind blows over the flower-beds **newly** turned, and the **gardens**, like women, seem to be getting ready for the summer fetes. Through the bars of the arbour and away beyond, the river seen in the fields, **meandering** through the **grass** in wandering **curves**. The evening vapours rose between the leafless poplars, touching their outlines with a violet **tint**, paler and more transparent than a **subtle** gauze **caught** athwart their branches. In the **distance** cattle moved about; neither their steps nor their lowing could be heard; and the bell, still ringing through the air, kept up its **peaceful** lamentation.

With this repeated **tinkling** the **thoughts** of the young woman lost themselves in old **memories** of her **youth** and school-days. She **remembered** the great candlesticks that rose above the vases full of **flowers** on the altar, and the **tabernacle** with its small columns. She would have liked to be once more lost in the long line of white veils, marked off here and there by the **stuff** black hoods of the good sisters bending over their **prie**-Dieu. At mass on Sundays, when she looked up, she saw the gentle face of the Virgin amid the blue **smoke** of the rising **incense**. Then she was moved; she felt herself **weak** and quite deserted,

Spanish

caught: cogido, asido, acertado.
curves: curvas.
distance: distancia, alejamiento.
flowers: las flores.
gardens: jardines.
grass: hierba, yerba, césped, la hierba, pasto.
incense: incienso, encolerizar.
meandering: con meandros, incoherente, largo y confuso, meandro, serpenteante, serpentear, vagar.

memories: memorias, recuerdos.
newly: nuevamente, recién, recientemente.
peaceful: tranquilo, pacífico.
prie-dieu: reclinatorio.
remembered: recordado.
smoke: fumar, fumo, fume, fumas, fuman, fumamos, fumáis, fumad, fuma, fumen, humo.
stuff: rellenar, cosas, material, llenar.
subtle: sutil.
tabernacle: tabernáculo.

thoughts: pensamientos.
tinkling: tilín, retintín, que hace tilín, cencerreo, cascabeleo, campanilleo.
tint: teñir, tinte.
trimming: adorno, adornos.
watching: tener cuidado, vigilar, observar, mirar, investigación, acechanza, reloj, velar, vigilante, vigilancia, acecho.
weak: débil, flojo.
youth: juventud, joven, jóvenes, adolescencia.

like the down of a bird whirled by the **tempest**, and it was **unconsciously** that she went towards the church, included to no matter what **devotions**, so that her soul was absorbed and all existence lost in it.

On the Place she met Lestivoudois on his way back, for, in order not to **shorten** his day's labour, he preferred **interrupting** his work, then beginning it again, so that he rang the Angelus to suit his own convenience. Besides, the ringing over a little earlier warned the lads of catechism hour.

Already a few who had arrived were playing **marbles** on the stones of the cemetery. Others, **astride** the wall, swung their legs, kicking with their clogs the large nettles growing between the little **enclosure** and the **newest** graves. This was the only green spot. All the rest was but stones, always covered with a fine **powder**, despite the vestry-broom.

The children in list shoes ran about there as if it were an enclosure made for them. The shouts of their voices could be heard through the humming of the bell. This grew less and less with the swinging of the great rope that, hanging from the top of the **belfry**, dragged its end on the ground. **Swallows flitted** to and fro uttering little **cries**, cut the air with the edge of their wings, and swiftly returned to their yellow nests under the tiles of the coping. At the end of the church a lamp was burning, the **wick** of a **night**-light in a glass hung up. Its light from a distance looked like a white **stain** trembling in the oil. A long ray of the sun fell across the **nave** and seemed to **darken** the lower sides and the corners.

"Where is the cure?" asked Madame Bovary of one of the lads, who was **amusing** himself by shaking a **swivel** in a hole too large for it.

"He is just coming," he answered.

And in fact the door of the presbytery **grated**; Abbe Bournisien appeared; the children, pell-mell, **fled** into the church.

"These young scamps!" murmured the priest, "always the same!"

Then, picking up a catechism all in rags that he had struck with is foot, "They respect nothing!" But as soon as he caught sight of Madame Bovary, "Excuse me," he said; "I did not recognise you."

Spanish

amusing: divertido, divirtiéndose, entreteniendo, cómico, entretenido, gracioso.
astride: a horcajadas.
belfry: campanario.
cries: llora.
darken: oscurecer, oscurezca, oscurecen, oscurezco, oscurece, oscureced, oscurecéis, oscurecemos, oscurezcan, oscureces.
devotions: oraciones.
enclosure: cercado, envolvente,

vallado, recinto, caja.
fled: huido.
flitted: aleteado, revoloteado, revoloteó.
grated: rallado.
interrupting: interrumpir.
marbles: bolita, canica, mármol.
nave: carrete de rueda.
newest: el mas nuevo.
night-light: luz nocturna.
powder: polvos, polvo, empolvar, pólvora, el polvo.

shorten: abreviar, abrevias, abreviad, abrevio, abrevien, abrevie, abrevia, abreviáis, abreviamos, abrevian, acortar.
stain: manchar, mancha, mancilla, teñir, tintura, la mancha.
swallows: traga.
swivel: eslabón giratorio, giratorio, pieza giratoria, pivote.
tempest: tormenta, tempestad.
unconsciously: inconscientemente.
wick: mecha.

He **thrust** the catechism into his pocket, and stopped short, **balancing** the heavy **vestry** key between his two fingers.

The light of the setting sun that fell full upon his face paled the lasting of his **cassock**, shiny at the elbows, **unravelled** at the hem. **Grease** and tobacco stains followed along his broad chest the lines of the buttons, and grew more numerous the farther they were from his neckcloth, in which the massive folds of his red chin rested; this was **dotted** with yellow **spots**, that disappeared beneath the coarse hair of his **greyish beard**. He had just dined and was **breathing noisily**.

"How are you?" he added.

"Not well," replied Emma; "I am ill."

"Well, and so am I," answered the priest. "These first warm days **weaken** one most **remarkably**, don't they? But, after all, we are born to suffer, as St. Paul says. But what does Monsieur Bovary think of it?"

"He!" she said with a gesture of **contempt**.

"What!" replied the good fellow, quite astonished, doesn't he **prescribe** something for you?"

"Ah!" said Emma, "it is no **earthly** remedy I need."

But the cure from time to time looked into the church, where the kneeling boys were shouldering one another, and tumbling over like packs of cards.

"I should like to know--" she went on.

"You look out, Riboudet," cried the priest in an angry voice; "I'll warm your ears, you imp!" Then turning to Emma, "He's Boudet the carpenter's son; his parents are well off, and let him do just as he **pleases**. Yet he could learn quickly if he would, for he is very sharp. And so sometimes for a joke I call him Riboudet (like the road one takes to go to Maromme) and I even say 'Mon Riboudet.' Ha! Ha! '**Mont** Riboudet.' The other day I repeated that just to Monsignor, and he laughed at it; he **condescended** to laugh at it. And how is Monsieur Bovary?"

She seemed not to hear him. And he went on--

Spanish

balancing: vacilando, equilibrando, de equilibrio, balanceando, balancear, restablecimiento de un equilibrio, pesar en la balanza, equilibrio, balance, equilibrarse, vacilante.
beard: barba, la barba, arista.
breathing: respirando, respiración, respirar.
cassock: sotana.
condescended: condescendido, se dignado, Dignado.
contempt: desprecio, menosprecio.

dotted: punteado.
earthly: terrenal, terrestre.
grease: grasa, engrasar, la grasa.
greyish: grisáceo.
mont: montana.
noisily: ruidosamente, clamorosamente, alborotadamente.
pleases: complace.
prescribe: prescribir, prescribo, prescribís, prescribimos, prescriben, prescribid, prescribe, prescriban, prescribes, prescriba, recetar.

remarkably: notablemente.
spots: lunares, granos, bienes con entrega inmediata.
thrust: empujar, empuje, empujón.
unravelled: desenredado, descifrado, desenlazado, desenmarañado, deshilachado, deshilado.
vestry: sacristía.
weaken: debilitar, debilite, debilitamos, debilito, debiliten, debilitan, debilitáis, debilitad, debilita, debilitas, amainar.

"Always very busy, no doubt; for he and I are certainly the busiest people in the parish. But he is doctor of the body," he added with a thick laugh, "and I of the soul."

She fixed her **pleading** eyes upon the priest. "Yes," she said, "you **solace** all sorrows."

"Ah! don't talk to me of it, Madame Bovary. This morning I had to go to Bas-**Diauville** for a **cow** that was ill; they thought it was under a **spell**. All their cows, I don't know how it is--But **pardon** me! Longuemarre and Boudet! **Bless** me! Will you leave off?"

And with a **bound** he ran into the church.

The boys were just then **clustering** round the large desk, **climbing** over the precentor's **footstool**, opening the **missal**; and others on tiptoe were just about to **venture** into the confessional. But the priest suddenly distributed a **shower** of cuffs among them. Seizing them by the collars of their coats, he **lifted** them from the ground, and **deposited** them on their knees on the stones of the choir, **firmly**, as if he meant **planting** them there.

"Yes," said he, when he returned to Emma, **unfolding** his large **cotton** handkerchief, one corner of which he put between his teeth, "farmers are much to be pitied."

"Others, too," she replied.

"**Assuredly**. Town-labourers, for example."

"It is not they--"

"Pardon! **I've** there known poor **mothers** of families, virtuous women, I **assure** you, real saints, who wanted even **bread**."

"But those," replied Emma, and the corners of her mouth **twitched** as she spoke, "those, Monsieur le Cure, who have bread and have no--"

"Fire in the winter," said the priest.

"Oh, what does that matter?"

Spanish

assure: asegurar, asegura, aseguren, aseguras, aseguran, aseguramos, aseguráis, asegurad, aseguro, asegure, garantizar.
assuredly: ciertamente.
bless: bendecir, bendecimos, bendigo, bendigan, bendices, bendicen, bendecís, bendecid, bendice, bendiga.
bound: encuadernado, saltar, salto, ligado, límite, obligado.
bread: pan, el pan.
climbing: alpinismo, escalar.

clustering: clasificación, arracimar, conglomeración.
cotton: algodón.
cow: vaca, la vaca.
deposited: depositado.
firmly: firmemente.
footstool: escabel.
ill: enfermo, malo, doliente.
i've: he, Tengo.
lifted: levantado.
missal: misal, devocionario.
mothers: las madres.

pardon: perdón, perdonar, indulto, indultar.
planting: plantío, cultivo.
pleading: suplicando, alegato.
shower: ducha, la ducha, chaparrón, chubasco.
solace: solaz, consolar, consuelo.
spell: deletrear, el hechizo, el encanto.
twitched: Retorcido.
unfolding: desplegando.
venture: arriesgar, ventura, aventurarse, aventurar, empresa.

"What! What does it matter? It seems to me that when one has firing and food--for, after all--"

"My God! my God!" she sighed.

"It is **indigestion**, no doubt? You must get home, Madame Bovary; **drink** a little tea, that will **strengthen** you, or else a glass of **fresh** water with a little moist sugar."

"Why?" And she looked like one **awaking** from a **dream**.

"Well, you see, you were **putting** your hand to your forehead. I thought you felt faint." Then, bethinking himself, "But you were asking me something? What was it? I really don't remember."

"I? Nothing! nothing!" repeated Emma.

And the **glance** she **cast** round her slowly fell upon the old man in the cassock. They looked at one another face to face without **speaking**.

"Then, Madame Bovary," he said at last, "excuse me, but duty first, you know; I must look after my good-for-nothings. The first communion will soon be upon us, and I fear we shall be behind after all. So after Ascension Day I keep them recta an extra hour every Wednesday. Poor children! One cannot lead them too soon into the path of the Lord, as, moreover, he has himself **recommended** us to do by the mouth of his Divine Son. Good health to you, madame; my respects to your husband."

And he went into the church making a **genuflexion** as soon as he reached the door.

Emma saw him **disappear** between the **double row** of forms, **walking** with a heavy tread, his head a little bent over his shoulder, and with his two hands half-open behind him.

Then she turned on her **heel** all of one piece, like a **statue** on a pivot, and went **homewards**. But the **loud** voice of the priest, the clear voices of the boys still reached her ears, and went on behind her.

"Are you a Christian?"

Spanish

awaking: Despertar.

cast: lanzar, lanzamiento, arrojar, echar, colar, elenco, molde.

disappear: desaparecer, desapareced, desaparecéis, desaparecemos, desaparecen, desapareces, desaparezcan, desaparezco, desaparece, desaparezca.

double: doble, doblar, doblado.

dream: soñar, sueño, ensueño.

drink: beber, bebida, tomar, el refresco, trago, copa.

fresh: fresco.

genuflexion: genuflexión.

glance: mirada, vistazo, ojeada.

heel: talón, tacón, calcañal, escorar, calcañar.

homewards: hacia la tierra natal, hacia casa, hacia la patria, hacia el país natal.

indigestion: indigestión, empacho.

loud: alto, fuerte, ruidoso, chillón.

putting: poniendo, metiendo, colocando.

recommended: recomendado, ensalzado, encarecido.

row: remar, fila, turno, hilera, bronca, línea.

speaking: hablando, parlante.

statue: estatua, la estatua.

strengthen: fortalecer, fortaleces, fortalezco, fortalezca, fortalecen, fortaleceis, fortaleced, fortalece, fortalecemos, fortalezcan.

walking: andando, caminando, ambulante.

"Yes, I am a Christian."

"What is a Christian?"

"He who, being baptized-baptized-baptized--"

She went up the steps of the staircase **holding** on to the **banisters**, and when she was in her room threw herself into an arm-chair.

The whitish light of the window-panes fell with **soft** undulations.

The furniture in its place seemed to have become more **immobile**, and to lose itself in the shadow as in an ocean of **darkness**. The fire was out, the clock went on **ticking**, and Emma **vaguely marvelled** at this calm of all things while within herself was such tumult. But little Berthe was there, between the window and the **work**-table, tottering on her knitted shoes, and trying to come to her mother to catch hold of the ends of her apron-strings.

"Leave me alone," said the latter, putting her from her with her hand.

The little girl soon came up **closer** against her knees, and leaning on them with her arms, she looked up with her large blue eyes, while a small thread of pure saliva **dribbled** from her lips on to the silk apron.

"Leave me alone," repeated the young woman quite **irritably**.

Her face frightened the child, who began to **scream**.

"Will you leave me alone?" she said, **pushing** her with her elbow.

Berthe fell at the foot of the drawers against the brass **handle**, **cutting** her cheek, which began to **bleed**, against it. Madame Bovary sprang to **lift** her up, **broke** the bell-rope, called for the servant with all her might, and she was just going to **curse** herself when Charles appeared. It was the dinner-hour; he had come home.

"Look, dear!" said Emma, in a calm voice, "the little one fell down while she was playing, and has **hurt** herself."

Charles **reassured** her; the case was not a serious one, and he went for some sticking plaster.

Spanish

banisters: balaustrada.
bleed: sangrar, sangras, sangrad, sangráis, sangran, sangra, sangren, sangro, sangramos, sangre.
broke: bollado, rotura, rompió, romper, pret de break, interrupción, fracturar, sin blanca, comienzo, pelado, descanso.
closer: íntimamente.
curse: maldecir, maldición, jurar.
cutting: recorte, cortante, corte, estaca.
darkness: tinieblas, oscuridad, la

oscuridad.
dribbled: goteado.
handle: asa, mango, manija, tratar, manejar, tacto, manivela, empuñadura, asidero, manubrio, palanca.
holding: mantenimiento, tenencia.
hurt: doler, herir, dañar, herida, lastimar.
immobile: inmóvil.
irritably: irasciblemente, coléricamente, irritablemente.

lift: ascensor, levantar, subir, alzar, elevar, elevación, levante, desnivel entre tramos, sustentación.
marvelled: Maravillado.
pushing: emprendedor, molesto, empujar, ambicioso, empuje.
reassured: tranquilizado.
scream: gritar, chillar, chillido.
soft: blando, suave, tierno, dulce.
ticking: terliz, tictac.
vaguely: vagamente.
work-table: mesa de trabajo.

Madame Bovary did not go **downstairs** to the **dining**-room; she wished to remain alone to look after the child. Then watching her sleep, the little anxiety she felt gradually wore off, and she seemed very stupid to herself, and very good to have been so worried just now at so little. Berthe, in fact, no longer sobbed.

Her breathing now **imperceptibly** raised the cotton covering. Big tears lay in the corner of the half-closed eyelids, through whose lashes one could see two pale **sunken** pupils; the plaster stuck on her cheek drew the skin obliquely.

"It is very strange," thought Emma, "how ugly this child is!"

When at eleven o'clock Charles came back from the chemist's shop, whither he had gone after dinner to return the remainder of the sticking-plaster, he found his wife standing by the **cradle**.

"I assure you it's nothing." he said, kissing her on the forehead. "Don't worry, my poor **darling**; you will make yourself ill."

He had stayed a long time at the chemist's. Although he had not seemed much moved, Homais, nevertheless, had **exerted** himself to **buoy** him up, to "keep up his spirits." Then they had talked of the various dangers that **threaten childhood**, of the **carelessness** of servants. Madame Homais knew something of it, having still upon her chest the marks left by a **basin** full of soup that a **cook** had formerly dropped on her **pinafore**, and her good parents took no end of trouble for her. The knives were not **sharpened**, nor the floors waxed; there were iron **gratings** to the windows and strong bars across the fireplace; the little Homais, in spite of their spirit, could not stir without someone watching them; at the slightest cold their father stuffed them with pectorals; and until they were turned four they all, without **pity**, had to wear **wadded** head-protectors. This, it is true, was a fancy of Madame Homais'; her husband was **inwardly afflicted** at it. Fearing the possible consequences of such **compression** to the **intellectual** organs. He even went so far as to say to her, "Do you want to make Caribs or Botocudos of them?"

Charles, however, had several times tried to **interrupt** the conversation. "I should like to speak to you," he had **whispered** in the clerk's ear, who went upstairs in front of him.

Spanish

afflicted: afligido.
basin: cuenca, recipiente de agua, fuente, pelvis, tazón, dársena, jofaina, palangana.
buoy: boya, baliza, balizar.
carelessness: descuido.
childhood: niñez, infancia.
compression: compresión, condensación.
cook: cocinar, cocinero, cocinera, cocer, el cocinero, guisar.
cradle: cuna, patria, horquilla,

plataforma.
darling: querido, amado.
dining-room: comedor.
downstairs: abajo, de abajo, en el fondo.
exerted: ejercido.
gratings: mallas reticulares, rejillas, rejillas de parrilla.
imperceptibly: imperceptiblemente.
intellectual: intelectual.
interrupt: interrumpir, interrupción.
inwardly: interiormente.

pinafore: falda con peto, pichi, delantal.
pity: dolerse por, piedad, compadecer a, lástima, compasión.
sharpened: afilado, aguzado.
sunken: hundido.
threaten: amenazar, amenacen, amenazad, amenazo, amenazas, amenazan, amenazáis, amenazamos, amenace, amenaza, conminar.
wadded: apretado, guata de relleno.
whispered: chuchicheado.

"Can he **suspect** anything?" Leon asked himself. His heart beat, and he **racked** his **brain** with surmises.

At last, Charles, having shut the door, asked him to see himself what would be the price at Rouen of a fine **daguerreotypes**. It was a sentimental **surprise** he intended for his wife, a delicate attention--his **portrait** in a frock-coat. But he wanted first to know "how much it would be." The inquiries would not put Monsieur Leon out, since he went to town almost every week.

Why? Monsieur Homais **suspected** some "young man's **affair**" at the **bottom** of it, an **intrigue**. But he was mistaken. Leon was after no love-making. He was sadder than ever, as Madame Lefrancois saw from the amount of food he left on his plate. To find out more about it she **questioned** the **tax**-collector. Binet answered roughly that he "wasn't paid by the police."

All the same, his companion seemed very strange to him, for Leon often threw himself back in his chair, and stretching out his arms. Complained vaguely of life.

"It's because you don't take enough recreation," said the **collector**.

"What recreation?"

"If I were you I'd have a lathe."

"But I don't know how to turn," answered the clerk.

"Ah! that's true," said the other, rubbing his chin with an air of mingled contempt and **satisfaction**.

Leon was weary of loving without any result; moreover he was beginning to feel that **depression** caused by the **repetition** of the same kind of life, when no interest **inspires** and no hope **sustains** it. He was so bored with Yonville and its inhabitants, that the **sight** of certain persons, of certain houses, irritated him beyond **endurance**; and the chemist, good **fellow** though he was, was becoming absolutely unbearable to him. Yet the **prospect** of a new condition of life frightened as much as it seduced him.

This **apprehension** soon changed into **impatience**, and then Paris from afar **sounded** its **fanfare** of masked balls with the laugh of grisettes. As he was to

Spanish

affair: asunto, caso, particular, aventura.
apprehension: arresto, detención, aprensión, aprehensión.
bottom: fondo, suelo, inferior, lado inferior, el fondo, culo, posaderas, trasero.
brain: cerebro, seso.
collector: colector, recaudador, coleccionista, recolector, cobrador.
daguerreotypes: daguerrotipos.
depression: crisis, depresión.

endurance: resistencia, aguante, endurancia.
fanfare: fanfarria.
fellow: compañero, hombre, socio, tipo, becario.
impatience: impaciencia.
inspires: inspira.
intrigue: intrigar, intriga.
portrait: retrato, vertical.
prospect: perspectiva.
questioned: preguntado.
racked: atormentado.

repetition: repetición.
satisfaction: satisfacción.
sight: vista, aspecto, mira, avistar.
sounded: sonado.
surprise: sorprender, sorpresa, la sorpresa.
suspect: sospechar, dudar, sospechoso.
suspected: sospechoso, desconfiar de, sospechado, sospechar.
sustains: sostiene.
tax-collector: exactor.

finish reading there, why not set out at once? What prevented him? And he began making home-preparations; he arranged his occupations beforehand. He furnished in his head an apartment. He would lead an artist's life there! He would take lessons on the **guitar**! He would have a dressing-gown, a Basque cap, blue velvet slippers! He even already was **admiring** two **crossed** foils over his chimney-piece, with a death's head on the guitar above them.

The difficulty was the **consent** of his mother; nothing, however, seemed more reasonable. Even his **employer** advised him to go to some other **chambers** where he could advance more **rapidly**. Taking a middle course, then, Leon looked for some place as second clerk at Rouen; found none, and at last wrote his mother a long letter full of details, in which he set forth the reasons for going to live at Paris immediately. She **consented**.

He did not hurry. Every day for a month Hivert carried **boxes**, valises, parcels for him from Yonville to Rouen and from Rouen to Yonville; and when Leon had **packed** up his **wardrobe**, had his three arm-chairs restuffed, bought a stock of neckties, in a word, had made more preparations than for a **voyage** around the world, he put it off from week to week, until he received a second letter from his mother urging him to leave, since he wanted to pass his examination before the **vacation**.

When the moment for the farewells had come, Madame Homais wept, Justin **sobbed**; Homais, as a man of **nerve**, concealed his emotion; he **wished** to carry his friend's **overcoat** himself as far as the **gate** of the notary, who was taking Leon to Rouen in his carriage.

The latter had just time to **bid** farewell to Monsieur Bovary.

When he reached the head of the stairs, he stopped, he was so out of **breath**. As he came in, Madame Bovary arose hurriedly.

"It is I again!" said Leon.

"I was sure of it!"

Spanish

admiring: admirando.
bid: ofrecer, licitación, postura, oferta, solicitar, licitar, pedir, demandar, rogar, puja.
boxes: las cajas.
breath: aliento, respiración, hálito.
chambers: recámara, compartimiento, cámara de comercio, aposento, cámara, cámara de paz.
consent: aprobación, acordar, declaración, declarar, consentimiento, autorización.

consented: Consentido.
crossed: cruzado.
employer: patrón, empleador, empresario, patrono.
finish: acabar, acabas, acabo, acabe, acaban, acabamos, acabáis, acabad, acaba, acaben, terminar.
gate: puerta, paso, verja, compuerta, barrera.
guitar: guitarra, la guitarra.
nerve: nervio.
overcoat: abrigo, el abrigo.

packed: guardado, empacado, embalado, comprimido, lleno, marcado, apuesto tendenciosamente, aborrotado, abarrotado, hasta los topes.
rapidly: rápidamente.
sobbed: sollozado.
vacation: vacaciones, vacación.
voyage: viaje.
wardrobe: armario, guardarropa, armario ropero, ropero, vestuario.
wished: deseado.

She bit her lips, and a rush of **blood** flowing under her **skin** made her red from the roots of her hair to the top of her collar. She remained **standing**, leaning with her shoulder against the wainscot.

"The doctor is not here?" he went on.

"He is out." She repeated, "He is out."

Then there was silence. They looked at one another and their thoughts, **confounded** in the same **agony**, **clung** close together like two throbbing **breasts**.

"I should like to **kiss** Berthe," said Leon.

Emma went down a few steps and called Felicite.

He threw one long look around him that took in the walls, the decorations, the fireplace, as if to **penetrate** everything, **carry** away everything. But she **returned**, and the servant brought Berthe, who was swinging a **windmill roof downwards** at the end of a string. Leon kissed her several times on the **neck**.

"Good-bye, poor child! good-bye, **dear** little one! good-bye!" And he gave her back to her mother.

"Take her away," she said.

They remained alone--Madame Bovary, her back turned, her face **pressed** against a window-pane; Leon held his cap in his hand, knocking it softly against his **thigh**.

"It is going to rain," said Emma.

"I have a cloak," he answered.

"Ah!"

She turned around, her chin lowered, her forehead bent forward.

The light **fell** on it as on a **piece** of marble, to the curve of the eyebrows, without one's being able to **guess** what Emma was **seeing** on the horizon or what she was **thinking** within herself.

"Well, good-bye," he sighed.

She **raised** her head with a **quick** movement.

Spanish

agony: agonía, angustia, miedo.
blood: sangre, la sangre.
breasts: pecho, pechos, seno.
carry: llevar, llevamos, lleváis, llevad, lleva, lleven, llevo, llevan, llevas, lleve, cargar.
clung: pret y pp de cling.
confounded: perplejo.
dear: caro, querido, estimado.
downwards: hacia abajo.
fell: talar, derribar.
guess: adivinar, suponer, suposición,

asumir.
kiss: besar, beso, besarse.
neck: cuello, el cuello, garganta, pescuezo, cerviz.
penetrate: penetrar, penetramos, penetro, penetra, penetráis, penetran, penetras, penetren, penetrad, penetre.
piece: pieza, pedazo, parte, trozo, tela.
pressed: prensado, apretado, planchado, plegado a presión.
quick: rápido, pronto.

raised: alzado, elevado, en relieve, levantado, peraltada, recrecido.
returned: devuelto.
roof: tejado, techo, el techo, techado, techar.
seeing: viendo, serrando.
skin: piel, cáscara, la piel, cutis, pelar.
standing: permanente, posición.
thigh: muslo, el muslo.
thinking: pensando, reflexionando, pensamiento, pensante.
windmill: molino de viento.

"Yes, good-bye--go!"

They **advanced** towards each other; he held out his hand; she hesitated.

"In the English **fashion**, then," she said, giving her own hand **wholly** to him, and **forcing** a laugh.

Leon felt it between his fingers, and the very **essence** of all his being seemed to pass down into that moist **palm**. Then he **opened** his hand; their eyes met again, and he disappeared.

When he **reached** the market-place, he **stopped** and hid behind a **pillar** to look for the last time at this white house with the four **green blinds**. He thought he saw a shadow behind the **window** in the room; but the curtain, **sliding** along the pole as though no one were touching it, **slowly** opened its long **oblique** folds that spread out with a single movement, and thus **hung** straight and motionless as a plaster wall. Leon set off **running**.

From afar he saw his employer's **gig** in the road, and by it a man in a coarse apron holding the **horse**. Homais and Monsieur Guillaumin were talking. They were waiting for him.

"Embrace me," said the druggist with **tears** in his eyes. "Here is your coat, my good friend. Mind the cold; take care of **yourself**; look after yourself."

"Come, Leon, jump in," said the notary.

Homais bend over the splash-board, and in a voice **broken** by sobs uttered these three sad words--

"A **pleasant** journey!"

"Good-night," said Monsieur Guillaumin. "Give him his head." They set out, and Homais went back.

Madame Bovary had opened her window overlooking the garden and **watched** the clouds. They **gathered** around the **sunset** on the side of Rouen and then **swiftly rolled** back their black columns, behind which the great rays of the sun looked out like the **golden** arrows of a **suspended trophy**, while the rest of

---

Spanish

advanced: avanzado, adelantado.
blinds: deslumbra, persianas.
broken: roto, estropeado, entrecortado, quebrado.
essence: esencia.
fashion: moda.
forcing: compulsión.
gathered: reunido, reunió.
gig: calesa.
golden: dorado, áureo, de oro.
green: verde.
horse: caballo, el caballo, potro, cabio.

hung: colgó, pret y pp de hang, colgado, continuado.
oblique: oblicuo, inclinado.
opened: abierto.
palm: palmera, palma.
pillar: columna, pilar.
pleasant: agradable, simpático, placentero, grato.
reached: alcanzado.
rolled: arrollado.
running: corriendo, funcionamiento.
sliding: corredizo, deslizamiento.

slowly: lentamente, despacio.
stopped: parado, detenido.
sun: sol, el sol.
suspended: suspendido.
swiftly: de prisa, pronto, rápidamente.
tears: desgarra, rasga.
trophy: trofeo.
watched: Mirado.
wholly: enteramente.
window: ventana, taquilla, la ventana, ventanilla.
yourself: tú mismo, se.

the **empty** heavens was white as porcelain. But a **gust** of **wind** bowed the poplars, and suddenly the **rain** fell; it pattered against the green leaves.

Then the sun **reappeared**, the hens clucked, sparrows **shook** their **wings** in the damp thickets, and the **pools** of water on the gravel as they flowed away carried off the **pink** flowers of an **acacia**.

"Ah! how far off he must be already!" she thought.

Monsieur Homais, as **usual**, came at half-past six during dinner.

"Well," said he, "so we've sent off our young friend!"

"So it seems," replied the doctor. Then turning on his chair; "Any news at home?"

"Nothing much. Only my wife was a little moved this **afternoon**. You know women--a nothing upsets them, especially my wife. And we should be wrong to **object** to that, since their nervous **organization** is much more **malleable** than ours."

"Poor Leon!" said Charles. "How will he live at Paris? Will he get used to it?"

Madame Bovary sighed.

"Get along!" said the chemist, **smacking** his lips. "The outings at restaurants, the masked balls, the champagne--all that'll be **jolly** enough, I assure you."

"I don't think he'll go wrong," objected Bovary.

"Nor do I," said Monsieur Homais quickly; "although he'll have to do like the rest for **fear** of passing for a Jesuit. And you don't know what a life those **dogs** lead in the Latin **quarter** with actresses. Besides, students are thought a great deal of in Paris. Provided they have a few accomplishments, they are **received** in the best society; there are even ladies of the Faubourg Saint-Germain who fall in love with them, which **subsequently furnishes** them opportunities for making very good matches."

"But," said the doctor, "I fear for him that down there--"

"You are right," interrupted the chemist; "that is the **reverse** of the **medal**. And one is constantly obliged to keep one's hand in one's **pocket** there. Thus, we

Spanish

acacia: acacia.
afternoon: tarde, la tarde.
dogs: los perros, las perras.
empty: vacío, vaciar, evacuar, desocupado, desocupar.
fear: temer, miedo, temor, angustia, recelar.
furnishes: amuebla.
gust: ráfaga, racha.
jolly: alegre, jovial.
malleable: maleable.
medal: medalla, la medalla.

object: objeto, el objeto, objetar.
organization: organización, organismo.
pink: rosado, rosa, clavel.
pocket: bolsillo, el bolsillo, bolsa, casilla.
pools: las piscinas.
quarter: barrio, cuarto, trimestre.
rain: llover, lluvia, la lluvia.
reappeared: reaparecido.
received: recibido.
reverse: inverso, reverso, marcha

atrás, revés, parte trasera, al contrario, al revés.
shook: sacudió, pret de shake.
smacking: paliza, azotaina, abofetear.
subsequently: después, subsiguientemente, posteriormente, luego, más adelante.
usual: común, general, universal, acostumbrado, habitual.
wind: viento, serpentear, el viento, enrollar, devanar.
wings: bastidores, alas.

will suppose you are in a public garden. An individual presents himself, well dressed, even wearing an order, and whom one would take for a **diplomatist**. He **approaches** you, he **insinuates** himself; offers you a **pinch** of **snuff**, or **picks** up your hat. Then you become more **intimate**; he takes you to a cafe, invites you to his country-house, **introduces** you, between two **drinks**, to all sorts of people; and three-fourths of the time it's only to **plunder** your watch or lead you into some **pernicious** step.

"That is true," said Charles; "but I was thinking especially of illnesses--of **typhoid fever**, for example, that attacks students from the provinces."

Emma shuddered.

"Because of the change of regimen," continued the chemist, "and of the **perturbation** that results **therefrom** in the whole system. And then the water at Paris, don't you know! The dishes at restaurants, all the spiced food, end by **heating** the blood, and are not worth, whatever people may say of them, a good soup. For my own part, I have always preferred plain living; it is more healthy. So when I was **studying** pharmacy at Rouen, I **boarded** in a **boarding** house; I dined with the professors."

And thus he went on, **expounding** his opinions generally and his personal likings, until Justin came to fetch him for a **mulled egg** that was wanted.

"Not a moment's peace!" he cried; "always at it! I can't go out for a minute! Like a plough-horse, I have always to be **moiling** and toiling. What drudgery!" Then, when he was at the door, "By the way, do you know the news?"

"What news?"

"That it is very likely," Homais went on, **raising** his eyebrows and **assuming** one of his most serious expression, "that the **agricultural** meeting of the Seine-Inferieure will be held this year at Yonville-l'Abbaye. The **rumour**, at all events, is going the round. This morning the paper **alluded** to it. It would be of the **utmost** importance for our district. But we'll talk it over later on. I can see, thank you; Justin has the lantern."

Spanish

agricultural: agrícola, agrario.
alluded: Aludido.
approaches: aproches.
assuming: asumiendo, arrogante.
boarded: Abordar.
boarding: embarque, entablado, abordaje.
diplomatist: diplomático.
drinks: bebidas.
egg: huevo, el huevo.
expounding: comentando, exponiendo.

fever: fiebre, calentura, la fiebre.
heating: calefacción, calentamiento.
insinuates: insinúa.
intimate: íntimo, cómodo, intimo.
introduces: presenta, introduce.
moiling: Bulliendo.
mulled: ponderado, vino hervido, Reflexionó, vino caliente.
pernicious: pernicioso.
perturbation: perturbación.
picks: pica.
pinch: pizca, apuro, pizcar, pellizco,

pellizcar.
plunder: pillaje, botín, saqueo.
raising: reunir, levantar, alza, alzar, aumento, aumento de sueldo, cría de ganado, criar, cultivar, elevación, elevar.
rumour: hambre, rumor.
snuff: rapé.
studying: estudiando.
therefrom: de eso, ahí dentro.
typhoid: tifoidea.
utmost: sumo.

CHAPTER SEVEN

The next day was a dreary one for Emma. Everything seemed to her enveloped in a black **atmosphere** floating **confusedly** over the **exterior** of things, and **sorrow** was **engulfed** within her soul with soft shrieks such as the winter wind makes in ruined castles. It was that reverie which we give to things that will not return, the **lassitude** that **seizes** you after everything was done; that pain, in fine, that the **interruption** of every **wonted** movement, the sudden **cessation** of any **prolonged vibration**, brings on.

As on the return from Vaubyessard, when the quadrilles were running in her head, she was full of a **gloomy** melancholy, of a **numb** despair. Leon reappeared, taller, handsomer, more charming, more vague. Though **separated** from her, he had not left her; he was there, and the walls of the house seemed to hold his shadow.

She could not **detach** her eyes from the **carpet** where he had walked, from those empty chairs where he had sat. The river still flowed on, and slowly **drove** its **ripples** along the slippery **banks**.

They had often walked there to the murmur of the **waves** over the moss-covered pebbles. How **bright** the sun had been! What happy afternoons they had seen along in the shade at the end of the garden! He read **aloud**, **bareheaded**, **sitting** on a footstool of dry sticks; the fresh wind of the meadow set trembling the **leaves** of the book and the nasturtiums of the arbour. **Ah**! he was gone, the

Spanish

ah: ay.
aloud: en voz alta.
atmosphere: atmósfera, ambiente.
banks: bancos.
bareheaded: descubierto.
bright: claro, luminoso, brillante, magnífico.
carpet: alfombra, la alfombra, alfombrar.
cessation: cese.
confusedly: confusamente.
detach: destacar, destaquen, destacad, destacamos, destacan, destacas, destaco, destaque, destaca, destacáis, desprender.
drove: manada.
engulfed: tragado.
exterior: aspecto, vista.
gloomy: oscuro, tenebroso, lóbrego.
interruption: interrupción.
lassitude: lasitud.
leaves: sale, deja, hojas, las hojas.
numb: entumecido, entorpecer, entorpece, entorpezco, entorpezcan, entorpezca, entorpeces, entorpecen, entorpecemos, entorpecéis, entorpeced.
prolonged: prolongado.
ripples: ondulaciones.
seizes: agarra, ase.
separated: separado.
sitting: sesión, sentada.
sorrow: tristeza, pena, dolor.
vibration: vibración.
waves: olas.
wonted: acostumbrado.

only charm of her life, the only possible hope of joy. Why had she not seized this happiness when it came to her? Why not have kept hold of it with both hands, with both knees, when it was about to flee from her? And she **cursed** herself for not having loved Leon. She thirsted for his lips. The wish took **possession** of her to run after and **rejoin** him, throw herself into his arms and say to him, "It is I; I am yours." But Emma recoiled beforehand at the difficulties of the enterprise, and her desires, increased by regret, became only the more acute.

Henceforth the memory of Leon was the centre of her boredom; it burnt there more **brightly** than the fire **travellers** have left on the snow of a Russian **steppe**. She sprang towards him, she pressed against him, she stirred carefully the dying **embers**, **sought** all around her anything that could **revive** it; and the most distant reminiscences, like the most immediate occasions, what she experienced as well as what she **imagined**, her **voluptuous** desires that were **unsatisfied**, her projects of happiness that crackled in the wind like dead boughs, her **sterile virtue**, her lost **hopes**, the domestic tete-a-tete--she gathered it all up, took everything, and made it all serve as fuel for her melancholy.

The flames, however, subsided, either because the supply had exhausted itself, or because it had been piled up too much. Love, little by little, was **quelled** by absence; regret stifled beneath habit; and this **incendiary** light that had empurpled her pale sky was **overspread** and faded by **degrees**. In the supineness of her **conscience** she even took her **repugnance** towards her husband for aspirations towards her lover, the burning of hate for the warmth of tenderness; but as the tempest still **raged**, and as passion burnt itself down to the very cinders, and no help came, no sun rose, there was night on all sides, and she was lost in the terrible cold that pierced her.

Then the **evil** days of Tostes began again. She thought herself now far more unhappy; for she had the experience of **grief**, with the **certainty** that it would not end.

A woman who had laid on herself such sacrifices could well allow herself certain **whims**. She bought a Gothic prie-dieu, and in a month spent **fourteen** francs on **lemons** for **polishing** her nails; she wrote to Rouen for a blue cashmere

Spanish

brightly: brillantemente.
certainty: certidumbre, certeza.
conscience: conciencia.
cursed: maldito.
degrees: grados.
embers: rescoldo, ascuas, ascua.
evil: mal, malo, malvado.
fourteen: catorce.
grief: pesar, dolor.
hopes: espera.
imagined: imaginado.
incendiary: incendiario.

lemons: limones.
overspread: esparcir, cubrir.
polishing: limpieza, pulido, satinado, pulidor, lucidatura.
possession: posesión, tenencia.
quelled: sofocado.
raged: rabiado.
rejoin: reincorporarse a, reunir, reunirse con, reunirse, volver a juntarse con, replicar, replicas, reúnan, reunís, reunimos, reunid.
repugnance: repugnancia.

revive: reponerse, reavivar, resucitar, reanimar, reavivan, reaviven, reavive, reavivas, reaviváis, reavivad, reaviva.
sought: buscado.
steppe: estepa.
sterile: estéril.
travellers: ver.
unsatisfied: insatisfecho.
virtue: virtud.
voluptuous: voluptuoso.
whims: caprichos.

gown; she chose one of Lheureux's **finest** scarves, and wore it knotted around her waist over her dressing-gown; and, with closed blinds and a book in her hand, she **lay** stretched out on a **couch** in this garb.

She often changed her **coiffure**; she did her hair a la Chinoise, in flowing curls, in **plaited** coils; she parted in on one side and rolled it under like a man's.

She wanted to learn Italian; she bought **dictionaries**, a **grammar**, and a supply of white paper. She tried serious reading, history, and **philosophy**. Sometimes in the night Charles woke up with a start, thinking he was being called to a **patient**. "I'm coming," he stammered; and it was the noise of a match Emma had struck to **relight** the lamp. But her reading fared like her piece of embroidery, all of which, only just begun, **filled** her cupboard; she took it up, left it, passed on to other books.

She had attacks in which she could easily have been **driven** to **commit** any **folly**. She maintained one day, in opposition to her husband, that she could drink off a large glass of brandy, and, as Charles was **stupid** enough to dare her to, she **swallowed** the brandy to the last drop.

In spite of her **vapourish** airs (as the housewives of Yonville called them), Emma, all the same, never seemed gay, and usually she had at the corners of her mouth that immobile **contraction** that **puckers** the faces of old maids, and those of men whose ambition has failed. She was pale all over, white as a **sheet**; the skin of her **nose** was drawn at the nostrils, her eyes looked at you vaguely. After **discovering** three grey hairs on her temples, she talked much of her old age.

She often fainted. One day she even spat blood, and, as Charles **fussed** around her showing his anxiety--

"Bah!" she answered, "what does it matter?"

Charles fled to his study and wept there, both his elbows on the table, sitting in an arm-chair at his bureau under the phrenological head.

Then he wrote to his mother **begging** her to come, and they had many long consultations together on the subject of Emma.

Spanish

begging: mendicidad, mendigando, mendigar.
coiffure: peinado.
commit: cometer, comete, cometo, cometes, cometen, cometed, cometan, cometéis, cometemos, cometa.
contraction: contracción, reducción.
couch: canapé, dyschatell, cama, sofá, sofá cama.
dictionaries: diccionarios.
discovering: descubriendo.
driven: conducido, manejado.

filled: llenar, completar, despachar, terraplén, relleno, rellenar, redondear, ocupar, lleno, atestado, llenó.
finest: mejor.
folly: tontería.
fussed: agitado.
grammar: gramática.
la: la, Loisiana.
nose: nariz, la nariz, proa.
patient: paciente.
philosophy: filosofía.

plaited: trenzado, fruncido, trenzó.
puckers: arruga, frunce, fruncidos.
relight: volver a arder.
sheet: hoja, lámina, sábana, libra, escota, folio, placa, chapa, plancha, sabana.
stupid: estúpido, bobo, zote, tonto, necio, torpe, menso.
swallowed: deglutido, dar crédito a, contener, golondrina, tragado, tragarse, tragar.
vapourish: vaporoso.

What should they decide? What was to be done since she **rejected** all medical treatment? "Do you know what your wife wants?" replied Madame Bovary senior.

"She wants to be forced to **occupy** herself with some **manual** work. If she were obliged, like so many others, to earn her living, she wouldn't have these vapours, that come to her from a lot of ideas she stuffs into her head, and from the idleness in which she lives.

Yet she is always busy," said Charles.

"Ah! always busy at what? Reading novels, bad books, works against **religion**, and in which they **mock** at priests in speeches taken from Voltaire. But all that **leads** you far **astray**, my poor child. Anyone who has no religion always ends by turning out badly."

So it was decided to stop Emma reading novels. The **enterprise** did not seem easy. The good lady **undertook** it. She was, when she passed through Rouen, to go herself to the lending-library and represent that Emma had **discontinued** her subscription. Would they not have a right to apply to the police if the **librarian** persisted all the same in his **poisonous** trade? The farewells of mother and daughter-in-law were cold. During the three weeks that they had been together they had not exchanged half-a-dozen words apart from the inquiries and phrases when they met at table and in the evening before going to bed.

Madame Bovary left on a Wednesday, the market-day at Yonville.

The Place since morning had been **blocked** by a row of carts, which, on end and their shafts in the air, spread all along the line of houses from the church to the inn. On the other side there were canvas booths, where cotton checks, blankets, and **woollen** stockings were **sold**, together with harness for **horses**, and packets of blue ribbon, whose ends fluttered in the wind. The coarse **hardware** was spread out on the ground between pyramids of **eggs** and hampers of cheeses, from which **sticky** straw stuck out.

Near the corn-machines clucking hens passed their necks through the bars of **flat cages**. The people, **crowding** in the same place and **unwilling** to move thence, sometimes **threatened** to **smash** the shop front of the chemist. On Wednesdays his shop was never empty, and the people **pushed** in less to buy **drugs** than for consultations. So great was Homais' **reputation** in the neighbouring villages. His **robust** aplomb had **fascinated** the **rustics**. They considered him a greater doctor than all the doctors.

Emma was leaning out at the window; she was often there. The window in the provinces **replaces** the **theatre** and the **promenade**, she was amusing herself with watching the **crowd** of boors when she saw a **gentleman** in a green velvet coat. He had on **yellow** gloves, although he wore heavy gaiters; he was coming towards the doctor's house, followed by a peasant walking with a bent head and quite a **thoughtful** air.

"Can I see the doctor?" he asked Justin, who was talking on the doorsteps with Felicite, and, taking him for a servant of the house--"Tell him that Monsieur Rodolphe Boulanger of La Huchette is here."

It was not from **territorial** vanity that the new arrival added "of La Huchette" to his name, but to make himself the better known.

La Huchette, in fact, was an estate near Yonville, where he had just bought the chateau and two farms that he cultivated himself, without, however, troubling very much about them. He lived as a **bachelor**, and was supposed to have "at least fifteen thousand francs a year."

Charles came into the room. Monsieur Boulanger introduced his man, who wanted to be bled because he felt "a **tingling** all over."

"That'll **purge** me," he **urged** as an **objection** to all **reasoning**.

So Bovary ordered a **bandage** and a basin, and asked Justin to hold it. Then addressing the peasant, who was already pale--

"Don't be afraid, my lad."

"No, no, sir," said the other; "get on."

And with an air of **bravado** he held out his great arm. At the prick of the lancet the blood **spurted** out, **splashing** against the looking-glass.

Spanish

bachelor: bachiller, soltero, solterón.
bandage: vendaje, venda, la venda, vendar.
bravado: valentía.
crowd: muchedumbre, multitud, gentío.
drugs: drogas, fármacos, medicamentos.
fascinated: fascinado.
gentleman: caballero, señor, gentilhombre.
objection: objeción.

promenade: paseo.
purge: purga, limpiar, purgar, depuración, depurar, purgante.
pushed: empujado.
reasoning: razonamiento.
replaces: sustituye, reemplaza.
reputation: reputación.
robust: robusto, sólido, fuerte.
rustics: rústico.
smash: rotura, golpear, romper.
splashing: chapoteo, riego, salpicar, salpicaduras.

spurted: chorreado.
territorial: territorial.
theatre: teatro.
thence: desde allí.
thoughtful: pensativo, atento, prudente, circunspecto.
threatened: amenazado, conminado.
tingling: zumbido, estremecimiento, hormiguear, hormigueo, picar, picazón, zumbar.
urged: Instado.
yellow: amarillo.

"Hold the basin nearer," exclaimed Charles.

"Lor!" said the peasant, "one would **swear** it was a little fountain flowing. How red my blood is! **That's** a good sign, isn't it?"

"Sometimes," answered the doctor, "one **feels** nothing at first, and then **syncope** sets in, and more especially with people of strong **constitution** like this man."

At these words the **rustic** let go the lancet-case he was **twisting** between his **fingers**. A shudder of his shoulders made the chair-back **creak**. His hat fell off.

"I thought as much," said Bovary, **pressing** his finger on the **vein**.

The basin was beginning to **tremble** in Justin's hands; his knees shook, he turned pale.

"Emma! Emma!" called Charles.

With one bound she came down the staircase.

"Some vinegar," he cried. "O dear! two at once!"

And in his emotion he could hardly put on the **compress**.

"It is nothing," said Monsieur Boulanger quietly, taking Justin in his arms. He seated him on the table with his back resting against the wall.

Madame Bovary began taking off his cravat. The strings of his shirt had got into a knot, and she was for some minutes moving her light fingers about the young fellow's neck. Then she poured some vinegar on her cambric handkerchief; she **moistened** his temples with little dabs, and then blew upon them softly. The **ploughman** revived, but Justin's syncope still lasted, and his eyeballs disappeared in the pale sclerotics like blue flowers in **milk**.

"We must **hide** this from him," said Charles.

Madame Bovary took the basin to put it under the table. With the movement she made in bending down, her dress (it was a summer dress with four flounces, yellow, long in the waist and wide in the **skirt**) spread out around her on the flags of the room; and as Emma **stooping**, **staggered** a little as she stretched out her arms.

Spanish

compress: comprimir, oprimir, compresa.
constitution: constitución, complexión.
creak: chirriar, chirrido, crujir, chirriad, chirrio, chirrien, chirrie, chirrias, chirrian, chirriáis, chirria.
feels: siente, palpa.
finger: dedo, el dedo, tocar, manga.
hat: sombrero, el sombrero.
hide: ocultar, oculto, oculta, oculte, ocultas, ocultan, ocultamos, ocultáis,
ocultad, oculten, piel.
milk: leche, ordeñar, la leche.
moistened: Humedecido.
ploughman: labrador, arador.
pressing: urgente, prensado.
rustic: rústico.
skirt: falda, la falda, base de blindaje, faldón.
staggered: alternado, asombrar, azorar, bamboleo, tambaleado, tambalear, tambalearse, tambaleo, tresbolillo, temblar.
stooping: inclinar, inclinarse, rebajamiento, rebajar, rebajarse, cargado de espaldas, agachado, agacharse, inclinación, humillarse, encorvado.
swear: jurar, jura, jurad, juráis, juramos, juran, juras, juren, juro, jure, maldecir.
syncope: síncope.
tremble: temblar, temblor.
twisting: retorcido.
vein: vena, veta, filón.

The stuff here and there gave with the inflections of her bust.

Then she went to fetch a bottle of water, and she was melting some pieces of sugar when the chemist arrived. The servant had been to fetch him in the tumult. Seeing his pupil's eyes **staring** he drew a long breath; then going around him he looked at him from head to foot.

"Fool!" he said, "really a little **fool**! A fool in four letters! A phlebotomy's a big affair, isn't it! And a fellow who isn't afraid of anything; a kind of **squirrel**, just as he is who climbs to **vertiginous** heights to **shake** down nuts. Oh, yes! you just talk to me, **boast** about yourself! Here's a fine **fitness** for **practising** pharmacy later on; for under serious circumstances you may be called before the **tribunals** in order to **enlighten** the minds of the **magistrates**, and you would have to keep your head then, to reason, show yourself a man, or else pass for an imbecile."

Justin did not answer. The chemist went on--

"Who asked you to come? You are always **pestering** the doctor and madame. On Wednesday, moreover, your presence is **indispensable** to me. There are now twenty people in the shop. I left everything because of the interest I take in you. Come, get along! Sharp! Wait for me, and keep an eye on the jars."

When Justin, who was **rearranging** his dress, had gone, they talked for a little while about **fainting**-fits. Madame Bovary had never fainted.

"That is **extraordinary** for a lady," said Monsieur Boulanger; "but some people are very **susceptible**. Thus in a **duel**, I have seen a second lose **consciousness** at the mere sound of the **loading** of pistols."

"For my part," said the chemist, "the sight of other people's blood doesn't affect me at all, but the mere thought of my own flowing would make me faint if I reflected upon it too much."

Monsieur Boulanger, however, **dismissed** his servant, **advising** him to calm himself, since his fancy was over.

"It **procured** me the advantage of making your acquaintance," he added, and he looked at Emma as he said this. Then he put three francs on the corner of the table, bowed **negligently**, and went out.

Spanish

advising: aconsejando.
boast: jactarse.
consciousness: conciencia, consciencia, conocimiento.
dismissed: despedido.
duel: duelo.
enlighten: iluminar, iluminas, ilumino, ilumine, iluminan, ilumináis, iluminad, ilumina, iluminamos, iluminen.
extraordinary: extraordinario.
faint: desmayarse, débil, desmayo, tenue.
fitness: capacidad, disposición, aptitud.
fool: engañar, necio, tonto.
indispensable: imprescindible, necesario, indispensable.
loading: carga.
magistrates: magistrados.
negligently: negligentemente.
pestering: importunando.
practising: ejercicio, ejercicios, entrenamiento, práctica, practicante, practicar, que ejerce.
procured: procurado.
rearranging: reorganizando.
shake: sacudir, sacuda, sacudimos, sacudís, sacudid, sacudes, sacuden, sacude, sacudan, sacudo, sacudida.
squirrel: ardilla, la ardilla.
staring: llamativo.
susceptible: sensible, propenso, impresionable.
tribunals: tribunales.
vertiginous: vertiginoso.

He was soon on the other side of the river (this was his way back to La Huchette), and Emma saw him in the meadow, walking under the poplars, **slackening** his **pace** now and then as one who reflects.

"She is very **pretty**," he said to himself; "she is very pretty, this doctor's wife. Fine teeth, black eyes, a dainty foot, a figure like a Parisienne's. Where the devil does she come from? **Wherever** did that fat fellow pick her up?"

Monsieur Rodolphe Boulanger was **thirty**-four; he was of **brutal** temperament and **intelligent perspicacity**, having, moreover, had much to do with women, and **knowing** them well. This one had seemed pretty to him; so he was thinking about her and her husband.

"I think he is very stupid. She is tired of him, no doubt. He has dirty nails, and hasn't **shaved** for three days. While he is trotting after his patients, she **sits** there botching **socks**. And she gets bored! She would like to live in town and dance polkas every evening. Poor little woman! She is gaping after love like a **carp** after water on a kitchen-table. With three words of **gallantry** she'd adore one, I'm sure of it. She'd be tender, charming. Yes; but how to get **rid** of her afterwards?"

Then the **difficulties** of love-making seen in the distance made him by **contrast** think of his mistress. She was an **actress** at Rouen, whom he kept; and when he had **pondered** over this image, with which, even in remembrance, he was satiated--

"Ah! Madame Bovary," he thought, "is much prettier, especially **fresher**. Virginie is **decidedly** beginning to **grow** fat. She is so finikin about her pleasures; and, besides, she has a mania for prawns."

The fields were empty, and around him Rodolphe only heard the regular **beating** of the grass **striking** against his boots, with a **cry** of the **grasshopper** hidden at a distance among the oats. He again saw Emma in her room, dressed as he had seen her, and he undressed her.

Spanish

actress: actriz, una actriz.
beating: paliza, pulsación, latido.
brutal: bronco, brusco, brutal.
carp: carpa.
contrast: contraste, contrastar.
cry: llorar, grito, gritar, lamento.
decidedly: decididamente.
difficulties: dificultades.
fresher: estudiante de primer año, fresco, mechón, novato, nuevo, puro, tierno.
gallantry: galantería, gallardía.

grasshopper: saltamontes, el saltamontes.
grow: crecer, crecen, crezco, crece, creced, crecemos, crezcan, crecéis, creces, crezca, cultivar.
intelligent: inteligente.
knowing: sabiendo, conociendo.
pace: paso.
perspicacity: perspicacia.
pondered: ponderado.
pretty: bonito, lindo, majo, amable, guapo, bastante, guapa.

rid: librar, libro, librad, librado, libráis, libramos, libran, libras, libre, libren, libra.
shaved: afeitado, rasurado.
sits: asienta, siente, sopla, empolla, se sienta.
slackening: aflojando.
socks: calcetines.
striking: llamativo.
thirty-four: treinta y cuatro.
wherever: dondequiera que, dondequiera.

"Oh, I will have her," he cried, striking a **blow** with his stick at a **clod** in **front** of him. And he at once began to **consider** the political part of the enterprise. He asked himself--

"Where shall we meet? By what means? We shall always be having the **brat** on our hands, and the servant, the neighbours, and **husband**, all sorts of **worries**. Pshaw! one would **lose** too much time over it."

Then he **resumed**, "She really has eyes that **pierce** one's **heart** like a **gimlet**. And that pale complexion! I adore pale women!"

When he reached the top of the Arguiel hills he had made up his mind. "It's only **finding** the opportunities. Well, I will call in now and then. I'll **send** them **venison**, poultry; I'll have **myself** bled, if need be. We shall become friends; I'll invite them to my place. By Jove!" **added** he, "there's the agricultural show coming on. She'll be there. I shall see her. We'll **begin boldly**, for that's the surest way."

CHAPTER EIGHT

At last it came, the famous agricultural show. On the morning of the **solemnity** all the inhabitants at their doors were **chatting** over the preparations. The **pediment** of the town hall had been hung with **garlands** of **ivy**; a **tent** had been **erected** in a meadow for the **banquet**; and in the middle of the Place, in front of the church, a kind of bombarde was to **announce** the arrival of the **prefect** and the names of the successful farmers who had obtained prizes. The National Guard of Buchy (there was none at Yonville) had come to join the **corps** of firemen, of whom Binet was captain. On that day he wore a collar even higher than usual; and, **tightly buttoned** in his **tunic**, his figure was so stiff and motionless that the whole vital portion of his person seemed to have **descended** into his legs, which rose in a cadence of set steps with a single movement. As there was some **rivalry** between the tax-collector and the **colonel**, both, to show off their **talents**, **drilled** their men **separately**. One saw the red **epaulettes** and the black breastplates pass and re-pass **alternately**; there was no end to it, and it constantly began again. There had never been such a display of **pomp**. Several citizens had scoured their houses the evening before; tri-coloured flags hung from half-open windows; all the public-houses were full; and in the lovely weather the **starched** caps, the golden crosses, and the coloured neckerchiefs seemed whiter than snow, shone in the sun, and **relieved** with the motley colours the sombre monotony of the frock-coats and blue smocks. The

Spanish

alternately: por rotación, alternadamente, alternamente, alternantemente, alternativamente, eventualmente.
announce: anunciar, anuncias, anuncien, anuncian, anunciamos, anunciáis, anunciad, anuncia, anuncie, anuncio, publicar.
banquet: banquete, banquetear, festín.
buttoned: abotonado, abrochado.
chatting: Charlar.
colonel: coronel.

corps: cuerpo.
descended: descendido, bajado.
drilled: taladró.
epaulettes: charreteras.
erected: erigido.
garlands: guirnaldas.
ivy: hiedra.
pediment: frontón.
pomp: pompa.
prefect: monitor, prefecto.
relieved: aliviado, relevado, desahogado.

rivalry: rivalidad.
separately: por separado, separadamente, aparte.
solemnity: solemnidad.
starched: acartonado, almidonado, almidonar, duro, plastificado, rígido, tieso, tirante.
talents: talentos.
tent: tienda de campaña, carpa, tienda.
tightly: apretadamente, herméticamente.
tunic: túnica.

neighbouring farmers' wives, when they got off their horses, pulled out the long **pins** that fastened around them their dresses, turned up for fear of mud; and the husbands, for their part, in order to save their hats, kept their handkerchiefs around them, holding one corner between their teeth.

The crowd came into the main street from both ends of the village. People poured in from the lanes, the **alleys**, the houses; and from time to time one heard **knockers** banging against **doors closing** behind women with their gloves, who were going out to see the **fete**. What was most admired were two long lamp-stands covered with lanterns, that flanked a **platform** on which the authorities were to sit. Besides this there were against the four columns of the town hall four kinds of poles, each **bearing** a small standard of **greenish** cloth, **embellished** with inscriptions in gold letters.

On one was written, "To Commerce"; on the other, "To Agriculture"; on the third, "To Industry"; and on the fourth, "To the Fine Arts."

But the **jubilation** that **brightened** all faces seemed to darken that of Madame Lefrancois, the **innkeeper**. Standing on her kitchen-steps she **muttered** to herself, "What **rubbish**! what rubbish! With their canvas **booth**! Do they think the prefect will be **glad** to dine down there under a tent like a **gipsy**? They call all this **fussing** doing good to the place! Then it wasn't worth while **sending** to Neufchatel for the keeper of a cookshop! And for whom? For cowherds! tatterdemalions!"

The druggist was passing. He had on a frock-coat, nankeen trousers, **beaver** shoes, and, for a wonder, a hat with a low crown.

"Your servant! **Excuse** me, I am in a hurry." And as the fat **widow** asked where he was going--

"It seems **odd** to you, doesn't it, I who am always more **cooped** up in my **laboratory** than the man's rat in his cheese."

"What cheese?" asked the landlady.

Spanish

alleys: paseos.
bearing: cojinete, abolas, rodamiento.
beaver: castor.
booth: cabina, puesto.
brightened: avivado, esclarecido, abrillantado, Aclarado.
closing: Cerrando, cierre, conexión, cerrar.
cooped: Encerrado.
doors: las puertas.
embellished: embellecido.
excuse: excusa, excusar, disculpa, disculpar.
fete: celebración, festejar, festejo, fiesta.
fussing: agitar.
gipsy: gitano.
glad: alegre, contento.
greenish: verdoso.
innkeeper: posadero.
jubilation: júbilo.
keeper: guardián, custodio, guarda, cortocircuito magnético.
knockers: tetas.
laboratory: laboratorio.
muttered: Mumurado.
odd: impar, extraño, raro.
pins: pines, patas.
platform: plataforma, andén, programa.
rat: rata, la rata.
rubbish: basura, derribos, desechos, detrito.
sending: enviando, mandando, despachando, envío.
widow: viuda.

"Oh, nothing! nothing!" Homais continued. "I merely wished to **convey** to you, Madame Lefrancois, that I usually live at home like a recluse. To-day, however, considering the circumstances, it is necessary--"

"Oh, you're going down there!" she said contemptuously.

"Yes, I am going," replied the druggist, astonished. "Am I not a member of the consulting commission?"

Mere Lefrancois looked at him for a few moments, and ended by saying with a smile--

"That's another pair of shoes! But what does agriculture matter to you? Do you understand anything about it?"

"Certainly I understand it, since I am a druggist--that is to say, a chemist. And the object of **chemistry**, Madame Lefrancois, being the knowledge of the **reciprocal** and **molecular** action of all natural bodies, it follows that agriculture is **comprised** within its **domain**. And, in fact, the composition of the manure, the **fermentation** of liquids, the **analyses** of gases, and the influence of miasmata, what, I ask you, is all this, if it isn't chemistry, pure and simple?"

The landlady did not answer. Homais went on--

"Do you think that to be an **agriculturist** it is necessary to have **tilled** the earth or **fattened** fowls oneself? It is necessary rather to know the composition of the substances in question--the **geological strata**, the **atmospheric** actions, the quality of the soil, the **minerals**, the waters, the **density** of the different bodies, their **capillarity**, and what not. And one must be master of all the principles of hygiene in order to direct, **criticize** the construction of buildings, the **feeding** of animals, the diet of **domestics**. And, moreover, Madame Lefrancois, one must know botany, be able to distinguish between plants, you understand, which are the **wholesome** and those that are **deleterious**, which are **unproductive** and which **nutritive**, if it is well to pull them up here and re-sow them there, to **propagate** some, **destroy** others; in brief, one must keep pace with science by means of pamphlets and public papers, be always on the **alert** to find out improvements."

Spanish

agriculturist: agricultor.
alert: alerta, alarma, alertar.
analyses: Analiza.
atmospheric: atmosférico.
capillarity: capilaridad.
chemistry: química.
comprised: Comprendido.
convey: alargar, entregar, llevar, entrega, entregan, entreguen, entregue, entregas, entregamos, entregáis, entregad.
criticize: criticar, critique, critiquen, criticad, criticáis, criticamos, critican, critico, critica, criticas, censurar.
deleterious: deletéreo.
density: densidad.
destroy: destruir, destruid, destruimos, destruís, destruyan, destruye, destruyen, destruyes, destruyo, destruya.
domain: dominio.
domestics: doméstico.
fattened: engordado.
feeding: alimentando, alimentación, cebando.
fermentation: fermentación.
geological: geológico.
minerals: los minerales.
molecular: molecular.
nutritive: nutritivo.
propagate: propagar.
reciprocal: recíproco.
strata: estratos.
tilled: embaldosado.
unproductive: improductivo.
wholesome: sano.

The landlady never took her eyes off the "Cafe Francois" and the chemist went on--

"Would to God our agriculturists were chemists, or that at least they would pay more **attention** to the counsels of **science**. Thus lately I myself **wrote** a considerable **tract**, a **memoir** of over **seventy**-two pages, **entitled**, 'Cider, its Manufacture and its Effects, together with some New Reflections on the Subject,' that I **sent** to the Agricultural Society of Rouen, and which even **procured** me the honour of being received among its members--Section, Agriculture; Class, Pomological. Well, if my work had been given to the public--" But the **druggist** stopped, Madame Lefrancois seemed so preoccupied.

"Just look at them!" she said. "It's past **comprehension**! Such a cookshop as that!" And with a **shrug** of the shoulders that stretched out over her breast the stitches of her knitted bodice, she pointed with both **hands** at her rival's inn, whence songs were **heard issuing**. "Well, it won't last long," she added. "It'll be over before a week."

Homais drew back with **stupefaction**. She came down three steps and whispered in his ear--

"What! you didn't know it? There is to be an **execution** in next week. It's Lheureux who is **selling** him out; he has **killed** him with bills."

"What a **terrible** catastrophe!" cried the druggist, who always found **expressions** in **harmony** with all imaginable **circumstances**.

Then the landlady began **telling** him the **story** that she had heard from Theodore, Monsieur Guillaumin's servant, and although she detested Tellier, she **blamed** Lheureux. He was "a wheedler, a sneak."

"There!" she said. "Look at him! he is in the market; he is **bowing** to Madame Bovary, who's got on a green bonnet. Why, she's taking Monsieur Boulanger's arm."

"Madame Bovary!" exclaimed Homais. "I must go at once and pay her my respects. Perhaps she'll be very glad to have a seat in the enclosure under the peristyle." And, without heeding Madame Lefrancois, who was **calling** him back

Spanish

attention: atención, firmes.
blamed: culpado.
bowing: reverencia, toque con el arco, inclinar, golpes de arco.
calling: llamando, llamada.
circumstances: circunstancias, circunstancia.
comprehension: comprensión.
druggist: droguero.
entitled: entitulado, tiene derecho, permitido, intitulado, con derecho, autorizado, acreedor.

execution: ejecución.
expressions: expresiones.
hands: las manos.
harmony: armonía.
heard: oído.
issuing: emisor.
killed: matado.
memoir: autobiografía, biografía, informe, memoria, memorias, nota biográfica.
procured: procurado.
science: ciencia, la ciencia.

selling: vendiendo, venta.
sent: enviado, mandado, despachado.
seventy-two: setenta y dos.
shrug: encogerse de hombros.
story: historia, piso, cuento, relato, el cuento.
stupefaction: estupefacción.
telling: contando, relatando, narración.
terrible: terrible.
tract: tracto.
wrote: escribió.

to tell him more about it, the druggist walked off rapidly with a **smile** on his lips, with straight knees, bowing copiously to right and left, and taking up much room with the large tails of his frock-coat that fluttered behind him in the wind.

Rodolphe, having caught sight of him from afar, **hurried** on, but Madame Bovary lost her breath; so he walked more slowly, and, smiling at her, said in a **rough** tone--

"It's only to get away from that fat fellow, you know, the druggist." She pressed his elbow.

"What's the **meaning** of that?" he asked himself. And he looked at her out of the corner of his eyes.

Her profile was so calm that one could guess nothing from it. It stood out in the light from the oval of her bonnet, with pale ribbons on it like the leaves of **weeds**. Her eyes with their long curved lashes looked straight before her, and though wide open, they seemed slightly puckered by the cheek-bones, because of the blood pulsing gently under the delicate skin. A pink line ran along the **partition** between her nostrils. Her head was bent upon her shoulder, and the **pearl** tips of her white teeth were seen between her lips.

"Is she making **fun** of me?" thought Rodolphe.

Emma's gesture, however, had only been meant for a **warning**; for Monsieur Lheureux was **accompanying** them, and **spoke** now and again as if to **enter** into the conversation.

"What a **superb** day! **Everybody** is out! The wind is east!"

And neither Madame Bovary nor Rodolphe answered him, whilst at the slightest movement made by them he drew near, saying, "I **beg** your pardon!" and raised his hat.

When they reached the farrier's house, **instead** of following the road up to the **fence**, Rodolphe suddenly turned down a path, **drawing** with him Madame Bovary. He called out--

"Good evening, Monsieur Lheureux! See you again presently."

Spanish

accompanying: acompañando.
beg: mendigar, mendigas, mendiguen, mendigan, mendigáis, mendiga, mendigad, mendigamos, mendigo, mendigue, pedir limosna.
drawing: dibujando, dibujo, encantando, trazando, plano, giro.
enter: entrar, entro, entra, entrad, entráis, entramos, entran, entras, entren, entre, inscribir.
everybody: todos, cada uno, cada, todo el mundo, todo.

fence: reja, valla, cerca, vallado, obstrucción, la cerca, cercado.
fun: diversión, divertido, placer, divertimento.
hurried: apresuradamente, apresurado, apurado, hecho de prisa, precipitado, superficial.
instead: en cambio.
meaning: intención, significado, sentido, significación.
partition: separación, partición, tabique, división.

pearl: perla, la perla.
rough: áspero, crudo, desigual, bronco, brusco, grosero.
smile: sonrisa, sonreír, la sonrisa, sonreírse.
spoke: decir, radio, rayo, raya, radioactivo, rayo de rueda, hablar, pret de speak, expresar.
superb: magnífico.
warning: aviso, avisando, advertencia, advirtiendo, amonestación.
weeds: malas hierbas, hierbajos.

"How you got rid of him!" she said, laughing.

"Why," he went on, "allow oneself to be **intruded** upon by others? And as to-day I have the happiness of being with you--"

Emma blushed. He did not finish his sentence. Then he talked of the fine weather and of the pleasure of walking on the grass. A few daisies had sprung up again.

"Here are some pretty Easter daisies," he said, "and enough of them to **furnish** oracles to all the amorous maids in the place."

He added, "Shall I pick some? What do you think?"

"Are you in love?" she asked, coughing a little.

"H'm, h'm! who knows?" answered Rodolphe.

The meadow began to **fill**, and the housewives **hustled** you with their great umbrellas, their baskets, and their **babies**. One had often to get out of the way of a long file of country **folk**, servant-maids with blue stockings, flat shoes, silver rings, and who smelt of milk, when one passed close to them. They walked along holding one another by the hand, and thus they spread over the whole field from the row of open trees to the banquet tent.

But this was the **examination** time, and the farmers one after the other entered a kind of enclosure **formed** by a long cord supported on sticks.

The **beasts** were there, their noses towards the cord, and making a confused line with their unequal rumps. **Drowsy** pigs were **burrowing** in the earth with their snouts, calves were **bleating**, lambs baaing; the cows, on knees folded in, were stretching their bellies on the grass, slowly **chewing** the cud, and **blinking** their heavy eyelids at the gnats that buzzed round them. Plough-men with bare arms were holding by the halter **prancing** stallions that **neighed** with **dilated** nostrils looking towards the mares. These stood **quietly**, stretching out their heads and flowing manes, while their **foals** rested in their shadow, or now and then came and **sucked** them. And above the long **undulation** of these **crowded** animals one saw some white mane rising in the wind like a **wave**, or some **sharp** horns sticking out, and the heads of men running about. Apart, outside the

Spanish

babies: criaturas, bebes.
beasts: ganado.
bleating: Balando.
blinking: intermitente, parpadear, parpadeo.
burrowing: excavación, hurgoneo.
chewing: masticando.
crowded: atestado.
dilated: dilatado.
drowsy: soñoliento.
examination: examen, contemplación, vista, interrogatorio.

fill: llenar, relleno, rellenar, ocupar, llenado.
foals: potrillos.
folk: pueblo, población, gente.
formed: formó, formado.
furnish: amueblar, amueblas, amueblen, amueblo, amueble, amueblamos, amuebláis, amuebla, amueblan, amueblad, suministrar.
hustled: Apresurado.
intruded: impuesto, estorbado, molestado, metido, intervenido,

incursionado.
neighed: Relinchó.
prancing: escarceos, encabritar.
quietly: calladamente, silenciosamente.
sharp: agudo, afilado, sostenido, justamente, acre, cortante, áspero.
sucked: chupado.
undulation: ondulación.
wave: ola, onda, ondulación, blandir, oleada, la ola, ondear, ondular, agitar.

enclosure, a hundred paces off, was a large black **bull**, **muzzled**, with an iron ring in its nostrils, and who moved no more than if he had been in **bronze**. A child in rags was holding him by a rope.

Between the two lines the committee-men were walking with heavy steps, **examining** each animal, then consulting one another in a low voice. One who seemed of more importance now and then took notes in a book as he walked along. This was the president of the **jury**, Monsieur Derozerays de la Panville. As soon as he recognised Rodolphe he came forward quickly, and smiling **amiably**, said--

"What! Monsieur Boulanger, you are **deserting** us?"

Rodolphe **protested** that he was just coming. But when the president had disappeared--

"Ma foi!" said he, "I shall not go. Your company is better than his."

And while **poking** fun at the show, Rodolphe, to move about more easily, showed the gendarme his blue card, and even stopped now and then in front of some fine **beast**, which Madame Bovary did not at all **admire**. He noticed this, and began **jeering** at the Yonville ladies and their dresses; then he apologised for the negligence of his own. He had that **incongruity** of common and **elegant** in which the **habitually vulgar** think they see the **revelation** of an **eccentric** existence, of the **perturbations** of sentiment, the tyrannies of art, and always a certain contempt for social conventions, that **seduces** or **exasperates** them. Thus his cambric shirt with plaited cuffs was **blown** out by the wind in the opening of his waistcoat of grey ticking, and his broad-striped trousers **disclosed** at the ankle nankeen boots with **patent** leather gaiters.

These were so polished that they reflected the grass. He **trampled** on horses's **dung** with them, one hand in the pocket of his jacket and his straw hat on one side.

"Besides," added he, "when one lives in the country--"

"It's waste of time," said Emma.

Spanish

admire: admirar, admiran, admiro, admiren, admiras, admiramos, admiráis, admirad, admira, admire.
amiably: amablemente.
beast: bestia, animal.
blown: soplado, hinchado, estropeado, jadeante, insípido, pp de blow.
bronze: bronce, bronceado, broncear.
bull: toro, alcista, el toro.
deserting: desertar.
disclosed: divulgado, revelado.

dung: estiércol.
eccentric: excéntrico, extravagante.
elegant: elegante.
examining: examinando, registrando, examinar.
exasperates: exaspera.
habitually: habitualmente.
incongruity: incongruidad, incoherencia, incongruencia.
jeering: mofándose.
jury: jurado.
muzzled: Abozalado.

patent: patente, patentar, evidente, patente de invención.
perturbations: inquietudes.
poking: meter.
protested: protestado.
revelation: revelación.
seduces: seduce.
trampled: pisoteado.
vulgar: chabacano, cursi, grosero, cutre, corriente, vulgo, vulgar, ramplón, ordinario, ordinaria, común.

"That is true," replied Rodolphe. "To think that not one of these people is **capable** of **understanding** even the cut of a coat!"

Then they talked about provincial mediocrity, of the lives it crushed, the illusions lost there.

"And I too," said Rodolphe, "am **drifting** into depression."

"You!" she said in astonishment; "I thought you very light-hearted."

"Ah! yes. I seem so, because in the midst of the world I know how to **wear** the **mask** of a **scoffer** upon my face; and yet, how many a time at the sight of a cemetery by moonlight have I not asked myself whether it were not better to **join** those sleeping there!"

"Oh! and your friends?" she said. "You do not think of them."

"My friends! What friends? Have I any? Who cares for me?" And he accompanied the last words with a kind of **whistling** of the lips.

But they were obliged to separate from each other because of a great pile of chairs that a man was carrying behind them. He was so overladen with them that one could only see the tips of his wooden shoes and the ends of his two **outstretched** arms. It was Lestiboudois, the gravedigger, who was carrying the church chairs about **amongst** the people. **Alive** to all that concerned his interests, he had **hit** upon this means of turning the show to account; and his idea was **succeeding**, for he no **longer** knew which way to turn. In fact, the villagers, who were hot, **quarreled** for these **seats**, whose straw smelt of incense, and they leant against the thick backs, **stained** with the wax of candles, with a certain veneration.

Madame Bovary again took Rodolphe's arm; he went on as if speaking to himself--

"Yes, I have **missed** so many things. Always **alone**! Ah! if I had some **aim** in life, if I had met some love, if I had found someone! Oh, how I would have **spent** all the energy of which I am capable, **surmounted** everything, **overcome** everything!"

"Yet it seems to me," said Emma, "that you are not to be pitied."

Spanish

aim: fin, objeto, objetivo, querer decir, apuntar, tratar de, esforzarse por, apuntáis, apunten, apuntas, apunto.
alive: vivo, viviente.
alone: solo, único, solamente, sólo.
amongst: entre.
capable: capaz, hábil.
drifting: llevar.
hit: golpear, acertar, golpe, pegar, llamar, éxito.
join: juntar, junta, junto, reunir, reunirse, junten, juntáis, juntamos, juntan, juntas, junte.
longer: más, más tiempo.
mask: máscara, careta, mascarilla, enmascarar, antifaz.
missed: perdido.
outstretched: extendido.
overcome: superar, superen, supera, superad, superado, superáis, superamos, superan, supere, supero, superas.
quarreled: Peleado.
scoffer: mofador.
seats: sillería.
spent: gastado, pasado.
stained: manchado.
succeeding: consiguiendo.
surmounted: vencido, superado.
understanding: entendiendo, comprendiendo, comprensión, relación, inteligencia, entendimiento, comprensivo, acuerdo.
wear: llevar, desgaste, usar, tener puesto, vestir, uso, llevar puesto.
whistling: silbido.

"Ah! you think so?" said Rodolphe.

"For, after all," she went on, "you are free-" she hesitated, "rich-"

"Do not mock me," he replied.

And she protested that she was not **mocking** him, when the report of a **cannon resounded**. Immediately all began **hustling** one another pell-mell towards the village.

It was a false alarm. The prefect seemed not to be coming, and the members of the jury felt much embarrassed, not knowing if they ought to begin the meeting or still wait.

At last at the end of the Place a large hired **landau** appeared, drawn by two thin horses, which a **coachman** in a white hat was **whipping lustily**. Binet had only just time to shout, "Present arms!" and the colonel to **imitate** him. All ran towards the enclosure; everyone pushed forward. A few even forgot their collars; but the equipage of the prefect seemed to anticipate the crowd, and the two **yoked** jades, trapesing in their harness, came up at a little trot in front of the **peristyle** of the town hall at the very moment when the National Guard and firemen **deployed**, beating **drums** and marking time.

"Present!" shouted Binet.

"Halt!" shouted the colonel. "Left about, march."

And after presenting arms, during which the **clang** of the band, letting loose, rang out like a brass **kettle** rolling downstairs, all the guns were lowered. Then was seen stepping down from the carriage a gentleman in a short coat with silver braiding, with bald brow, and wearing a **tuft** of hair at the back of his head, of a **sallow** complexion and the most **benign** appearance. His eyes, very large and covered by heavy lids, were half-closed to look at the crowd, while at the same time he raised his sharp nose, and forced a smile upon his sunken mouth. He recognised the mayor by his scarf, and explained to him that the prefect was not able to come. He himself was a councillor at the **prefecture**; then he added a few **apologies**. Monsieur Tuvache answered them with compliments; the other **confessed** himself nervous; and they remained thus, face to face, their foreheads

---

Spanish

apologies: disculpas aceptadas, disculpas.
benign: benigno.
cannon: cañón.
clang: sonar, sonido metálico, sonido metálico resonante, resonar, estruendo, hacer sonar, hacer estruendo.
coachman: cochero.
confessed: confesado, reconocido.
deployed: desplegado.
drums: batería.

hustling: buscarse la vida, Apresurar.
imitate: imitar, imite, imito, imitamos, imitas, imitáis, imitan, imitad, imita, imiten.
kettle: hervidor.
landau: landó.
lustily: lozanamente, cachondo, lujuriosamente.
mocking: burlarse, falso, imitar, burlas, burlador, burlón, burla, fingido, escarnecer, engañar, imitado.
peristyle: peristilo.

prefecture: prefectura.
resounded: Resonado.
sallow: pálido, sauce.
tuft: manojo de vasos sanguíneos, cresta, mata, mechón, penacho, copete, copo.
whipping: paliza, vapuleo, miembro de una Cámara, latigazo, látigo, fustigar, fustigación, fusta, flagelación, dar una paliza a, dar latigazos a.
yoked: Unió.

almost touching, with the members of the jury all round, the **municipal** council, the **notable** personages, the National Guard and the crowd. The **councillor** pressing his little **cocked** hat to his breast repeated his **bows**, while Tuvache, bent like a bow, also smiled, stammered, tried to say something, protested his **devotion** to the **monarchy** and the honour that was being done to Yonville.

Hippolyte, the groom from the inn, took the head of the horses from the coachman, and, **limping** along with his club-foot, led them to the door of the "Lion d'Or", where a number of peasants **collected** to look at the carriage. The **drum** beat, the **howitzer thundered**, and the gentlemen one by one **mounted** the platform, where they sat down in red utrecht velvet arm-chairs that had been lent by Madame Tuvache.

All these people looked **alike**. Their fair flabby faces, somewhat **tanned** by the sun, were the colour of sweet cider, and their **puffy** whiskers **emerged** from stiff collars, kept up by white cravats with **broad** bows. All the waist-coats were of velvet, **double**-breasted; all the watches had, at the end of a long ribbon, an oval **cornelian seal**; everyone rested his two hands on his **thighs**, carefully stretching the **stride** of their trousers, whose unsponged glossy cloth shone more **brilliantly** than the leather of their heavy boots.

The ladies of the company stood at the back under the vestibule between the pillars while the common **herd** was opposite, standing up or sitting on chairs. As a matter of fact, Lestiboudois had brought thither all those that he had moved from the field, and he even kept running back every minute to fetch others from the church. He caused such **confusion** with this piece of business that one had great difficulty in getting to the small steps of the platform.

"I think," said Monsieur Lheureux to the chemist, who was passing to his place, "that they ought to have put up two Venetian masts with something rather severe and rich for **ornaments**; it would have been a very pretty effect."

"To be sure," replied Homais; "but what can you expect? The mayor took everything on his own shoulders. He hasn't much taste. Poor Tuvache! and he is even completely **destitute** of what is called the **genius** of art."

Spanish

alike: semejante, igual, por igual.
bow: proa, arco, reverencia, inclinarse, lazo.
brilliantly: brillantemente.
broad: ancho.
cocked: Montado, de tres picos, tres picos.
collected: recogido, coleccionado, reunido, Cobrado.
confusion: confusión.
cornelian: cornalina.
councillor: consejero, concejal,
eclesiasta, vocal.
destitute: destituir, indigente.
devotion: devoción.
double-breasted: cruzado.
drum: tambor, bidón, el tambor, barril.
emerged: aparecido, emergido.
genius: genio, ingenio.
herd: manada, grupo, rebaño.
howitzer: obús.
limping: cojera, cojear.
monarchy: monarquía.
mounted: montado.
municipal: municipal.
notable: señalado, memorable, excelente, personaje, notabilidad, insigne.
ornaments: adornos.
puffy: hinchado.
seal: foca, sello, sellar, precinto, precintar.
stride: paso, paso largo, zancada.
tanned: bronceado, curtido, moreno.
thighs: muslos.
thundered: Tronado.

Rodolphe, meanwhile, with Madame Bovary, had gone up to the first floor of the town hall, to the "council-room," and, as it was empty, he declared that they could enjoy the sight there more **comfortably**. He **fetched** three stools from the round table under the bust of the **monarch**, and having carried them to one of the windows, they sat down by each other.

There was **commotion** on the platform, long whisperings, much **parleying**. At last the councillor got up. They knew now that his name was Lieuvain, and in the crowd the name was passed from one to the other. After he had **collated** a few pages, and bent over them to see better, he began--

"Gentlemen! May I be **permitted** first of all (before addressing you on the object of our meeting to-day, and this sentiment will, I am sure, be **shared** by you all), may I be permitted, I say, to pay a **tribute** to the higher administration, to the government to the monarch, gentle men, our **sovereign**, to that **beloved** king, to whom no branch of public or private **prosperity** is a matter of indifference, and who **directs** with a hand at once so firm and **wise** the **chariot** of the state amid the **incessant** perils of a **stormy** sea, knowing, moreover, how to make peace respected as well as war, industry, commerce, **agriculture**, and the fine arts?"

"I ought," said Rodolphe, "to get back a little further."

"Why?" said Emma.

But at this moment the voice of the councillor rose to an extraordinary pitch. He declaimed--

"This is no longer the time, gentlemen, when civil **discord** ensanguined our public places, when the landlord, the business-man, the working-man himself, falling asleep at night, lying down to peaceful sleep, trembled **lest** he should be awakened suddenly by the noise of incendiary tocsins, when the most **subversive** doctrines **audaciously sapped** foundations."

"Well, someone down there might see me," Rodolphe resumed, "then I should have to **invent excuses** for a **fortnight**; and with my bad reputation--"

"Oh, you are **slandering** yourself," said Emma.

Spanish

agriculture: agricultura.
audaciously: atrevidamente, audazmente, osadamente.
beloved: querido, amado, novio, dilecto.
chariot: carro.
collated: intercalado.
comfortably: cómodamente.
commotion: escándalo, conmoción, alboroto.
directs: dirige.
discord: discordia, disonancia.

excuses: deshechas.
fetched: traído, sacado.
fortnight: quincena, quince días.
incessant: incesante.
invent: inventar, invente, invento, inventas, inventen, inventan, inventamos, inventáis, inventad, inventa.
lest: para que no, a no ser que, con el fin de, no sea que, si es necesario.
monarch: monarca.
parleying: parlamentando,

debatiendo.
permitted: lícito, permitido.
prosperity: prosperidad.
sapped: agotó.
shared: compartido.
slandering: calumnia, calumniar, difamación, difamar, maledicencia.
sovereign: soberano.
stormy: tempestuoso, tormentoso.
subversive: subversivo.
tribute: tributo.
wise: sabio, sensato, guisa.

"No! It is **dreadful**, I assure you."

"But, gentlemen," continued the councillor, "if, **banishing** from my memory the remembrance of these sad **pictures**, I carry my eyes back to the actual situation of our dear country, what do I see there? **Everywhere** commerce and the **arts** are **flourishing**; everywhere new means of **communication**, like so many new **arteries** in the body of the state, **establish** within it new relations. Our great industrial centres have **recovered** all their activity; religion, more **consolidated**, smiles in all **hearts**; our **ports** are full, confidence is born again, and France **breathes** once more!"

"Besides," added Rodolphe, "perhaps from the world's point of view they are right."

"How so?" she asked.

"What!" said he. "Do you not know that there are souls constantly **tormented**? They need by **turns** to dream and to act, the purest passions and the most **turbulent** joys, and thus they **fling** themselves into all sorts of fantasies, of follies."

Then she looked at him as one looks at a **traveller** who has **voyaged** over strange lands, and went on--

"We have not even this distraction, we poor women!"

"A sad distraction, for happiness isn't found in it."

"But is it ever found?" she asked.

"Yes; one day it comes," he answered.

"And this is what you have understood," said the councillor.

"You, farmers, agricultural **labourers**! you **pacific** pioneers of a work that **belongs** wholly to **civilization**! you, men of progress and **morality**, you have understood, I say, that political storms are even more **redoubtable** than atmospheric disturbances!"

"It comes one day," repeated Rodolphe, "one day suddenly, and when one is despairing of it. Then the horizon expands; it is as if a voice cried, 'It is here!' You

Spanish

arteries: las arterias.
arts: letras, artes.
banishing: desterrando.
belongs: pertenece.
breathes: respira.
civilization: civilización.
communication: comunicación, noticia, noticias, publicación.
consolidated: consolidado, fusionado.
dreadful: terrible, espantoso.
establish: establecer, establezcan, establezco, estableces, establece,

estableced, establecemos, establecen, establecéis, establezca, edificar.
everywhere: en todas partes, por todas partes.
fling: arrojado, tiro, tirar, lanzar, lanzamiento, lanza, lance, echar al suelo, echar, echada, aventura amorosa.
flourishing: floreciendo, floreciente.
hearts: corazones, copas.
labourers: peones, braceros.
morality: moralidad, virtud, moral.

pacific: pacífico, Océano Pacífico, pacifico.
pictures: cine, Gráficas.
ports: puertos.
recovered: sanado, recuperado, recobrado.
redoubtable: temible.
tormented: atormentado.
traveller: viajero, viajante.
turbulent: turbulento.
turns: gira, vuelve, trastorna.
voyaged: navegado, viajado.

feel the need of **confiding** the whole of your life, of giving everything, **sacrificing** everything to this being. There is no need for explanations; they understand one another. They have seen each other in dreams!"

(And he looked at her.) "In fine, here it is, this **treasure** so sought after, here before you. It **glitters**, it **flashes**; yet one still **doubts**, one does not believe it; one remains dazzled, as if one went out iron darkness into light."

And as he ended Rodolphe suited the action to the word. He passed his hand over his face, like a man seized with giddiness. Then he let it fall on Emma's. She took hers away.

"And who would be surprised at it, gentlemen? He only who is so **blind**, so **plunged** (I do not fear to say it), so plunged in the prejudices of another age as still to **misunderstand** the spirit of agricultural populations. Where, indeed, is to be found more **patriotism** than in the country, greater devotion to the public welfare, more intelligence, in a word? And, gentlemen, I do not mean that **superficial** intelligence, **vain ornament** of **idle** minds, but rather that **profound** and **balanced** intelligence that **applies** itself above all else to useful objects, thus **contributing** to the good of all, to the common **amelioration** and to the support of the state, born of respect for law and the practice of duty--"

"Ah! again!" said Rodolphe. "Always 'duty.' I am sick of the word. They are a lot of old **blockheads** in flannel vests and of old women with foot-warmers and rosaries who constantly **drone** into our ears 'Duty, duty!' Ah! by Jove! one's duty is to feel what is great, **cherish** the beautiful, and not accept all the conventions of society with the **ignominy** that it **imposes** upon us."

"Yet--yet--" objected Madame Bovary.

"No, no! Why cry out against the passions? Are they not the one beautiful thing on the earth, the source of **heroism**, of **enthusiasm**, of **poetry**, music, the arts, of everything, in a word?"

"But one must," said Emma, "to some extent bow to the opinion of the world and accept its moral code."

Spanish

amelioration: mejora.
applies: emplea, aplica.
balanced: equilibrado.
blind: ciego, persiana, deslumbrar, deslumbrad, deslumbre, deslumbras, deslumbran, deslumbro, deslumbramos, deslumbráis, deslumbren.
blockheads: tonto.
cherish: querer, quered, quieran, quiero, quieres, quiere, quiera, queremos, queréis, quieren, apreciar.

confiding: confiando, crédulo.
contributing: contribuyendo.
doubts: duda.
drone: zumbido, zángano.
enthusiasm: entusiasmo.
flashes: bocadillos, intermitentes.
glitters: brilla.
heroism: heroísmo.
idle: ocioso, haraganear, perezoso, inactivo, en reposo.
ignominy: ignominia.
imposes: impone.

misunderstand: entender mal.
ornament: alhaja, decorar, ornamento, adorno.
patriotism: patriotismo.
plunged: hundido.
poetry: poesía.
profound: profundo.
sacrificing: sacrificar.
superficial: somero, superficial, de poca profundidad.
treasure: tesoro, atesorar.
vain: vano, hueco, vanidoso.

"Ah! but there are two," he replied. "The small, the conventional, that of men, that which constantly changes, that **brays** out so loudly, that makes such a commotion here below, of the earth earthly, like the mass of imbeciles you see down there. But the other, the eternal, that is about us and above, like the landscape that surrounds us, and the blue heavens that give us light."

Monsieur Lieuvain had just wiped his mouth with a **pocket**-handkerchief. He continued--

"And what should I do here gentlemen, pointing out to you the uses of agriculture? Who **supplies** our wants? Who provides our means of **subsistence**? Is it not the agriculturist? The agriculturist, gentlemen, who, **sowing** with **laborious** hand the **fertile** furrows of the country, brings forth the **corn**, which, being ground, is made into a powder by means of **ingenious machinery**, comes out thence under the name of flour, and from there, transported to our cities, is soon **delivered** at the **baker's**, who makes it into food for poor and rich alike. Again, is it not the agriculturist who **fattens**, for our **clothes**, his **abundant** flocks in the pastures? For how should we clothe ourselves, how **nourish** ourselves, without the agriculturist? And, gentlemen, is it even necessary to go so far for examples? Who has not frequently reflected on all the **momentous** things that we get out of that **modest** animal, the ornament of poultry-yards, that provides us at once with a soft pillow for our bed, with **succulent** flesh for our tables, and eggs? But I should never end if I were to **enumerate** one after the other all the different products which the earth, well cultivated, like a **generous** mother, **lavishes** upon her children. Here it is the vine, elsewhere the apple tree for cider, there colza, farther on cheeses and **flax**. Gentlemen, let us not forget flax, which has made such great **strides** of late years, and to which I will more particularly call your attention."

He had no need to call it, for all the mouths of the **multitude** were wide open, as if to drink in his words. Tuvache by his side listened to him with staring eyes. Monsieur Derozerays from time to time softly closed his eyelids, and farther on the chemist, with his son Napoleon between his knees, put his hand behind his ear in order not to lose a **syllable**. The chins of the other members of the jury

Spanish

abundant: abundante.
baker's: panadería.
brays: rebuznos.
clothe: vestir, vestid, vistes, visten, viste, vistan, vestís, vestimos, visto, vista.
corn: maíz, callo, grano.
delivered: entregado.
enumerate: enumerar, enumerad, enumeráis, enumeramos, enumeran, enumeras, enumeren, enumero, enumera, enumere.

fattens: engorda.
fertile: fértil, fecundo.
flax: lino.
generous: generoso, dadivoso.
ingenious: ingenioso.
laborious: laborioso, tabajoso.
lavishes: prodiga.
machinery: maquinaria.
modest: modesto.
momentous: importante.
multitude: multitud, la multitud.
nourish: alimentar, alimentáis,

alimento, alimenten, alimentas, alimentamos, alimentad, alimenta, alimentan, alimente, nutrir.
pocket-handkerchief: pañuelo.
sowing: siembra.
strides: zancadas.
subsistence: subsistencia.
succulent: zumoso, carnoso, suculento, jugoso, planta carnosa, sabroso, suculenta.
supplies: suministros.
syllable: sílaba.

went slowly up and down in their **waistcoats** in sign of **approval**. The firemen at the foot of the platform rested on their bayonets; and Binet, motionless, stood with out-turned elbows, the point of his sabre in the air. Perhaps he could hear, but certainly he could see nothing, because of the **visor** of his helmet, that fell down on his nose. His **lieutenant**, the **youngest** son of Monsieur Tuvache, had a **bigger** one, for his was **enormous**, and shook on his head, and from it an end of his cotton scarf **peeped** out. He **smiled beneath** it with a **perfectly** infantine sweetness, and his pale little face, whence drops were running, wore an expression of **enjoyment** and sleepiness.

The **square** as far as the houses was crowded with people. One saw folk leaning on their elbows at all the windows, others standing at doors, and Justin, in front of the chemist's shop, seemed quite **transfixed** by the sight of what he was looking at. In spite of the silence Monsieur Lieuvain's voice was lost in the air. It reached you in fragments of phrases, and interrupted here and there by the creaking of chairs in the crowd; then you suddenly heard the long **bellowing** of an **ox**, or else the bleating of the lambs, who answered one another at street corners. In fact, the cowherds and **shepherds** had driven their beasts thus far, and these lowed from time to time, while with their tongues they tore down some scrap of **foliage** that hung above their mouths.

Rodolphe had **drawn** nearer to Emma, and said to her in a low voice, speaking rapidly--

"Does not this **conspiracy** of the world **revolt** you? Is there a single sentiment it does not **condemn**? The noblest instincts, the purest sympathies are persecuted, slandered; and if at length two poor souls do meet, all is so **organised** that they cannot **blend** together. Yet they will make the attempt; they will flutter their wings; they will call upon each other. Oh! no matter. **Sooner** or later, in six months, ten years, they will come together, will love; for **fate** has **decreed** it, and they are born one for the other."

His arms were folded across his knees, and thus **lifting** his face towards Emma, close by her, he looked **fixedly** at her. She noticed in his eyes small

Spanish

approval: aprobación, homologación, aplauso, autorización, visto bueno.
bellowing: bramar.
beneath: debajo de, debajo, abajo.
bigger: más grande, mayor, más.
blend: mezcla, mezclar, combinar.
condemn: condenar, condenas, condenen, condenan, condenamos, condenáis, condenad, condeno, condene, condena, desaprobar.
conspiracy: conspiración.
decreed: decretado.

drawn: dibujado, encantado, trazado.
enjoyment: goce, disfrute.
enormous: enorme, ingente.
fate: destino, suerte, sino, hado.
fixedly: fijamente.
foliage: follaje.
lieutenant: teniente, lugarteniente.
lifting: levantamiento, elevación, levantar.
organised: organizado.
ox: buey.
peeped: pipió.

perfectly: perfectamente.
revolt: revuelta, sublevarse, rebelarse.
shepherds: los pastores.
smiled: sonreído.
sooner: más pronto.
square: plaza, cuadrado, cuadro, escuadra, el cuadro, en Ángulo Recto, glorieta, cuadrar, casilla.
transfixed: traspasado.
visor: visera.
waistcoats: poniente.
youngest: más joven.

golden lines **radiating** from black pupils; she even smelt the perfume of the pomade that made his hair glossy.

Then a **faintness** came over her; she recalled the Viscount who had waltzed with her at Vaubyessard, and his beard exhaled like this air an odour of **vanilla** and **citron**, and mechanically she half-closed her eyes the better to breathe it in. But in making this movement, as she leant back in her chair, she saw in the distance, right on the line of the horizon, the old **diligence**, the "Hirondelle," that was slowly **descending** the hill of Leux, dragging after it a long trail of dust. It was in this yellow carriage that Leon had so often come back to her, and by this route down there that he had gone for ever. She fancied she saw him opposite at his windows; then all grew confused; clouds gathered; it seemed to her that she was again turning in the waltz under the light of the lustres on the arm of the Viscount, and that Leon was not far away, that he was coming; and yet all the time she was conscious of the **scent** of Rodolphe's head by her side. This sweetness of sensation pierced through her old desires, and these, like **grains** of sand under a gust of wind, eddied to and fro in the subtle breath of the perfume which **suffused** her soul. She opened wide her nostrils several times to drink in the freshness of the ivy round the capitals. She took off her gloves, she wiped her hands, then **fanned** her face with her handkerchief, while athwart the throbbing of her temples she heard the murmur of the crowd and the voice of the councillor **intoning** his phrases. He said--"Continue, **persevere**; listen neither to the suggestions of routine, nor to the over-hasty councils of a **rash empiricism**.

"Apply **yourselves**, above all, to the amelioration of the soil, to good manures, to the development of the **equine**, **bovine**, ovine, and **porcine** races. Let these shows be to you pacific arenas, where the victor in leaving it will hold forth a hand to the **vanquished**, and will **fraternise** with him in the hope of better success. And you, aged servants, humble domestics, whose hard labour no Government up to this day has taken into consideration, come **hither** to receive the reward of your silent virtues, and be assured that the state **henceforward** has its eye upon you; that it **encourages** you, **protects** you; that it will **accede** to your

Spanish

accede: acceder, accedéis, accedes, accedo, accedemos, accede, accedan, acceden, acceded, acceda, acordar.
bovine: bovino, bovina, vacuno.
citron: cidra.
descending: descendiendo, bajando, descendente, descender, descendiente.
diligence: diligencia.
empiricism: empirismo.
encourages: anima, alienta, espolea.
equine: equino.

faintness: debilidad.
fanned: ventilado.
fraternise: fraternice.
grains: cereales.
henceforward: de aquí en adelante.
hither: acá.
intoning: entonando.
ovine: ovino, Ovina.
persevere: perseverar, perseveramos, persevero, perseveren, persevere, perseveran, perseveráis, perseverad, persevera, perseveras.

porcine: porcino.
protects: protégé.
radiating: radiando.
rash: sarpullido, erupción, precipitado, salpullido, erupción cutánea.
scent: olor, perfume, aroma.
suffused: difundido.
vanilla: vainilla, la vainilla.
vanquished: vencido, derrotado, rendido, logrado.
yourselves: ustedes mismos.

just demands, and **alleviate** as much as in it lies the **burden** of your **painful** sacrifices."

Monsieur Lieuvain then sat down; Monsieur Derozerays got up, beginning another speech. His was not perhaps so **florid** as that of the councillor, but it recommended itself by a more direct style, that is to say, by more special knowledge and more **elevated** considerations. Thus the **praise** of the Government took up less space in it; religion and agriculture more. He showed in it the relations of these two, and how they had always contributed to **civilisation**. Rodolphe with Madame Bovary was talking dreams, presentiments, **magnetism**. Going back to the cradle of society, the **orator** painted those fierce times when men lived on **acorns** in the heart of **woods**. Then they had left off the **skins** of beasts, had put on cloth, tilled the **soil**, **planted** the vine. Was this a good, and in this **discovery** was there not more of **injury** than of gain? Monsieur Derozerays set himself this problem. From magnetism little by little Rodolphe had come to **affinities**, and while the president was **citing** Cincinnatus and his **plough**, Diocletian, planting his cabbages, and the Emperors of China **inaugurating** the year by the sowing of **seed**, the young man was **explaining** to the young woman that these **irresistible** attractions find their cause in some previous state of existence.

"Thus we," he said, "why did we come to know one another? What chance willed it? It was because across the infinite, like two streams that **flow** but to **unite**; our special bents of mind had driven us towards each other."

And he seized her hand; she did not **withdraw** it.

"For good farming generally!" cried the president.

"Just now, for example, when I went to your house."

"To Monsieur Bizat of Quincampoix."

"Did I know I should accompany you?"

"**Seventy** francs."

"A hundred times I wished to go; and I followed you--I remained."

"Manures!"

Spanish

acorns: bellotas.
affinities: n - afinidades -f.
alleviate: aliviar, aliviáis, alivias, alivien, aliviamos, alivia, alivian, aliviad, alivio, alivie.
burden: carga, cargar, peso, gravamen, agobio, gravar.
citing: citando, mencionando.
civilisation: civilización.
discovery: descubrimiento.
elevated: elevado.
explaining: explicando.

florid: florido.
flow: flujo, corriente, fluir, correr.
inaugurating: inaugurando.
injury: lesión, herida, daño.
irresistible: irresistible.
magnetism: magnetismo.
orator: orador.
painful: doloroso, penoso.
planted: plantado.
plough: arado, arar.
praise: alabar, alabanza, elogio, elogiar.

seed: semilla, la semilla, grano, simiente, semen, sembrar.
seventy: setenta.
skins: hollejo, batería.
soil: tierra, ensuciar, suelo, manchar.
unite: reunir, reunimos, reunís, reúno, reúnes, reunid, reúna, reúne, reúnan, reúnen, juntar.
withdraw: retirar, retiro, retire, retira, retiras, retiren, retiran, retiramos, retiráis, retirad, quitar.
woods: bosque.

"And I shall remain to-night, to-morrow, all other days, all my life!"

"To Monsieur Caron of Argueil, a **gold** medal!"

"For I have never in the society of any other person found so complete a charm."

"To Monsieur Bain of Givry-Saint-Martin."

"And I shall carry away with me the remembrance of you."

"For a merino ram!"

"But you will **forget** me; I shall pass away like a shadow."

"To Monsieur Belot of Notre-Dame."

"Oh, no! I shall be something in your thought, in your life, shall I not?"

"Porcine **race**; prizes--equal, to Messrs. Leherisse and Cullembourg, **sixty** francs!"

Rodolphe was pressing her hand, and he felt it all warm and **quivering** like a **captive dove** that wants to **fly** away; but, whether she was trying to take it away or whether she was **answering** his pressure; she made a movement with her fingers. He exclaimed--

"Oh, I thank you! You do not **repulse** me! You are good! You understand that I am **yours**! Let me look at you; let me **contemplate** you!"

A gust of wind that blew in at the window **ruffled** the cloth on the table, and in the square below all the great caps of the peasant women were **uplifted** by it like the wings of white butterflies fluttering.

"Use of oil-cakes," continued the president. He was **hurrying** on: "Flemish manure-flax-growing-drainage-long leases-domestic service."

Rodolphe was no longer speaking. They looked at one another. A **supreme desire** made their dry lips tremble, and **wearily**, without an effort, their fingers **intertwined**.

"Catherine Nicaise Elizabeth Leroux, of Sassetot-la-Guerriere, for **fifty**-four years of service at the same farm, a silver medal--value, twenty-five francs!"

Spanish

answering: contestar, respuesta.
captive: cautivo.
contemplate: contemplar, contemplan, contemplen, contemplo, contemplas, contempláis, contempla, contemplamos, contemplad, contemple, meditar.
desire: desear, deseo, tener, querer, gana, codiciar.
dove: pichón, paloma, la palomita.
fifty-four: cincuenta y cuatro, cinquenta y cuatro.

fly: volar, voláis, vuelen, vuele, vuelas, volamos, vuela, volad, vuelan, vuelo, mosca.
forget: olvidar, olvidan, olviden, olvidas, olvidamos, olvidáis, olvidad, olvida, olvide, olvido, olvidarse.
gold: oro, el oro, de oro.
hurrying: apurar.
intertwined: entrelazado.
quivering: estremecimiento, vibrante, vibración, tembloroso, vibrar, temblor, parpadeante, estremecerse,

carcaj, aljaba, temblador.
race: raza, carrera, correr, regata.
repulse: repulsión, repulsar.
ruffled: erizado.
sixty: sesenta.
supreme: supremo.
uplifted: inspiró.
wearily: hastiadamente, fatigadamente, cansadamente, fastidiosamente, fatigosamente, abrumadoramente.
yours: vuestro, suyo, el tuyo.

"Where is Catherine Leroux?" repeated the councillor.

She did not present herself, and one could hear voices whispering--

"Go up!"

"Don't be afraid!"

"Oh, how stupid she is!"

"Well, is she there?" cried Tuvache. ·--

"Yes; here she is."

"Then let her come up!"

Then there came forward on the platform a little old woman with **timid** bearing, who seemed to **shrink** within her poor clothes. On her feet she wore heavy wooden clogs, and from her hips hung a large blue apron. Her pale face framed in a borderless cap was more **wrinkled** than a **withered russet** apple. And from the sleeves of her red **jacket** looked out two large hands with **knotty** joints, the dust of barns, the **potash** of washing the grease of **wools** had so **encrusted**, roughened, **hardened** these that they seemed dirty, although they had been **rinsed** in clear water; and by dint of long service they remained half open, as if to bear humble **witness** for themselves of so much **suffering endured**. Something of **monastic rigidity dignified** her face. Nothing of sadness or of emotion **weakened** that pale look. In her constant living with animals she had caught their **dumbness** and their calm. It was the first time that she found herself in the midst of so large a company, and inwardly **scared** by the flags, the drums, the gentlemen in frock-coats, and the order of the councillor, she stood motionless, not knowing whether to **advance** or run away, nor why the crowd was pushing her and the jury were smiling at her.

Thus stood before these **radiant bourgeois** this half-century of **servitude**.

"Approach, **venerable** Catherine Nicaise Elizabeth Leroux!" said the councillor, who had taken the list of prize-winners from the president; and, looking at the piece of paper and the old woman by turns, he repeated in a **fatherly** tone--"Approach! approach!"

Spanish

advance: avance, adelanto, anticipo, acercarse, progreso, adelantar, proponer, aproximarse, avanzar, anticipar.
bourgeois: burgués.
dignified: dignificado, digno.
dumbness: mudez, tonterías comprensibles, estupidez.
encrusted: incrustó.
endured: durado, soportado.
fatherly: paternal, paternalmente.
hardened: endurecido.

jacket: chaqueta, americana, la chaqueta, cubierta, funda, envoltura, camisa, cazadora.
knotty: nudoso.
monastic: monástico, monacal.
potash: potasa.
radiant: resplandeciente, radiante, brillante.
rigidity: rigidez.
rinsed: enjuagado.
russet: bermejo.
scared: asustado.

servitude: servidumbre.
shrink: encoger, mermar.
suffering: sufriendo, padeciendo, sufrimiento.
timid: tímido, encogido, miedo.
venerable: venerado.
weakened: debilitado.
withered: marchito, marchitado.
witness: testigo, presenciar, atestiguar, testimonio.
wools: lana.
wrinkled: arrugado.

"Are you deaf?" said Tuvache, **fidgeting** in his armchair; and he began shouting in her ear, "Fifty-four years of service. A silver medal! Twenty-five francs! For you!"

Then, when she had her medal, she looked at it, and a smile of **beatitude** spread over her face; and as she walked away they could hear her **muttering** "I'll give it to our cure up home, to say some **masses** for me!"

"What fanaticism!" exclaimed the chemist, leaning across to the notary.

The meeting was over, the crowd dispersed, and now that the speeches had been read, each one fell back into his place again, and everything into the old **grooves**; the masters **bullied** the **servants**, and these struck the **animals**, **indolent** victors, going back to the stalls, a green-crown on their horns.

The National Guards, however, had gone up to the first floor of the town hall with buns **spitted** on their bayonets, and the **drummer** of the **battalion** carried a basket with bottles. Madame Bovary took Rodolphe's arm; he saw her home; they separated at her door; then he walked about alone in the meadow while he waited for the time of the banquet.

The feast was long, **noisy**, ill served; the guests were so crowded that they could hardly move their elbows; and the **narrow planks** used for forms almost broke down under their weight. They ate **hugely**. Each one stuffed himself on his own account. **Sweat** stood on every brow, and a whitish steam, like the **vapour** of a **stream** on an **autumn** morning, **floated** above the table between the hanging lamps. Rodolphe, leaning against the calico of the tent was thinking so **earnestly** of Emma that he heard nothing. Behind him on the grass the servants were **piling** up the dirty plates, his neighbours were talking; he did not answer them; they filled his glass, and there was silence in his thoughts in spite of the growing noise. He was dreaming of what she had said, of the line of her lips; her face, as in a **magic mirror**, shone on the plates of the shakos, the folds of her gown fell along the walls, and days of love **unrolled** to all **infinity** before him in the vistas of the future.

He saw her again in the evening during the **fireworks**, but she was with her husband, Madame Homais, and the druggist, who was **worrying** about the

Spanish

animals: animales.
autumn: otoño.
battalion: batallón.
beatitude: beatitud.
bullied: intimidado.
drummer: tambor.
earnestly: seriamente.
fidgeting: manoseando, meneando.
fireworks: fuegos artificiales, pirotecnia.
floated: fratasado, flotado.
grooves: surcos, ranuras.

hugely: enormemente, inmensamente, muy.
indolent: indolente.
infinity: infinidad, infinito.
magic: magia, mágico.
masses: masas, vulgo.
mirror: espejo, el espejo, reflejar.
muttering: barboteo, mumurar, murmullo, rezongo.
narrow: estrecho, angosto.
noisy: ruidoso, bullicioso.
piling: acopio, apilamiento,

amontonar, pilotaje.
planks: vertical de desviadores, tablazón, poste con tablas.
servants: servicio.
spitted: escupió.
stream: arroyo, corriente, flujo, chorro, riachuelo, secuencia.
sweat: sudor, sudar, transpirar.
unrolled: devanado.
vapour: vapor, vaho.
worrying: inquietante, molesto, preocupar.

danger of **stray** rockets, and every moment he left the company to go and give some **advice** to Binet.

The **pyrotechnic** pieces sent to Monsieur Tuvache had, through an **excess** of **caution**, been shut up in his cellar, and so the damp powder would not light, and the **principal** set piece, that was to represent a **dragon** biting his **tail**, failed completely. Now and then a meagre Roman-candle went off; then the gaping crowd sent up a **shout** that mingled with the cry of the women, whose waists were being **squeezed** in the darkness. Emma silently **nestled** against Charles's shoulder; then, raising her chin, she watched the **luminous** rays of the rockets against the dark sky. Rodolphe **gazed** at her in the light of the burning lanterns.

They went out one by one. The stars shone out. A few crops of rain began to fall. She knotted her fichu round her bare head.

At this moment the councillor's carriage came out from the inn.

His coachman, who was **drunk**, suddenly **dozed** off, and one could see from the distance, above the **hood**, between the two lanterns, the mass of his body, that **swayed** from right to left with the giving of the traces.

"Truly," said the druggist, "one ought to **proceed** most **rigorously** against **drunkenness**! I should like to see written up **weekly** at the door of the town hall on a board ad **hoc** the names of all those who during the week got **intoxicated** on **alcohol**. Besides, with regard to **statistics**, one would thus have, as it were, public records that one could **refer** to in case of need. But excuse me!"

And he once more ran off to the captain. The latter was going back to see his lathe again.

"Perhaps you would not do ill," Homais said to him, "to send one of your men, or to go yourself--"

"Leave me alone!" answered the tax-collector. "It's all right!"

"Do not be uneasy," said the druggist, when he returned to his friends. "Monsieur Binet has **assured** me that all **precautions** have been taken. No sparks have fallen; the **pumps** are full. Let us go to rest."

Spanish

ad: anuncio, aviso.
alcohol: alcohol.
assured: asegurado.
caution: cautela, precaución, avisar, advertencia.
dozed: dormitado.
dragon: dragón.
drunk: borracho, bebido, ebrio.
drunkenness: embriaguez, ebriedad, borrachera.
excess: exceso, excedente.
gazed: mirado.

hoc: éste.
hood: capucha, tapa, capot, campana, capota, capó.
intoxicated: ebrio, intoxicado, borracho, aturdido.
luminous: luminoso.
nestled: se acurrucado, anidado.
precautions: precauciones.
principal: principal, mandante, comitente, ordenante.
proceed: proceder, actuar.
pumps: bombas.

pyrotechnic: pirotécnico, sustancia pirotécnica.
refer: remitir, referirse, referir.
rigorously: rigurosamente.
shout: gritar, grito.
squeezed: apretado, exprimido.
statistics: estadística, estadísticas.
stray: extraviarse, perdido.
swayed: Oscilado.
tail: cola, rabo, el rabio.
weekly: semanalmente, semanal, semanario.

"Ma foi! I want it," said Madame Homais, **yawning** at large. "But never mind; we've had a beautiful day for our fete."

Rodolphe repeated in a low voice, and with a tender look, "Oh, yes! very beautiful!"

And having bowed to one another, they separated.

Two days later, in the "Final de Rouen," there was a long **article** on the show. Homais had composed it with **verve** the very next morning.

"Why these festoons, these flowers, these garlands? Whither hurries this crowd like the waves of a **furious** sea under the torrents of a tropical sun **pouring** its **heat** upon our heads?"

Then he spoke of the **condition** of the peasants. Certainly the Government was doing much, but not enough. "Courage!" he cried to it; "a **thousand** reforms are indispensable; let us **accomplish** them!" Then touching on the **entry** of the councillor, he did not forget "the **martial** air of our militia;" nor "our most **merry** village maidens;" nor the "bald-headed old men like patriarchs who were there, and of whom some, the **remnants** of our phalanxes, still felt their hearts **beat** at the **manly** sound of the drums." He cited himself among the first of the members of the jury, and he even called attention in a note to the fact that Monsieur Homais, chemist, had sent a memoir on cider to the agricultural society.

When he came to the **distribution** of the prizes, he painted the joy of the prize-winners in dithyrambic strophes. "The father embraced the son, the **brother** the brother, the husband his **consort**. More than one showed his humble medal with **pride**; and no doubt when he got home to his good housewife, he hung it up weeping on the modest walls of his **cot**.

"About six o'clock a banquet **prepared** in the meadow of Monsieur Leigeard brought together the principal personages of the fete. The **greatest** cordiality **reigned** here. **Divers** toasts were **proposed**: Monsieur Lieuvain, the King; Monsieur Tuvache, the Prefect; Monsieur Derozerays, Agriculture; Monsieur Homais, Industry and the Fine Arts, those **twin** sisters; Monsieur Leplichey, Progress. In the evening some **brilliant** fireworks on a sudden **illumined** the air.

Spanish

accomplish: realizar, realizad, realizo, realizáis, realice, realicen, realizan, realiza, realizamos, realizas, lograr.
article: artículo, objeto.
beat: golpear, batido, batir, pegar, apalear, pulsación, latido, batimiento.
brilliant: brillante, magnífico, genial.
brother: hermano, el hermano, cofrade.
condition: condición, acondicionar, estado.
consort: consorte.

cot: camita de niño, catre.
distribution: distribución.
divers: varios, diversos.
entry: entrada, asiento, ingreso, partida, inscripción, acceso.
furious: torcido, furioso, furibundo.
greatest: máximo, máxima.
heat: calor, calentar, el calor, hornada, carga de fusión.
illumined: iluminado.
manly: varonil.
martial: marcial.

merry: alegre.
pouring: trasvase, vertir, colada, torrencial.
prepared: preparado.
pride: orgullo.
proposed: propuesto.
reigned: Reinado.
remnants: remanentes.
thousand: mil.
twin: gemelo, gemelos.
verve: brío.
yawning: bostezante, bostezando.

One would have called it a **veritable kaleidoscope**, a real **operatic scene**; and for a moment our little **locality** might have thought itself **transported** into the **midst** of a **dream** of the 'Thousand and One Nights.' "Let us state that no **untoward event disturbed** this family meeting." And he **added** "Only the **absence** of the **clergy** was **remarked**. No **doubt** the priests **understand progress** in another **fashion**. Just as you **please, messieurs** the **followers** of Loyola!"

CHAPTER NINE

Six **weeks** passed. Rodolphe did not come again. At last one **evening** he appeared.

The day after the show he had said to himself--"We mustn't go back too **soon;** that would be a mistake."

And at the end of a week he had **gone** off **hunting.** After the hunting he had thought it was too **late,** and then he **reasoned** thus--

"If from the first day she **loved** me, she must from **impatience** to see me again love me more. **Let's** go on with it!"

And he knew that his **calculation** had been right when, on **entering** the room, he saw Emma **turn pale.**

She was alone. The day was drawing in. The small **muslin curtain along** the **windows deepened** the **twilight,** and the **gilding** of the **barometer,** on which the rays of the sun fell, **shone** in the **looking**-glass between the meshes of the **coral.**

Rodolphe remained standing, and Emma **hardly answered** his first **conventional phrases.**

"I," he said, "have been busy. I have been ill."

"Seriously?" she **cried.**

Spanish

along: a lo largo de, por.
answered: contesta, Contestado.
barometer: barómetro.
calculation: cálculo, cuenta.
conventional: convencional.
coral: coral.
cried: Lloró.
curtain: cortina, la cortina.
deepened: ahondado.
entering: entrando, inscribiendo, montando.
evening: tarde, noche, anochecer.

gilding: dorado, dorando.
gone: ido, marchado.
hardly: apenas.
hunting: cazando, caza, penduleo, cacería.
impatience: impaciencia.
late: tarde, tardío, tardo.
let's: permitanos.
looking-glass: espejo.
loved: amado, estimado, querido, considerado.
muslin: muselina.

pale: pálido, palidecer, descolorido.
phrases: batería libre de mantenimiento -- menor tiempo de respuesta de servicio.
reasoned: razonado.
shone: brillado, pret y pp de shine.
soon: pronto, luego.
turn: girar, gira, giro, giráis, giramos, giran, giras, gire, giren, girad, vuelta.
twilight: crepúsculo, anochecer.
weeks: semanas.
windows: ventanas, ojal.

"Well," said Rodolphe, sitting down at her side on a footstool, "no; it was because I did not want to come back."

"Why?"

"Can you not guess?"

He looked at her again, but so **hard** that she lowered her head, **blushing**. He went on--

"Emma!"

"Sir," she said, drawing back a little.

"Ah! you see," replied he in a melancholy voice, "that I was right not to come back; for this name, this name that **fills** my whole soul, and that escaped me, you **forbid** me to use! Madame Bovary! why all the world **calls** you thus! Besides, it is not your name; it is the name of another!"

He repeated, "of another!" And he hid his face in his hands.

"Yes, I think of you constantly. The **memory** of you **drives** me to despair. Ah! **forgive** me! I will leave you! Farewell! I will go far away, so far that you will never **hear** of me again; and yet-- to-day--I know not what **force impelled** me towards you. For one does not **struggle** against Heaven; one cannot **resist** the smile of angels; one is **carried** away by that which is beautiful, charming, adorable."

It was the first time that Emma had heard such words spoken to herself, and her pride, like one who **reposes bathed** in warmth, **expanded** softly and **fully** at this **glowing** language.

"But if I did not come," he continued, "if I could not see you, at least I have gazed long on all that surrounds you. At night-every night-I arose; I came hither; I watched your house, its glimmering in the moon, the **trees** in the garden swaying before your window, and the little lamp, a gleam shining through the window-panes in the darkness. Ah! you never knew that there, so near you, so far from you, was a **poor** wretch!"

She **turned** towards him with a **sob**.

Spanish

bathed: se bañado.
blushing: ruborizado, rubor.
calls: llama, llamadas.
carried: Llevado, cargado, transportado.
drives: conduce, maneja.
expanded: se expandido.
fills: artículos de relleno, llena.
forbid: prohibir, prohibid, prohiban, prohibo, prohibimos, prohibes, prohiben, prohibe, prohibís, prohiba.
force: fuerza, forzar, obligar, virtud.

forgive: perdonar, perdona, perdonad, perdono, perdonen, perdonas, perdonan, perdonamos, perdonáis, perdone.
fully: completamente.
glowing: resplandeciente.
hard: duro, difícil, tieso.
hear: oír, oigan, oyes, oyen, oye, oís, oigo, oíd, oímos, oiga.
impelled: impulsado, espoleado.
memory: memoria, recuerdo, la memoria.

poor: pobre, malo, deplorable, indigente, miserable.
reposes: reposos.
resist: resistir, resista, resistan, resisto, resistís, resistimos, resistid, resistes, resisten, resiste, oponerse.
sob: sollozar, sollozo.
struggle: batalla, forcejeo, lucha, contienda.
trees: árboles.
turned: girado, vuelto, trastornado.

"Oh, you are good!" she said.

"No, I love you, that is all! You do not doubt that! Tell me--one word--only one word!"

And Rodolphe imperceptibly glided from the footstool to the ground; but a sound of wooden shoes was heard in the **kitchen**, and he noticed the door of the room was not closed.

"How kind it would be of you," he went on, rising, "if you would **humour** a **whim** of mine." It was to go over her house; he wanted to know it; and Madame Bovary seeing no objection to this, they both **rose**, when **Charles** came in.

"Good morning, doctor," Rodolphe said to him.

The doctor, **flattered** at this **unexpected title**, **launched** out into obsequious phrases. Of this the other took **advantage** to **pull** himself together a little.

"Madame was speaking to me," he then said, "about her health."

Charles interrupted him; he had indeed a thousand anxieties; his wife's palpitations of the heart were beginning again. Then Rodolphe asked if **riding** would not be good.

"Certainly! **excellent**! just the thing! There's an idea! You **ought** to **follow** it up."

And as she objected that she had no horse, Monsieur Rodolphe **offered** one. She **refused** his offer; he did not **insist**. Then to explain his visit he said that his ploughman, the man of the **blood**-letting, still **suffered** from giddiness.

"I'll call around," said Bovary.

"No, no! I'll send him to you; we'll come; that will be more convenient for you."

"Ah! very good! I thank you."

And as soon as they were alone, "Why don't you **accept** Monsieur Boulanger's kind offer?"

She **assumed** a **sulky** air, invented a thousand excuses, and **finally** declared that perhaps it would look odd.

Spanish

accept: aceptar, acepta, acepten, acepto, aceptas, aceptan, aceptamos, aceptáis, aceptad, acepte, admitir.
advantage: ventaja, provecho, la ventaja.
assumed: asumido, supuesto.
blood-letting: sangría.
charles: Carlos.
excellent: excelente.
finally: finalmente, al fin, por fin.
flattered: adulado.
follow: seguir, seguid, sigues, siguen,

sigue, sigo, sigan, seguís, seguimos, siga, venir después.
humour: humor.
insist: insistir, insista, insiste, insisto, insistís, insistimos, insistid, insistes, insisten, insistan, instar.
kitchen: cocina, la cocina.
launched: Lanzado.
offered: ofrecido.
ought: haber que, deba, deber, haber de.
pull: tirar, tiramos, tiráis, tirad, tiran,

tiras, tiren, tire, tira, tiro, halar.
refused: rehusado.
riding: paseo a caballo, cabalgar, de equitación, de montar, equitación, ir montado en, montar, paseo, paseo en coche.
rose: rosa, la rosa.
suffered: sufrido, padecido.
sulky: malhumorado.
title: título, titular, título.
unexpected: inesperado, imprevisto.
whim: capricho, antojo.

"Well, what the **deuce** do I care for that?" said Charles, making a **pirouette**. "Health before everything! You are wrong."

"And how do you think I can **ride** when I **haven't** got a habit?"

"You must order one," he answered.

The riding-habit **decided** her.

When the habit was ready, Charles wrote to Monsieur Boulanger that his wife was at his **command**, and that they counted on his good-nature.

The next day at **noon** Rodolphe appeared at Charles's door with two **saddle-horses**. One had pink **rosettes** at his ears and a **deerskin** side-saddle.

Rodolphe had put on high soft boots, saying to himself that no doubt she had never seen anything like them. In fact, Emma was charmed with his appearance as he stood on the **landing** in his great velvet coat and white **corduroy** breeches. She was ready; she was waiting for him.

Justin escaped from the chemist's to see her start, and the chemist also came out. He was giving Monsieur Boulanger a little good **advice**.

"An **accident happens** so **easily**. Be **careful**! Your horses perhaps are mettlesome."

She heard a noise above her; it was Felicite **drumming** on the windowpanes to amuse little Berthe. The child blew her a kiss; her mother answered with a wave of her whip.

"A pleasant ride!" cried Monsieur Homais. "**Prudence**! above all, prudence!" And he **flourished** his **newspaper** as he saw them disappear.

As soon as he felt the ground, Emma's horse set off at a gallop.

Rodolphe **galloped** by her side. Now and then they exchanged a word. Her figure **slightly** bent, her hand well up, and her right arm stretched out, she gave herself up to the cadence of the movement that rocked her in her saddle. At the bottom of the **hill** Rodolphe gave his horse its head; they started together at a bound, then at the top suddenly the horses stopped, and her large **blue** veil fell about her.

Spanish

accident: accidente, desgracia, un accidente, el accidente.
advice: consejo, noticias, asesoramiento, publicación, noticia, el consejo.
blue: azul, azular.
careful: cuidadoso, prudente, circunspecto, precavido.
command: mando, orden, mandato, comando, instrucción, capitanear, acaudillar.
corduroy: pana, la pana.

decided: decidido.
deerskin: piel de ciervo, de gamuza.
deuce: diablo.
drumming: envasado en bidones.
easily: fácilmente.
flourished: florecido.
galloped: galopado.
happens: pasa, acontece, ocurre, sucede, acaece.
haven't: no tener.
hill: colina, loma, cerro, la colina, la loma.

landing: aterrizaje, desembarco, rellano, descansillo.
newspaper: periódico, diario, gaceta.
noon: mediodía.
pirouette: pirueta.
prudence: prudencia.
ride: montar, conducir, paseo, cabalgar, cabalgata.
rosettes: rosetones.
saddle: montura.
slightly: ligeramente, un poco, levemente.

It was early in October. There was fog over the land. **Hazy** clouds **hovered** on the horizon between the outlines of the hills; others, rent asunder, floated up and disappeared. Sometimes through a **rift** in the clouds, beneath a ray of **sunshine**, gleamed from afar the roots of Yonville, with the gardens at the water's edge, the yards, the walls and the church **steeple**. Emma half closed her eyes to pick out her house, and never had this poor village where she lived appeared so small. From the **height** on which they were the whole valley seemed an immense pale **lake** sending off its vapour into the air. Clumps of trees here and there stood out like black **rocks**, and the tall lines of the poplars that rose above the mist were like a **beach** stirred by the wind.

By the side, on the **turf** between the **pines**, a brown light **shimmered** in the warm atmosphere. The earth, **ruddy** like the powder of tobacco, deadened the noise of their steps, and with the edge of their shoes the horses as they walked **kicked** the **fallen fir cones** in front of them.

Rodolphe and Emma thus went along the skirt of the wood. She turned away from time to time to avoid his look, and then she saw only the pine trunks in lines, whose monotonous **succession** made her a little **giddy**. The horses were panting; the leather of the **saddles** creaked.

Just as they were entering the forest the sun shone out.

"God protects us!" said Rodolphe.

"Do you think so?" she said.

"Forward! forward!" he continued.

He "tchk'd" with his **tongue**. The two beasts set off at a trot.

Long ferns by the **roadside** caught in Emma's **stirrup**.

Rodolphe leant forward and **removed** them as they **rode** along. At other times, to turn aside the branches, he passed close to her, and Emma felt his knee **brushing** against her leg. The sky was now blue, the leaves no longer stirred. There were **spaces** full of **heather** in **flower**, and plots of **violets alternated** with the confused patches of the trees that were grey, **fawn**, or golden coloured, according to the nature of their leaves. Often in the **thicket** was heard the

Spanish

alternated: polarización alternada.
beach: playa, la playa, varar.
brushing: cepillado, cepillar.
cones: conos.
fallen: se caído, caído, decrecido, derribado.
fawn: cervato.
fir: abeto.
flower: flor, la flor, florecer.
giddy: mareado.
hazy: brumoso, neblinoso.
heather: brezo.

height: altura, altitud, elevación, la altura, estatura, cerro.
hovered: Cernido, flotado, revoloteado, rondado.
kicked: pateado.
lake: lago, el lago, laca.
pine: pino, languidecer.
removed: quitado, alejado, removido.
rift: hendidura.
roadside: orilla del camino.
rocks: risco.
rode: Cabalgue, pret de ride.

ruddy: rojo.
saddles: monturas para equitación.
shimmered: brilló.
spaces: espacios.
steeple: campanario, torre, aguja.
stirrup: estribo.
succession: sucesión.
sunshine: sol, solana.
thicket: matorral.
tongue: lengua, la lengua, lengüeta.
turf: césped, tepe.
violets: huevas de mar.

fluttering of wings, or else the **hoarse**, soft cry of the ravens **flying** off amidst the oaks.

They **dismounted**. Rodolphe fastened up the horses. She walked on in front on the moss between the **paths**. But her long habit got in her way, although she held it up by the skirt; and Rodolphe, walking behind her, saw between the black cloth and the black **shoe** the **fineness** of her white stocking, that seemed to him as if it were a part of her **nakedness**.

She stopped. "I am tired," she said.

"Come, try again," he went on. "Courage!"

Then some hundred paces farther on she again stopped, and through her veil, that fell **sideways** from her man's hat over her hips, her face appeared in a **bluish transparency** as if she were floating under azure waves.

"But where are we going?"

He did not answer. She was breathing **irregularly**. Rodolphe looked round him biting his **moustache**. They came to a **larger space** where the **coppice** had been cut. They **sat** down on the trunk of a fallen tree, and Rodolphe began **speaking** to her of his love. He did not begin by **frightening** her with compliments. He was calm, **serious**, melancholy.

Emma listened to him with bowed head, and stirred the bits of **wood** on the ground with the tip of her **foot**. But at the words, "Are not our **destinies** now one?"

"Oh, no! she replied. "You know that well. It is impossible!" She rose to go. He seized her by the **wrist**. She stopped. Then, having gazed at him for a few moments with an amorous and **humid** look, she said hurriedly--

"Ah! do not speak of it again! Where are the horses? Let us go back."

He made a gesture of **anger** and **annoyance**. She repeated:

"Where are the horses? Where are the horses?"

Then smiling a strange smile, his pupil fixed, his teeth set, he advanced with outstretched **arms**. She recoiled trembling. She stammered:

Spanish

anger: cólera, enojo, enfado, ira, enojar, furia.
annoyance: molestia.
arms: brazos, los brazos, armas.
bluish: azulado.
coppice: matorral.
destinies: destinos.
dismounted: desmontado.
fineness: ley, fineza, finura.
flying: volando, volante.
foot: pie, pata, el pie, pujamen.
frightening: espantando, asustando,
espantoso.
hoarse: ronco.
humid: húmedo.
irregularly: irregularmente.
larger: Mayor.
moustache: bigote, el bigote.
nakedness: desnudez.
paths: trayectos.
sat: pret y pp de sit, sáb, servicio de administración tributaria, sentado, sábado, soplado, asentado, empollado, se sentado, sentido.
serious: serio, grave, importante, crítico.
shoe: zapato, el zapato, herrar, zapata.
sideways: de lado.
space: espacio, el espacio, espaciar.
speak: hablar, hablamos, hablo, hablas, habláis, hablad, hablen, habla, hablan, hable.
transparency: transparencia.
wood: madera, leño, bosque, la madera.
wrist: muñeca.

"Oh, you frighten me! You hurt me! Let me go!"

"If it must be," he went on, his face changing; and he again became **respectful**, caressing, timid. She gave him her arm. They went back. He said--

"What was the matter with you? Why? I do not understand. You were mistaken, no doubt. In my soul you are as a Madonna on a pedestal, in a place lofty, **secure**, **immaculate**. But I need you to live! I must have your eyes, your voice, your thought! Be my friend, my **sister**, my angel!"

And he put out his arm round her waist. She feebly tried to **disengage** herself. He **supported** her thus as they walked along.

But they heard the two horses **browsing** on the leaves.

"Oh! one moment!" said Rodolphe. "Do not let us go! Stay!"

He drew her farther on to a small **pool** where duckweeds made a **greenness** on the water. Faded water lilies lay motionless between the reeds. At the noise of their steps in the grass, **frogs** jumped away to hide themselves.

"I am wrong! I am wrong!" she said. "I am mad to **listen** to you!"

"Why? Emma! Emma!"

"Oh, Rodolphe!" said the young woman slowly, leaning on his shoulder.

The cloth of her habit caught against the velvet of his coat. She threw back her white neck, **swelling** with a sigh, and **faltering**, in tears, with a long shudder and **hiding** her face, she gave herself up to him--

The shades of night were falling; the horizontal sun passing between the branches dazzled the eyes. Here and there around her, in the leaves or on the ground, trembled luminous patches, as it hummingbirds flying about had scattered their feathers. Silence was everywhere; something sweet seemed to come forth from the trees; she felt her heart, whose beating had begun again, and the blood **coursing** through her **flesh** like a stream of milk. Then far away, **beyond** the wood, on the other hills, she heard a vague prolonged cry, a voice which **lingered**, and in silence she heard it mingling like **music** with the last

Spanish

beyond: más allá de, a través de, luego, después, allende, más allá.
browsing: explorar, hojeada, examen rápido, examinar, navegador, navegar, ojear, vistazo, hojear, navegación, recorrido.
coursing: caza de liebres.
disengage: separar, desembragar.
faltering: titubeando.
flesh: carne, pulpa.
frogs: ranas.
greenness: verdura.

hiding: ocultando, escondiendo, ocultamiento.
immaculate: inmaculado.
lingered: Demorado, quedado, durado, tardado, remoloneado, permanecido, pausado, persistido.
listen: escuchar, escuche, escucha, escuchas, escuchad, escuchen, escucho, escucháis, escuchamos, escuchan, oír.
music: música.
pool: piscina, charco, juntarse, unirse,

charca, consorcio, estanque, la piscina, juego de billar.
respectful: respetuoso.
secure: seguro, fijar, fija, fijen, fije, fijas, fijan, fijamos, fijo, fijad, fijáis.
sister: hermana, la hermana, cuñada.
supported: apoyo, apoyar, sustento, sustentar, sostenido, sostener, sostén, soportar, soportado, manutención, mantener.
swelling: hinchazón, chichón, tumefacción, protuberancia, bulto.

pulsations of her throbbing nerves. Rodolphe, a cigar between his lips, was **mending** with his **penknife** one of the two broken bridles.

They returned to Yonville by the same road. On the mud they saw again the traces of their horses side by side, the same thickets, the same stones to the grass; nothing around them seemed **changed**; and yet for her something had **happened** more **stupendous** than if the **mountains** had **moved** in their places. Rodolphe now and again bent **forward** and took her hand to kiss it.

She was charming on horseback--upright, with her slender waist, her knee bent on the **mane** of her horse, her face somewhat **flushed** by the fresh **air** in the **red** of the evening.

On entering Yonville she made her horse **prance** in the road. People looked at her from the windows.

At dinner her husband thought she looked well, but she pretended not to hear him when he inquired about her ride, and she remained sitting there with her elbow at the side of her plate between the two lighted candles.

"Emma!" he said.

"What?"

"Well, I spent the afternoon at Monsieur Alexandre's. He has an old **cob**, still very **fine**, only a little brokenkneed, and that could be **bought**; I am **sure**, for a **hundred** crowns." He added, "And thinking it might please you, I have **bespoken** it--bought it. Have I done right? Do tell me?"

She nodded her head in **assent**; then a quarter of an **hour** later--

"Are you going out to-night?" she asked.

"Yes. Why?"

"Oh, nothing, nothing, my dear!"

And as soon as she had got rid of Charles she went and shut herself up in her room.

Spanish

air: aire, airear, el aire, aéreo, orear.
assent: asentir, asentimiento, confirmar.
bespoken: indicado, pp de bespeak.
bought: comprado.
changed: cambio, cambió, cambiado.
cob: avellano, cisne, cisne macho, cisne mancho, comer pan redondo, elote, mazorca, jaca, zuro, tusa, panoja.
fine: multa, fino, multar, excelente, bonito, delgado, bien, estupendo, bueno.

flushed: derramarse, sofoco, vaciar, afluir, cisterna, sonrojo, inundar, limpiado, llenarse de agua, rubor, ruborizarse.
forward: adelante, delantero, reenviar, hacia delante, enviar, remitir, hacia adelante.
happened: pasado, acontecido, ocurrido, sucedido, acaecido.
hour: hora, la hora.
hundred: ciento, cien, centenar.
mane: melena, crin.

mending: remendón, reparar, zurcir, ropa de repaso, reparación, remiendo, remendar, ir mejorando, enmendarse, enmendar, apaño.
mountains: sierra, monta a.
moved: emotiva, movido, emocionado, afectado.
penknife: cortaplumas.
prance: cabriola.
red: rojo, tinto, encarnado.
stupendous: estupendo.
sure: seguro, cierto.

At first she felt stunned; she saw the trees, the paths, the ditches, Rodolphe, and she again felt the **pressure** of his arm, while the leaves rustled and the reeds whistled.

But when she saw herself in the **glass** she wondered at her face. Never had her eyes been so large, so black, of so profound a **depth**. Something subtle about her being **transfigured** her. She repeated, "I have a lover! a lover!" **delighting** at the idea as if a second **puberty** had come to her. So at last she was to know those joys of love, that fever of happiness of which she had despairedl She was entering upon marvels where all would be passion, ecstasy, **delirium**. An azure infinity **encompassed** her, the heights of sentiment **sparkled** under her thought, and **ordinary existence** appeared only afar off, down below in the shade, through the interspaces of these heights.

Then she recalled the heroines of the books that she had read, and the **lyric legion** of these adulterous women began to **sing** in her memory with the voice of sisters that charmed her. She became herself, as it were, an **actual** part of these imaginings, and realised the love-dream of her youth as she saw herself in this type of amorous women whom she had so envied. Besides, Emma felt a satisfaction of revenge. Had she not suffered enough? But now she **triumphed**, and the love so long **pent** up burst forth in full joyous bubblings. She tasted it without **remorse**, without anxiety, without **trouble**.

The day following passed with a new sweetness. They made vows to one another She told him of her sorrows. Rodolphe interrupted her with kisses; and she looking at him through half-closed eyes, asked him to call her again by her name--to say that he loved her They were in the **forest**, as yesterday, in the **shed** of some woodenshoe **maker**. The walls were of straw, and the roof so low they had to stoop. They were seated side by side on a bed of dry leaves.

From that day forth they wrote to one another regularly every evening. Emma **placed** her letter at the end of the garden, by the river, in a **fissure** of the wall. Rodolphe came to fetch it, and put another there, that she always found fault with as too short.

Spanish

actual: real, actual, verdadero, efectivo.
delighting: deleitar.
delirium: delirio.
depth: profundidad, hondura, puntal, fondo.
encompassed: rodeado.
existence: existencia.
fissure: hendidura, fisura, grieta.
forest: bosque, el bosque, selva.
glass: vidrio, vaso, cristal, copa, el vidrio.

legion: legión.
lyric: texto.
maker: fabricante.
ordinary: ordinario, común.
pent: reprimido, encerrado.
placed: situado.
pressure: presión, instancia, insistencia, empuje.
puberty: pubertad.
remorse: remordimiento.
shed: cobertizo, derramar, derramáis, derramo, derramen, derrame,

derramas, derramamos, derramado, derramad, derrama.
sing: cantar, cantan, cantas, canten, cantamos, cantáis, canta, cantad, canto, cante.
sparkled: chispeado.
transfigured: Transfigurado.
triumphed: Triunfado.
trouble: molestar, prueba, inconveniente, incomodar, molestia, perturbación, problema, dificultad, avería, esfuerzo.

One morning, when Charles had gone out before day break, she was seized with the fancy to see Rodolphe at once. She would go quickly to La Huchette, stay there an hour, and be back again at Yonville while everyone was still asleep. This idea made her **pant** with desire, and she soon found herself in the middle of the field, walking with rapid steps, without looking behind her.

Day was just **breaking**. Emma from afar **recognised** her lover's house. Its two dove-tailed weathercocks stood out black against the pale **dawn**.

Beyond the farmyard there was a **detached** building that she thought must be the chateau She entered--it was if the doors at her approach had opened wide of their own accord. A large straight staircase led up to the corridor. Emma raised the **latch** of a door, and suddenly at the end of the room she saw a man sleeping. It was Rodolphe. She uttered a cry.

"You here? You here?" he repeated. "How did you **manage** to come? Ah! your dress is damp."

"I love you," she answered, throwing her arms about his neck.

This first piece of daring successful, now every time Charles went out early Emma dressed quickly and **slipped** on tiptoe down the steps that led to the **waterside**.

But when the **plank** for the cows was taken up, she had to go by the walls **alongside** of the river; the bank was slippery; in order not to fall she caught hold of the tufts of faded wallflowers. Then she went across **ploughed** fields, in which she **sank**, **stumbling**; and **clogging** her **thin** shoes. Her scarf, knotted round her head, fluttered to the wind in the meadows. She was **afraid** of the **oxen**; she began to run; she **arrived** out of breath, with rosy cheeks, and breathing out from her whole person a fresh perfume of **sap**, of **verdure**, of the open air. At this hour Rodolphe still slept. It was like a spring morning coming into his room.

The yellow curtains along the windows let a heavy, whitish light enter softly. Emma felt about, **opening** and closing her eyes, while the drops of dew hanging from her hair formed, as it were, a **topaz** aureole around her face. Rodolphe, laughing, drew her to him, and pressed her to his breast.

Spanish

afraid: miedoso, temeroso, asustado, medroso, miedo, encogido, angustioso, tímido, be - tener miedo.
alongside: a lo largo de, junto a, al lado de.
arrived: llegado.
breaking: ruptura, rotura.
clogging: traba, obstructor, estorbar, zueco, obstrucción, obstáculo, estorbo, atrancar, atasco, obstruir, atascamiento.
dawn: amanecer, alba, madrugada,

aurora.
detached: destacado, separado, aislado.
latch: pestillo, cerrojo.
manage: administrar, administras, administro, administren, administre, administrad, administráis, administramos, administra, administran, mandar.
opening: abriendo, abertura, apertura, entrada, inauguración, abrir.
oxen: buey.

pant: jadear.
plank: tabla, tablón.
ploughed: aró.
recognised: reconocido, reconocico.
sank: pret de sink.
sap: savia, jugo, zumo.
slipped: resbalado.
stumbling: tropezar.
thin: delgado, fino, flaco, ralo.
topaz: topacio.
verdure: verdura.
waterside: ribera.

Then she **examined** the **apartment**, opened the **drawers** of the **tables**, **combed** her **hair** with his comb, and looked at herself in his shaving-glass. Often she even put between her teeth the big **pipe** that lay on the table by the bed, **amongst lemons** and **pieces** of **sugar near** a **bottle** of water.

It took them a good quarter of an hour to say **goodbye**. Then Emma **cried**. She would have **wished** never to **leave** Rodolphe. Something stronger than herself **forced** her to him; so much so, that one day, seeing her come **unexpectedly**, he frowned as one put out.

"What is the **matter** with you?" she said. "Are you **ill**? Tell me!"

At last he **declared** with a serious air that her **visits** were **becoming** imprudent--that she was **compromising** herself.

Spanish

amongst: entre.
apartment: apartamento, piso, cuarto.
becoming: conveniente, aconteciendo.
bed: cama, lecho, cauce, la cama, bancada, cuadro, madre.
bottle: botella, la botella, embotellar, vaciar, frasco, biberón.
comb: peine, peinar, el peine.
combed: peinado.
compromising: comprometido, comprometedor.
cried: Lloró.

declared: declarado.
drawers: calzoncillos.
examined: examinado, registrado.
forced: forzado.
goodbye: adiós, despedida, hasta luego, hasta la vista.
hair: pelo, cabello, el pelo, vello.
ill: enfermo, malo, doliente.
leave: salir, sal, sale, salís, salimos, salgo, salgan, salga, sales, salen, saled.
lemons: limones.

matter: materia, asunto, particular, caso, importar.
near: cerca, próximo, cerca de, cercano, entrante, casi.
pieces: material de artillería.
pipe: pipa, cañería, tubo, tubería, conducto, la pipa.
sugar: azúcar, azucarar.
tables: mesas, tablas.
unexpectedly: inesperadamente.
visits: visita.
wished: deseado.

CHAPTER TEN

Gradually Rodolphe's fears took possession of her. At first, love had **intoxicated** her; and she had thought of nothing beyond. But now that he was **indispensable** to her life, she feared to lose anything of this, or even that it should be disturbed. When she came back from his house she looked all about her, **anxiously** watching every form that passed in the horizon, and every village window from which she could be seen. She listened for steps, cries, the noise of the **ploughs**, and she stopped short, white, and trembling more than the **aspen** leaves **swaying overhead**.

One morning as she was thus **returning**, she suddenly thought she saw the long barrel of a **carbine** that seemed to be **aimed** at her. It stuck out sideways from the end of a small **tub** half-buried in the grass on the edge of a ditch. Emma, half-fainting with **terror**, nevertheless walked on, and a man **stepped** out of the tub like a Jack-in-the-box. He had gaiters **buckled** up to the knees, his cap pulled down over his eyes, trembling lips, and a red nose. It was Captain Binet **lying** in **ambush** for **wild** ducks.

"You ought to have called out long ago!" he exclaimed; "When one **sees** a **gun**, one should always give warning."

The **tax**-collector was thus trying to hide the **fright** he had had, for a prefectorial order having **prohibited** duckhunting **except** in boats, Monsieur Binet, despite his **respect** for the **laws**, was **infringing** them, and so he every

Spanish

aimed: Apuntado.
ambush: emboscada, acecho.
anxiously: ansiosamente.
aspen: Álamo.
buckled: Abrochado.
carbine: carabina.
except: excepto, menos, exceptuar, además de, amén de.
fright: espanto, susto, miedo, angustia, terror.
gun: escopeta, pistola, fusil, arma de fuego.

indispensable: imprescindible, necesario, indispensable.
infringing: infringiendo.
intoxicated: ebrio, intoxicado, borracho, aturdido.
laws: las leyes.
lying: mentiroso.
overhead: arriba, gastos generales.
ploughs: arados.
prohibited: prohibido.
respect: respetar, respeto, estima, estimación.

returning: volver.
sees: Ve, serra.
stepped: escalonado.
swaying: oscilación, oscilar, ladearse, tambalear, vaivén, que balancea, oscilante, mimbrear, influir en, inclinarse, inclinación lateral.
tax-collector: exactor.
terror: terror.
tub: bañera.
wild: fiero, salvaje, silvestre.

moment **expected** to see the **rural guard** turn up. But this anxiety **whetted** his pleasure, and, all alone in his tub, he **congratulated** himself on his **luck** and on his **cuteness**. At sight of Emma he seemed relieved from a great **weight**, and at once entered upon a conversation.

"It isn't warm; it's nipping."

Emma answered nothing. He went on--

"And you're out so early?"

"Yes," she said stammering; "I am just coming from the nurse where my child is."

"Ah! very good! very good! For myself, I am here, just as you see me, since **break** of day; but the weather is so **muggy**, that **unless** one had the **bird** at the **mouth** of the gun--"

"Good evening, Monsieur Binet," she interrupted him, turning on her heel.

"Your servant, madame," he replied **drily**; and he went back into his tub.

Emma regretted having left the tax-collector so **abruptly**. No doubt he would form **unfavourable** conjectures. The story about the nurse was the **worst** possible excuse, everyone at Yonville knowing that the little Bovary had been at home with her parents for a year. Besides, no one was **living** in this **direction**; this path **led** only to La Huchette. Binet, then, would guess whence she came, and he would not keep silence; he would talk, that was certain. She remained until evening **racking** her brain with every **conceivable** lying project, and had constantly before her eyes that imbecile with the **game**-bag.

Charles after dinner, seeing her gloomy, proposed, by way of distraction, to take her to the chemist's, and the first person she caught sight of in the **shop** was the taxcollector again. He was standing in front of the **counter**, lit up by the gleams of the red bottle, and was saying--

"Please give me half an **ounce** of vitriol."

"Justin," cried the druggist, "bring us the **sulphuric** acid." Then to Emma, who was going up to Madame Homais' room, "No, stay here; it isn't **worth** while

Spanish

abruptly: bruscamente, abruptamente.
bird: pájaro, ave.
break: romper, descanso, interrupción, rotura, quebrar, corte, pausa, adiestrar, fractura, interrumpir.
conceivable: concebible.
congratulated: Felicitado, congratulado.
counter: contador, mostrador, barra.
cuteness: monería, gracia.
direction: dirección, rumbo.
drily: secamente.

expected: esperado, previsto.
game-bag: escarcela.
guard: guardia, guardar, vigilar, cobrador, guarda, revisor, defender, proteger, amparar.
led: guiado, conducido, dirigido.
living: viviendo, habitando, vivo, viviente.
luck: suerte, la suerte.
mouth: boca, desembocadura, la boca.
muggy: húmedo, bochornoso.
ounce: onza.

racking: trasiego.
rural: rústico, campestre, rural.
shop: tienda, hacer las compras, ir de compras, almacén, taller.
sulphuric: sulfúrico.
unfavourable: desfavorable.
unless: a menos que, a no ser que.
weight: peso, carga, el peso, asignar un peso a, la pesa, pesa.
whetted: Afilado.
worst: peor.
worth: valor.

going up; she is just coming down. Warm yourself at the stove in the meantime. Excuse me. Good-day, doctor," (for the chemist much **enjoyed pronouncing** the word "doctor," as if addressing another by it reflected on himself some of the **grandeur** that he found in it). "Now, take care not to upset the mortars! You'd better fetch some chairs from the little room; you know very well that the arm-chairs are not to be taken out of the drawing-room."

And to put his arm-chair back in its place he was **darting** away from the counter, when Binet asked him for half an ounce of sugar **acid**.

"Sugar acid!" said the chemist **contemptuously**, "don't know it; I'm ignorant of it! But perhaps you want **oxalic** acid. It is oxalic acid, isn't it?"

Binet explained that he wanted a **corrosive** to make himself some copperwater with which to **remove rust** from his hunting things.

Emma shuddered. The chemist began saying--

"Indeed the weather is not **propitious** on account of the damp."

"Nevertheless," replied the tax-collector, with a sly look, "there are people who like it."

She was stifling.

"And give me--"

"Will he never go?" thought she.

"Half an ounce of **resin** and **turpentine**, four ounces of **yellow** wax, and three half ounces of **animal charcoal**, if you please, to **clean** the **varnished** leather of my togs."

The druggist was beginning to cut the wax when Madame Homais appeared, Irma in her arms, Napoleon by her side, and Athalie following. She sat down on the velvet seat by the window, and the lad **squatted** down on a footstool, while his **eldest** sister hovered round the **jujube** box near her **papa**. The latter was **filling** funnels and **corking** phials, sticking on labels, making up parcels. Around him all were silent; only from time to time, were heard the weights **jingling** in the **balance**, and a few low words from the chemist giving directions to his pupil.

Spanish

acid: ácido, agrio, agudo, afilado.
animal: bestia, animal, el animal.
balance: equilibrio, saldo, balancear, balanza, balance, saldar, equilibrar.
charcoal: carbón, carbón de leña, carbón vegetal.
clean: limpio, limpiar, limpiáis, limpiad, limpien, limpie, limpias, limpiamos, limpian, limpia, puro.
contemptuously: desdeñosamente.
corking: estupendo, corcho, de primera, excelente, encorchar,

taponar.
corrosive: corrosivo.
darting: rápido.
eldest: mayor.
enjoyed: disfrutado, gozado.
filling: relleno, empaste.
grandeur: grandeza.
jingling: tintineando, cascabeleo.
jujube: pastilla, jinjolero, azufaifa, azufaifo.
low: bajo, depresión.
oxalic: oxálico.

papa: papá.
pronouncing: pronunciando.
propitious: propicio, favorable.
remove: quitar, eliminar, quite, quiten, quitas, quitan, quitamos, quito, quitad, quita, quitáis.
resin: resina.
rust: óxido, herrumbre, moho, oxidación, el moho, aherrumbrar.
squatted: agachado.
turpentine: trementina.
varnished: barnizado.

"And how's the little woman?" suddenly asked Madame Homais.

"Silence!" exclaimed her husband, who was **writing** down some **figures** in his waste-book.

"Why didn't you **bring** her?" she went on in a low voice.

"**Hush!** hush!" said Emma, pointing with her finger to the druggist.

But Binet, quite absorbed in looking over his **bill**, had probably heard nothing. At last he went out. Then Emma, relieved, uttered a **deep** sigh.

"How hard you are breathing!" said Madame Homais.

"Well, you see, it's rather warm," she replied.

So the next day they talked over how to **arrange** their **rendezvous**. Emma wanted to **bribe** her servant with a present, but it would be better to find some **safe** house at Yonville. Rodolphe **promised** to look for one.

All through the winter, three or four times a week, in the **dead** of night he came to the garden. Emma had on **purpose** taken away the key of the gate, which Charles thought **lost**.

To call her, Rodolphe threw a **sprinkle** of sand at the shutters. She jumped up with a start; but sometimes he had to **wait**, for Charles had a mania for chatting by the fireside, and he would not **stop**. She was wild with impatience; if her eyes could have done it, she would have **hurled** him out at the window. At last she would begin to **undress**, then take up a book, and go on **reading** very quietly as if the book amused her. But Charles, who was in bed, called to her to come too.

"Come, now, Emma," he said, "it is time."

"Yes, I am coming," she answered.

Then, as the candles dazzled him; he turned to the wall and fell asleep. She escaped, smiling, palpitating, undressed. Rodolphe had a large cloak; he wrapped her in it, and putting his arm round her waist, he drew her without a word to the end of the garden.

Spanish

arrange: arreglar, arreglen, arreglan, arreglamos, arregláis, arregla, arreglad, arreglas, arreglo, arregle, organizar.
bill: cuenta, billete, pico, factura, proyecto de ley, podadera, efecto, letra de cambio, nota, facturar.
bribe: soborno, sobornar, cohecho, cohechar.
bring: traer, traigan, trae, traed, traéis, traemos, traen, traigo, traes, traiga, llevar.
dead: muerto.
deep: profundo, hondo.
figures: cifras.
hurled: arrojado, lanzado, tirado.
hush: silencio, acallar.
lost: perdido, adelgazado.
promised: prometido.
purpose: fin, objeto, finalidad, propósito, intención.
reading: leyendo, lectura, la lectura.
rendezvous: cita.
safe: seguro, caja fuerte, salvo, a salvo, caja de caudales.
sprinkle: salpicar, espolvorear, rociar.
stop: parar, paran, paras, paren, paráis, parad, paramos, pare, para, paro, parada.
undress: bata, desnudarse, desnudar, desvestir.
wait: esperar, espera, espere, esperad, espero, esperen, esperas, esperan, esperamos, esperáis, aguardar.
writing: escribiendo, escritura, letra, inscripción.

It was in the arbour, on the same seat of old sticks where formerly Leon had looked at her so **amorously** on the summer evenings. She never thought of him now.

The **stars** shone through the leafless jasmine branches. Behind them they heard the river flowing, and now and again on the bank the rustling of the dry reeds. Masses of shadow here and there **loomed** out in the darkness, and sometimes, **vibrating** with one movement, they rose up and swayed like immense black waves pressing forward to engulf them. The cold of the nights made them clasp closer; the sighs of their lips seemed to them deeper; their eyes that they could hardly see, larger; and in the midst of the silence low words were spoken that fell on their souls sonorous, **crystalline**, and that **reverberated** in multiplied **vibrations**.

When the night was rainy, they took **refuge** in the consulting-room between the cart-shed and the **stable**. She lighted one of the kitchen candles that she had hidden behind the books. Rodolphe **settled** down there as if at home. The sight of the **library**, of the bureau, of the whole apartment, in fine, **excited** his **merriment**, and he could not **refrain** from making jokes about Charles, which rather embarrassed Emma. She would have liked to see him more serious, and even on occasions more **dramatic**; as, for example, when she thought she heard a noise of **approaching** steps in the **alley**.

"Someone is coming!" she said.

He blew out the light.

"Have you your pistols?"

"Why?"

"Why, to **defend** yourself," replied Emma.

"From your husband? Oh, poor devil!" And Rodolphe finished his sentence with a gesture that said, "I could **crush** him with a **flip** of my finger."

She was wonder-stricken at his **bravery**, although she felt in it a sort of **indecency** and a naive **coarseness** that **scandalised** her.

Spanish

alley: callejón, calleja.
amorously: amorosamente, tiernamente.
approaching: acercamiento, acercar, aproximado, acercarse, aproximar, aproximarse, dirigirse a uno, venidero, tocar un tema, semejante, que se acerca.
bravery: valentía, el valor.
coarseness: grosería.
crush: compresión, aplastar.
crystalline: cristalino.

defend: defender, defiendes, defiendo, defendéis, defendemos, defiendan, defienden, defended, defiende, defienda.
dramatic: dramático.
excited: excitado, instigado, emocionado.
flip: capirotazo, poco serio, invertir, echar de un capirotazo, arrojar, Voltear, tablero flipchart, girar.
indecency: indecencia.
library: biblioteca, la biblioteca.

loomed: Asomado.
merriment: alegría.
refrain: estribillo, abstenerse.
refuge: refugio, asilo.
reverberated: reverberado.
scandalised: escandalizado.
settled: despachado.
stable: cuadra, establo, estable, fijo, caballeriza.
stars: estrellas.
vibrating: vibrando.
vibrations: vibraciones, vibración.

Rodolphe reflected a good deal on the affair of the pistols. If she had spoken **seriously**, it was very **ridiculous**, he thought, even odious; for he had no reason to hate the good Charles, not being what is called devoured by jealousy; and on this subject Emma had taken a great vow that he did not think in the best of taste.

Besides, she was growing very sentimental. She had **insisted** on **exchanging** miniatures; they had cut off handfuls of hair, and now she was asking for a ring-- a real wedding-ring, in sign of an eternal union. She often spoke to him of the evening chimes, of the voices of nature. Then she talked to him of her mother-- hers! and of his mother--his! Rodolphe had lost his twenty years ago. Emma **none** the less consoled him with caressing words as one would have done a lost child, and she sometimes even said to him, **gazing** at the moon

"I am sure that above there together they **approve** of our love."

But she was so pretty. He had possessed so few women of such **ingenuousness**. This love without **debauchery** was a new experience for him, and, drawing him out of his **lazy** habits, **caressed** at once his pride and his **sensuality**. Emma's enthusiasm, which his bourgeois good sense **disdained**, seemed to him in his heart of hearts charming, since it was **lavished** on him. Then, sure of being loved, he no longer kept up **appearances**, and **insensibly** his ways changed.

He had no longer, as formerly, words so gentle that they made her cry, nor passionate caresses that made her mad, so that their great love, which **engrossed** her life, seemed to **lessen** beneath her like the water of a stream absorbed into its **channel**, and she could see the bed of it. She would not believe it; she **redoubled** in tenderness, and Rodolphe concealed his indifference less and less.

She did not know if she regretted having yielded to him, or whether she did not wish, on the contrary, to **enjoy** him the more. The **humiliation** of feeling herself weak was turning to **rancour**, tempered by their voluptuous pleasures. It was not affection; it was like a **continual** seduction. He **subjugated** her; she almost feared him.

Spanish

appearances: apariciones.
approve: aprobar, aprueban, apruebo, apruebas, aprueba, aprobamos, aprobáis, aprobad, aprueben, apruebe.
caressed: Cariciado.
channel: canal, cauce, estrecho, conducto.
continual: continuo.
debauchery: libertinaje.
disdained: desdeñado.
engrossed: acaparado, copiado,

absorbido, absorto.
enjoy: disfrutar, disfrutas, disfrutan, disfrutamos, disfrutáis, disfrutad, disfruta, disfruto, disfruten, disfrute, gozar.
exchanging: cambiar.
gazing: mirar.
humiliation: humillación.
ingenuousness: ingenuidad.
insensibly: insensiblemente.
insisted: insistido, instado.
lavished: Prodigó.

lazy: perezoso, holgazán, vago, guapo.
lessen: minorar, achicar, disminuir, minora, minore, minoras, minoran, minoramos, achicas, minoráis, minoro.
none: ninguno, nadie, nada.
rancour: encono, ojeriza, rencor.
redoubled: redoblado.
ridiculous: ridículo.
sensuality: sensualidad.
seriously: seriamente, gravemente.
subjugated: subyugado.

Appearances, nevertheless, were calmer than ever, Rodolphe having **succeeded** in carrying out the **adultery** after his own fancy; and at the end of six months, when the spring-time came, they were to one another like a married couple, **tranquilly** keeping up a domestic flame.

It was the time of year when old Rouault sent his turkey in remembrance of the setting of his **leg**. The present always arrived with a letter. Emma cut the string that **tied** it to the basket, and read the following lines:--

"My Dear Children--I hope this will find you well, and that this one will be as good as the others. For it seems to me a little more tender, if I may venture to say so, and heavier. But next time, for a change, I'll give you a turkeycock, unless you have a **preference** for some dabs; and send me back the **hamper**, if you please, with the two old ones. I have had an accident with my cart-sheds, whose covering flew off one windy night among the trees. The **harvest** has not been overgood either. Finally, I don't know when I shall come to see you. It is so difficult now to leave the house since I am alone, my poor Emma."

Here there was a break in the lines, as if the old fellow had **dropped** his pen to dream a little while.

"For myself, I am very well, except for a cold I caught the other day at the fair at Yvetot, where I had gone to **hire** a **shepherd**, having turned away **mine** because he was too dainty. How we are to be pitied with such a lot of **thieves**! Besides, he was also **rude**. I heard from a pedlar, who, **travelling** through your part of the country this winter, had a **tooth** drawn, that Bovary was as usual working hard. That doesn't surprise me; and he showed me his tooth; we had some coffee together. I asked him if he had seen you, and he said not, but that he had seen two horses in the stables, from which I **conclude** that business is looking up. So much the better, my dear children, and may God send you every imaginable happiness! It **grieves** me not yet to have seen my dear little **grand-daughter**, Berthe Bovary. I have planted an Orleans **plum**-tree for her in the garden under your room, and I won't have it **touched** unless it is to have **jam** made for her by and **bye**, that I will keep in the cupboard for her when she comes.

Spanish

adultery: adulterio.
bye: adiós, hasta luego, hasta la vista.
conclude: despachar, despacháis, despacho, despachen, despache, despachas, despachan, despachamos, despacha, despachad, concluir.
dropped: soltar.
grand-daughter: nieta.
grieves: aflige, apena.
hamper: dificultar, cesta, canasta.
harvest: cosecha, cosechar, siega, recolección, vendimia.

hire: alquilar, arrendar, alquila, alquilo, alquilen, alquile, alquilas, alquilan, alquilamos, alquilad, alquiláis.
jam: mermelada.
leg: pierna, la pierna, pata, tramo.
mine: mina, mío, minar.
plum-tree: ciruelo.
preference: preferencia.
rude: grosero, rudo, insolente, descortés.
shepherd: pastor.

succeeded: conseguido.
thieves: ladrones, roba.
tied: atado.
tooth: diente, el diente.
touched: palpar, tocar, tocado, pulsación, toque, emocionado, conmover, chiflado, alcanzar, tacto, conmovido.
tranquilly: tranquilamente.
travelling: corredizo, de viaje, ambulante, el viajar, itinerante, viajar, viajes.

"Good-bye, my dear children. I kiss you, my girl, you too, my son-in-law, and the little one on both cheeks. I am, with best compliments, your loving father.

"Theodore Rouault."

She held the coarse paper in her fingers for some minutes. The **spelling mistakes** were interwoven one with the other, and Emma followed the **kindly** thought that **cackled** right through it like a hen half hidden in the hedge of thorns. The writing had been dried with **ashes** from the hearth, for a little grey powder slipped from the letter on to her dress, and she almost thought she saw her father bending over the hearth to take up the tongs. How long since she had been with him, sitting on the footstool in the chimney-corner, where she used to burn the end of a **bit** of wood in the great flame of the sea-sedges! She remembered the **summer** evenings all full of sunshine. The colts neighed when anyone passed by, and galloped, galloped. Under her window there was a **beehive**, and sometimes the bees **wheeling** round in the light struck against her window like **rebounding** balls of gold. What happiness there had been at that time, what **freedom**, what hope! What an **abundance** of illusions! Nothing was left of them now. She had got rid of them all in her soul's life, in all her **successive** conditions of lifemaidenhood, her marriage, and her love--thus constantly **losing** them all her life through, like a traveller who leaves something of his **wealth** at every inn along his road.

But what then, made her so unhappy? What was the extraordinary **catastrophe** that had **transformed** her? And she raised her head, looking round as if to **seek** the cause of that which made her **suffer**.

An April ray was dancing on the china of the **whatnot**; the fire **burned**; beneath her slippers she felt the softness of the carpet; the day was bright, the air warm, and she heard her child shouting with **laughter**.

In fact, the little girl was just then rolling on the **lawn** in the midst of the grass that was being turned. She was lying flat on her **stomach** at the top of a **rick**. The servant was holding her by her skirt. Lestiboudois was **raking** by her side, and every time he came near she lent forward, beating the air with both her arms.

Spanish

abundance: abundancia, riqueza.
ashes: cenizas.
beehive: colmena.
bit: pedazo, tela, trozo, broca.
burned: quemó.
cackled: Cacareó.
catastrophe: catástrofe.
freedom: libertad.
kindly: amablemente, bondadosamente, amable.
laughter: risa, la risa, carcajada.
lawn: césped, el césped, batista, el prado.
losing: perdiendo, perdedor, adelgazando.
mistakes: errores.
raking: rastrillaje, rastro, atizar, rastrear, rasguear, rastrillar, rastrillo.
rebounding: rebotar.
rick: almiar.
seek: buscar, busque, busca, buscan, buscamos, busquen, buscas, buscáis, buscad, busco.
spelling: ortografía.
stomach: estómago, aguantar.
successive: sucesivo.
suffer: sufrir, sufres, sufro, sufrís, sufrid, sufren, sufre, sufran, sufrimos, sufra, padecer.
summer: verano, el verano, estival.
transformed: transformado.
wealth: riqueza, abundancia, caudal.
whatnot: estante, cualquier cosa.
wheeling: rodar, transporte, ruedas, ruedo, rueden, ruede, rueda, rodamos, rodáis, rodad, ruedan.

"Bring her to me," said her mother, **rushing** to **embrace** her. "How I love you, my poor child! How I love you!"

Then **noticing** that the **tips** of her ears were rather dirty, she rang at once for warm water, and washed her, changed her **linen**, her **stockings**, her shoes, asked a thousand **questions** about her health, as if on the return from a long **journey**, and finally, **kissing** her again and crying a little, she gave her back to the servant, who **stood** quite thunderstricken at this excess of tenderness.

That evening Rodolphe found her more serious than usual.

"That will pass over," he **concluded**; "it's a whim:"

And he missed three **rendezvous** running. When he did come, she **showed** herself cold and almost **contemptuous**.

"Ah! you're losing your time, my lady!"

And he **pretended** not to **notice** her **melancholy** sighs, **nor** the **handkerchief** she took out.

Then Emma **repented**. She even asked herself why she **detested** Charles; if it had not been better to have been able to love him? But he gave her no opportunities for such a **revival** of **sentiment**, so that she was much embarrassed by her desire for **sacrifice**, when the **druggist** came just in time to provide her with an **opportunity**.

Spanish

concluded: despachado.
contemptuous: despectivo, despreciativo.
detested: detestado.
druggist: droguero.
embrace: abrazar, abarcar.
handkerchief: pañuelo.
journey: viaje, viajar.
kissing: besar.
linen: lino, lencería, ropa blanca.
melancholy: melancolía, melancólico.
nor: ni, tampoco.

notice: cartel, aviso, anuncio, notar, advertir, nota, notificación, noticias, noticia, percibir, publicación.
noticing: notando.
opportunity: acontecimiento, oportunidad, ocasión.
pretended: fingido, pretendido.
questions: preguntas.
rendezvous: cita.
repented: Arrepentido, se arrepentido.
revival: reavivamiento, resurgimiento, reanimación.

rushing: apresurar.
sacrifice: sacrificio, sacrificar, ofrecer, presentar.
sentiment: sentimiento, opinión, sensibilidad, parecer, sentimentalismo.
showed: mostrado, pret de show.
stockings: las medias.
stood: pret y pp de stand.
tips: propinas.

CHAPTER ELEVEN

He had recently read a **eulogy** on a new method for curing club-foot, and as he was a **partisan** of progress, he **conceived** the patriotic idea that Yonville, in order to keep to the **fore**, ought to have some **operations** for strephopody or club-foot.

"For," said he to Emma, "what risk is there? See--" (and he **enumerated** on his fingers the **advantages** of the attempt), "success, almost certain **relief** and **beautifying** of the patient, **celebrity acquired** by the **operator**. Why, for example, should not your husband **relieve** poor Hippolyte of the 'Lion d'Or'? Note that he would not **fail** to tell about his cure to all the travellers, and then" (Homais lowered his voice and looked round him) "who is to **prevent** me from sending a short **paragraph** on the subject to the paper? Eh! goodness me! an article gets about; it is talked of; it ends by making a **snowball**! And who knows? who knows?"

In fact, Bovary might **succeed**. Nothing **proved** to Emma that he was not clever; and what a satisfaction for her to have urged him to a step by which his reputation and fortune would be increased! She only wished to lean on something more **solid** than love.

Charles, urged by the druggist and by her, allowed himself to be **persuaded**. He sent to Rouen for Dr. Duval's **volume**, and every evening, holding his head between both hands, plunged into the reading of it.

Spanish

acquired: adquirido.
advantages: ventajas.
beautifying: embelleciendo.
celebrity: celebridad.
conceived: concebido.
eh: cómo.
enumerated: enumerado.
eulogy: elogio.
fail: fallar, fracasar, faltar.
fore: frente, delantero.
operations: operaciones.
operator: operador, operadora, operario, corredor de bolsa.
paragraph: párrafo, apartado, parágrafo.
partisan: partidista, partisano.
persuaded: convencido, persuadido.
prevent: impedir, impedid, impido, impides, impiden, impide, impidan, impida, impedimos, impedís, prevenir.
proved: evidenciar, demostrar, pret de prove, probado, probar, poner a prueba.
relief: alivio, relieve, socorro, asistencia, relevo.
relieve: aliviar, alivie, alivias, aliviad, alivio, alivien, aliviamos, aliviáis, alivian, alivia, relevar.
snowball: bola de nieve.
solid: sólido, fuerte, macizo.
succeed: tener éxito, conseguir, consigan, consiguen, consigue, consigo, conseguís, conseguimos, conseguid, consigues, consiga.
volume: volumen, tomo.

While he was studying equinus, varus, and valgus, that is to say, katastrephopody, endostrephopody, and exostrephopody (or better, the various **turnings** of the foot downwards, **inwards**, and **outwards**, with the hypostrephopody and anastrephopody), otherwise **torsion** downwards and **upwards**, Monsier Homais, with all sorts of arguments, was **exhorting** the lad at the inn to **submit** to the operation.

"You will **scarcely** feel, probably, a slight pain; it is a simple prick, like a little blood-letting, less than the **extraction** of certain corns."

Hippolyte, **reflecting**, rolled his stupid eyes.

"However," continued the chemist, "it doesn't concern me. It's for your **sake**, for pure humanity! I should like to see you, my friend, rid of your **hideous** caudication, together with that **waddling** of the **lumbar regions** which, whatever you say, must **considerably** interfere with you in the exercise of your calling."

Then Homais **represented** to him how much jollier and brisker he would feel afterwards, and even gave him to understand that he would be more likely to please the women; and the stable-boy began to smile **heavily**. Then he **attacked** him through his vanity:

"Aren't you a man? **Hang** it! what would you have done if you had had to go into the army, to go and fight beneath the standard? Ah! Hippolyte!"

And Homais retired, **declaring** that he could not understand this obstinacy, this **blindness** in **refusing** the **benefactions** of science.

The poor fellow gave way, for it was like a conspiracy. Binet, who never interfered with other people's business, Madame Lefrancois, Artemise, the neighbours, even the mayor, Monsieur Tuvache--everyone persuaded him, lectured him, **shamed** him; but what finally decided him was that it would cost him nothing. Bovary even undertook to provide the machine for the operation. This **generosity** was an idea of Emma's, and Charles consented to it, thinking in his heart of hearts that his wife was an **angel**.

So by the advice of the chemist, and after three fresh starts, he had a kind of box made by the **carpenter**, with the aid of the **locksmith**, that **weighed** about

Spanish

angel: ángel.
attacked: Atacado.
benefactions: donaciones.
blindness: ceguera.
carpenter: carpintero, el carpintero.
considerably: considerablemente.
declaring: declarando.
exhorting: exhortando.
extraction: extracción.
generosity: generosidad.
hang: colgar.
heavily: pesadamente, fuertemente.

hideous: horroroso, abominable, horrible.
inwards: tripas, hacia el centro, hacia adentro.
locksmith: cerrajero, el cerrajero.
lumbar: lumbar.
outwards: exteriormente, hacia fuera, exterior.
reflecting: reflejando.
refusing: Rehusar.
regions: regiones.
represented: representado.

sake: motivo, fin, bien, causa.
scarcely: apenas, escasamente.
shamed: avergonzado.
submit: someter, sometan, sometes, someto, someten, sometemos, sometéis, someted, somete, someta, presentar.
torsion: torsión.
turnings: torneaduras.
upwards: hacia arriba.
waddling: zanqueamiento, Anadear.
weighed: Pesado.

eight pounds, and in which iron, wood, sheer-iron, leather, **screws**, and nuts had not been spared.

But to know which of Hippolyte's **tendons** to cut, it was necessary first of all to find out what kind of club-foot he had.

He had a foot **forming** almost a straight line with the leg, which, however, did not prevent it from being turned in, so that it was an equinus together with something of a varus, or else a slight varus with a strong **tendency** to equinus. But with this equinus, wide in foot like a horse's **hoof**, with rugose skin, dry tendons, and large **toes**, on which the black nails looked as if made of iron, the **clubfoot** ran about like a **deer** from **morn** till night. He was constantly to be seen on the Place, jumping round the carts, **thrusting** his limping foot **forwards**. He seemed even stronger on that leg than the other. By dint of hard service it had acquired, as it were, **moral** qualities of **patience** and energy; and when he was given some heavy work, he stood on it in preference to its fellow.

Now, as it was an equinus, it was necessary to cut the tendon of Achilles, and, if need were, the **anterior** tibial **muscle** could be seen to afterwards for getting rid of the varus; for the doctor did not dare to risk both operations at once; he was even trembling already for fear of **injuring** some important region that he did not know.

Neither Ambrose Pare, **applying** for the first time since Celsus, after an **interval** of fifteen centuries, a **ligature** to an **artery**, nor Dupuytren, about to open an abscess in the brain, nor Gensoul when he first took away the **superior maxilla**, had hearts that trembled, hands that shook, minds so **strained** as Monsieur Bovary when he **approached** Hippolyte, his tenotome between his fingers. And as at **hospitals**, near by on a table lay a heap of **lint**, with waxed thread, many bandages--a **pyramid** of bandages--every bandage to be found at the druggist's. It was Monsieur Homais who since morning had been **organising** all these preparations, as much to **dazzle** the multitude as to keep up his illusions. Charles pierced the skin; a dry **crackling** was heard. The tendon was cut, the operation over. Hippolyte could not get over his surprise, but bent over Bovary's hands to cover them with kisses.

Spanish

anterior: anterior, anterior a, previo.
applying: aplicando, empleando.
approached: Acercado.
artery: arteria.
clubfoot: pata de palo.
crackling: crepitaciones.
dazzle: deslumbrar, deslumbramiento.
deer: ciervo, venado.
forming: formación.
forwards: adelante.
hoof: pezuña, casco.
hospitals: hospitales.

injuring: hiriendo.
interval: intervalo, intervalo logarítmico de frecuencia.
ligature: ligadura.
lint: hilas.
maxilla: maxilar superior.
moral: moral, moraleja.
morn: mañana.
muscle: músculo.
organising: organizar.
patience: paciencia.
pyramid: pirámide.

screws: tornillos.
strained: torcer, entiesar, torcido, torcedura, tirantez, tirante, tenso, tensión, rasgo heredado, poner tirante, pasado.
superior: jefe, superior.
tendency: tendencia, tentación.
tendon: tendón.
tendons: tendones.
thrusting: empujar.
toes: dedos del pie, los dedos de los pies.

"Come, be calm," said the druggist; "later on you will show your gratitude to your benefactor."

And he went down to tell the result to five or six inquirers who were waiting in the **yard**, and who fancied that Hippolyte would **reappear** walking **properly**. Then Charles, having buckled his patient into the machine, went home, where Emma, all anxiety, **awaited** him at the door. She threw herself on his neck; they sat down to table; he ate much, and at dessert he even wanted to take a cup of coffee, a luxury he only permitted himself on Sundays when there was company.

The evening was charming, full of **prattle**, of dreams together. They talked about their future fortune, of the improvements to be made in their house; he saw people's **estimation** of him **growing**, his comforts **increasing**, his wife always loving him; and she was happy to **refresh** herself with a new sentiment, healthier, better, to feel at last some tenderness for this poor fellow who adored her. The thought of Rodolphe for one moment passed through her mind, but her eyes turned again to Charles; she even noticed with surprise that he had not bad teeth.

They were in bed when Monsieur Homais, in spite of the servant, suddenly entered the room, holding in his hand a sheet of paper just written. It was the paragraph he **intended** for the "Fanal de Rouen." He brought it for them to read.

"Read it yourself," said Bovary.

He read--

" 'Despite the prejudices that still **invest** a part of the face of Europe like a **net**, the light **nevertheless begins** to penetrate our country places. Thus on Tuesday our little town of Yonville found itself the scene of a **surgical** operation which is at the same time an, act of loftiest **philanthropy**. Monsieur Bovary, one of our, most **distinguished** practitioners--'"

"Oh, that is too much! too much!" said Charles, **choking** with emotion.

"No, no! not at all! What next!"

Spanish

awaited: esperado, aguardado.
begins: empieza, principia.
choking: la obstrucción aérea, estrangular, atragantamiento, ahogarse.
distinguished: distinguido.
estimation: estimación.
growing: creciendo, aumentando, creciente, crecimiento.
increasing: creciente.
intended: destinado, destinado a, intencional, intentar, pensar,

proponerse, proyectado, querer, ser destinado a, tener la intención de, a propósito.
invest: invertir, invierta, invertimos, invertís, invierto, inviertes, invierten, invierte, inviertan, invertid, colocar.
net: red, neto, la red.
nevertheless: no obstante, sin embargo.
philanthropy: filantropía.
prattle: cháchara, balbuceo, charlar, parlotear, parloteo, balbucear.

properly: correctamente, como es debido, debidamente.
reappear: reaparecer, reaparecen, reaparezcan, reapareces, reaparezco, reaparecemos, reaparecéis, reaparece, reapareced, reaparezca.
refresh: refrescar, refresco, actualizar, refresque, refresca, refresquen, refrescas, refrescan, refrescamos, refrescad, refrescáis.
surgical: quirúrgico.
yard: patio, corral, yarda, grave.

" '--Performed an operation on a club-footed man.' I have not used the scientific term, because you know in a newspaper everyone would not perhaps understand. The masses must--'"

"No doubt," said Bovary; "go on!"

"I proceed," said the chemist. "'Monsieur Bovary, one of our most distinguished **practitioners**, performed an operation on a club-footed man called Hippolyte Tautain, **stableman** for the last twenty-five years at the hotel of the "Lion d'Or," kept by Widow Lefrancois, at the Place d'Armes. The **novelty** of the attempt, and the interest incident to the subject, had **attracted** such a **concourse** of persons that there was a veritable **obstruction** on the threshold of the establishment. The operation, moreover, was performed as if by magic, and **barely** a few drops of blood appeared on the skin, as though to say that the **rebellious** tendon had at last given way beneath the efforts of art. The patient, **strangely** enough--we **affirm** it as an eye-witness--complained of no pain. His condition up to the present time leaves nothing to be **desired**. Everything **tends** to show that his convelescence will be brief; and who knows even if at our next village **festivity** we shall not see our good Hippolyte **figuring** in the **bacchic** dance in the midst of a **chorus** of joyous boon-companions, and thus **proving** to all eyes by his verve and his **capers** his complete cure? Honour, then, to the generous savants! Honour to those **indefatigable spirits** who **consecrate** their vigils to the amelioration or to the **alleviation** of their kind! Honour, **thrice** honour! Is it not time to cry that the blind shall see, the deaf hear, the **lame** walk? But that which fanaticism formerly promised to its **elect**, science now **accomplishes** for all men. We shall keep our readers informed as to the successive phases of this remarkable cure.' "

This did not prevent Mere Lefrancois, from coming five days after, scared, and crying out--

"Help! he is dying! I am going crazy!"

Charles **rushed** to the "Lion d'Or," and the chemist, who caught sight of him passing along the Place **hatless**, **abandoned** his shop. He appeared himself breathless, red, anxious, and asking everyone who was going up the stairs--

Spanish

abandoned: abandonado, desamparado, dejado, abandonados, abandonada, olvidado, abandonadas.
accomplishes: realiza.
affirm: afirmar, confirmar, confirmad, afirmamos, confirme, confirmas, confirman, confirmen, confirmamos, confirmo, confirmáis.
alleviation: alivio.
attracted: atraído, encantado.
bacchic: báquico.
barely: apenas.

capers: alcaparras.
chorus: coro.
concourse: concurso.
consecrate: consagrar.
desired: deseado.
elect: elegir, escoger.
festivity: festividad.
figuring: figurar, computación.
hatless: descubierto.
indefatigable: infatigable.
lame: cojo.
novelty: novedad, noticias.

obstruction: obstrucción, obstáculo.
practitioners: profesionales.
proving: probando, verificando.
rebellious: rebelde.
rushed: apresurarse, a prisa, apresurado, con prisas, prisa, precipitar.
spirits: alcohol.
stableman: mozo de cuadra.
strangely: extrañamente.
tends: cuida, tiende.
thrice: tres veces.

"Why, what's the matter with our interesting strephopode?"

The strephopode was **writhing** in hideous convulsions, so that the machine in which his leg was **enclosed** was knocked against the wall enough to break it.

With many precautions, in order not to disturb the position of the **limb**, the box was removed, and an **awful** sight presented itself. The outlines of the foot disappeared in such a swelling that the **entire** skin seemed about to burst, and it was **covered** with **ecchymosis**, caused by the famous machine. Hippolyte had already complained of suffering from it. No attention had been paid to him; they had to **acknowledge** that he had not been altogether wrong, and he was **freed** for a few hours. But, hardly had the **oedema** gone down to some extent, than the two savants thought fit to put back the limb in the **apparatus**, **strapping** it tighter to **hasten** matters. At last, three days after, Hippolyte being unable to endure it any longer, they once more removed the machine, and were much **surprised** at the result they saw. The **livid tumefaction** spread over the leg, with blisters here and there, whence there oozed a black **liquid**. Matters were taking a serious turn. Hippolyte began to worry himself, and Mere Lefrancois, had him installed in the little room near the kitchen, so that he might at least have some distraction.

But the tax-collector, who dined there every day, complained **bitterly** of such **companionship**. Then Hippolyte was removed to the billiard-room. He lay there **moaning** under his heavy coverings, pale with long beard, sunken eyes, and from time to time turning his **perspiring** head on the dirty pillow, where the flies **alighted**. Madame Bovary went to see him. She brought him linen for his poultices; she **comforted**, and **encouraged** him. Besides, he did not want for company, especially on market-days, when the peasants were knocking about the billiard-balls round him, fenced with the cues, smoked, drank, sang, and **brawled**.

"How are you?" they said, clapping him on the shoulder. "Ah! you're not up to much, it seems, but it's your own fault. You should do this! do that!" And then they told him stories of people who had all been cured by other **remedies** than his. Then by way of consolation they added--

Spanish

acknowledge: reconocer, reconoce, reconocen, reconozcan, reconoces, reconozco, reconocemos, reconoced, reconocéis, reconozca, confirmar.
alighted: Bajado.
apparatus: aparato.
awful: horrible, abominable, horroroso, atroz, tremendo.
bitterly: amargamente.
brawled: Peleado.
comforted: aliviado.
companionship: compañerismo,

compañía.
covered: cubierto, cubierto de verdor.
ecchymosis: equimosis.
enclosed: adjunto, encerrado.
encouraged: animado, alentado, espoleado.
entire: entero, todo, completo, cabal, total.
freed: liberado.
hasten: acelerar, apresurar.
limb: miembro, limbo.
liquid: líquido.

livid: lívido.
moaning: gimiendo.
oedema: edema.
perspiring: sudando.
remedies: recursos.
strapping: correaje, tira, robusto, fuerte, fornido, fajando, afilar, encintado, encintar, correa, atar.
surprised: sorprendido.
tumefaction: tumefacción.
writhing: retorcer, retorcimiento, retorciendo.

"You give way too much! Get up! You **coddle** yourself like a king! All the same, old **chap**, you don't smell nice!"

Gangrene, in fact, was spreading more and more. Bovary himself turned sick at it. He came every hour, every moment. Hippolyte looked at him with eyes full of terror, sobbing--

"When shall I get well? Oh, save me! How **unfortunate** I am! How unfortunate I am!"

And the doctor left, always **recommending** him to diet himself.

"Don't listen to him, my lad," said Mere Lefrancois, "Haven't they tortured you enough already? You'll grow still weaker. Here! swallow this."

And she gave him some good beef-tea, a **slice** of mutton, a piece of **bacon**, and sometimes small **glasses** of brandy, that he had not the strength to put to his lips.

Abbe Bournisien, hearing that he was growing worse, asked to see him. He began by **pitying** his sufferings, declaring at the same time that he ought to rejoice at them since it was the will of the Lord, and take advantage of the occasion to **reconcile** himself to Heaven.

"For," said the **ecclesiastic** in a paternal tone, "you rather **neglected** your duties; you were rarely seen at divine **worship**. How many years is it since you approached the **holy** table? I understand that your work, that the **whirl** of the world may have kept you from care for your salvation. But now is the time to reflect. Yet don't despair. I have known great sinners, who, about to appear before God (you are not yet at this point I know), had implored His **mercy**, and who certainly died in the best frame of mind. Let us hope that, like them, you will set us a good example. Thus, as a **precaution**, what is to prevent you from saying morning and evening a 'Hail Mary, full of grace,' and 'Our Father which art in heaven'? Yes, do that, for my sake, to **oblige** me. That won't cost you anything. Will you promise me?"

The poor devil promised. The cure came back day after day. He chatted with the landlady; and even told anecdotes **interspersed** with jokes and puns that

Spanish

abbe: abate.

bacon: tocino, el tocino, beicon, lardo, tocino ahumado.

chap: raja.

coddle: consentir.

ecclesiastic: eclesiástico.

gangrene: gangrena.

glasses: gafas, lentes, anteojos.

holy: santo, sagrado.

interspersed: esparcido.

mercy: misericordia, compasión.

neglected: abandonado, descuidado.

oblige: obligar, obligad, obligo, obligas, obligan, obliga, obligáis, obliguen, obligamos, obligue, compeler.

pitying: compasión, compadecer, compasivo, de lástima, piedad, tener lástima de, apiadarse de.

precaution: precaución.

recommending: recomendando, encareciendo, ensalzando.

reconcile: reconciliar, se reconcilian, reconcíliate, reconcíliense,

reconcilíese, reconciliados, se reconcilia, me reconcilio, os reconciliáis, te reconcilias, nos reconciliamos.

slice: rebanar, tajada, cortar, trozo, rodaja, rebanada, filete, corte, loncha.

unfortunate: desgraciado, infortunado.

whirl: giro rápido, torbellino, dar vueltas.

worship: adorar, adoración, culto, veneración.

Hippolyte did not understand. Then, as soon as he could, he fell back upon matters of religion, putting on an appropriate expression of face.

His zeal seemed successful, for the club-foot soon **manifested** a desire to go on a **pilgrimage** to Bon-Secours if he were cured; to which Monsieur Bournisien replied that he saw no objection; two precautions were better than one; it was no risk **anyhow**.

The druggist was indignant at what he called the manoeuvres of the priest; they were **prejudicial**, he said, to Hippolyte's **convalescence**, and he kept repeating to Madame Lefrancois, "Leave him alone! leave him alone! You **perturb** his morals with your mysticism." But the good woman would no longer listen to him; he was the cause of it all. From a spirit of contradiction she hung up near the bedside of the patient a basin filled with holy-water and a branch of box.

Religion, however, seemed no more able to **succour** him than surgery, and the **invincible** gangrene still spread from the **extremities** towards the stomach. It was all very well to vary the potions and change the poultices; the muscles each day **rotted** more and more; and at last Charles replied by an **affirmative** nod of the head when Mere Lefrancois, asked him if she could not, as a **forlorn** hope, send for Monsieur Canivet of Neufchatel, who was a celebrity.

A doctor of medicine, fifty years of age, enjoying a good position and **self-possessed**, Charles's colleague did not refrain from laughing **disdainfully** when he had uncovered the leg, **mortified** to the knee. Then having flatly declared that it must be **amputated**, he went off to the chemist's to rail at the asses who could have reduced a poor man to such a state. Shaking Monsieur Homais by the button of his coat, he shouted out in the shop--

"These are the inventions of Paris! These are the ideas of those gentry of the capital! It is like **strabismus**, **chloroform**, lithotrity, a heap of **monstrosities** that the Government ought to **prohibit**. But they want to do the clever, and they **cram** you with remedies without, troubling about the consequences. We are not so clever, not we! We are not savants, coxcombs, **fops**! We are practitioners; we cure people, and we should not dream of operating on anyone who is in perfect

Spanish

affirmative: afirmativo.
amputated: amputado.
anyhow: sin embargo.
chloroform: cloroformo.
convalescence: convalecencia.
cram: atestar, empollar, apretura, abarrotado, repaso de última hora, rellenar con, hartarse de comer, emborrar, cebar, atiborrar, atiborramiento.
disdainfully: desdeñosamente, altaneramente.

extremities: extremidades.
fops: petimetres.
forlorn: abandonado, desamparado.
invincible: invencible.
manifested: Manifestado.
monstrosities: Monstruosidades.
mortified: mortificado.
perturb: perturbar, perturba, perturbad, perturbo, perturben, perturbe, perturbas, perturban, perturbáis, perturbamos.
pilgrimage: peregrinación, romería,

peregrinaje.
prejudicial: perjudicial.
prohibit: prohibir, prohiban, prohibís, prohibimos, prohibid, prohibes, prohiben, prohibe, prohibo, prohiba.
rotted: pudrido, descompuesto, envanecido, podrido, se macado, corrompido.
self-possessed: dueño de sí mismo.
strabismus: estrabismo.
succour: prestar ayuda, socorrer, asistir, acudir, socorro.

health. **Straighten** club- feet! As if one could straighten club-feet! It is as if one wished, for example, to make a **hunchback** straight!"

Homais suffered as he listened to this **discourse**, and he concealed his **discomfort** beneath a courtier's smile; for he needed to humour Monsier Canivet, whose prescriptions sometimes came as far as Yonville. So he did not take up the defence of Bovary; he did not even make a single **remark**, and, **renouncing** his **principles**, he **sacrificed** his **dignity** to the more serious interests of his business.

This **amputation** of the thigh by Doctor Canivet was a great event in the village. On that day all the inhabitants got up earlier, and the Grande Rue, although full of people, had something **lugubrious** about it, as if an execution had been expected. At the grocer's they **discussed** Hippolyte's **illness**; the **shops** did no business, and Madame Tuvache, the mayor's wife, did not stir from her window, such was her impatience to see the operator **arrive**.

He came in his gig, which he drove himself. But the springs of the right side having at length given way beneath the weight of his **corpulence**, it happened that the carriage as it rolled along leaned over a little, and on the other **cushion** near him could be seen a large box covered in red sheep-leather, whose three brass clasps shone **grandly**.

After he had entered like a **whirlwind** the porch of the "Lion d'Or," the doctor, shouting very loud, ordered them to unharness his horse. Then he went into the stable to see that he was eating his oats all right; for on **arriving** at a patient's he first of all looked after his mare and his gig. People even said about this--

"Ah! Monsieur Canivet's a character!"

And he was the more **esteemed** for this imperturbable **coolness**. The **universe** to the last man might have died, and he would not have missed the **smallest** of his habits.

Homais presented himself.

"I **count** on you," said the doctor. "Are we ready? Come along!"

Spanish

amputation: amputación.
arrive: llegar, llega, llego, llegas, llegan, llegamos, lleguen, llegad, llegáis, llegue, arribar.
arriving: llegando.
coolness: frescura, calma, desapego, frescor, frialdad, igualdad, serenidad, indiferencia.
corpulence: corpulencia.
count: contar, recuento, cuenta, conde, calcular, entrar en cuenta, computar, unidad de cuenta, cargo.

cushion: cojín, almohada, colchón.
dignity: dignidad.
discomfort: incomodidad.
discourse: discurso.
discussed: discutido, debatido.
esteemed: estimado.
grandly: grandiosamente, grandemente.
hunchback: jorobado.
illness: enfermedad.
lugubrious: lúgubre.
principles: principios.

remark: comentario, observación, reparo, censura, nota, notar.
renouncing: renunciando.
sacrificed: sacrificado.
shops: denuncia, negocios.
smallest: menor.
straighten: enderezarse, enderezar, enderece, enderezas, enderezan, enderezo, enderezamos, enderezáis, enderezad, endereza, enderecen.
universe: universo.
whirlwind: torbellino.

But the druggist, turning red, confessed that he was too **sensitive** to **assist** at such an operation.

"When one is a **simple** spectator," he said, "the imagination, you know, is impressed. And then I have such a nervous system!"

"Pshaw!" interrupted Canivet; "on the contrary, you seem to me inclined to **apoplexy**. Besides, that doesn't **astonish** me, for you chemist fellows are always poking about your kitchens, which must end by spoiling your constitutions. Now just look at me. I get up every day at four o'clock; I shave with cold water (and am never cold). I don't wear flannels, and I never catch cold; my **carcass** is good enough! I live now in one way, now in another, like a **philosopher**, taking **pot**-luck; that is why I am not squeamish like you, and it is as **indifferent** to me to **carve** a Christian as the first **fowl** that turns up. Then, perhaps, you will say, habit! habit!"

Then, without any **consideration** for Hippolyte, who was **sweating** with agony between his **sheets**, these gentlemen entered into a conversation, in which the druggist **compared** the coolness of a **surgeon** to that of a general; and this comparison was **pleasing** to Canivet, who launched out on the **exigencies** of his art. He looked upon, it as a sacred office, although the ordinary practitioners **dishonoured** it. At last, coming back to the patient, he examined the bandages **brought** by Homais, the same that had appeared for the club-foot, and asked for someone to hold the limb for him. Lestiboudois was sent for, and Monsieur Canivet having turned up his sleeves, passed into the billiard-room, while the druggist **stayed** with Artemise and the landlady, both whiter than their **aprons**, and with ears strained towards the door.

Bovary during this time did not dare to stir from his house.

He **kept** downstairs in the sitting-room by the side of the fireless chimney, his chin on his breast, his hands **clasped**, his eyes staring. "What a mishap!" he thought, "what a mishap!" Perhaps, after all, he had made some slip. He thought it over, but could hit upon nothing. But the most **famous** surgeons also made mistakes; and that is what no one would ever believe! People, on the contrary, would laugh, jeer! It would spread as far as Forges, as Neufchatel, as Rouen,

Spanish

apoplexy: apoplejía.
aprons: sendero.
assist: ayudar, ayudad, ayudo, ayuden, ayudas, ayudan, ayudáis, ayudamos, ayuda, ayude, asistir.
astonish: asombrar, asombramos, asombren, asombran, asombras, asombra, asombrad, asombráis, sorprender, asombro, asombre.
brought: Traído.
carcass: cadáver, canal.
carve: tallar, tallad, talláis, tallamos, tallan, tallas, tallen, tallo, labrar, talle, talla.
clasped: apretado, abrochado.
compared: Comparado, cotejado.
consideration: consideración, contraprestación, contemplación.
constitutions: constituciones.
dishonoured: deshonrado.
exigencies: exigencias.
famous: famoso, afamado, conocido.
fowl: gallina, aves, ave.
indifferent: indiferente.
kept: guardado, vigilado, conservado, preservado.
philosopher: filósofo.
pleasing: agradable.
pot-luck: comida en la que cada uno trae un plato.
sensitive: sensible.
sheets: hoja, folio.
simple: sencillo, simple.
stayed: quedado, permanecido.
surgeon: cirujano, el cirujano.
sweating: sudar.

everywhere! Who could say if his colleagues would not write against him. **Polemics** would **ensue**; he would have to answer in the papers. Hippolyte might even **prosecute** him. He saw himself dishonoured, ruined, lost; and his imagination, **assailed** by a world of hypotheses, **tossed** amongst them like an empty cask **borne** by the sea and floating upon the waves.

Emma, **opposite**, watched him; she did not share his humiliation; she felt another--that of having supposed such a man was worth anything. As if twenty times already she had not **sufficiently** perceived his mediocrity.

Charles was walking up and down the room; his boots creaked on the floor.

"Sit down," she said; "you **fidget** me."

He sat down again.

How was it that she--she, who was so intelligent--could have allowed herself to be **deceived** again? and through what deplorable **madness** had she thus ruined her life by continual sacrifices? She recalled all her instincts of luxury, all the privations of her soul, the **sordidness** of marriage, of the household, her dream sinking into the **mire** like wounded swallows; all that she had longed for, all that she had **denied** herself, all that she might have had! And for what? for what?

In the midst of the silence that hung over the village a heart-rending cry rose on the air. Bovary turned white to fainting. She **knit** her brows with a nervous gesture, then went on. And it was for him, for this **creature**, for this man, who understood nothing, who felt nothing! For he was there quite quiet, not even **suspecting** that the **ridicule** of his name would **henceforth sully** hers as well as his. She had made **efforts** to love him, and she had repented with tears for having yielded to another!

"But it was perhaps a valgus!" suddenly exclaimed Bovary, who was **meditating**.

At the unexpected shock of this phrase falling on her thought like a **leaden bullet** on a silver plate, Emma, **shuddering**, raised her head in order to find out what he meant to say; and they looked at the other in silence, almost **amazed** to

Spanish

amazed: asombrado, maravillado, pasmado, atónito.
assailed: Asaltado.
borne: Soportado, pp de bear, pagado.
bullet: bala, bola, viñeta.
creature: criatura.
deceived: engañado.
denied: negado, desmentido.
efforts: afán.
ensue: suceder, suceda, sucedes, suceden, sucedemos, sucedéis, suceded, sucede, sucedan, sucedo.

fidget: estar inquieto, agitarse.
henceforth: de aquí en adelante.
knit: tejer.
leaden: de plomo, plomizo.
madness: locura, demencia, chifladura.
meditating: meditando.
mire: fango.
opposite: enfrente de, opuesto, contra, enfrente, contrario, frente a, frontero.
polemics: polémica, polémico.
prosecute: procesar, procesáis,

procesad, procesamos, procesen, procesan, procesas, procesa, proceso, procese, perseguir.
ridicule: ridiculizar, ridículo.
shuddering: estremecer.
sordidness: suciedad, sordidez, lo miserable, lo asqueroso, vileza.
sufficiently: suficientemente, bastante.
sully: tachar a, manchar, mancharse, mancillar, mancille.
suspecting: Sospechar.
tossed: Tirado.

see each other, so far **sundered** were they by their **inner** thoughts. Charles gazed at her with the dull look of a **drunken** man, while he listened motionless to the last cries of the **sufferer**, that followed each other in long-drawn modulations, broken by sharp spasms like the far-off **howling** of some beast being **slaughtered**. Emma bit her **wan** lips, and rolling between her fingers a piece of coral that she had broken, fixed on Charles the burning glance of her eyes like two arrows of fire about to **dart** forth. Everything in him irritated her now; his face, his dress, what he did not say, his whole person, his existence, in fine. She repented of her past virtue as of a **crime**, and what still remained of it **rumbled** away beneath the furious blows of her pride. She revelled in all the evil ironies of **triumphant** adultery. The memory of her lover came back to her with dazzling attractions; she threw her whole soul into it, borne away towards this **image** with a fresh enthusiasm; and Charles seemed to her as much removed from her life, as **absent forever**, as **impossible** and **annihilated**, as if he had been about to **die** and were passing under her eyes.

There was a sound of steps on the pavement. Charles looked up, and through the lowered blinds he saw at the **corner** of the market in the broad sunshine Dr. Canivet, who was wiping his brow with his handkerchief. Homais, behind him, was carrying a large red box in his hand, and both were going towards the chemist's.

Then with a **feeling** of sudden tenderness and discouragement Charles turned to his wife saying to her--

"Oh, kiss me, my own!"

"Leave me!" she said, red with anger.

"What is the matter?" he asked, **stupefied**. "Be calm; **compose** yourself. You know well enough that I love you. Come!"

"Enough!" she cried with a terrible look.

And **escaping** from the room, Emma closed the door so **violently** that the barometer fell from the wall and **smashed** on the floor.

Spanish

absent: ausente.
annihilated: aniquilado, anonadado.
compose: componer, compongan, compongo, compones, componen, componéis, componed, compone, compon, componemos, componga.
corner: esquina, ángulo, rincón.
crime: crimen, delito, el crimen.
dart: dardo.
die: morir, morid, mueran, muere, morís, mueren, mueres, muero, morimos, muera, molde.

drunken: borracho, ebrio.
escaping: escapar.
feeling: sentimiento, sintiendo, palpando, sensación.
forever: para siempre, siempre.
howling: aullido, lamentarse, clamoroso, aullador, alarido, aullar, lamento, gritar, rugir, grito, dar alaridos.
image: imagen, grabado, retrato, reproducción.
impossible: imposible.

inner: interior, interno, interna.
rumbled: retumbado.
slaughtered: matado.
smashed: golpeado.
stupefied: aturdido, entorpecido.
sufferer: doliente, enfermo, paciente, víctima.
sundered: partió.
triumphant: triunfante.
violently: violentamente.
wan: red de área extensa, lívido, pálido.

Charles **sank** back into his **arm**-chair **overwhelmed**, **trying** to **discover** what could be **wrong** with her, fancying some **nervous illness**, **weeping**, and **vaguely feeling** something **fatal** and **incomprehensible whirling** round him.

When Rodolphe came to the **garden** that evening, he found his **mistress waiting** for him at the **foot** of the **steps** on the **lowest stair**. They **threw** their **arms** round one another, and all their **rancour melted** like **snow beneath** the **warmth** of that **kiss**.

Spanish

arm-chair: sillón, butaca.
arms: brazos, los brazos, armas.
beneath: debajo de, debajo, abajo.
discover: descubrir, descubrimos, descubrís, descubrid, descubres, descubren, descubre, descubran, descubro, descubra.
fatal: mortal.
feeling: sentimiento, sintiendo, palpando, sensación.
foot: pie, pata, el pie, pujamen.
garden: jardín, el jardín.

illness: enfermedad.
incomprehensible: incomprensible.
kiss: besar, beso, besarse.
lowest: ínfimo, bajo.
melted: derretido, fundido.
mistress: señora.
nervous: nervioso.
overwhelmed: enterrado.
rancour: encono, ojeriza, rencor.
sank: pret de sink.
snow: nevar, nieve, la nieve.
stair: escalón, escalera.

steps: pasos.
threw: pret de throw, Tiró, tiro.
trying: molesto.
vaguely: vagamente.
waiting: esperando, espera, aguardando, servicio.
warmth: calor moderado, calor.
weeping: llorando, lloroso, llanto, llorón.
whirling: turbulencia.
wrong: malo, mal, falso, incorrecto, entuerto, agravio, impropio, erróneo.

CHAPTER TWELVE

They began to love one another again. Often, even in the **middle** of the day, Emma suddenly wrote to him, then from the window made a **sign** to Justin, who, taking his **apron** off, quickly **ran** to La Huchette. Rodolphe would come; she had sent for him to tell him that she was **bored**, that her husband was **odious**, her life frightful.

"But what can I do?" he **cried** one day **impatiently**.

"Ah! if you would--"

She was sitting on the **floor** between his **knees**, her hair **loose**, her look lost.

"Why, what?" said Rodolphe.

She **sighed**.

"We would go and **live** elsewhere--somewhere!"

"You are really mad!" he said **laughing**. "How could that be possible?"

She returned to the **subject**; he **pretended** not to understand, and turned the conversation.

What he did not understand was all this **worry** about so simple an affair as love. She had a **motive**, a **reason**, and, as it were, a **pendant** to her **affection**.

Her **tenderness**, in fact, **grew** each day with her **repulsion** to her husband. The more she gave up herself to the one, the more she **loathed** the other. Never

Spanish

affection: afecto, cariño, afectuosidad, amor.
apron: delantal, el delantal, mandil.
bored: aburrido.
cried: Lloró.
floor: piso, suelo, el suelo, pavimento.
grew: creció, pret de grow, crecida.
impatiently: impacientemente, con impaciencia.
knees: rodillas.
laughing: riendo.
live: vivir, viven, vive, vivo, vivan,

vivís, vivimos, vives, viva, vivid, habitar.
loathed: detestado.
loose: suelto, flojo.
middle: medio, centro.
motive: motivo, lugar, móvil.
odious: odioso.
pendant: colgante, pendiente.
pretended: fingido, pretendido.
ran: corrió, participio pasivo del verbo run, pret de run.
reason: motivo, causa, razón, lugar,

razonar.
repulsion: repulsión.
sighed: suspirado.
sign: firmar, señal, seña, signo, agüero, letrero, prueba, el letrero, rótulo, muestra.
subject: asunto, tema, asignatura, someter, sujeto, cuestión, materia.
tenderness: ternura.
worry: preocuparse, cuidar, preocupación, inquietar, inquietud, preocupar, molestar.

had Charles seemed to her so disagreeable, to have such **stodgy** fingers, such vulgar ways, to be so dull as when they found themselves together after her meeting with Rodolphe. Then, while **playing** the spouse and virtue, she was burning at the thought of that head whose black hair fell in a **curl** over the **sunburnt** brow, of that form at once so strong and elegant, of that man, in a word, who had such experience in his reasoning, such passion in his desires. It was for him that she **filed** her nails with the care of a **chaser**, and that there was never enough cold-cream for her skin, nor of **patchouli** for her handkerchiefs. She **loaded** herself with bracelets, rings, and **necklaces**. When he was coming she filled the two large blue glass vases with roses, and prepared her room and her person like a **courtesan** expecting a **prince**. The servant had to be constantly washing linen, and all day Felicite did not stir from the kitchen, where little Justin, who often kept her company, watched her at work.

With his elbows on the long board on which she was **ironing**, he **greedily** watched all these women's **clothes** spread about him, the **dimity** petticoats, the fichus, the collars, and the drawers with running strings, **wide** at the hips and growing narrower below.

"What is that for?" asked the young fellow, passing his hand over the **crinoline** or the **hooks** and eyes.

"Why, haven't you ever seen anything?" Felicite answered laughing. "As if your mistress, Madame Homais, didn't wear the same."

"Oh, I **daresay**! Madame Homais!" And he added with a **meditative** air, "As if she were a **lady** like madame!"

But Felicite grew impatient of seeing him hanging round her. She was six years older than he, and Theodore, Monsieur Guillaumin's servant, was **beginning** to pay court to her.

"Let me alone," she said, **moving** her **pot** of starch. "You'd better be off and pound almonds; you are always **dangling** about women. Before you **meddle** with such things, bad **boy**, wait till you've got a beard to your chin."

"Oh, don't be **cross**! I'll go and clean her boots."

Spanish

beginning: empezando, comienzo, principio, principiando, inicio, origen, el principio.
boy: chico, muchacho, niño, el muchacho, criado, chamaco.
chaser: perseguidor.
clothes: ropa, viste, la ropa, ropaje.
courtesan: cortesana.
crinoline: miriñaque.
cross: cruz, atravesar, cruzar, transversal, aspa, cruce.
curl: rizo, bucle, rizar, rizarse,

rotacional, encrespar.
dangling: balancear, colgado, balanceando, bamboleándose, colgando, pendiendo.
daresay: dicho atrevido.
dimity: bombasí.
filed: archivado.
greedily: vorazmente.
hooks: ganchos, manos, garfios.
ironing: férreo, planchar, hierro, plancha, planchado, ferrizo, férrico.
lady: dama, señora.

loaded: cargado.
meddle: entrometerse.
meditative: meditativo.
moving: conmovedor.
necklaces: gargantillas.
patchouli: pachulí, pachuli, patchuli.
playing: jugando, tocando, jugar.
pot: olla, orinal, jarro.
prince: príncipe.
stodgy: aburrido, pesado.
sunburnt: tostado por el sol.
wide: ancho, amplio, vasto, lejos.

And he at once took down from the **shelf** Emma's boots, all **coated** with mud, the mud of the rendezvous, that **crumbled** into powder beneath his fingers, and that he watched as it gently rose in a ray of sunlight.

"How afraid you are of spoiling them!" said the servant, who wasn't so particular when she cleaned them herself, because as soon as the stuff of the boots was no longer fresh madame **handed** them over to her.

Emma had a number in her cupboard that she squandered one after the other, without Charles allowing himself the slightest **observation**. So also he **disbursed** three hundred francs for a wooden leg that she thought proper to make a present of to Hippolyte. Its top was covered with **cork**, and it had spring joints, a **complicated mechanism**, covered over by black trousers **ending** in a patent-leather boot. But Hippolyte, not daring to use such a **handsome** leg every day, begged Madame Bovary to get him another more convenient one. The doctor, of course, had again to **defray** the **expense** of this purchase.

So little by little the stable-man took up his work again. One saw him running about the village as before, and when Charles heard from afar the sharp noise of the wooden leg, he at once went in another direction.

It was Monsieur Lheureux, the shopkeeper, who had **undertaken** the order; this provided him with an excuse for **visiting** Emma. He chatted with her about the new goods from Paris, about a thousand **feminine trifles**, made himself very **obliging**, and never asked for his money. Emma yielded to this lazy **mode** of **satisfying** all her caprices. Thus she wanted to have a very handsome ridding-whip that was at an umbrella-maker's at Rouen to give to Rodolphe. The week after Monsieur Lheureux placed it on her table.

But the next day he called on her with a bill for two hundred and seventy francs, not counting the centimes. Emma was much embarrassed; all the drawers of the writing-table were empty; they owed over a fortnight's wages to Lestiboudois, two **quarters** to the servant, for any quantity of other things, and Bovary was impatiently expecting Monsieur Derozeray's account, which he was in the habit of paying every year about Midsummer.

Spanish

coated: chaqueta, cuché, cubrir, cubierta, cubierto de pintura, dar una capa, grageado, mano de pintura, revistió, saburral, saco.
complicated: complicado, complejo.
cork: corcho, el corcho, tapón.
crumbled: desmenuzado, se desmoronado.
defray: costear, costeas, costead, costeen, costee, costeo, costeáis, costea, costeamos, costean, sufragar.
disbursed: desembolsado.

ending: final, fin, término, terminación, conclusión.
expense: gasto, gastos, expensas.
feminine: femenino.
handed: entregado.
handsome: guapo, bonito, bien parecido.
mechanism: mecanismo.
mode: moda, modo.
obliging: obligando, complaciente, servicial.
observation: observación, reparo,

censura.
quarters: cuarta, cuartel, cuarteles, cuarto, alojamiento, cuartos traseros, domicilio, puesto de combate, trasero.
satisfying: complaciendo, satisfaciendo.
shelf: estante, tabla, el estante, repisa, anaquel.
trifles: zarandajas.
undertaken: Emprendido.
visiting: visitando, visitante.

She succeeded at first in putting off Lheureux. At last he lost patience; he was being **sued**; his **capital** was out, and unless he got some in he should be forced to take back all the **goods** she had received.

"Oh, very well, take them!" said Emma.

"I was only joking," he replied; "the only thing I regret is the whip. My word! I'll ask monsieur to return it to me."

"No, no!" she said.

"Ah! I've got you!" thought Lheureux.

And, certain of his discovery, he went out repeating to himself in an undertone, and with his usual low whistle--

"Good! we shall see! we shall see!"

She was thinking how to get out of this when the servant **coming** in put on the mantelpiece a small **roll** of blue paper "from Monsieur Derozeray's." Emma **pounced** upon and opened it. It **contained fifteen** napoleons; it was the account. She heard Charles on the stairs; threw the gold to the back of her drawer, and took out the key.

Three days after Lheureux reappeared.

"I have an **arrangement** to **suggest** to you," he said. "If, instead of the **sum agreed** on, you would take--"

"Here it is," she said **placing** fourteen napoleons in his hand.

The **tradesman** was **dumfounded**. Then, to **conceal** his disappointment, he was **profuse** in apologies and proffers of service, all of which Emma declined; then she remained a few moments **fingering** in the pocket of her apron the two five-franc pieces that he had given her in change. She promised herself she would **economise** in order to pay back later on. "Pshaw!" she thought, "he won't think about it again."

Besides the riding-whip with its silver-gilt handle, Rodolphe had received a seal with the **motto** Amor nel cor **furthermore**, a scarf for a **muffler**, and, finally, a cigar-case exactly like the Viscount's, that Charles had formerly picked up in

Spanish

agreed: acordado, convenido, de acuerdo, vale, entendido, conforme, asentido, concordado, en orden.
arrangement: arreglo, acuerdo, construcción, disposición, orden, combinación.
capital: capital, capitel, mayúscula, la capital.
coming: viniendo, proveniente, próximo, originario, natural.
conceal: ocultar, ocultamos, oculten, ocultan, ocultáis, ocultad, oculta,

ocultas, oculto, oculte, recatar.
contained: contenido.
dumfounded: confundido.
economise: economizar, guardar, economice, ahorrar, reservar.
fifteen: quince.
fingering: tecleo, digitación, tocar.
furthermore: además.
goods: bienes, géneros, mercancías, mercancía.
motto: lema.
muffler: silenciador, bufanda.

placing: colocación.
pounced: estarcido, precipitado, repujado, abalanzado.
profuse: profuso.
roll: rollo, rodar, panecillo, bocadillo, balanceo, bollo, arrollar, bobina.
sued: demandado.
suggest: sugerir, sugerid, sugiero, sugieres, sugieren, sugiere, sugieran, sugerís, sugerimos, sugiera, indicar.
sum: suma, importe, cantidad.
tradesman: comerciante.

the road, and that Emma had kept. These presents, however, humiliated him; he refused several; she insisted, and he ended by **obeying, thinking** her **tyrannical** and overexacting.

Then she had strange ideas.

"When midnight **strikes**," she said, "you must think of me."

And if he confessed that he had not thought of her, there were floods of reproaches that always ended with the eternal question--

"Do you love me?"

"Why, of **course** I love you," he answered.

"A great deal?"

"Certainly!"

"You **haven't** loved any others?"

"Did you think you'd got a virgin?" he exclaimed laughing.

Emma cried, and he tried to console her, **adorning** his protestations with puns.

"Oh," she went on, "I love you! I love you so that I could not live without you, do you see? There are times when I long to see you again, when I am **torn** by all the anger of love. I **ask** myself, Where is he? Perhaps he is **talking** to other women. They smile upon him; he approaches. Oh no; no one else **pleases** you. There are some more beautiful, but I love you best. I know how to love best. I am your servant, your **concubine**! You are my king, my idol! You are good, you are beautiful, you are clever, you are strong!"

He had so often heard these things said that they did not strike him as **original**. Emma was like all his mistresses; and the charm of novelty, gradually falling away like a **garment**, laid bare the eternal **monotony** of passion, that has always the same **forms** and the same **language**. He did not distinguish, this man of so much experience, the **difference** of sentiment beneath the **sameness** of **expression**. Because lips **libertine** and **venal** had murmured such words to him, he **believed** but little in the **candour** of hers; **exaggerated** speeches hiding

Spanish

adorning: decorando.
ask: preguntar, preguntáis, preguntad, pregunto, pregunten, preguntas, preguntan, preguntamos, pregunte, pregunta, pedir.
believed: Creído.
candour: sinceridad, franqueza, candor.
concubine: concubina.
course: curso, plato, cursillo, rumbo, transcurso, recorrido.
difference: diferencia.

exaggerated: exagerado.
expression: expresión.
forms: formas, Formularios.
garment: prenda.
haven't: no tener.
king: rey, el rey.
language: lengua, lenguaje, idioma, el idioma, la lengua, el lenguaje.
libertine: libertino.
monotony: monotonía.
obeying: obedeciendo.
original: original.

pleases: complace.
sameness: identidad, igualdad, monótono, monotonía, similaridad, uniformidad.
strike: huelga, golpear, llamar, declararse en huelga, acertar, paro, golpe.
talking: hablando, parlante, charlando, hablar.
torn: roto.
tyrannical: tiránico.
venal: corruptible, venal.

mediocre affections must be **discounted**; as if the **fullness** of the soul did not sometimes overflow in the emptiest **metaphors**, since no one can ever give the **exact** measure of his needs, nor of his conceptions, nor of his sorrows; and since human speech is like a cracked **tin** kettle, on which we **hammer** out tunes to make bears dance when we long to move the stars.

But with that superior critical judgment that belongs to him who, in no matter what **circumstance**, holds back, Rodolphe saw other delights to be got out of this love. He thought all modesty in the way. He treated her quite **sans** facon. He made of her something **supple** and **corrupt**. Hers was an **idiotic** sort of **attachment**, full of **admiration** for him, of voluptuousness for her, a beatitude that **benumbed** her; her soul sank into this drunkenness, **shrivelled** up, drowned in it, like Clarence in his **butt** of Malmsey.

By the mere effect of her love Madame Bovary's manners changed. Her looks grew bolder, her speech more free; she even **committed** the **impropriety** of walking out with Monsieur Rodolphe, a **cigarette** in her mouth, "as if to **defy** the people." At last, those who still doubted doubted no longer when one day they saw her getting out of the "Hirondelle," her waist squeezed into a waistcoat like a man; and Madame Bovary senior, who, after a **fearful** scene with her husband, had taken refuge at her son's, was not the least scandalised of the women-folk. Many other things displeased her. First, Charles had not **attended** to her advice about the forbidding of novels; then the "ways of the house" annoyed her; she allowed herself to make some remarks, and there were quarrels, especially one on account of Felicite.

Madame Bovary senior, the evening before, passing along the passage, had surprised her in company of a man--a man with a brown collar, about forty years old, who, at the sound of her step, had quickly escaped through the kitchen. Then Emma began to laugh, but the good lady grew angry, declaring that unless morals were to be laughed at one ought to look after those of one's servants.

"Where were you brought up?" asked the daughter-in-law, with so impertinent a look that Madame Bovary asked her if she were not perhaps **defending** her own case.

Spanish

admiration: admiración.
attachment: afectuosidad, fijación, conexión, anexo, enlace, embargo, adjunto, acoplamiento, atadura, apego, unión.
attended: asistido.
benumbed: embotado, congelado, entumecido.
butt: culata, colilla, extremo, tope.
cigarette: cigarrillo, el cigarrillo.
circumstance: condición, circunstancia.

committed: cometido, comprometido.
corrupt: corrupto, corromper, adulterar, corrompa, corrompido, corrompan, corrompo, corrompes, corrompemos, corromped, corrompe.
defending: defendiendo.
defy: desafiar, desafiáis, desafío, desafíen, desafías, desafiamos, desafiad, desafía, desafían, desafíe.
discounted: descontado.
exact: exacto, preciso.
fearful: temeroso, medroso,

angustioso.
fullness: plenitud.
hammer: martillo, el martillo, martillar.
idiotic: idiota, tonto.
impropriety: impropiedad.
metaphors: metáforas.
sans: sin.
shrivelled: marchito, consumido, apergaminado, arrugado, secado.
supple: suave.
tin: lata, estaño, hojalata, estañar, bote.

"Leave the room!" said the young woman, **springing** up with a bound.

"Emma! Mamma!" cried Charles, trying to **reconcile** them.

But both had fled in their **exasperation**. Emma was **stamping** her **feet** as she repeated--

"Oh! what manners! What a peasant!"

He ran to his mother; she was **beside** herself. She **stammered**

"She is an **insolent**, giddy-headed thing, or perhaps worse!"

And she was for **leaving** at once if the other did not **apologise**. So Charles went back again to his **wife** and **implored** her to give way; he **knelt** to her; she ended by saying--

"Very well! I'll go to her."

And in fact she held out her hand to her mother-in-law with the dignity of a **marchioness** as she said--

"Excuse me, madame."

Then, having gone up again to her room, she threw herself flat on her bed and cried there like a child, her face **buried** in the pillow.

She and Rodolphe had agreed that in the event of anything extraordinary **occurring**, she should **fasten** a small piece of white **paper** to the blind, so that if by **chance** he happened to be in Yonville, he could hurry to the **lane** behind the house. Emma made the **signal**; she had been waiting three-quarters of an hour when she suddenly caught sight of Rodolphe at the corner of the market. She felt **tempted** to open the window and call him, but he had already disappeared. She fell back in despair.

Soon, however, it seemed to her that someone was walking on the pavement. It was he, no doubt. She went downstairs, crossed the yard. He was there outside. She threw herself into his arms.

"Do take care!" he said.

"Ah! if you knew!" she replied.

Spanish

apologise: discúlpese.
beside: cerca de, junto a, al lado de, al lado.
buried: enterrado.
chance: azar, suerte, acontecimiento, acaso, oportunidad.
exasperation: exasperación.
fasten: fijar, fije, fijas, fijan, fijamos, fijáis, fijad, fija, fijen, fijo, atar.
feet: los pies, pies.
implored: implorado, suplicado.
insolent: insolente, procaz.

knelt: pret y pp de kneel, Arrodillado.
lane: calleja, senda, carril, pista, camino.
leaving: saliendo, dejando.
marchioness: marquesa.
occurring: ocurriendo.
paper: papel, documento, el papel, papel pintado, ponencia, tapizar, periódico.
reconcile: reconciliar, se reconcilian, reconcíliate, reconcíliense, reconcíliese, reconciliados, se

reconcilia, me reconcilio, os reconciliáis, te reconcilias, nos reconciliamos.
signal: señal, seña.
springing: saltar.
stammered: tartamudeó.
stamping: timbrado, estampación.
tempted: Tentado.
wife: esposa, mujer, la esposa.

And she began telling him everything, hurriedly, **disjointedly**, **exaggerating** the **facts**, **inventing** many, and so prodigal of **parentheses** that he understood nothing of it.

"Come, my poor angel, **courage**! Be comforted! be patient!"

"But I have been patient; I have suffered for four years. A love like **ours** ought to show itself in the face of **heaven**. They **torture** me! I can **bear** it no longer! Save me!"

She clung to Rodolphe. Her eyes, full of tears, **flashed** like flames beneath a wave; her breast **heaved**; he had never loved her so much, so that he lost his head and said "What is, it? What do you **wish**?"

"Take me away," she cried, "carry me off! Oh, I **pray** you!"

And she threw herself upon his mouth, as if to seize there the unexpected consent if breathed forth in a kiss.

"But--" Rodolphe resumed.

"What?"   "Your little girl!" She reflected a few moments, then replied--

"We will take her! It can't be helped!"

"What a woman!" he said to himself, watching her as she went. For she had run into the garden. Someone was calling her.

On the following days Madame Bovary **senior** was much surprised at the change in her daughter-in-law. Emma, in fact, was **showing** herself more **docile**, and even carried her **deference** so far as to ask for a **recipe** for **pickling gherkins**.

Was it the better to **deceive** them both? Or did she wish by a sort of voluptuous stoicism to feel the more **profoundly** the bitterness of the things she was about to leave?

But she **paid** no **heed** to them; on the contrary, she lived as lost in the **anticipated** delight of her coming happiness.

It was an eternal subject for conversation with Rodolphe. She leant on his shoulder murmuring--

Spanish

anticipated: previsto.
bear: oso, llevar, el oso, bajista, producir, dar a luz, parir, portar, soportar.
courage: valor, coraje, ánimo, virtud.
deceive: engañar, engaño, engañe, engaña, engañamos, engañen, engañan, engañáis, engañad, engañas, embaucar.
deference: deferencia.
disjointedly: desarticuladamente, descoyuntadamente, inconexamente.

docile: dócil.
exaggerating: exagerando.
facts: datos.
flashed: destellado.
gherkins: pepinillos, pepinillos en vinagre, pepinillo.
heaved: tirado.
heaven: cielo.
heed: atención.
inventing: inventando.
ours: nuestro.
paid: pagado.

parentheses: paréntesis.
pickling: decapado.
pray: rezar, rezáis, rezas, rezamos, rezad, reza, recen, rece, rezan, rezo, rogar.
profoundly: profundamente.
recipe: receta, la receta.
senior: mayor, superior.
showing: mostrando, exhibición.
torture: tortura, tormento, torturar.
wish: desear, deseo, voluntad, querer, tener, gana.

"Ah! when we are in the mail-coach! Do you think about it? Can it be? It seems to me that the moment I feel the carriage start, it will be as if we were rising in a **balloon**, as if we were **setting** out for the clouds. Do you know that I count the hours? And you?"

Never had Madame Bovary been so beautiful as at this period; she had that **indefinable beauty** that results from joy, from enthusiasm, from success, and that is only the harmony of temperament with circumstances. Her desires, her sorrows, the experience of pleasure, and her ever-young illusions, that had, as soil and rain and winds and the sun make flowers grow, gradually **developed** her, and she at **length** blossomed forth in all the **plenitude** of her nature. Her eyelids seemed **chiselled** expressly for her long amorous **looks** in which the pupil disappeared, while a strong **inspiration** expanded her delicate nostrils and raised the **fleshy** corner of her lips, shaded in the light by a little black down. One would have thought that an artist **apt** in **conception** had arranged the curls of hair upon her neck; they fell in a thick mass, negligently, and with the changing **chances** of their adultery, that **unbound** them every day. Her voice now took more **mellow** infections, her figure also; something subtle and penetrating escaped even from the folds of her gown and from the line of her foot. Charles, as when they were first **married**, thought her **delicious** and quite irresistible.

When he came home in the middle of the night, he did not dare to wake her. The porcelain night-light threw a round trembling gleam upon the ceiling, and the drawn curtains of the little cot formed as it were a white **hut** standing out in the shade, and by the bedside Charles looked at them. He seemed to hear the light breathing of his child. She would grow big now; every season would bring rapid progress. He already saw her coming from school as the day drew in, laughing, with ink-stains on her jacket, and carrying her basket on her arm. Then she would have to be sent to the boarding-school; that would cost much; how was it to be done? Then he reflected. He thought of **hiring** a small **farm** in the neighbourhood, that he would **superintend** every morning on his way to his patients. He would **save** up what he brought in; he would put it in the savings-

Spanish

apt: apropiado.
balloon: globo, aeróstato.
beauty: belleza, la belleza.
chances: posibilidades.
chiselled: escopleado, timado, cincelado.
conception: concepción, concepto.
delicious: delicioso.
developed: revelado, desarrollado.
farm: granja, finca, agrario, la granja, cultivar, la hacienda.
fleshy: carnoso.

hiring: alquilando, arrendando, contratando.
hut: cabaña, choza, barraca.
indefinable: indefinible.
inspiration: inspiración.
length: longitud, largura, eslora, duración.
looks: mira.
married: casado, casada, se casado, conyugal.
mellow: maduro, suave.
plenitude: plenitud, abundancia.

save: guardar, guarda, guardan, guardáis, guardamos, guardas, guarde, guardo, guardad, guarden, salvar.
setting: puesta, ajuste, escena, configuración, cuajado, escenario.
superintend: vigilas, supervisas, supervisen, superviso, vigila, vigilad, vigiláis, vigilan, vigilen, vigile, supervisan.
unbound: pret y pp de unbind, no unido.

bank. Then he would buy **shares somewhere**, no matter where; besides, his practice would increase; he counted upon that, for he wanted Berthe to be well-educated, to be **accomplished**, to **learn** to play the piano. Ah! how pretty she would be later on when she was fifteen, when, **resembling** her mother, she would, like her, wear large straw hats in the summer-time; from a distance they would be taken for two sisters. He **pictured** her to himself working in the evening by their side beneath the light of the lamp; she would embroider him slippers; she would look after the house; she would fill all the home with her charm and her gaiety. At last, they would think of her marriage; they would find her some good young fellow with a **steady** business; he would make her happy; this would last for ever.

Emma was not asleep; she pretended to be; and while he dozed off by her side she awakened to other dreams.

To the gallop of four horses she was carried away for a week towards a new land, whence they would return no more. They went on and on, their arms **entwined**, without a word. Often from the top of a **mountain** there suddenly **glimpsed** some **splendid** city with **domes**, and bridges, and **ships**, forests of citron trees, and cathedrals of white marble, on whose pointed steeples were storks' nests. They went at a walking-pace because of the great flag-stones, and on the ground there were bouquets of flowers, offered you by women dressed in red bodices. They heard the **chiming** of **bells**, the **neighing** of mules, together with the murmur of guitars and the noise of fountains, whose rising spray refreshed **heaps** of **fruit** arranged like a pyramid at the foot of pale **statues** that smiled beneath playing **waters**. And then, one night they came to a fishing village, where **brown nets** were drying in the wind along the cliffs and in front of the huts. It was there that they would stay; they would live in a low, flat-roofed house, shaded by a **palm**-tree, in the heart of a gulf, by the sea. They would row in gondolas, **swing** in hammocks, and their existence would be **easy** and large as their silk gowns, warm and star-spangled as the nights they would contemplate. However, in the immensity of this future that she **conjured** up, nothing special stood forth; the days, all **magnificent**, **resembled** each other like waves; and it

Spanish

accomplished: realizado, cumplido, consumado, dotado, talentoso, terminado.
bells: las campanas.
brown: marrón, pardo, moreno, dorar, castaño.
chiming: Tocar, repique.
conjured: conjurado.
domes: domos.
easy: fácil.
entwined: entrelazado.
fruit: fruta, la fruta, fruto.

glimpsed: vislumbrado.
heaps: muchísimo.
learn: aprender, aprenda, aprendemos, aprendes, aprendo, aprenden, aprended, aprendan, aprende, aprendéis, estudiar.
magnificent: magnífico, lucido.
mountain: montaña, monte.
neighing: relinchos.
nets: redes.
palm-tree: palma.
pictured: imaginado.

resembled: Parecido.
resembling: parecido a, Parecer, pareciendo.
shares: acciones.
ships: envía, despacha, expide.
somewhere: en alguna parte.
splendid: espléndido.
statues: estatuas.
steady: estable.
swing: balancear, columpio, balancearse, oscilación.
waters: aguas.

swayed in the horizon, **infinite, harmonised, azure,** and **bathed** in sunshine. But the child began to **cough** in her **cot** or Bovary **snored** more **loudly,** and Emma did not fall asleep till morning, when the dawn **whitened** the windows, and when little Justin was already in the square taking down the **shutters** of the chemist's shop.

She had sent for Monsieur Lheureux, and had said to him--

"I want a **cloak**--a large **lined** cloak with a deep collar."

"You are going on a journey?" he asked.

"No; but--never mind. I may count on you, may I not, and quickly?"

He **bowed**.

"Besides, I shall want," she went on, "a trunk--not too heavy-- handy."

"Yes, yes, I understand. About three feet by a foot and a half, as they are being made just now."

"And a travelling bag."

"Decidedly," thought Lheureux. "there's a row on here."

"And," said Madame Bovary, taking her **watch** from her **belt,** "take this; you can pay yourself out of it."

But the **tradesman** cried out that she was wrong; they knew one another; did he doubt her? What **childishness**!

She insisted, however, on his taking at least the **chain,** and Lheureux had already put it in his pocket and was going, when she called him back.

"You will leave **everything** at your place. As to the cloak"--she seemed to be reflecting--"do not bring it either; you can give me the maker's **address,** and tell him to have it ready for me."

It was the next **month** that they were to run away. She was to leave Yonville as if she was going on some business to Rouen. Rodolphe would have **booked** the seats, **procured** the **passports,** and even have **written** to Paris in order to have the whole mail-coach **reserved** for them as far as Marseilles, where they would **buy** a carriage, and go on **thence** without stopping to Genoa. She would

Spanish

address: dirección, dirigir, discurso, señas, dirigirse a, alocución, dirigirse, domicilio, dirigir la palabra a.
azure: azul celeste, azur.
bathed: se bañado.
belt: cinturón, correa, cinto, pretina.
booked: reservó.
bowed: agobiado, arqueado, cabizbajo, encorvado, inclinado.
buy: comprar, compra, procurarse, adquisición.
chain: cadena, la cadena, encadenar.

childishness: puerilidad.
cloak: abrigo, capa.
cot: camita de niño, catre.
cough: toser, tos, la tos.
everything: todo.
harmonised: armonizado.
infinite: infinito.
lined: rayado.
loudly: en alta voz, ruidosamente.
month: mes, el mes.
passports: pasaportes.
procured: procurado.

reserved: reservado, reservada.
shutters: obturadores, obturador.
snored: roncado.
swayed: Oscilado.
thence: desde allí.
tradesman: comerciante.
watch: reloj, mirar, observar, reloj de pulsera, ver, contemplar, el reloj, prestar atención, vigilar, guardia, guardar.
whitened: blanqueado.
written: escrito.

take care to send her **luggage** to Lheureux **whence** it would be taken direct to the "Hirondelle," so that no one would have any **suspicion**. And in all this there never was any **allusion** to the child. Rodolphe **avoided** speaking of her; perhaps he no longer thought about it.

He wished to have two more weeks before him to arrange some **affairs**; then at the end of a week he wanted two more; then he said he was ill; next he went on a journey. The month of August passed, and, after all these delays, they decided that it was to be **irrevocably** fixed for the 4th September--a Monday.

At length the Saturday before arrived.

Rodolphe came in the evening earlier than usual.

"Everything is ready?" she asked him.

"Yes."

Then they walked round a garden-bed, and went to **sit** down near the terrace on the kerb-stone of the wall.

"You are sad," said Emma.

"No; why?"

And yet he looked at her **strangely** in a **tender** fashion.

"It is because you are going away?" she went on; "because you are leaving what is dear to you--your life? Ah! I understand. I have nothing in the world! you are all to me; so shall I be to you. I will be your people, your country; I will tend, I will love you!"

"How sweet you are!" he said, **seizing** her in his arms.

"Really!" she said with a **voluptuous** laugh. "Do you love me? **Swear** it then!"

"Do I love you--love you? I **adore** you, my love."

The moon, full and purple-coloured, was rising right out of the earth at the end of the **meadow**. She rose quickly between the branches of the poplars, that **hid** her here and there like a black **curtain pierced** with holes. Then she appeared **dazzling** with **whiteness** in the empty **heavens** that she lit up, and now **sailing** more slowly along, let fall upon the river a great **stain** that broke up into an

Spanish

adore: adorar, adoran, adoren, adore, adoro, adoras, adoramos, adoráis, adora, adorad.
affairs: asuntos.
allusion: alusión.
avoided: Evitado, eludido, rehuido.
curtain: cortina, la cortina.
dazzling: deslumbrante.
heavens: cielo, cielos.
hid: escondió, pret de hide.
irrevocably: irrevocablemente.
luggage: equipaje, equipajes.

meadow: prado, pradera.
pierced: agujereado.
sailing: navegación.
seizing: agarrando, asiendo.
sit: sentarse, estar sentado, sentar.
stain: manchar, mancha, mancilla, teñir, tintura, la mancha.
strangely: extrañamente.
suspicion: sospecha, recelo, recelocaz.
swear: jurar, jura, jurad, juráis, juramos, juran, juras, juren, juro, jure, maldecir.

tend: cuidar, cuidas, cuidan, cuido, cuide, cuida, cuidáis, cuidamos, cuidad, cuiden, tender.
tender: tierno, oferta, dulce, subasta, proposición, ofrecer, destajo, licitación, presentar, reproducir, retratar.
voluptuous: voluptuoso.
whence: de dónde.
whiteness: albura.

infinity of stars; and the silver **sheen** seemed to **writhe** through the very depths like a **heedless** serpent covered with luminous **scales**; it also resembled some **monster** candelabra all along which sparkled drops of diamonds running together. The soft night was about them; masses of shadow filled the branches. Emma, her eyes half closed, breathed in with deep sighs the fresh wind that was blowing. They did not speak, lost as they were in the rush of their reverie. The tenderness of the old days came back to their hearts, full and silent as the flowing river, with the softness of the perfume of the syringas, and threw across their memories shadows more immense and more sombre than those of the still willows that lengthened out over the grass. Often some night-animal, **hedgehog** or **weasel**, setting out on the **hunt**, disturbed the **lovers**, or sometimes they heard a **ripe peach** falling all alone from the espalier.

"Ah! what a **lovely** night!" said Rodolphe.

"We shall have others," replied Emma; and, as if speaking to herself: "Yet, it will be good to **travel**. And yet, why should my heart be so **heavy**? Is it **dread** of the **unknown**? The effect of habits left? Or rather--? No; it is the excess of happiness. How weak I am, am I not? Forgive me!"

"There is still time!" he cried. "**Reflect!** perhaps you may repent!"

"Never!" she cried **impetuously**. And coming closer to him: "What ill could come to me? There is no **desert**, no **precipice**, no ocean I would not traverse with you. The longer we live together the more it will be like an embrace, every day closer, more heart to heart. There will be nothing to trouble us, no cares, no obstacle. We shall be alone, all to **ourselves** eternally. Oh, speak! Answer me!"

At **regular** intervals he answered, "Yes--Yes--" She had passed her hands through his hair, and she repeated in a **childlike** voice, despite the big tears which were falling, "Rodolphe! Rodolphe! Ah! Rodolphe! dear little Rodolphe!"

Midnight struck.

"Midnight!" said she. "Come, it is to-morrow. One day more!"

He rose to go; and as if the **movement** he made had been the signal for their **flight**, Emma said, suddenly assuming a gay air--

Spanish

childlike: infantil.
desert: desierto, abandonar, desertar, el desierto.
dread: miedo.
flight: vuelo, huida, escape.
heavy: pesado.
hedgehog: erizo.
heedless: distraído, desatento.
hunt: cazar, cazo, caza, cazáis, cazas, cazamos, cazad, cacen, cace, cazan, acosar.
impetuously: impetuosamente.

lovely: hermoso, bonito, encantador, agradable, magnífico, adorable, caro, lindo.
lovers: amantes.
monster: monstruo.
movement: movimiento, el movimiento.
ourselves: nosotros mismos.
peach: melocotón, durazno.
precipice: precipicio, despeñadero, abismo, derrumbadero.
reflect: reflejar, reflejo, refleje, reflejen,

reflejas, reflejan, reflejamos, reflejáis, reflejad, refleja, reflexionar.
regular: regular, normal.
ripe: maduro.
scales: balanza.
sheen: brillo, lustre.
travel: viajar, viaje, viajo, viaja, viajas, viajan, viajamos, viajen, viajad, viajáis, conducir.
unknown: desconocido, incógnita.
weasel: comadreja.
writhe: retorcerse.

"You have the passports?"

"Yes."

"You are **forgetting** nothing?"

"No."

"Are you sure?"

"Certainly."

"It is at the Hotel de Provence, is it not, that you will wait for me at midday?"

He nodded.

"Till **to**-morrow then!" said Emma in a last **caress**; and she watched him go.

He did not turn round. She ran after him, and, **leaning** over the water's **edge** between the bulrushes

"To-morrow!" she cried.

He was already on the other side of the river and walking **fast** across the **meadow**.

After a **few** moments Rodolphe stopped; and when he saw her with her white **gown** gradually **fade** away in the **shade** like a **ghost**, he was seized with such a **beating** of the heart that he **leant** against a tree **lest** he should fall.

"What an **imbecile** I am!" he said with a **fearful oath**. "No matter! She was a pretty mistress!"

And **immediately** Emma's beauty, with all the pleasures of their love, came back to him. For a moment he **softened**; then he **rebelled** against her.

"For, after all," he **exclaimed, gesticulating**, "I **can't exile** myself--have a child on my hands."

He was **saying** these things to give himself **firmness**.

"And besides, the worry, the expense! Ah! no, no, no, no! a thousand times no! That would be too stupid."

Spanish

beating: paliza, pulsación, latido.
can't: no puede.
caress: acariciar, caricia.
edge: borde, orilla, filo, canto, arista, baranda, ribetear, margen.
exclaimed: exclamado.
exile: destierro, exilio, desterrado, desterrar.
fade: marchitarse, marchitar.
fast: rápido, ayunar, fijo, de prisa, pronto, veloz, ligero, firme, ayuno.
fearful: temeroso, medroso,

angustioso.
few: pocos.
firmness: firmeza.
forgetting: olvidando.
gesticulating: gesticulando.
ghost: fantasma, el fantasma, imagen fantasma, aparición.
gown: vestido, toga.
imbecile: imbécil.
immediately: inmediatamente, ahora mismo, directamente, en seguida, en el acto.

leaning: inclinación.
leant: pret y pp de lean.
lest: para que no, a no ser que, con el fin de, no sea que, si es necesario.
meadow: prado, pradera.
oath: juramento.
rebelled: rebelado.
saying: diciendo, dicho, decir, refrán.
shade: sombra, sombrear, pantalla, matizar, tono, matiz.
softened: ablandado.
to-morrow: mañana.

CHAPTER THIRTEEN

No sooner was Rodolphe at home than he sat down quickly at his bureau under the stag's head that hung as a trophy on the wall. But when he had the pen between his fingers, he could think of nothing, so that, resting on his elbows, he began to reflect. Emma seemed to him to have **receded** into a **far**-off past, as if the **resolution** he had taken had suddenly placed a distance between them.

To get back something of her, he **fetched** from the cupboard at the bedside an old Rheims biscuit-box, in which he **usually** kept his **letters** from women, and from it came an odour of dry dust and **withered** roses. First he saw a handkerchief with pale little spots. It was a handkerchief of hers. Once when they were walking her nose had **bled**; he had **forgotten** it. Near it, **chipped** at all the corners, was a miniature given him by Emma: her **toilette** seemed to him **pretentious**, and her **languishing** look in the worst possible **taste**. Then, from looking at this image and **recalling** the memory of its original, Emma's **features** little by little grew confused in his **remembrance**, as if the living and the painted face, rubbing one against the other, had **effaced** each other. Finally, he read some of her letters; they were full of explanations **relating** to their journey, **short**, **technical**, and **urgent**, like business **notes**. He wanted to see the long **ones** again, those of old times. In order to find them at the bottom of the **box**, Rodolphe disturbed all the others, and **mechanically** began **rummaging** amidst this mass of **papers** and things, finding **pell**-mell bouquets, **garters**, a black mask, pins, and

Spanish

bled: Sangrado.
box: caja, estuche, arca, casilla, boxear, la caja, jarro, recuadro, olla, palco, cajetín.
chipped: astillado.
effaced: borrado.
far-off: remoto.
features: características, funciones.
fetched: traído, sacado.
forgotten: olvidado.
garters: ligas.
languishing: languideciendo.

letters: letras.
mechanically: mecánicamente.
notes: notas.
ones: unos.
papers: papeles.
pell-mell: atropelladamente.
pretentious: pretencioso, engreído.
recalling: recordar.
receded: retrocedido.
relating: contando, relacionando.
remembrance: recuerdo.
resolution: resolución, definición,

poder de resolución.
rummaging: registrando.
short: corto, bajo, breve.
taste: gusto, saborear, sabor, probar, catar.
technical: técnico.
toilette: wáter, de tocador, inodoro, lavabo, retrete, sanitario, servicios, tocado, vestido, atavío, baño.
urgent: urgente.
usually: normalmente, usualmente.
withered: marchito, marchitado.

hair--hair! **dark** and **fair**, some even, **catching** in the **hinges** of the box, broke when it was opened.

Thus **dallying** with his souvenirs, he examined the writing and the **style** of the letters, as **varied** as their **orthography**. They were tender or **jovial**, **facetious**, melancholy; there were some that asked for love, others that asked for money. A word recalled faces to him, certain gestures, the **sound** of a voice; sometimes, however, he remembered nothing at all.

In fact, these women, rushing at once into his thoughts, **cramped** each other and **lessened**, as **reduced** to a uniform level of love that **equalised** them all. So taking handfuls of the mixed-up letters, he amused himself for some moments with letting them fall in **cascades** from his right into his left hand. At last, bored and weary, Rodolphe took back the box to the cupboard, saying to himself, "What a **lot** of rubbish!" Which **summed** up his **opinion**; for pleasures, like **schoolboys** in a school courtyard, had so trampled upon his heart that no green thing grew there, and that which passed through it, more **heedless** than children, did not even, like them, leave a name carved upon the wall.

"Come," said he, "let's begin."

He wrote--

"Courage, Emma! courage! I would not bring misery into your life."

"After all, that's true," thought Rodolphe. "I am **acting** in her interest; I am honest."

"Have you **carefully** weighed your resolution? Do you know to what an **abyss** I was dragging you, poor angel? No, you do not, do you? You were coming **confident** and **fearless**, believing in happiness in the **future**. Ah! unhappy that we are--insensate!"

Rodolphe stopped here to think of some good excuse.

"If I told her all my fortune is lost? No! Besides, that would stop nothing. It would all have to be begun over again later on. As if one could make women like that listen to reason!" He reflected, then went on--

Spanish

abyss: abismo, despeñadero, precipicio.
acting: acción, interino.
carefully: cuidadosamente.
cascades: cascadas.
catching: cogiendo, contagioso, asiendo, acertando.
confident: seguro.
cramped: estrecho.
dallying: tardando.
dark: oscuro, tenebroso.
equalised: igualado.

facetious: jocoso, gracioso, chistoso.
fair: justo, rubio, mercado, feria, verbena, bazar, equitativo, hermoso.
fearless: intrépido, arrojado.
future: futuro, porvenir, próximo, entrante, el futuro.
heedless: distraído, desatento.
hinges: goznes, bisagras.
jovial: jovial.
lessened: achicado, minorado.
lot: lote, porción, solar.
opinion: opinión, dictamen, juicio,

parecer.
orthography: ortografía.
reduced: reducido, reducir, achicado.
schoolboys: colegiales.
sound: sonido, sonar, ruido, tocar, sano, sondear, legítimo, auscultar, sólido, oscilación acústica, vibración acústica.
style: estilo.
summed: sumado.
varied: variado.

"I shall not forget you, oh believe it; and I shall ever have a profound devotion for you; but some day, sooner or later, this **ardour** (such is the fate of human things) would have **grown** less, no doubt. Lassitude would have come to us, and who knows if I should not even have had the atrocious pain of **witnessing** your remorse, of **sharing** it myself, since I should have been its cause? The mere idea of the grief that would come to you **tortures** me, Emma. Forget me! Why did I ever know you? Why were you so beautiful? Is it my fault? O my God! No, no! **Accuse** only fate."

"That's a word that always tells," he said to himself.

"Ah, if you had been one of those frivolous women that one sees, certainly I might, through egotism, have tried an **experiment**, in that case without **danger** for you. But that delicious **exaltation**, at once your charm and your torment, has prevented you from understanding, **adorable** woman that you are, the **falseness** of our future position. Nor had I reflected upon this at first, and I rested in the shade of that **ideal** happiness as beneath that of the **manchineel** tree, without **foreseeing** the consequences."

"Perhaps she'll think I'm giving it up from **avarice**. Ah, well! so much the worse; it must be stopped!"

"The world is **cruel**, Emma. Wherever we might have gone, it would have persecuted us. You would have had to put up with indiscreet questions, **calumny**, contempt, insult perhaps. Insult to you! Oh! And I, who would place you on a **throne**! I who bear with me your memory as a **talisman**! For I am going to **punish** myself by exile for all the ill I have done you. I am going away. Whither I know not. I am mad. **Adieu**! Be good always. **Preserve** the memory of the unfortunate who has lost you. **Teach** my name to your child; let her **repeat** it in her prayers."

The wicks of the candles **flickered**. Rodolphe got up to, shut the window, and when he had sat down again--

"I think it's all right. Ah! and this for fear she should come and hunt me up."

Spanish

accuse: acusar, acusamos, acuso, acusen, acusan, acusáis, acusad, acusa, acusas, acuse, denunciar.
adieu: adiós.
adorable: cute, adorable.
ardour: exaltación, vehemencia, entusiasmo, ardor.
avarice: avaricia.
calumny: calumnia.
cruel: cruel.
danger: peligro, el peligro.
exaltation: exaltación.

experiment: experimento, experimentar.
falseness: falsedad.
flickered: parpadeó.
foreseeing: previendo.
grown: crecido, aumentado, adulto.
ideal: ideal.
manchineel: manzanillo, mancinella.
preserve: conservar, guardar, preservar, confitura, conserva.
punish: castigar, castigad, castiguen, castigas, castigan, castigáis, castiga,

castigamos, castigue, castigo, penar.
repeat: repetir, repita, repitan, repito, repites, repetid, repite, repetís, repetimos, repiten, reiterar.
sharing: compartir.
talisman: talismán.
teach: enseñar, enseñáis, enseñamos, enseñad, enseñan, enseñas, enseñen, enseño, Enseñe, enseña, instruir.
throne: trono.
tortures: torturas.
witnessing: presenciar.

"I shall be far away when you read these sad **lines**, for I have wished to flee as quickly as possible to **shun** the temptation of seeing you again. No weakness! I shall **return**, and perhaps later on we shall **talk** together very **coldly** of our old love. Adieu!"

And there was a last "adieu" **divided** into two words! "A Dieu!" which he thought in very excellent taste.

"Now how am I to sign?" he said to himself. " 'Yours devotedly?' No! 'Your friend?' Yes, that's it."

"Your friend."

He re-read his **letter**. He considered it very good.

"Poor little woman!" he thought with emotion. "She'll think me harder than a **rock**. There ought to have been some tears on this; but I **can't** cry; it isn't my fault." Then, having **emptied** some water into a glass, Rodolphe **dipped** his finger into it, and let a big drop fall on the paper, that made a pale **stain** on the ink. Then looking for a seal, he came upon the one "Amor nel cor."

"That doesn't at all **fit** in with the circumstances. **Pshaw**! never mind!"

After which he smoked three pipes and went to bed.

The next day when he was up (at about two o'clock--he had slept late), Rodolphe had a basket of apricots picked. He put his letter at the bottom under some **vine** leaves, and at once ordered Girard, his **ploughman**, to take it with care to Madame Bovary. He made use of this means for **corresponding** with her, sending **according** to the **season** fruits or **game**.

"If she asks after me," he said, "you will tell her that I have gone on a journey. You must give the basket to her herself, into her own hands. Get along and take care!"

Girard put on his new blouse, **knotted** his handkerchief round the apricots, and walking with great heavy steps in his thick iron-bound galoshes, made his way to Yonville.

Spanish

according: conforme, de acuerdo con.
can't: no puede.
coldly: fríamente.
corresponding: correspondiente, correspondiendo, empalmando.
dipped: mojado.
divided: dividido, separado, apartado, segregado, compartido.
emptied: desocupado, vaciado.
fit: adaptar, acomodar, ajustar, apoplejía, ajuste, caber, ataque, en forma, encajar.
game: juego, el juego, partido, caza.
knotted: anudado.
letter: carta, letra, la carta.
lines: partida de matrimonio, destino, pauta, especificado de líneas, líneas, papel.
ploughman: labrador, arador.
pshaw: bah.
return: volver, devolver, regresar, retorno, devolución, rendimiento, vuelta.
rock: roca, balancear, piedra, mecer, peña.
season: estación, temporada, condimentar.
shun: rehuir, rehuyo, rehuid, rehuimos, rehuís, rehuyan, rehuye, rehuyen, rehuyes, rehuya.
stain: manchar, mancha, mancilla, teñir, tintura, la mancha.
talk: hablar, hablas, hablan, hablad, habláis, hablamos, hablo, hable, hablen, habla, charla.
vine: parra, viña, vid.

Madame Bovary, when he got to her house, was arranging a bundle of linen on the kitchen-table with Felicite.

"Here," said the **ploughboy**, "is something for you--from the master."

She was seized with apprehension, and as she sought in her pocket for some coppers, she looked at the peasant with **haggard** eyes, while he himself looked at her with amazement, not understanding how such a present could so move **anyone**. At last he went out. Felicite remained. She could bear it no longer; she ran into the sitting room as if to take the apricots there, **overturned** the basket, tore away the leaves, found the letter, opened it, and, as if some fearful **fire** were behind her, Emma flew to her room **terrified**.

Charles was there; she saw him; he spoke to her; she heard nothing, and she went on quickly up the stairs, breathless, **distraught**, dumb, and ever holding this **horrible** piece of paper, that crackled between her fingers like a plate of sheet-iron. On the second floor she stopped before the attic door, which was closed.

Then she tried to calm herself; she recalled the letter; she must finish it; she did not dare to. And where? How? She would be seen! "Ah, no! here," she thought, "I shall be all right."

Emma pushed open the door and went in.

The **slates** threw straight down a heavy heat that **gripped** her temples, stifled her; she dragged herself to the closed garret-window. She drew back the bolt, and the dazzling **light** burst in with a **leap**.

Opposite, beyond the roofs, stretched the open country till it was lost to sight. Down **below**, underneath her, the **village** square was empty; the stones of the pavement glittered, the weathercocks on the **houses** were motionless. At the corner of the street, from a **lower storey**, rose a kind of humming with **strident** modulations. It was Binet turning.

She leant against the **embrasure** of the window, and **reread** the letter with **angry** sneers. But the more she fixed her attention upon it, the more confused were her ideas. She saw him again, heard him, **encircled** him with her arms, and

Spanish

angry: enojado, enfadado, furioso.
anyone: alguien, cualquiera.
below: abajo, debajo de, debajo, bajo, por debajo de, en el fondo.
distraught: aturrullado.
embrasure: alféizar, Apertura, cañonera.
encircled: rodeado.
fire: fuego, incendio, despedir, disparar, el fuego, tirar, animar, incitar, lumbre, hacer fuego, encender.

gripped: agarrado.
haggard: ojeroso, macilento, demacrado.
horrible: temeroso, abominable, lúgubre, horroroso, horrible.
houses: casas.
leap: saltar, salto, brincar, el salto.
light: luz, claro, ligero, encender, alumbrar, débil, liviano, la luz, radiación visible, lámpara, iluminar.
lower: bajar, baja, bajo, bajen, baje, bajas, bajan, bajamos, bajáis, bajad,

inferior.
overturned: invertido, trastornado, volcado.
ploughboy: mozo de labranza.
reread: releer.
slates: pizarra.
storey: piso.
strident: estridente.
terrified: aterrorizado, aterrado.
village: aldea, pueblo, el pueblo, caserío.

throbs of her heart, that **beat** against her breast like blows of a sledge-hammer, grew **faster** and faster, with **uneven** intervals. She looked about her with the wish that the earth might crumble into pieces. Why not end it all? What restrained her? She was free. She advanced, looking at the paving-stones, saying to herself, "Come! come!"

The luminous ray that came straight up from below drew the weight of her body towards the abyss. It seemed to her that the **ground** of the **oscillating** square went up the walls and that the floor dipped on end like a **tossing boat**. She was right at the edge, almost hanging, surrounded by **vast** space. The blue of the heavens suffused her, the air was whirling in her **hollow** head; she had but to **yield**, to let herself be taken; and the humming of the lathe never ceased, like an angry voice calling her.

"Emma! Emma!" cried Charles.

She stopped.

"Wherever are you? Come!"

The thought that she had just escaped from death almost made her faint with terror. She closed her eyes; then she shivered at the **touch** of a hand on her **sleeve**; it was Felicite.

"**Master** is waiting for you, madame; the soup is on the table."

And she had to go down to sit at table.

She tried to eat. The food choked her. Then she unfolded her napkin as if to **examine** the **darns**, and she really thought of applying herself to this work, counting the threads in the linen. Suddenly the remembrance of the letter returned to her. How had she lost it? Where could she find it? But she felt such weariness of **spirit** that she could not even invent a **pretext** for leaving the table. Then she became a coward; she was afraid of Charles; he knew all, that was certain! Indeed he **pronounced** these words in a strange **manner**:

"We are not likely to see Monsieur Rodolphe soon again, it seems."

"Who told you?" she said, shuddering.

Spanish

boat: barco, bote, barca, el barco.
darns: zurce.
eat: comer, comemos, comes, coméis, comed, coman, como, comen, coma, Come.
examine: examinar, examina, examinen, examine, examinas, examinan, examinamos, examináis, examinad, examino, registrar.
faster: ayunador, más rápido, asegurado.
ground: suelo, terreno, tierra, molido, masa, conexión a tierra, el suelo, fondo, fundamento.
hollow: hueco, cavidad, hondonada, vacuo.
manner: manera.
master: maestro, amo, dueño, patrón, principal, magister.
oscillating: oscilando, oscilante, fluctuando.
pretext: pretexto.
pronounced: pronunciado, marcado.
sleeve: manga, manguito, la manga, camisa.
spirit: espíritu.
throbs: latidos.
tossing: tirar.
touch: tocar, toque, tacto, palpar, contacto, rozar.
uneven: desigual, impar, irregular.
vast: vasto.
yield: ceder, cedemos, cedes, cedo, ceden, cedéis, ceded, cede, ceda, cedan, rendimiento.

"Who told me!" he replied, rather astonished at her **abrupt tone**. "Why, Girard, **whom** I **met** just now at the door of the Cafe Francais. He has gone on a journey, or is to go."

She gave a sob.

"What surprises you in that? He **absents** himself like that from time to time for a change, and, **ma foi**, I think he's right, when one has a fortune and is a bachelor. Besides, he has jolly times, has our **friend**. He's a bit of a **rake**. Monsieur Langlois told me--"

He stopped for propriety's sake because the servant came in. She put back into the basket the apricots scattered on the **sideboard**. Charles, without **noticing** his wife's **colour**, had them brought to him, took one, and bit into it.

"Ah! perfect!" said he; "just taste!"

And he handed her the basket, which she put away from her gently.

"Do just **smell**! What an odour!" he remarked, passing it under her nose several times.

"I am choking," she cried, **leaping** up. But by an **effort** of will the **spasm** passed; then--

"It is nothing," she said, "it is nothing! It is **nervousness**. Sit down and go on eating." For she **dreaded lest** he should begin **questioning** her, attending to her, that she should not be left alone.

Charles, to **obey** her, sat down again, and he **spat** the stones of the apricots into his hands, **afterwards** putting them on his plate.

Suddenly a blue tilbury passed across the square at a rapid **trot**. Emma **uttered** a cry and fell back rigid to the ground.

In fact, Rodolphe, after many reflections, had decided to set out for Rouen. Now, as from La Huchette to Buchy there is no other way than by Yonville, he had to go through the village, and Emma had recognised him by the rays of the lanterns, which like **lightning** flashed through the **twilight**.

Spanish

abrupt: brusco, escarpado, abrupto, bronco, repentino.
absents: ausentes.
afterwards: después, luego, más adelante.
colour: color, colorear, coloración.
dreaded: temido.
effort: esfuerzo, afán.
friend: amigo, amiga, el amigo.
leaping: saltar.
lest: para que no, a no ser que, con el fin de, no sea que, si es necesario.

lightning: relámpago, rayo, el relámpago.
ma: Título Universitario, Massachusetts, Mamá.
met: encontrado, hallado.
nervousness: nerviosidad, nerviosismo.
noticing: notando.
obey: obedecer, obedecemos, obedezco, obedezcan, obedecen, obedecéis, obedeced, obedece, obedeces, obedezca.

questioning: interrogatorio.
rake: rastrillo, rastro, rastrear.
sideboard: armario, aparador.
smell: oler, olor, apestar, oler mal, olfatear, olfato.
spasm: espasmo.
spat: reñir.
tone: tono.
trot: trote, trotar.
twilight: crepúsculo, anochecer.
uttered: pronunciado.
whom: quien, quién, que.

The chemist, at the **tumult** which broke out in the house ran **thither**. The table with all the plates was upset; **sauce, meat, knives**, the **salt**, and cruet-stand were **strewn** over the room; Charles was calling for help; Berthe, scared, was crying; and Felicite, **whose** hands **trembled**, was **unlacing** her mistress, whose whole body **shivered** convulsively.

"I'll run to my laboratory for some **aromatic** vinegar," said the **druggist**.

Then as she opened her eyes on **smelling** the bottle--

"I was sure of it," he remarked; "that would wake any dead person for you!"

"Speak to us," said Charles; "collect yourself; it is your Charles, who loves you. Do you know me? See! here is your little **girl**! Oh, kiss her!"

The child stretched out her arms to her mother to **cling** to her neck. But turning away her head, Emma said in a broken voice "No, no! no one!"

She **fainted** again. They carried her to her bed. She lay there stretched at full length, her lips apart, her eyelids closed, her hands open, **motionless**, and white as a **waxen** image. Two streams of tears **flowed** from her eyes and fell slowly upon the **pillow**.

Charles, standing up, was at the back of the **alcove**, and the chemist, near him, maintained that **meditative** silence that is becoming on the serious occasions of life.

"Do not be uneasy," he said, touching his elbow; "I think the **paroxysm** is past."

"Yes, she is resting a little now," answered Charles, watching her **sleep**. "Poor girl! poor girl! She had gone off now!"

Then Homais asked how the accident had come about. Charles answered that she had been taken ill suddenly while she was eating some apricots.

"Extraordinary!" continued the chemist. "But it might be that the apricots had brought on the **syncope**. Some natures are so sensitive to certain **smells**; and it would even be a very fine question to study both in its **pathological** and **physiological relation**. The priests know the **importance** of it, they who have

Spanish

alcove: alcoba, nicho.
aromatic: aromático.
cling: agarrarse.
druggist: droguero.
fainted: pasmado, desfallecido, amortecido, desmayado.
flowed: fluido.
girl: muchacha, chica, niña, la muchacha.
importance: importancia.
knives: cuchillo.
meat: carne, la carne, carnes.

meditative: meditativo.
motionless: inmóvil, estático.
paroxysm: paroxismo, acceso.
pathological: patológico.
physiological: fisiológico.
pillow: almohada, la almohada.
relation: relación, conexión.
salt: sal, la sal, salar, salado.
sauce: salsa, la salsa.
shivered: tiritado.
sleep: dormir, duerme, duermes, dormimos, duermen, duermo,

dormís, dormid, duerma, duerman, sueño.
smelling: oler.
smells: malos olores.
strewn: regado, pp de strew.
syncope: síncope.
thither: allá.
trembled: Temblado, tembló.
tumult: tumulto, ruido.
unlacing: desenlazar.
waxen: ceroso.
whose: cuyo, cuya.

introduced aromatics into all their **ceremonies**. It is to **stupefy** the senses and to bring on ecstasies--a thing, moreover, very easy in persons of the weaker **sex**, who are more delicate than the other. Some are cited who faint at the smell of burnt hartshorn, of new bread--"

"Take care; you'll wake her!" said Bovary in a low voice.

"And not only," the druggist went on, "are human beings subject to such **anomalies**, but animals also. Thus you are not ignorant of the **singularly aphrodisiac** effect produced by the Nepeta **cataria**, **vulgarly** called catmint, on the **feline** race; and, on the other hand, to **quote** an example whose **authenticity** I can answer for. Bridaux (one of my old comrades, at present established in the Rue Malpalu) **possesses** a **dog** that falls into convulsions as soon as you hold out a snuff-box to him. He often even makes the experiment before his friends at his **summer**-house at Guillaume Wood. Would anyone believe that a simple **sternutation** could produce such **ravages** on a **quadrupedal organism**? It is extremely curious, is it not?"

"Yes," said Charles, who was not listening to him.

"This shows us," went on the other, smiling with benign **self**-sufficiency, "the **innumerable** irregularities of the nervous system. With **regard** to madame, she has always seemed to me, I confess, very susceptible. And so I should by no means recommend to you, my dear friend, any of those **so**-called remedies that, under the **pretence** of **attacking** the **symptoms**, attack the constitution. No; no useless physicking! **Diet**, that is all; sedatives, emollients, dulcification. Then, don't you think that perhaps her imagination should be worked upon?"

"In what way? How?" said Bovary.

"Ah! that is it. Such is indeed the question. 'That is the question,' as I lately read in a newspaper."

But Emma, awaking, cried out--

"The letter! the letter!"

They thought she was **delirious**; and she was by midnight. Brain-fever had set in.

Spanish

anomalies: Anomalías.
aphrodisiac: afrodisíaco.
aromatics: aromático.
attacking: agredir, atentado, acometer, atacante, agresor, atacar, ataque.
authenticity: autenticidad.
cataria: gatera.
ceremonies: feriar.
delirious: delirante.
diet: dieta.
dog: perro, el perro, la perra, can.
feline: felino.

innumerable: innumerable.
introduced: presentado, introducido.
organism: organismo.
possesses: posee.
pretence: pretensión, derecho.
quadrupedal: cuadrúpedo.
quote: citar, mencionar, cotizar, conulla.
ravages: estragos.
regard: mirar, considerar, mira, miran, miráis, miro, miramos, mirad, miras, mire, miren.

self-sufficiency: autosuficiencia.
sex: sexo, el sexo, tener sexo.
singularly: particularmente, singularmente.
so-called: llamado.
sternutation: el estornudo.
stupefy: aturdir, aturdid, aturda, aturdan, aturde, aturdes, aturdimos, aturdís, aturdo, aturden, entorpecer.
summer-house: glorieta.
symptoms: las síntomas.
vulgarly: vulgarmente.

For **forty**-three days Charles did not leave her. He gave up all his **patients**; he no longer went to bed; he was constantly feeling her **pulse**, putting on sinapisms and cold-water compresses. He sent Justin as far as Neufchatel for **ice**; the ice melted on the way; he sent him back again. He called Monsieur Canivet into **consultation**; he sent for Dr. Lariviere, his old master, from Rouen; he was in despair. What alarmed him most was Emma's **prostration**, for she did not speak, did not listen, did not even **seem** to suffer, as if her body and soul were both resting together after all their troubles.

About the middle of October she could sit up in bed supported by pillows. Charles **wept** when he saw her eat her first bread-and-jelly. Her strength returned to her; she got up for a few **hours** of an afternoon, and one day, when she felt better, he tried to take her, leaning on his arm, for a **walk** round the garden. The sand of the paths was disappearing beneath the dead leaves; she walked slowly, dragging along her **slippers**, and leaning against Charles's shoulder. She smiled all the time.

They went thus to the bottom of the garden near the terrace. She drew herself up slowly, **shading** her eyes with her hand to look. She looked far off, as far as she could, but on the horizon were only great **bonfires** of grass **smoking** on the hills.

"You will **tire** yourself, my darling!" said Bovary. And, pushing her gently to make her go into the **arbour**, "Sit down on this seat; you'll be comfortable."

"Oh! no; not there!" she said in a **faltering** voice.

She was seized with **giddiness**, and from that evening her illness recommenced, with a more **uncertain character**, it is **true**, and more **complex** symptoms. Now she suffered in her heart, then in the chest, the head, the limbs; she had **vomitings**, in which Charles thought he saw the first **signs** of **cancer**.

And besides this, the poor fellow was **worried** about money matters.

Spanish

arbour: cenador, emparrado.
bonfires: fogatas.
cancer: cáncer.
character: carácter, seña, naturaleza, índole, personaje.
complex: complejo, complicado.
consultation: consulta, reflexión.
faltering: titubeando.
forty-three: cuarenta y tres, curenta y tres.
giddiness: mareo.
hours: horas, las horas.

ice: hielo, el hielo, helado.
patients: paciente, los pacientes.
prostration: postración.
pulse: pulso, impulso, pulsación.
seem: parecer, parezca, parecen, parezcan, pareces, parezco, parecemos, parecéis, parece, pareced.
shading: sombreado.
signs: señales, carteles de señalización, signo.
slippers: zapatillas.
smoking: fumando, humeando,

fumar, ahumar.
tire: neumático, llanta, cansar, cansarse, la llanta, fatigar.
true: verdadero, cierto.
uncertain: incierto.
vomitings: vómitos.
walk: andar, andamos, ando, anden, ande, andas, andáis, andad, anda, andan, caminar.
wept: Llorado.
worried: preocupado, angustiado, inquieto.

CHAPTER FOURTEEN

To begin with, he did not know how he could pay Monsieur Homais for all the **physic supplied** by him, and though, as a **medical** man, he was not obliged to pay for it, he nevertheless blushed a little at such an **obligation**. Then the **expenses** of the household, now that the servant was mistress, became terrible. **Bills rained** in upon the house; the **tradesmen** grumbled; Monsieur Lheureux especially **harassed** him. In fact, at the height of Emma's illness, the latter, taking advantage of the circumstances to make his bill larger, had hurriedly brought the cloak, the travelling-bag, two trunks instead of one, and a number of other things. It was very well for Charles to say he did not want them. The tradesman answered **arrogantly** that these articles had been ordered, and that he would not take them back; besides, it would **vex** madame in her convalescence; the doctor had better think it over; in short, he was **resolved** to **sue** him rather than give up his rights and take back his goods. Charles subsequently ordered them to be sent back to the shop. Felicite forgot; he had other things to attend to; then thought no more about them. Monsieur Lheureux returned to the **charge**, and, by turns **threatening** and **whining**, so **managed** that Bovary ended by **signing** a bill at six months. But hardly had he **signed** this bill than a **bold** idea occurred to him: it was to **borrow** a thousand francs from Lheureux. So, with an embarrassed air, he asked if it were possible to get them, **adding** that it would be for a year, at any interest he wished. Lheureux ran off to his shop, brought back the money, and

Spanish

adding: sumando, agregando, añadiendo.
arrogantly: atorrantemente, altaneramente, altivo, altivamente, arrogantemente.
bills: efectos, billetes.
bold: grueso, negrita, audaz.
borrow: prestar, tomar prestado, pedir prestado.
charge: carga, cargo, acusación, gastos, cargar, cobro, cobrar, imputación.
expenses: gastos, expensas.

harassed: acosado, atormentado, acosada.
managed: administrado, Manejado, gestionado, dirigido.
medical: médico.
obligation: obligación, deber, compromiso.
physic: medicamento, remedio.
rained: llovido.
resolved: resuelto.
signed: firmado.
signing: firma, firmar.

sue: poner pleito a, demandar, demandad, demandas, demanden, demando, demandáis, demandamos, demandan, demanda, demande.
supplied: suministrado.
threatening: amenazando, amenazador, conminando, amenazante.
tradesmen: trabajadores especializados.
vex: vejar.
whining: gimoteando.

dictated another bill, by which Bovary undertook to pay to his order on the 1st of September next the sum of one thousand and seventy francs, which, with the hundred and **eighty** already agreed to, made just twelve hundred and **fifty**, thus lending at six per **cent** in addition to **one**-fourth for commission: and the things **bringing** him in a good third at the least, this ought in twelve months to give him a profit of a hundred and **thirty** francs. He **hoped** that the business would not stop there; that the bills would not be paid; that they would be **renewed**; and that his poor little money, having **thriven** at the doctor's as at a hospital, would come back to him one day considerably more **plump**, and fat enough to burst his bag.

Everything, moreover, succeeded with him. He was **adjudicator** for a supply of cider to the hospital at Neufchatel; Monsieur Guillaumin promised him some shares in the turf-pits of Gaumesnil, and he **dreamt** of **establishing** a new diligence service between Arcueil and Rouen, which no doubt would not be long in **ruining** the **ramshackle van** of the "Lion d'Or," and that, travelling faster, at a **cheaper** rate, and carrying more luggage, would thus put into his hands the whole commerce of Yonville.

Charles several times asked himself by what means he should next year be able to pay back so much money. He reflected, imagined **expedients**, such as applying to his father or selling something. But his father would be **deaf**, and he--he had nothing to sell. Then he **foresaw** such worries that he quickly dismissed so disagreeable a subject of **meditation** from his mind. He reproached himself with forgetting Emma, as if, all his thoughts belonging to this woman, it was **robbing** her of something not to be constantly thinking of her.

The winter was **severe**, Madame Bovary's convalescence slow. When it was fine they **wheeled** her arm-chair to the window that overlooked the square, for she now had an **antipathy** to the garden, and the blinds on that side were always down. She wished the horse to be sold; what she formerly liked now displeased her. All her ideas seemed to be **limited** to the care of herself. She stayed in bed taking little **meals**, rang for the servant to inquire about her **gruel** or to chat with her. The snow on the market-roof threw a white, still light into the room; then the

Spanish

adjudicator: juez.
antipathy: antipatía.
bringing: trayendo.
cent: centavo, céntimo, centésima, el centavo.
cheaper: más barato.
deaf: sordo.
dreamt: pret y pp de dream.
eighty: ochenta.
establishing: estableciendo, edificando.
expedients: conveniente, material de

circunstancias.
fifty: cincuenta.
foresaw: pret de foresee, previo.
gruel: gachas.
hoped: esperado.
limited: limitado, limitada.
meals: las comidas.
meditation: meditación.
one-fourth: un cuarto.
plump: engordáis, engordamos, engordan, engordas, engorde, engorden, engordad, dilaten,

engordo, dilato, dilata.
ramshackle: ruinoso.
renewed: renovado.
robbing: robando, despojando, hurtando.
ruining: arruinar.
severe: severo, inclemente, áspero, grave.
thirty: treinta.
thriven: pp de thrive.
van: furgoneta, furgón.
wheeled: de ruedas, rodado.

rain began to fall; and Emma waited **daily** with a mind full of **eagerness** for the **inevitable** return of some **trifling events** which nevertheless had no relation to her. The most important was the arrival of the "Hirondelle" in the evening. Then the landlady **shouted** out, and other voices answered, while Hippolyte's lantern, as he fetched the boxes from the boot, was like a **star** in the darkness. At mid-day Charles came in; then he went out again; next she took some beef-tea, and **towards** five o'clock, as the day drew in, the children coming back from school, dragging their wooden shoes along the pavement, knocked the **clapper** of the shutters with their **rulers** one after the other.

It was at this hour that Monsieur Bournisien came to see her. He inquired after her health, gave her **news, exhorted** her to religion, in a **coaxing** little **prattle** that was not without its charm. The mere thought of his **cassock** comforted her.

One day, when at the height of her illness, she had thought herself dying, and had asked for the communion; and, while they were making the preparations in her room for the **sacrament**, while they were turning the night table covered with syrups into an altar, and while Felicite was **strewing dahlia** flowers on the floor, Emma felt some power passing over her that freed her from her **pains**, from all **perception**, from all feeling. Her body, relieved, no longer thought; another life was beginning; it seemed to her that her being, mounting toward God, would be **annihilated** in that love like a burning incense that melts into vapour. The **bed**-clothes were **sprinkled** with holy water, the priest drew from the holy **pyx** the white **wafer**; and it was **fainting** with a celestial joy that she put out her lips to accept the body of the Saviour presented to her. The curtains of the alcove floated gently round her like clouds, and the rays of the two tapers burning on the night-table seemed to shine like dazzling **halos**. Then she let her head fall back, fancying she heard in space the music of **seraphic** harps, and perceived in an **azure** sky, on a golden throne in the midst of saints holding green palms, God the Father, **resplendent** with **majesty**, who with a sign sent to earth angels with wings of fire to carry her away in their arms.

Spanish

annihilated: aniquilado, anonadado.
azure: azul celeste, azur.
bed-clothes: ropa de la cama.
cassock: sotana.
clapper: badajo, palmoteador.
coaxing: halagando.
dahlia: dalia.
daily: diariamente, diario, cotidiano, de todos los días, todos los días.
eagerness: deseo, ansia, avidez.
events: eventos.
exhorted: exhortado.

fainting: desmayo, desvanecimiento.
halos: aureolas.
inevitable: inevitable.
majesty: majestad.
news: noticias, noticia, nueva, las noticias.
pains: dolores del parto, esfuerzos, desvelos.
perception: percepción.
prattle: cháchara, balbuceo, charlar, parlotear, parloteo, balbucear.
pyx: píxide.

resplendent: resplandeciente.
rulers: gobernantes.
sacrament: sacramento.
seraphic: seráfico.
shouted: gritado.
sprinkled: rociado.
star: estrella, la estrella, astro.
strewing: esparciendo.
toward: hacia, a.
trifling: fútil.
wafer: oblea, galleta, oblea de silicio, barquillo, el barquillo, hostia.

This splendid vision **dwelt** in her memory as the most beautiful thing that it was possible to dream, so that now she **strove** to recall her sensation. That still lasted, however, but in a less **exclusive** fashion and with a deeper sweetness. Her soul, tortured by pride, at length found rest in Christian **humility**, and, tasting the joy of weakness, she saw within herself the **destruction** of her will, that must have left a wide entrance for the inroads of **heavenly grace**. There **existed**, then, in the place of happiness, still greater joys--another love beyond all loves, without **pause** and without end, one that would grow eternally! She saw amid the illusions of her hope a state of **purity** floating above the earth mingling with heaven, to which she **aspired**. She wanted to become a **saint**. She bought chaplets and wore amulets; she wished to have in her room, by the side of her bed, a **reliquary** set in emeralds that she might kiss it every evening.

The cure marvelled at this humour, although Emma's religion, he thought, might, from its **fervour**, end by touching on **heresy**, extravagance. But not being much **versed** in these matters, as soon as they went beyond a certain limit he wrote to Monsieur Boulard, **bookseller** to Monsignor, to send him "something good for a lady who was very clever." The bookseller, with as much indifference as if he had been sending off hardware to niggers, packed up, **pellmell**, everything that was then the fashion in the pious book trade. There were little manuals in questions and answers, pamphlets of **aggressive** tone after the manner of Monsieur de Maistre, and certain novels in rose-coloured bindings and with a honied style, **manufactured** by **troubadour** seminarists or **penitent** blue-stockings. There were the "*Think of it; the Man of the World at Mary's Feet, by Monsieur de ---, decorated with many Orders*"; "*The Errors of Voltaire, for the Use of the Young,*" etc.

Madame Bovary's mind was not yet sufficiently clear to apply herself seriously to anything; moreover, she began this reading in too much hurry. She grew **provoked** at the doctrines of religion; the **arrogance** of the **polemic** writings displeased her by their **inveteracy** in attacking people she did not know; and the **secular** stories, relieved with religion, seemed to her written in such ignorance of the world, that they insensibly estranged her from the truths for whose **proof** she was looking. Nevertheless, she **persevered**; and when the volume slipped from

Spanish

aggressive: agresivo.
arrogance: arrogancia, soberbia, altanería.
aspired: ambicionado, Aspirado.
bookseller: librero.
decorated: decorado, adornado.
destruction: destrucción, ruina.
dwelt: pret de dwell, pp de dwell.
exclusive: exclusivo.
existed: existido.
fervour: celo.
grace: gracia, garbo, honrar.

heavenly: celestial, celeste.
heresy: herejía.
humility: humildad.
inveteracy: costumbre arraigada.
manufactured: fabricado, manufacturado.
pause: descanso, pausa, pausar, hacer una pausa, la pausa.
pellmell: a la desbandada, a trochemoche, barahúnda, caótico, desordenado, en desorden, lío.
penitent: penitente, arrepentido.

persevered: perseverado.
polemic: polémica, polémico.
proof: prueba, demostración, probanza.
provoked: provocado.
purity: pureza, limpieza, virtud.
reliquary: relicario.
saint: santo, santa, san.
secular: seglar.
strove: pret de strive.
troubadour: trovador.
versed: versado.

her hands, she fancied herself seized with the finest Catholic melancholy that an **ethereal** soul could **conceive**.

As for the memory of Rodolphe, she had thrust it back to the bottom of her heart, and it remained there more **solemn** and more motionless than a **king's mummy** in a **catacomb**. An **exhalation escaped** from this **embalmed** love, that, penetrating through everything, **perfumed** with tenderness the immaculate atmosphere in which she longed to live. When she knelt on her Gothic prie-Dieu, she **addressed** to the Lord the same suave words that she had murmured formerly to her lover in the outpourings of adultery. It was to make faith come; but no delights descended from the heavens, and she arose with tired limbs and with a vague feeling of a gigantic dupery.

This **searching** after faith, she thought, was only one **merit** the more, and in the pride of her **devoutness** Emma compared herself to those grand ladies of long ago whose glory she, had dreamed of over a portrait of La Valliere, and who, **trailing** with so much majesty the lace-trimmed trains of their long gowns, retired into **solitudes** to shed at the feet of Christ all the tears of hearts that life had wounded.

Then she gave herself up to **excessive charity**. She sewed clothes for the poor, she sent wood to women in **childbed**; and Charles one day, on coming home, found three good-for-nothings in the kitchen seated at the table eating soup. She had her little girl, whom during her illness her husband had sent back to the nurse, brought home. She wanted to teach her to read; even when Berthe cried, she was not **vexed**. She had made up her mind to **resignation**, to **universal indulgence**. Her language about everything was full of ideal expressions. She said to her child, "Is your **stomach**-ache better, my angel?"

Madame Bovary senior found nothing to **censure** except perhaps this mania of **knitting** jackets for **orphans** instead of mending her own house-linen; but, harassed with domestic quarrels, the good woman took pleasure in this quiet house, and she even stayed there till after Easter, to escape the sarcasms of old Bovary, who never failed on Good Friday to order chitterlings.

Spanish

addressed: dirigido.
catacomb: catacumba.
censure: censurar, reprobación, criticar, desaprobación.
charity: caridad, limosna, misericordia, beneficencia.
childbed: parto, cama para niños.
conceive: concebir, conciban, concibo, concibes, concibe, concebís, concebimos, conceived, conciben, conciba.
devoutness: devoción.

embalmed: embalsamado.
escape: escaparse, escapar, huida, fuga, escape, evadir, escapada, huir.
ethereal: etéreo.
excessive: excesivo, desmesurado.
exhalation: exhalación.
indulgence: indulgencia, bula.
king's: inglés correcto.
knitting: tejido de punto.
merit: merecer, mérito.
mummy: momia.
orphans: huérfanos.

perfumed: perfumado.
resignation: resignación, dimisión, renuncia.
searching: minucioso, búsqueda.
solemn: solemne.
solitudes: soledades.
stomach-ache: dolor de barriga.
trailing: estela, rastrear, rastreo, rastro, seguir, seguir la pista de, sendero, vereda, arrastrar, pista, huella.
universal: universal.
vexed: enfadado.

Besides the companionship of her mother-in-law, who **strengthened** her a little by the **rectitude** of her **judgment** and her grave **ways**, Emma almost every day had other visitors. These were Madame Langlois, Madame Caron, Madame Dubreuil, Madame Tuvache, and regularly from two to five o'clock the excellent Madame Homais, who, for her part, had never believed any of the tittle-tattle about her **neighbour**. The little Homais also came to see her; Justin accompanied them. He went up with them to her bedroom, and remained standing near the door, motionless and **mute**. Often even Madame Bovary; taking no heed of him, began her toilette. She began by taking out her comb, **shaking** her head with a quick movement, and when he for the first time saw all this mass of hair that fell to her knees **unrolling** in black ringlets, it was to him, poor child! like a sudden **entrance** into something new and strange, whose splendour terrified him.

Emma, no doubt, did not notice his silent attentions or his **timidity**. She had no suspicion that the love vanished from her life was there, palpitating by her side, beneath that coarse holland shirt, in that **youthful** heart open to the emanations of her beauty. Besides, she now enveloped all things with such indifference, she had words so affectionate with looks so **haughty**, such **contradictory** ways, that one could no longer distinguish egotism from charity, or **corruption** from virtue. One evening, for **example**, she was angry with the servant, who had asked to go out, and stammered as she tried to find some pretext. Then suddenly--

"So you love him?" she said.

And without waiting for any answer from Felicite, who was blushing, she added, "There! run along; enjoy yourself!"

In the beginning of spring she had the garden turned up from end to end, **despite** Bovary's **remonstrances**. However, he was glad to see her at last **manifest** a wish of any kind. As she grew stronger she **displayed** more **wilfulness**. First, she found **occasion** to **expel** Mere Rollet, the nurse, who during her convalescence had contracted the habit of coming too often to the kitchen with her two nurslings and her **boarder**, better off for teeth than a **cannibal**. Then she got rid of the Homais family, **successively** dismissed all the other visitors,

Spanish

boarder: huésped, pupilo, pensionista, interno.
cannibal: caníbal.
contradictory: opuesto, contradictorio.
corruption: corrupción, deterioración, putrefacción.
despite: a pesar de.
displayed: manifestado, expuesto, acusado, desplegado, lúcido, ostentado, presentado, demostrado.
entrance: entrada, la entrada.
example: ejemplo, el ejemplo.

expel: expulsar, expulsa, expulsad, expulso, expulsen, expulsas, expulsan, expulsamos, expulsáis, expulse.
haughty: orgulloso, altivo, altanero.
judgment: juicio, fallo, sentencia, criterio.
manifest: manifiesto, evidente, manifestar.
mute: mudo, muda, sordina.
neighbour: vecino.
occasion: motivo, ocasión, lugar,

oportunidad.
rectitude: rectitud.
remonstrances: protestas.
shaking: sacudiendo, sacudida.
strengthened: fortalecido.
successively: sucesivamente.
timidity: timidez.
unrolling: devanando.
ways: maneras.
wilfulness: intención, testarudez, voluntariedad.
youthful: juvenil, joven.

and even **frequented** church less **assiduously**, to the great approval of the druggist, who said to her in a **friendly** way--

"You were going in a bit for the cassock!"

As formerly, Monsieur Bournisien dropped in every day when he came out after catechism class. He preferred staying out of doors to taking the air "in the grove," as he called the arbour. This was the time when Charles came home. They were hot; some sweet cider was brought out, and they drank together to madame's **complete** restoration.

Binet was there; that is to say, a little lower down against the terrace wall, fishing for **crayfish**. Bovary **invited** him to have a drink, and he **thoroughly** understood the **uncorking** of the **stone** bottles.

"You must," he said, throwing a **satisfied** glance all round him, even to the very **extremity** of the **landscape**, "hold the bottle **perpendicularly** on the table, and after the strings are **cut**, **press** up the cork with little thrusts, gently, gently, as indeed they do seltzer-water at restaurants."

But during his **demonstration** the cider often spurted right into their faces, and then the ecclesiastic, with a thick laugh, never missed this joke--

"Its goodness strikes the eye!"

He was, in fact, a good fellow and one day he was not even scandalised at the chemist, who advised Charles to give madame some distraction by taking her to the theatre at Rouen to hear the illustrious **tenor**, Lagardy. Homais, surprised at this silence, wanted to know his opinion, and the priest declared that he considered music less **dangerous** for morals than literature.

But the chemist took up the **defence** of letters. The theatre, he **contended**, served for **railing** at prejudices, and, beneath a mask of pleasure, **taught** virtue.

"'Castigat ridendo mores,' Monsieur Bournisien! Thus consider the **greater** part of Voltaire's **tragedies**; they are cleverly strewn with philosophical reflections, that made them a vast school of morals and **diplomacy** for the people."

Spanish

assiduously: asiduamente.
complete: completo, lleno, completar, llenar, cabal, concluir, cumplido.
contended: Contendido.
crayfish: cangrejo, cangrejo de río.
cut: cortar, corte, cortado, cortadura.
dangerous: peligroso.
defence: defensa, retaguardia.
demonstration: demostración, manifestación.
diplomacy: diplomacia.
extremity: extremidad, extremo,

extremidades.
frequented: frecuentado, asendereado.
friendly: amistoso, amable, bonito, gracioso, amigable.
greater: mayor.
invited: invitado.
landscape: paisaje, panorama, horizontal.
perpendicularly: perpendicularmente.
press: prensa, apretar, presionar, prensar, pulsar, oprimir.
railing: barandilla, balaustrada,

pasamano, baranda.
satisfied: satisfecho, contento, complacido.
stone: piedra, la piedra, cálculo.
taught: enseñado, instruido, desacostumbrado.
tenor: vencimiento de un efecto, curso, de tenor, para tenor, rumbo, tenor, camino, tendencia.
thoroughly: completamente.
tragedies: tragedias.
uncorking: descorchando.

"I," said Binet, "once saw a piece called the 'Gamin de Paris,' in which there was the character of an old general that is really hit off to a T. He sets down a young **swell** who had seduced a working girl, who at the ending--"

"Certainly," continued Homais, "there is bad literature as there is bad pharmacy, but to condemn in a **lump** the most important of the fine arts seems to me a stupidity, a Gothic idea, **worthy** of the **abominable** times that **imprisoned** Galileo."

"I know very well," objected the cure, "that there are good works, good authors. However, if it were only those persons of different sexes united in a **bewitching** apartment, decorated **rouge**, those lights, those **effeminate** voices, all this must, in the long-run, engender a certain mental libertinage, give rise to **immodest** thoughts and **impure temptations**. Such, at any rate, is the opinion of all the Fathers. Finally," he added, suddenly assuming a mystic tone of voice while he rolled a pinch of snuff between his fingers, "if the Church has **condemned** the theatre, she must be right; we must submit to her decrees."

"Why," asked the druggist, "should she **excommunicate actors**? For formerly they **openly** took part in religious ceremonies. Yes, in the middle of the **chancel** they acted; they performed a kind of **farce** called 'Mysteries,' which often **offended** against the laws of decency."

The ecclesiastic contented himself with uttering a **groan**, and the chemist went on--

"It's like it is in the Bible; there there are, you know, more than one **piquant** detail, matters really libidinous!"

And on a gesture of irritation from Monsieur Bournisien--

"Ah! you'll admit that it is not a book to place in the hands of a young girl, and I should be sorry if Athalie--"

"But it is the Protestants, and not we," cried the other impatiently, "who recommend the Bible."

"No matter," said Homais. "I am surprised that in our days, in this century of **enlightenment**, anyone should still **persist** in **proscribing** an intellectual

Spanish

abominable: abominable, horrible, horroroso.
actors: los actores.
bewitching: embrujando, fascinante.
chancel: presbiterio.
condemned: condenado.
effeminate: afeminado.
enlightenment: esclarecimiento, ilustración.
excommunicate: excomulgar, excomulgad, excomulguen, excomulgo, excomulgas,

excomulgan, excomulgáis, excomulga, excomulgamos, excomulgue.
farce: farsa.
groan: gemir, gemido.
immodest: inmodesto.
imprisoned: encarcelado.
impure: impuro.
lump: pedazo, masa, terrón, pieza, bola, tela, grumo, bulto, chichón, pella.
offended: ofendido, injuriado,

ultrajado, insultado, delinquido.
openly: abiertamente, públicamente.
persist: persistir, persistimos, persistid, persisto, persistís, persisten, persistes, persiste, persistan, persista.
piquant: picante.
proscribing: proscribiendo, proscribir.
rouge: colorete.
swell: hincharse, oleaje, hinchar.
temptations: tentaciones.
worthy: digno.

relaxation that is **inoffensive, moralising,** and sometimes even hygienic; is it not, doctor?"

"No doubt," replied the doctor carelessly, either because, sharing the same ideas, he wished to **offend** no one, or else because he had not any ideas.

The conversation seemed at an end when the chemist thought fit to **shoot** a Parthian **arrow.**

"I've known priests who put on ordinary clothes to go and see dancers kicking about."

"Come, come!" said the cure.

"Ah! I've known some!" And **separating** the words of his **sentence,** Homais repeated, "I--have--known--some!"

"Well, they were wrong," said Bournisien, **resigned** to anything.

"By Jove! they go in for more than that," exclaimed the druggist.

"Sir!" replied the ecclesiastic, with such angry eyes that the druggist was **intimidated** by them.

"I only mean to say," he replied in less brutal a tone, "that **toleration** is the surest way to **draw** people to religion."

"That is true! that is true!" agreed the good fellow, sitting down again on his chair. But he stayed only a few moments.

Then, as soon as he had gone, Monsieur Homais said to the doctor--

"That's what I call a cock-fight. I beat him, did you see, in a way!--Now take my advice. Take madame to the theatre, if it were only for once in your life, to **enrage** one of these ravens, hang it! If anyone could take my place, I would accompany you myself. Be quick about it. Lagardy is only going to give one **performance;** he's **engaged** to go to England at a high **salary.** From what I hear, he's a regular dog; he's rolling in money; he's taking three mistresses and a cook along with him. All these great artists burn the **candle** at both ends; they **require** a **dissolute** life, that suits the imagination to some extent. But they die at the

Spanish

arrow: flecha, la flecha, saeta.
candle: vela, la vela, bujía, candela, cirio.
dissolute: disoluto.
draw: dibujar, dibujáis, dibujad, dibujen, dibuje, dibujas, dibujamos, dibuja, dibujan, dibujo, tirar.
engaged: ocupado, comprometido, engranado, prometido.
enrage: enfurecer, enfurecerse.
inoffensive: inofensivo, cándido, ingenuo, inofensiva.

intimidated: intimidado.
moralising: moralizar.
offend: ofender, ofendo, ofendan, ofende, ofended, ofendéis, ofendemos, ofenden, ofendes, ofenda, injuriar.
performance: rendimiento, representación, actuación, desempeño, función, funcionamiento, cumplimiento.
relaxation: relajación.
require: necesitar, necesita, necesiten,

necesite, necesitas, necesito, necesitan, necesitamos, necesitáis, necesitad, exigir.
resigned: dimitido, resignado.
salary: salario, sueldo, el sueldo.
sentence: frase, condenar, sentencia, oración, la frase, pena, punición, condena.
separating: separar.
shoot: tirar, tiren, tiráis, tiramos, tiran, tirad, tire, tiras, tiro, tira, disparar.
toleration: tolerancia.

hospital, because they **haven't** the sense when young to lay by. Well, a pleasant dinner! Goodbye till to-morrow."

The idea of the theatre quickly **germinated** in Bovary's head, for he at once **communicated** it to his wife, who at first refused, **alleging** the **fatigue**, the worry, the expense; but, for a **wonder**, Charles did not give in, so sure was he that this recreation would be good for her. He saw nothing to prevent it: his mother had sent them three hundred francs which he had no longer expected; the **current** debts were not very large, and the falling in of Lheureux's bills was still so far off that there was no need to think about them. Besides, **imagining** that she was refusing from delicacy, he insisted the more; so that by dint of worrying her she at last made up her mind, and the next day at **eight** o'clock they set out in the "Hirondelle."

The **druggist**, whom nothing **whatever** kept at Yonville, but who thought himself bound not to **budge** from it, sighed as he saw them go.

"Well, a pleasant journey!" he said to them; "happy **mortals** that you are!"

Then addressing himself to Emma, who was wearing a blue silk gown with four flounces--

"You are as lovely as a Venus. You'll cut a **figure** at Rouen."

The diligence stopped at the "Croix-Rouge" in the Place Beauvoisine. It was the inn that is in every provincial faubourg, with large stables and small **bedrooms**, where one sees in the middle of the court **chickens pilfering** the oats under the muddy gigs of the **commercial** travellers--a good old house, with **worm**-eaten balconies that creak in the wind on winter nights, always full of people, noise, and feeding, whose black tables are sticky with coffee and brandy, the thick windows made yellow by the flies, the damp **napkins** stained with **cheap wine**, and that always smells of the village, like ploughboys dressed in Sunday clothes, has a cafe on the street, and towards the **countryside** a kitchen-garden. Charles at once set out. He **muddled** up the stage-boxes with the **gallery**, the pit with the boxes; asked for explanations, did not understand them; was sent from the box-office to the acting-manager; came back to the inn, returned to the

Spanish

alleging: alegando.
bedrooms: el dormitorios.
budge: mover, mueve, muevan, muevo, mueves, mueva, moved, movemos, movéis, mueven, moverse.
cheap: barato.
chickens: pollos.
commercial: comercial, anuncio.
communicated: Comunicado.
countryside: campo, campiña.
current: corriente, actual, contemporáneo, en curso, común.

druggist: droguero.
eight: ocho.
fatigue: fatiga, fatigar.
figure: figura, cifra, calcular, figurar, computar, retrato, reproducción, ilustración.
gallery: galería.
germinated: germinado.
haven't: no tener.
hospital: hospital, el hospital.
imagining: imaginando.
mortals: mortales.

muddled: desordenó.
napkins: servilletas.
pilfering: ratería.
pit: zanja, pozo, hoyo, foso, fosa, picadura.
whatever: cualquier, lo que, cualquier cosa.
wine: vino, el vino.
wonder: preguntarse, maravilla, asombrarse, prodigio, preguntar.
worm-eaten: picado por los gusanos, carcomido, apolillado.

theatre, and thus several times **traversed** the whole length of the **town** from the theatre to the **boulevard**.

Madame Bovary bought a bonnet, gloves, and a bouquet. The doctor was much afraid of **missing** the beginning, and, without having had time to swallow a plate of soup, they presented themselves at the doors of the theatre, which were still closed. **Chapter** Fifteen

The crowd was waiting against the wall, **symmetrically** enclosed between the **balustrades**. At the corner of the neighbouring **streets huge** bills repeated in **quaint** letters "Lucie de Lammermoor-Lagardy-Opera-etc." The weather was fine, the people were hot, perspiration trickled amid the curls, and handkerchiefs taken from pockets were **mopping** red **foreheads**; and now and then a warm wind that blew from the river gently stirred the **border** of the **tick awnings** hanging from the doors of the public-houses. A little lower down, however, one was refreshed by a current of icy air that smelt of **tallow**, leather, and **oil**. This was an **exhalation** from the Rue des Charrettes, full of large black warehouses where they made casks.

For fear of seeming ridiculous, Emma before going in wished to have a little **stroll** in the **harbour**, and Bovary **prudently** kept his tickets in his hand, in the pocket of his trousers, which he pressed against his stomach.

Her heart began to beat as soon as she reached the vestibule. She involuntarily smiled with vanity on seeing the crowd rushing to the right by the other corridor while she went up the staircase to the reserved seats. She was as **pleased** as a child to **push** with her finger the large tapestried door. She breathed in with all her might the dusty smell of the lobbies, and when she was seated in her box she bent forward with the air of a **duchess**.

The theatre was beginning to fill; **opera**-glasses were taken from their cases, and the **subscribers**, catching sight of one another, were bowing. They came to seek relaxation in the fine arts after the anxieties of business; but "business" was not forgotten; they still talked cottons, spirits of wine, or **indigo**. The heads of old men were to be seen, **inexpressive** and peaceful, with their hair and complexions looking like silver medals **tarnished** by steam of **lead**. The young beaux were

Spanish

awnings: toldos, entoldado.
balustrades: barandillas.
border: borde, orilla, frontera, límite, margen, baranda.
boulevard: bulevar.
chapter: capítulo, capitulo, sección.
duchess: duquesa.
exhalation: exhalación.
harbour: puerto.
heads: cabezas, administradores.
huge: enorme, inmenso, ingente.
indigo: índigo, añil.

inexpressive: inexpresivo.
lead: plomo, guiar, guía, conducir, guiáis, guiamos, guían, guías, guíe, guíen, guío.
missing: desaparecido.
mopping: trapear.
oil: aceite, el aceite, engrasar, petróleo, aceitar.
opera-glasses: gemelos de teatro.
pleased: contento.
prudently: prudentemente.
push: empujar, empujón, empuje.

quaint: pintoresco.
streets: calles, las calles.
stroll: paseo, andar.
subscribers: suscriptores.
symmetrically: simétricamente.
tallow: sebo.
tarnished: deslustrado, empañado, manchado.
tick: tictac, garrapata, marcar.
town: ciudad, pueblo, población, el pueblo.
traversed: Atravesado.

strutting about in the pit, showing in the opening of their waistcoats their pink or applegreen cravats, and Madame Bovary from above admired them leaning on their canes with golden knobs in the open palm of their yellow gloves.

Now the lights of the orchestra were lit, the lustre, let down from the ceiling, throwing by the glimmering of its facets a sudden gaiety over the theatre; then the musicians came in one after the other; and first there was the protracted hubbub of the basses grumbling, violins squeaking, cornets trumpeting, flutes and flageolets fifing. But three knocks were heard on the stage, a rolling of drums began, the brass instruments played some chords, and the curtain rising, discovered a country-scene.

It was the cross-roads of a wood, with a fountain shaded by an oak to the left. Peasants and lords with plaids on their shoulders were singing a hunting-song together; then a captain suddenly came on, who evoked the spirit of evil by lifting both his arms to heaven. Another appeared; they went away, and the hunters started afresh. She felt herself transported to the reading of her youth, into the midst of Walter Scott. She seemed to hear through the mist the sound of the Scotch bagpipes re-echoing over the heather. Then her remembrance of the novel helping her to understand the libretto, she followed the story phrase by phrase, while vague thoughts that came back to her dispersed at once again with the bursts of music. She gave herself up to the lullaby of the melodies, and felt all her being vibrate as if the violin bows were drawn over her nerves. She had not eyes enough to look at the costumes, the scenery, the actors, the painted trees that shook when anyone walked, and the velvet caps, cloaks, swords--all those imaginary things that floated amid the harmony as in the atmosphere of another world. But a young woman stepped forward, throwing a purse to a squire in green. She was left alone, and the flute was heard like the murmur of a fountain or the warbling of birds. Lucie attacked her cavatina in G major bravely. She plained of love; she longed for wings. Emma, too, fleeing from life, would have liked to fly away in an embrace. Suddenly Edgar-Lagardy appeared.

He had that splendid pallor that gives something of the majesty of marble to the ardent races of the South. His vigorous form was tightly clad in a brown-

Spanish

afresh: de nuevo, otra vez.
ardent: ardiente.
bagpipes: gaitas, gaita.
birds: aves.
bravely: valientemente.
canes: bastones.
captain: capitán.
costumes: vestuario.
facets: facetas.
fleeing: huyendo.
flute: flauta.
gives: da.

helping: ración.
instruments: accesorios, instrumentos.
knocks: Golpes.
libretto: libreto.
lights: luces.
lullaby: arrullo, canción de cuna.
novel: novela, nuevo, la novela.
oak: roble.
orchestra: orquesta, la orquesta.
plaids: jugado.
plained: afinado, fino.
played: jugado, tocado.

protracted: prolongado.
scenery: paisaje, decorado.
squire: escudero.
stage: escenario, fase, etapa, escena, plataforma, estrado, organizar.
started: comenzado, encaminado.
strutting: pavoneo, pavoneándose.
vibrate: vibrar, vibre, vibrad, vibro, vibren, vibras, vibran, vibráis, vibra, vibramos.
vigorous: vigoroso.
warbling: Trinando.

coloured **doublet**; a small **chiselled poniard** hung against his left thigh, and he cast round laughing looks showing his white teeth. They said that a Polish **princess** having heard him sing one night on the beach at Biarritz, where he mended boats, had fallen in love with him. She had ruined herself for him. He had deserted her for other women, and this sentimental celebrity did not fail to **enhance** his artistic reputation. The **diplomatic mummer** took care always to slip into his **advertisements** some **poetic** phrase on the **fascination** of his person and the **susceptibility** of his soul. A fine organ, imperturbable coolness, more temperament than **intelligence**, more power of **emphasis** than of real singing, made up the charm of this admirable **charlatan** nature, in which there was something of the hairdresser and the toreador.

From the first scene he evoked enthusiasm. He pressed Lucy in his arms, he left her, he came back, he seemed **desperate**; he had outbursts of rage, then **elegiac** gurglings of infinite sweetness, and the notes escaped from his bare neck full of sobs and kisses. Emma leant forward to see him, clutching the velvet of the box with her nails. She was filling her heart with these **melodious** lamentations that were drawn out to the **accompaniment** of the double-basses, like the cries of the **drowning** in the tumult of a tempest. She recognised all the intoxication and the anguish that had almost killed her. The voice of a **prima** donna seemed to her to be but echoes of her conscience, and this illusion that charmed her as some very thing of her own life. But no one on earth had loved her with such love. He had not wept like Edgar that last **moonlit** night when they said, "To-morrow! to-morrow!" The theatre rang with **cheers**; they recommenced the entire movement; the lovers spoke of the flowers on their tomb, of vows, exile, fate, hopes; and when they uttered the final **adieu**, Emma gave a sharp cry that mingled with the vibrations of the last chords.

"But why," asked Bovary, "does that gentleman **persecute** her?"

"No, no!" she answered; "he is her lover!"

"Yet he vows **vengeance** on her family, while the other one who came on before said, 'I love Lucie and she loves me!' Besides, he went off with her father

---

Spanish

accompaniment: acompañamiento.
adieu: adiós.
advertisements: anuncios, publicidad.
charlatan: charlatán.
cheers: salud, a su salud.
chiselled: escopleado, timado, cincelado.
desperate: desesperado.
diplomatic: diplomático.
doublet: jubón, doblete.
drowning: ahogándose, el ahogamiento, ahogar, ahogo, ahogamiento.
elegiac: elegíaco.
emphasis: énfasis, realce.
enhance: mejorar, mejoro, mejoras, mejoran, mejoramos, mejoráis, mejorad, mejoren, mejore, mejora, realzar.
fascination: fascinación.
intelligence: inteligencia.
melodious: melodioso.
moonlit: luz de la luna, iluminado por la luna.
mummer: bufón, mimo, máscara.
persecute: perseguir, persigue, perseguid, persigues, persiguen, persigan, perseguimos, perseguís, persigo, persiga.
poetic: poético.
poniard: apuñalar, puñal.
prima: primero, primer.
princess: princesa.
susceptibility: susceptibilidad.
vengeance: venganza.

arm in arm. For he certainly is her father, isn't he--the ugly little man with a cock's feather in his hat?"

Despite Emma's explanations, as soon as the **recitative duet** began in which Gilbert **lays** bare his abominable machinations to his master Ashton, Charles, seeing the **false** troth-ring that is to deceive Lucie, thought it was a love-gift sent by Edgar. He confessed, moreover, that he did not understand the story because of the music, which interfered very much with the words.

"What does it matter?" said Emma. "Do be quiet!"

"Yes, but you know," he went on, leaning against her shoulder, "I like to understand things."

"Be quiet! be quiet!" she cried impatiently.

Lucie advanced, half supported by her women, a **wreath** of orange blossoms in her hair, and paler than the white satin of her gown. Emma dreamed of her marriage day; she saw herself at home again amid the corn in the little path as they walked to the church. Oh, why had not she, like this woman, **resisted**, implored? She, on the contrary, had been joyous, without seeing the abyss into which she was throwing herself. Ah! if in the freshness of her beauty, before the soiling of marriage and the **disillusions** of adultery, she could have **anchored** her life upon some great, strong heart, then virtue, tenderness, voluptuousness, and duty blending, she would never have fallen from so high a happiness. But that happiness, no doubt, was a lie invented for the despair of all desire. She now knew the **smallness** of the passions that art exaggerated. So, **striving** to **divert** her thoughts, Emma determined now to see in this **reproduction** of her sorrows only a plastic **fantasy**, well enough to please the eye, and she even smiled **internally** with **disdainful** pity when at the back of the stage under the velvet **hangings** a man appeared in a black cloak.

His large Spanish hat fell at a gesture he made, and immediately the instruments and the singers began the **sextet**. Edgar, flashing with **fury**, **dominated** all the others with his **clearer** voice; Ashton hurled **homicidal** provocations at him in deep notes; Lucie uttered her shrill **plaint**, Arthur at one side, his **modulated** tones in the middle **register**, and the **bass** of the minister

Spanish

anchored: anclado.
bass: bajo, perca, róbalo, lubina.
clearer: aclarar, limpio, liquidador, claro, borrar, eliminar, puro, vaciar, el que despeja, despejado, anular.
disdainful: desdeñoso.
disillusions: desilusiona.
divert: desviar, desvían, desvíen, desvíe, desvías, desviamos, desviáis, desvía, desviad, desvío, distraer.
dominated: dominado.
duet: dúo.

false: falso.
fantasy: fantasía.
fury: furia, furor.
hangings: papel pintado.
homicidal: homicida.
internally: internamente.
lays: pone, coloca.
modulated: modulado.
plaint: lamento, querella, demanda, reclamación.
recitative: recitativo, recitado.
register: registro, registrar, certificar,

inscribir, recomendar, ensalzar, hacer inscribir, registrarse, registrador, encarecer, matricular.
reproduction: reproducción, lectura.
resisted: Resistido.
sextet: sexteto.
smallness: pequeñez.
striving: luchando, forcejeando, esforzándose, desviviéndose, afanando, pugnando, esforzar, esfuerzos.
wreath: guirnalda, corona.

pealed forth like an organ, while the voices of the women repeating his words took them up in chorus **delightfully**. They were all in a row gesticulating, and anger, vengeance, jealousy, terror, and stupefaction breathed forth at once from their half-opened mouths. The **outraged** lover **brandished** his **naked sword**; his guipure **ruffle** rose with jerks to the movements of his chest, and he walked from right to left with long strides, clanking against the **boards** the silver-gilt spurs of his soft boots, **widening** out at the ankles. He, she thought must have an **inexhaustible** love to lavish it upon the crowd with such **effusion**. All her small fault-findings faded before the poetry of the part that absorbed her; and, drawn towards this man by the illusion of the character, she tried to **imagine** to herself his life--that life **resonant**, extraordinary, splendid, and that might have been hers if fate had willed it. They would have known one another, loved one another. With him, through all the **kingdoms** of Europe she would have **travelled** from capital to capital, sharing his fatigues and his pride, **picking** up the flowers thrown to him, herself **embroidering** his costumes. Then each evening, at the back of a box, behind the golden trellis-work she would have drunk in **eagerly** the expansions of this soul that would have sung for her alone; from the stage, even as he **acted**, he would have looked at her. But the mad idea seized her that he was looking at her; it was certain. She longed to run to his arms, to take refuge in his strength, as in the **incarnation** of love itself, and to say to him, to cry out, "Take me away! carry me with you! let us go! **Thine**, thine! all my ardour and all my dreams!"

The curtain fell.

The smell of the gas mingled with that of the breaths, the **waving** of the **fans**, made the air more **suffocating**. Emma wanted to go out; the crowd filled the corridors, and she fell back in her arm-chair with palpitations that choked her. Charles, fearing that she would faint, ran to the refreshment-room to get a glass of barley-water.

He had great **difficulty** in getting back to his seat, for his elbows were jerked at every step because of the glass he held in his hands, and he even **spilt** three-fourths on the shoulders of a Rouen lady in short sleeves, who feeling the cold

---

Spanish

acted: Actuado.
boards: tablazón, valla de madera.
brandished: Blandido.
delightfully: deleitablemente, deleitosamente, deliciosamente, encantadamente, encantado.
difficulty: dificultad, inconveniente.
eagerly: ansiosamente, ávidamente.
effusion: derrame, efusión.
embroidering: bordando.
fans: hinchada, ventiladores.
imagine: figurarse, imaginar,

imaginad, imaginen, imagine, imaginas, imaginan, imagino, imaginamos, imagináis, imagina.
incarnation: encarnación, renacer.
inexhaustible: inagotable.
kingdoms: reinos.
naked: desnudo.
outraged: despavorido, ultrajado.
picking: picando.
resonant: resonante.
ruffle: faralá, fruncir, agitar, agitarse, arruga, arrugar, arrugarse, chorrera,

confundir, enmarañar, erizar.
spilt: pret y pp de spill.
suffocating: sofocando, sofocante, ahogándose, asfixiar.
sword: espada.
thine: tuyo, tuyos, tuyas, tuya, tus.
travelled: viaje, moverse, viajado, viajar, viajar por, camino.
waving: ondear, señalar, cimbreante, señal, ondular, ondeante, onda, oleada, indicar, ola.
widening: ensanchando, ensanche.

liquid running down to her **loins**, **uttered** cries like a **peacock**, as if she were being **assassinated**. Her husband, who was a millowner, railed at the **clumsy** fellow, and while she was with her handkerchief wiping up the **stains** from her handsome cherry-coloured **taffeta** gown, he **angrily** muttered about **indemnity**, **costs**, **reimbursement**. At last Charles reached his wife, saying to her, quite out of breath--

"Ma foi! I thought I should have had to **stay** there. There is such a crowd-- SUCH a crowd!"

He added--

"Just guess whom I met up there! Monsieur Leon!"

"Leon?"

"Himself! He's coming along to pay his respects." And as he **finished** these words the ex-clerk of Yonville entered the box.

He **held** out his hand with the **ease** of a gentleman; and Madame Bovary **extended** hers, without doubt **obeying** the **attraction** of a stronger will. She had not felt it since that spring evening when the rain fell upon the green leaves, and they had said **good**-bye standing at the window. But soon recalling herself to the **necessities** of the **situation**, with an effort she shook off the **torpor** of her memories, and began **stammering** a few hurried words.

"Ah, good-day! What! you here?"

"Silence!" cried a voice from the pit, for the third act was beginning.

"So you are at Rouen?"

"Yes."

"And since when?"

"Turn them out! turn them out!" People were looking at them. They were silent.

But from that moment she listened no more; and the chorus of the guests, the scene between Ashton and his servant, the **grand duet** in D major, all were for her as far off as if the instruments had grown less **sonorous** and the characters

Spanish

angrily: con enojo, enconadamente, airadamente, enojadamente.
assassinated: asesinado.
attraction: atracción.
clumsy: torpe.
costs: costes, cuesta, expensas, costas.
duet: dúo.
ease: facilidad, comodidad, mitigar.
extended: ampliado, alargado, extendido.
finished: acabado, terminado, listo, concluido.

good-bye: despedida, adiós.
grand: magnífico, grande, grandioso.
held: tuvo lugar, sostuvo.
indemnity: indemnización, indemnidad.
loins: los lomos.
necessities: artículos de primera necesidad.
obeying: obedeciendo.
peacock: pavo real.
reimbursement: reembolso, reintegro.
situation: situación.

sonorous: sonoro.
stains: manchas.
stammering: balbuceo, tartamudo, estropajoso, balbuciente, tartamudear, tartamudeo, tartamudez, tartamudeando.
stay: quedarse, quedar, queden, quede, quedas, quedan, quedamos, quedáis, quedad, queda, quedo.
taffeta: tafetán, tafeta.
torpor: estupor.
uttered: pronunciado.

more **remote**. She remembered the **games** at cards at the druggist's, and the walk to the nurse's, the reading in the **arbour**, the tete-a-tete by the fireside--all that poor love, so calm and so **protracted**, so **discreet**, so **tender**, and that she had nevertheless forgotten. And why had he come back? What **combination** of circumstances had brought him back into her life? He was standing behind her, **leaning** with his shoulder against the wall of the box; now and again she felt herself **shuddering** beneath the hot breath from his nostrils falling upon her hair.

"Does this **amuse** you?" said he, **bending** over her so **closely** that the end of his **moustache brushed** her cheek. She replied carelessly--

"Oh, dear me, no, not much."

Then he proposed that they should leave the theatre and go and take an ice somewhere.

"Oh, not yet; let us stay," said Bovary. "Her hair's **undone**; this is going to be tragic."

But the mad scene did not at all interest Emma, and the acting of the **singer** seemed to her **exaggerated**.

"She **screams** too loud," said she, turning to Charles, who was listening.

"Yes--a little," he replied, **undecided** between the **frankness** of his pleasure and his respect for his wife's opinion.

Then with a **sigh** Leon said--

"The heat is--"

"**Unbearable**! Yes!"

"Do you feel unwell?" asked Bovary.

"Yes, I am **stifling**; let us go."

Monsieur Leon put her long **lace shawl** carefully about her shoulders, and all three went off to sit down in the harbour, in the open air, outside the windows of a **cafe**.

Spanish

amuse: divertir, diviértete, diviértase, diviértanse, divértidos, me divierto, nos divertimos, os divertís, se divierte, se divierten, te diviertes.
arbour: cenador, emparrado.
bending: flexión, torcimiento.
brushed: cepillado.
cafe: café, cafés.
closely: estrechamente.
combination: combinación.
discreet: discreto.
exaggerated: exagerado.

frankness: franqueza.
games: juegos.
lace: encaje, lazo, cordón, el encaje, la cinta.
leaning: inclinación.
moustache: bigote, el bigote.
protracted: prolongado.
remote: remoto, lejano, apartado, aislado, separado.
screams: carcajadas.
shawl: chal.
shuddering: estremecer.

sigh: suspirar, suspiro.
singer: cantor, cantora, cantante, el cantor.
stifling: sofocante, ahogante.
tender: tierno, oferta, dulce, subasta, proposición, ofrecer, destajo, licitación, presentar, reproducir, retratar.
unbearable: insufrible, insoportable.
undecided: indeciso.
undone: deshecho.

First they spoke of her illness, although Emma interrupted Charles from time to time, for fear, she said, of **boring** Monsieur Leon; and the latter told them that he had come to **spend** two years at Rouen in a large office, in order to get **practice** in his **profession**, which was different in Normandy and Paris. Then he **inquired** after Berthe, the Homais, Mere Lefrancois, and as they had, in the husband's **presence**, nothing more to say to one another, the conversation soon came to an end.

People coming out of the theatre passed along the pavement, **humming** or shouting at the **top** of their voices, "O bel ange, ma Lucie!" Then Leon, playing the **dilettante**, began to talk music. He had seen Tambourini, Rubini, Persiani, Grisi, and, compared with them, Lagardy, despite his grand outbursts, was **nowhere**.

"Yet," interrupted Charles, who was slowly **sipping** his rum-sherbet, "they say that he is quite **admirable** in the last act. I regret leaving before the end, because it was beginning to **amuse** me."

"Why," said the clerk, "he will soon give another performance."

But Charles replied that they were going back next day. "Unless," he added, turning to his wife, "you would like to stay alone, kitten?"

And changing his **tactics** at this unexpected opportunity that presented itself to his hopes, the young man sang the praises of Lagardy in the last number. It was really superb, **sublime**. Then Charles insisted--

"You would get back on Sunday. Come, make up your mind. You are wrong if you feel that this is doing you the least good."

The tables round them, however, were **emptying**; a **waiter** came and stood **discreetly** near them. Charles, who understood, took out his purse; the clerk held back his arm, and did not forget to leave two more pieces of silver that he made **chink** on the marble.

"I am really sorry," said Bovary, "about the money which you are--"

The other made a **careless** gesture full of **cordiality**, and taking his hat said--

"It is settled, isn't it? **To**-morrow at six o'clock?"

Spanish

admirable: admirable, estupendo.
amuse: divertir, diviértete, diviértase, diviértanse, divértidos, me divierto, nos divertimos, os divertís, se divierte, se divierten, te diviertes.
boring: aburrido, perforación, taladrar.
careless: descuidado, sin cuidado, negligente.
chink: grieta.
cordiality: cordialidad.
dilettante: diletante, aficionado.

discreetly: discreta, discretamente, recatadamente.
emptying: vaciado.
humming: zumbador.
inquired: inquirido, preguntado.
nowhere: en ninguna parte.
practice: ejercicio, practicar, emplear, práctica, ejercer.
presence: presencia.
profession: profesión, oficio.
sipping: beborrotear.
spend: gastar, gastáis, gastas, gasten,

gastad, gasta, gastamos, gastan, gasto, gaste, pasar.
sublime: sublimas, sublima, sublimen, sublimo, sublime, sublimamos, sublimad, sublimáis, subliman, admirable, bello.
tactics: táctica.
to-morrow: mañana.
top: cima, superficie, parte superior, superior, cumbre.
waiter: camarero, el camarero, el mozo, mozo.

Charles **explained** once more that he could not **absent** himself **longer**, but that nothing **prevented** Emma--

"But," she **stammered**, with a **strange smile**, "I am not sure--"

"Well, you must think it over. **We'll** see. Night **brings** counsel." Then to Leon, who was **walking along** with them, "Now that you are in our part of the world, I **hope** you'll come and **ask** us for some **dinner** now and then."

The **clerk declared** he would not **fail** to do so, being **obliged**, **moreover**, to go to Yonville on some business for his office. And they **parted** before the Saint-Herbland Passage just as the **clock** in the **cathedral struck** half-past eleven.

PART THREE

CHAPTER ONE

Monsieur Leon, while studying law, had gone pretty often to the dancing-rooms, where he was even a great **success** amongst the grisettes, who thought he had a **distinguished** air. He was the best-mannered of the students; he wore his hair **neither** too long nor too short, didn't spend all his quarter's money on the first day of the month, and kept on good terms with his professors. As for excesses, he had always **abstained** from them, as much from **cowardice** as from **refinement**.

Often when he stayed in his room to read, or else when sitting of an evening under the lime-trees of the Luxembourg, he let his Code fall to the ground, and the memory of Emma came back to him. But gradually this feeling grew weaker, and other desires gathered over it, although it still **persisted** through them all. For Leon did not lose all hope; there was for him, as it were, a **vague promise floating** in the future, like a golden fruit **suspended** from some **fantastic** tree.

Then, seeing her again after three years of absence his passion reawakened. He must, he thought, at last make up his mind to **possess** her. Moreover, his **timidity** had worn off by **contact** with his **gay** companions, and he returned to the provinces **despising everyone** who had not with **varnished** shoes **trodden** the **asphalt** of the boulevards. By the side of a Parisienne in her **laces**, in the **drawing**-room of some **illustrious physician**, a person **driving** his carriage and wearing many orders, the poor **clerk** would no doubt have **trembled** like a child;

Spanish

abstained: se abstenido, abstinente.
asphalt: asfalto, asfaltar.
clerk: empleado, dependiente, oficinista, secretario, el dependiente.
contact: contacto, contactar, ponerse en contacto.
cowardice: cobardía.
despising: despreciando.
distinguished: distinguido.
drawing-room: estrado.
driving: conduciendo, manejando, conducción, conducir.

everyone: todo el mundo, todos.
fantastic: fantástico, hueco.
floating: flotante, flotación.
gay: alegre, homosexual.
illustrious: ilustre.
laces: cintas.
neither: tampoco, ninguno, nadie, ni.
persisted: persistido.
physician: médico, doctor.
possess: poseer, poseen, posees, poseo, posean, poseéis, posee, poseed, poseemos, posea, tener.

promise: prometer, prometéis, prometemos, prometen, prometo, promete, prometan, prometa, prometes, prometed, promesa.
refinement: refinamiento, finura.
success: éxito, acierto, desarrollo.
suspended: suspendido.
timidity: timidez.
trembled: Temblado, tembló.
trodden: pisado, pp de tread.
vague: vago.
varnished: barnizado.

but here, at Rouen, on the harbour, with the wife of this small doctor he felt at his ease, sure beforehand he would shine. Self-possession **depends** on its **environment**. We **don't** speak on the first floor as on the fourth; and the **wealthy** woman seems to have, about her, to guard her virtue, all her banknotes, like a **cuirass** in the lining of her corset.

On leaving the Bovarys the night before, Leon had followed them through the streets at a distance; then having seen them stop at the "Croix-Rouge," he turned on his heel, and spent the night meditating a **plan**.

So the next day about five o'clock he walked into the kitchen of the inn, with a choking sensation in his **throat**, pale cheeks, and that resolution of cowards that **stops** at nothing.

"The gentleman isn't in," answered a servant.

This seemed to him a good **omen**. He went **upstairs**.

She was not disturbed at his **approach**; on the contrary, she apologised for having neglected to tell him where they were staying.

"Oh, I divined it!" said Leon.

He pretended he had been guided towards her by chance, by, **instinct**. She began to smile; and at once, to **repair** his folly, Leon told her that he had spent his morning in looking for her in all the **hotels** in the town one after the other.

"So you have made up your mind to stay?" he added.

"Yes," she said, "and I am wrong. One ought not to **accustom** oneself to impossible pleasures when there are a thousand demands upon one."

"Oh, I can imagine!"

"Ah! no; for you, you are a man!"

But men too had had their **trials**, and the conversation went off into certain philosophical reflections. Emma **expatiated** much on the misery of earthly affections, and the eternal **isolation** in which the heart **remains entombed**.

To show off, or from a naive **imitation** of this melancholy which called forth his, the young man declared that he had been **awfully** bored during the whole

Spanish

accustom: acostumbrar, acostumbren, acostumbran, acostumbro, acostumbras, acostumbráis, acostumbrad, acostumbra, acostumbramos, acostumbre, habituar.
approach: aproximación, enfoque, aproximarse, acercarse, acercar, acercamiento, método, planteamiento.
awfully: terriblemente.
cuirass: coraza.

depends: depende.
don't: no.
entombed: sepultó.
environment: entorno, ambiente, alrededores, medio ambiente.
expatiated: explayado, espaciado.
hotels: hoteles, los hoteles.
imitation: imitación, remedo.
instinct: instinto.
isolation: aislamiento, separación, retiro.
omen: agüero, augurio, presagio.

plan: plano, propósito, proyectar, diseño, planificar, plan, intención, proyecto, planear, esquema.
remains: restos, resta, permanece.
repair: reparar, reparación, compostura.
stops: para, detiene.
throat: garganta, la garganta.
trials: juicios.
upstairs: arriba.
wealthy: adinerado, rico, pudiente, acaudalado.

course of his **studies**. The law irritated him, other vocations attracted him, and his mother never ceased worrying him in every one of her letters. As they talked they explained more and more fully the motives of their sadness, working **themselves** up in their **progressive confidence**. But they sometimes stopped short of the complete **exposition** of their thought, and then sought to invent a phrase that might **express** it all the same. She did not confess her passion for another; he did not say that he had forgotten her.

Perhaps he no longer remembered his suppers with **girls** after masked balls; and no doubt she did not **recollect** the **rendezvous** of old when she ran across the fields in the morning to her lover's house. The noises of the town hardly reached them, and the room seemed small, as if on purpose to hem in their solitude more closely. Emma, in a **dimity** dressing-gown, leant her head against the back of the old **arm**-chair; the yellow **wall**-paper formed, as it were, a golden **background** behind her, and her bare head was **mirrored** in the glass with the white **parting** in the middle, and the tip of her ears **peeping** out from the folds of her hair.

"But pardon me!" she said. "It is wrong of me. I weary you with my eternal complaints."

"No, never, never!"

"If you knew," she went on, raising to the ceiling her beautiful eyes, in which a tear was trembling, "all that I had dreamed!"

"And I! Oh, I too have suffered! Often I went out; I went away. I dragged myself along the quays, **seeking** distraction amid the **din** of the crowd without being able to **banish** the **heaviness** that weighed upon me. In an engraver's shop on the **boulevard** there is an Italian **print** of one of the Muses. She is draped in a **tunic**, and she is looking at the moon, with forget-me-nots in her flowing hair. Something drove me there **continually**; I stayed there hours together." Then in a trembling voice, "She resembled you a little."

Madame Bovary turned away her head that he might not see the **irrepressible** smile she felt rising to her lips.

Spanish

arm-chair: sillón, butaca.
background: fondo, antecedentes, segundo plano, trasfondo, de fondo, movimiento propio, luminancia de fondo.
banish: desterrar, destierran, destierras, destierra, desterramos, desterráis, desterrad, destierren, destierre, destierro.
boulevard: bulevar.
confidence: confianza, confidencia.
continually: continuamente, siempre.

dimity: bombasí.
din: ruido, fragor.
exposition: exposición.
express: expresar, expresa, expresas, expresen, expresan, expresamos, expresáis, expresad, expreso, exprese.
girls: las muchachas.
heaviness: pesadez.
hem: dobladillo.
irrepressible: irreprimible, incontrolable.
mirrored: reflejado.

parting: separación.
peeping: pipiando.
print: imprimir, impresión, copiar, estampa, escribir con letras de imprenta, huella.
progressive: progresivo.
recollect: recordar.
rendezvous: cita.
seeking: buscando.
studies: estudios.
tunic: túnica.
wall-paper: papel pintado.

"Often," he went on, "I wrote you letters that I tore up."

She did not **answer**. He continued--

"I sometimes fancied that some chance would bring you. I thought I recognised you at street-corners, and I ran after all the carriages through whose windows I saw a **shawl fluttering**, a veil like yours."

She seemed resolved to let him go on speaking without **interruption**. **Crossing** her arms and bending down her face, she looked at the **rosettes** on her **slippers**, and at intervals made little movements **inside** the satin of them with her toes.

At last she sighed.

"But the most wretched thing, is it not--is to **drag** out, as I do, a useless existence. If our pains were only of some use to **someone**, we should find consolation in the thought of the sacrifice."

He started off in praise of virtue, **duty**, and silent **immolation**, having himself an **incredible** longing for self-sacrifice that he could not **satisfy**.

"I should much like," she said, "to be a nurse at a hospital."

"Alas! men have none of these holy missions, and I see nowhere any calling-- unless perhaps that of a doctor."

With a slight shrug of her shoulders, Emma interrupted him to speak of her illness, which had almost killed her. What a pity! She should not be suffering now! Leon at once **envied** the calm of the tomb, and one evening he had even made his will, asking to be buried in that beautiful rug with velvet stripes he had received from her. For this was how they would have wished to be, each setting up an ideal to which they were now **adapting** their past life. Besides, **speech** is a rolling-mill that always **thins** out the sentiment.

But at this **invention** of the rug she asked, "But why?"

"Why?" He **hesitated**. "Because I loved you so!" And **congratulating** himself at having **surmounted** the difficulty, Leon watched her face out of the corner of his eyes.

Spanish

adapting: adaptando.
answer: respuesta, responder, contestar, contestación, responder a, corresponder al, contestar a, la respuesta, réplica.
congratulating: felicitando, congratulando.
crossing: cruce, cruzamiento, travesía.
drag: arrastrar, arrastro, arrastrad, arrastráis, arrastramos, arrastran, arrastras, arrastren, arrastra, arrastre, remolcar.

duty: deber, servicio, obligación, impuesto.
envied: envidiado.
fluttering: revolotear.
hesitated: vacilado, titubeado.
immolation: inmolación.
incredible: increíble.
inside: dentro, dentro de, interior, adentro, en, por, interna.
interruption: interrupción.
invention: invención, invento.
rosettes: rosetones.

satisfy: complacer, complacen, complazca, complazcan, complaces, complazco, complacéis, complace, complaced, complacemos, satisfacer.
shawl: chal.
slippers: zapatillas.
someone: alguien, alguno, cierto.
speech: discurso, habla, lenguaje, oración, conversación, dialecto, idioma.
surmounted: vencido, superado.
thins: afina.

It was like the sky when a **gust** of wind **drives** the clouds across. The mass of sad thoughts that **darkened** them seemed to be lifted from her blue eyes; her whole face **shone**. He waited. At last she replied--

"I always suspected it."

Then they went over all the **trifling** events of that **far**-off existence, whose joys and sorrows they had just **summed** up in one **word**. They recalled the **arbour** with **clematis**, the **dresses** she had worn, the furniture of her room, the whole of her house.

"And our poor **cactuses**, where are they?"

"The cold killed them this winter."

"Ah! how I have thought of them, do you know? I often saw them again as of **yore**, when on the summer mornings the sun beat down upon your **blinds**, and I saw your two bare arms passing out amongst the flowers."

"Poor friend!" she said, holding out her hand to him.

Leon swiftly pressed his lips to it. Then, when he had taken a deep breath--

"At that time you were to me I know not what **incomprehensible** force that took **captive** my life. Once, for **instance**, I went to see you; but you, no doubt, do not **remember** it."

"I do," she said; "go on."

"You were **downstairs** in the **ante**-room, ready to go out, standing on the last stair; you were wearing a **bonnet** with small blue flowers; and without any **invitation** from you, in **spite** of myself, I went with you. Every moment, however, I grew more and more **conscious** of my **folly**, and I went on walking by you, not **daring** to follow you **completely**, and unwilling to leave you. When you went into a shop, I waited in the street, and I watched you through the window taking off your **gloves** and **counting** the change on the counter. Then you rang at Madame Tuvache's; you were let in, and I stood like an **idiot** in front of the great heavy door that had closed after you."

Spanish

ante-room: antesala, antecámara, vestíbulo.
arbour: cenador, emparrado.
blinds: deslumbra, persianas.
bonnet: capot, capó, gorro, capota.
cactuses: cactos.
captive: cautivo.
clematis: clemátide.
completely: completamente.
conscious: consciente.
counting: contar, cuenta.
daring: atrevido.

darkened: oscurecido.
dresses: los vestidos.
drives: conduce, maneja.
far-off: remoto.
folly: tontería.
gloves: guantes, los guantes.
gust: ráfaga, racha.
idiot: idiota, bobo, estúpido.
incomprehensible: incomprensible.
instance: instancia, ejemplo, ejemplar.
invitation: invitación, convite.
remember: recordar, recuerde,

recuerdo, recuerdan, recuerdas, recuerden, recordamos, recordad, recordáis, recuerda, acordarse de.
shone: brillado, pret y pp de shine.
spite: rencor.
stair: escalón, escalera.
summed: sumado.
trifling: fútil.
word: palabra, la palabra, vocablo, término, formular.
yore: antaño, de antaño, hace tiempo, tiempos pasados.

Madame Bovary, as she listened to him, wondered that she was so old. All these things **reappearing** before her seemed to **widen** out her life; it was like some sentimental **immensity** to which she returned; and from time to time she said in a low voice, her eyes half closed--

"Yes, it is true--true--true!"

They heard eight strike on the different clocks of the Beauvoisine quarter, which is full of **schools**, churches, and large empty hotels. They no longer spoke, but they felt as they looked upon each other a **buzzing** in their heads, as if something **sonorous** had escaped from the fixed eyes of each of them. They were hand in hand now, and the past, the future, reminiscences and dreams, all were **confounded** in the **sweetness** of this **ecstasy**. Night was **darkening** over the walls, on which still **shone**, half hidden in the shade, the coarse **colours** of four bills **representing** four scenes from the "Tour de Nesle," with a **motto** in Spanish and French at the bottom. Through the **sash**-window a **patch** of dark sky was seen between the pointed roofs.

She rose to light two wax-candles on the drawers, then she sat down again.

"Well!" said Leon.

"Well!" she replied.

He was thinking how to **resume** the interrupted conversation, when she said to him--

"How is it that no one until now has ever **expressed** such sentiments to me?"

The clerk said that ideal natures were difficult to understand. He from the first moment had loved her, and he **despaired** when he thought of the happiness that would have been **theirs**, if thanks to fortune, **meeting** her **earlier**, they had been **indissolubly** bound to one another.

"I have sometimes thought of it," she went on.

"What a dream!" murmured Leon. And **fingering** gently the blue **binding** of her long white sash, he added, "And who **prevents** us from beginning now?"

Spanish

binding: encuadernación, vinculante, vinculación, obligatorio, atadura, ligamiento.
buzzing: zumbido.
colours: bandera.
confounded: perplejo.
darkening: oscureciendo.
despaired: desesperado.
earlier: mas temprano.
ecstasy: éxtasis.
expressed: expresado.
fingering: tecleo, digitación, tocar.

immensity: inmensidad.
indissolubly: indisolublemente.
meeting: encontrando, reunión, encuentro, hallando, sesión, entrevista, cita, asamblea.
motto: lema.
patch: remendar, parche.
prevents: impide, previene.
reappearing: reapareciendo.
representing: representando.
resume: reanudar, reanudan, reanuden, reanudo, reanudas,

reanudáis, reanudad, reanuda, reanude, reanudamos, resumir.
sash: faja, banda, marco de ventana.
schools: escuelas.
shone: brillado, pret y pp de shine.
sonorous: sonoro.
sweetness: dulzura.
theirs: suyo, sus.
widen: ensanchar, ensanche, ensanchen, ensanchas, ensanchan, ensancho, ensanchamos, ensancháis, ensanchad, ensancha, ensancharse.

"No, my friend," she replied; "I am too old; you are too young. Forget me! Others will love you; you will love them."

"Not as you!" he cried.

"What a child you are! Come, let us be **sensible**. I wish it."

She showed him the **impossibility** of their love, and that they must remain, as formerly, on the simple terms of a **fraternal** friendship.

Was she speaking thus seriously? No doubt Emma did not herself know, quite **absorbed** as she was by the **charm** of the **seduction**, and the **necessity** of **defending** herself from it; and **contemplating** the young man with a moved look, she gently **repulsed** the **timid caresses** that his **trembling** hands **attempted**.

"Ah! **forgive** me!" he cried, drawing back.

Emma was seized with a vague fear at this **shyness**, more dangerous to her than the **boldness** of Rodolphe when he advanced to her open-armed. No man had ever seemed to her so beautiful. An **exquisite candour emanated** from his being. He **lowered** his long fine **eyelashes**, that **curled** upwards. His cheek, with the soft skin **reddened**, she thought, with desire of her person, and Emma felt an **invincible longing** to press her lips to it. Then, leaning towards the clock as if to see the time--

"Ah! how late it is!" she said; "how we do chatter!"

He understood the **hint** and took up his hat.

"It has even made me forget the theatre. And poor Bovary has left me here especially for that. Monsieur Lormeaux, of the Rue Grand-Pont, was to take me and his wife."

And the opportunity was lost, as she was to leave the next day.

"Really!" said Leon.

"Yes."

"But I must see you again," he went on. "I wanted to tell you--"

"What?"

Spanish

absorbed: absorbido, absorto.
attempted: intentado.
boldness: intrepidez.
candour: sinceridad, franqueza, candor.
caresses: caricias.
charm: encanto, hechizar, encantar, gracia, embelesar, amuleto.
contemplating: contemplando, meditando.
curled: rizado, ondulado.
defending: defendiendo.

emanated: emanado.
exquisite: exquisito.
eyelashes: las pestañas, pestañas.
forgive: perdonar, perdona, perdonad, perdono, perdonen, perdonas, perdonan, perdonamos, perdonáis, perdone.
fraternal: fraternal.
hint: indirecta.
impossibility: imposibilidad.
invincible: invencible.
longing: anhelo, anhelante.

lowered: bajado, arriado.
necessity: necesidad.
reddened: enrojecido.
repulsed: Repeló.
seduction: seducción.
sensible: sensato, razonable.
shyness: timidez.
timid: tímido, encogido, miedo.
trembling: temblar, temblando.

"Something--important--serious. Oh, no! Besides, you will not go; it is impossible. If you should--listen to me. Then you have not understood me; you have not guessed--"

"Yet you speak plainly," said Emma.

"Ah! you can **jest**. Enough! enough! Oh, for pity's sake, let me see you once-- only once!"

"Well--"She stopped; then, as if thinking better of it, "Oh, not here!"

"Where you will."

"Will you--"She seemed to reflect; then **abruptly**, "To-morrow at eleven o'clock in the cathedral."

"I shall be there," he cried, **seizing** her hands, which she **disengaged**.

And as they were both standing up, he behind her, and Emma with her head **bent**, he **stooped** over her and pressed long **kisses** on her neck.

"You are mad! Ah! you are mad!" she said, with **sounding** little laughs, while the kisses **multiplied**.

Then **bending** his head over her shoulder, he seemed to **beg** the consent of her eyes. They fell upon him full of an **icy dignity**.

Leon stepped back to go out. He stopped on the **threshold**; then he whispered with a **trembling** voice, "Tomorrow!"

She answered with a **nod**, and disappeared like a bird into the next room.

In the evening Emma wrote the clerk an **interminable** letter, in which she **cancelled** the **rendezvous**; all was over; they must not, for the sake of their **happiness, meet** again. But when the letter was finished, as she did not know Leon's address, she was **puzzled**.

"I'll give it to him myself," she said; "he will come."

The next morning, at the open window, and **humming** on his **balcony**, Leon himself **varnished** his **pumps** with several coatings. He put on white trousers, fine **socks**, a green coat, **emptied** all the **scent** he had into his **handkerchief**, then

Spanish

abruptly: bruscamente, abruptamente.
balcony: balcón.
beg: mendigar, mendigas, mendiguen, mendigan, mendigáis, mendiga, mendigad, mendigamos, mendigo, mendigue, pedir limosna.
bending: flexión, torcimiento.
bent: inclinación, torcido.
cancelled: cancelado, anulado.
dignity: dignidad.
disengaged: desembarazado.
emptied: desocupado, vaciado.

handkerchief: pañuelo.
happiness: felicidad, alegría, dicha.
humming: zumbador.
icy: helado, álgido.
interminable: incabable.
jest: bromear, broma.
kisses: besos.
meet: encontrar, encontrad, encuentro, encuentren, encuentre, encuentras, encuentran, encontramos, encontráis, encuentra, quedar.
multiplied: multiplicado.

nod: inclinación, cabecear.
pumps: bombas.
puzzled: perplejo, desconcertado.
rendezvous: cita.
scent: olor, perfume, aroma.
seizing: agarrando, asiendo.
socks: calcetines.
sounding: sondeo.
stooped: rebajado.
threshold: umbral.
trembling: temblar, temblando.
varnished: barnizado.

having had his hair curled, he uncurled it again, in order to give it a more **natural** elegance.

"It is still too early," he thought, looking at the hairdresser's cuckoo-clock, that pointed to the hour of **nine**. He read an old fashion journal, went out, smoked a cigar, walked up three streets, thought it was time, and went slowly towards the porch of Notre Dame.

It was a beautiful summer morning. Silver plate **sparkled** in the jeweller's windows, and the light falling **obliquely** on the cathedral made mirrors of the corners of the grey stones; a **flock** of birds **fluttered** in the grey sky round the **trefoil** bell-turrets; the square, **resounding** with cries, was **fragrant** with the flowers that bordered its pavement, roses, **jasmines**, pinks, narcissi, and tube-roses, **unevenly spaced** out between moist grasses, catmint, and **chickweed** for the birds; the fountains gurgled in the centre, and under large umbrellas, amidst melons, piled up in heaps, flower-women, bare-headed, were twisting paper round **bunches** of **violets**.

The young man took one. It was the first time that he had bought flowers for a woman, and his breast, as he smelt them, **swelled** with pride, as if this homage that he meant for another had recoiled upon himself.

But he was afraid of being seen; he **resolutely** entered the church. The **beadle**, who was just then standing on the threshold in the middle of the left **doorway**, under the "Dancing Marianne," with feather cap, and **rapier** dangling against his calves, came in, more **majestic** than a **cardinal**, and as shining as a saint on a holy **pyx**.

He came towards Leon, and, with that smile of **wheedling benignity** assumed by ecclesiastics when they question children--

"The gentleman, no doubt, does not **belong** to these **parts**? The gentleman would like to see the **curiosities** of the church?"

"No!" said the other.

And he first went round the lower **aisles**. Then he went out to look at the Place. Emma was not coming yet. He went up again to the choir.

Spanish

aisles: pasillos.
beadle: bedel.
belong: pertenecer, pertenecemos, pertenezcan, pertenezco, pertenecen, perteneced, pertenece, pertenecéis, perteneces, pertenezca.
benignity: benignidad.
bunches: coletas.
cardinal: cardenal.
chickweed: pamplina.
curiosities: curiosidades.
doorway: puerta.

flock: bandada, rebaño, manada.
fluttered: revoloteado.
fragrant: fragante, oloroso.
jasmines: jazmines.
majestic: majestuoso.
natural: natural.
nine: nueve.
obliquely: oblicuamente.
parts: talento, regiones, piezas, partes.
pyx: píxide.
rapier: estoque.
resolutely: determinadamente,

resueltamente.
resounding: resonando.
spaced: espació.
sparkled: chispeado.
swelled: hinchado.
trefoil: trébol.
unevenly: irregularmente, disparejamente, desigualmente, accidentadamente, desniveladamente.
violets: huevas de mar.
wheedling: engatusando.

The nave was reflected in the full **fonts** with the beginning of the arches and some portions of the glass windows. But the reflections of the **paintings**, broken by the marble **rim**, were continued farther on upon the flag-stones, like a many-coloured carpet. The broad daylight from without **streamed** into the church in three enormous rays from the three opened **portals**. From time to time at the **upper** end a **sacristan** passed, making the oblique **genuflexion** of **devout** persons in a hurry. The crystal lustres hung motionless. In the choir a silver lamp was burning, and from the side **chapels** and dark places of the church sometimes rose sounds like sighs, with the clang of a closing grating, its **echo reverberating** under the lofty vault.

Leon with solemn steps walked along by the walls. Life had never seemed so good to him. She would come **directly**, charming, **agitated**, looking back at the glances that followed her, and with her **flounced** dress, her gold **eyeglass**, her thin shoes, with all sorts of elegant trifles that he had never enjoyed, and with the **ineffable** seduction of **yielding** virtue. The church like a huge **boudoir** spread around her; the arches bent down to **gather** in the shade the confession of her love; the windows shone resplendent to **illumine** her face, and the censers would burn that she might appear like an angel amid the fumes of the **sweet**-smelling odours.

But she did not come. He sat down on a chair, and his eyes fell upon a blue stained window representing boatmen carrying baskets. He looked at it long, **attentively**, and he counted the scales of the fishes and the button-holes of the **doublets**, while his thoughts **wandered** off towards Emma.

The beadle, standing **aloof**, was inwardly angry at this **individual** who took the liberty of admiring the cathedral by himself. He seemed to him to be **conducting** himself in a **monstrous** fashion, to be robbing him in a sort, and almost **committing sacrilege**.

But a **rustle** of silk on the flags, the tip of a bonnet, a lined cloak--it was she! Leon rose and ran to meet her.

Emma was pale. She walked fast.

"Read!" she said, holding out a paper to him. "Oh, no!"

Spanish

agitated: agitado, inquieto.
aloof: apartado.
attentively: atentamente.
boudoir: tocador.
chapels: iglesias.
committing: cometiendo.
conducting: en conducción, conductor, conductible, conducir.
devout: devoto.
directly: directamente, seguido.
doublets: jubones.
echo: eco, resonar, el eco.

eyeglass: ocular.
flounced: sacudido.
fonts: fuentes.
gather: recoger, deducir, reunir, recolectar, cosechar.
genuflexion: genuflexión.
illumine: poner luminarias, ilumine, iluminar, dar focos, aclarar.
individual: individuo, individual.
ineffable: inefable.
monstrous: monstruoso.
paintings: cuadros.

portals: portales.
reverberating: reverberando.
rim: llanta, borde, baranda, margen.
rustle: susurro.
sacrilege: sacrilegio.
sacristan: sacristán.
streamed: corrido.
sweet-smelling: fragante, perfumado.
upper: superior, alto.
wandered: Vagado.
yielding: cediendo, rindiendo, rentando.

And she abruptly withdrew her hand to enter the chapel of the Virgin, where, **kneeling** on a chair, she began to pray.

The young man was irritated at this **bigot** fancy; then he nevertheless **experienced** a certain charm in seeing her, in the middle of a **rendezvous**, thus lost in her **devotions**, like an Andalusian **marchioness**; then he grew bored, for she seemed never coming to an end.

Emma **prayed**, or rather **strove** to pray, **hoping** that some sudden resolution might **descend** to her from heaven; and to draw down divine aid she filled full her eyes with the splendours of the **tabernacle**. She breathed in the perfumes of the **full**-blown flowers in the large vases, and listened to the **stillness** of the church, that only heightened the **tumult** of her heart.

She rose, and they were about to leave, when the **beadle** came forward, hurriedly saying--

"Madame, no doubt, does not belong to these parts? Madame would like to see the **curiosities** of the church?"

"Oh, no!" cried the clerk.

"Why not?" said she. For she clung with her **expiring** virtue to the Virgin, the sculptures, the tombs--anything.

Then, in order to proceed "by rule," the beadle **conducted** them right to the entrance near the square, where, pointing out with his cane a large **circle** of block-stones without **inscription** or carving--

"This," he said **majestically**, "is the **circumference** of the beautiful bell of Ambroise. It weighed **forty** thousand pounds. There was not its **equal** in all Europe. The **workman** who cast it died of the joy--"

"Let us go on," said Leon.

The old fellow started off again; then, having got back to the chapel of the Virgin, he stretched forth his arm with an **all**-embracing gesture of demonstration, and, prouder than a country squire showing you his **espaliers**, went on--

"This simple stone covers Pierre de Breze, **lord** of Varenne and of Brissac, grand **marshal** of Poitou, and **governor** of Normandy, who **died** at the **battle** of Montlhery on the 16th of July, 1465."

Leon bit his lips, fuming.

"And on the right, this gentleman all **encased** in **iron**, on the **prancing** horse, is his **grandson**, Louis de Breze, lord of Breval and of Montchauvet, Count de Maulevrier, Baron de Mauny, **chamberlain** to the king, Knight of the Order, and also governor of Normandy; died on the 23rd of July, 1531--a Sunday, as the inscription **specifies**; and below, this figure, about to descend into the tomb, **portrays** the same person. It is not possible, is it, to see a more **perfect representation** of annihilation?"

Madame Bovary put up her **eyeglasses**. Leon, motionless, looked at her, no longer even **attempting** to speak a **single** word, to make a gesture, so **discouraged** was he at this two-fold obstinacy of **gossip** and indifference.

The **everlasting guide** went on--

"Near him, this kneeling woman who **weeps** is his spouse, Diane de Poitiers, Countess de Breze, Duchess de Valentinois, **born** in 1499, died in 1566, and to the left, the one with the child is the Holy Virgin. Now turn to this side; here are the tombs of the Ambroise. They were both cardinals and archbishops of Rouen. That one was minister under Louis XII. He did a great **deal** for the cathedral. In his will he left thirty thousand gold crowns for the poor."

And without stopping, still talking, he pushed them into a chapel full of **balustrades**, some put away, and disclosed a kind of **block** that **certainly** might once have been an ill-made statue.

"Truly," he said with a groan, "it adorned the tomb of Richard Coeur de Lion, King of England and Duke of Normandy. It was the Calvinists, **sir**, who reduced it to this condition. They had buried it for spite in the earth, under the **episcopal** seat of Monsignor. See! this is the door by which Monsignor passes to his house. Let us pass on quickly to see the **gargoyle** windows."

Spanish

attempting: intentando.
balustrades: barandillas.
battle: batalla, pelea.
block: bloque, manzana, bloquear, bloqueo, motón, polea, taco.
born: nacido, nato.
certainly: ciertamente, desde luego.
chamberlain: chambelán.
deal: trato, transacción.
died: muerto.
discouraged: espantado, desanimado.
encased: encajonado.

episcopal: episcopal.
everlasting: eterno.
eyeglasses: anteojos, ojos.
gargoyle: gárgola.
gossip: cotillear, cotilleo, chismear, chismes, los chismes, chismorreo.
governor: gobernador, regulador.
grandson: nieto, el nieto.
guide: guía, guiar, mandar, dirigir, conducir.
iron: hierro, planchar, plancha, de hierro, el hierro, fierro.

lord: señor, caballero.
marshal: mariscal, ordenar.
perfect: perfecto, perfeccionar.
portrays: retrata.
prancing: escarceos, encabritar.
representation: representación, retrato, reproducción, declaración.
single: soltero, solo, único, simple, individual.
sir: señor.
specifies: especifica, detalla.
weeps: llora.

But Leon **hastily** took some silver from his pocket and seized Emma's arm. The beadle stood dumfounded, not able to understand this **untimely munificence** when there were still so many things for the **stranger** to see. So calling him back, he cried--

"Sir! sir! The steeple! the steeple!"

"No, thank you!" said Leon.

"You are wrong, sir! It is four hundred and forty feet high, nine less than the great pyramid of Egypt. It is all cast; it--"

Leon was fleeing, for it seemed to him that his love, that for **nearly** two hours now had become **petrified** in the church like the stones, would **vanish** like a vapour through that sort of **truncated funnel**, of **oblong** cage, of open chimney that rises so **grotesquely** from the cathedral like the **extravagant attempt** of some fantastic **brazier**.

"But where are we going?" she said.

Making no answer, he walked on with a rapid **step**; and Madame Bovary was already, **dipping** her finger in the holy water when behind them they heard a panting breath interrupted by the regular sound of a cane. Leon turned back.

"Sir!"

"What is it?"

And he recognised the beadle, holding under his arms and balancing against his stomach some **twenty** large **sewn** volumes. They were **works** "which **treated** of the cathedral."

"Idiot!" **growled** Leon, rushing out of the church.

A lad was playing about the close.

"Go and get me a cab!"

The child **bounded** off like a **ball** by the Rue Quatre-Vents; then they were alone a few minutes, face to face, and a little embarrassed.

"Ah! Leon! Really--I don't know--if I ought," she whispered. Then with a more serious air, "Do you know, it is very improper--"

Spanish

attempt: intentar, intenta, intentad, intentáis, intentamos, intentas, intente, intenten, intentan, intento, tentativa.
ball: pelota, bola, baile, la pelota, balón, ovillo.
bounded: amordazado, saltado, definido, encerrado.
brazier: latonero, brasero.
dipping: mojar, mojadura, lavado, inmersión.
extravagant: extravagante.

funnel: embudo.
grotesquely: grotescamente.
growled: gruñido.
hastily: precipitadamente, apresuradamente.
munificence: munificencia.
nearly: casi.
oblong: oblongo, apaisado, rectangular.
petrified: petrificado.
sewn: cosido, pegado.
step: paso, escalón, peldaño.

stranger: forastero, extraño, desconocido.
treated: tratado.
truncated: truncado.
twenty: veinte.
untimely: inoportuno, intempestivo.
vanish: desaparecer, desaparezca, desaparezcan, desapareces, desaparecen, desaparecemos, desaparecéis, desapareced, desaparece, desaparezco.
works: fábrica, obras.

"How so?" replied the **clerk**. "It is done at Paris."

And that, as an **irresistible argument**, decided her.

Still the **cab** did not come. Leon was afraid she might go back into the church. At last the cab appeared.

"At all events, go out by the north porch," cried the **beadle**, who was left alone on the **threshold**, "so as to see the Resurrection, the Last Judgment, Paradise, King David, and the Condemned in Hell-flames."

"Where to, sir?" asked the **coachman**.

"Where you like," said Leon, **forcing** Emma into the cab.

And the **lumbering machine** set out. It went down the Rue Grand-Pont, **crossed** the Place des Arts, the Quai Napoleon, the Pont Neuf, and stopped short before the **statue** of Pierre Corneille.

"Go on," cried a voice that came from within.

The cab went on again, and as soon as it reached the Carrefour Lafayette, set off down-hill, and entered the **station** at a **gallop**.

"No, straight on!" cried the same voice.

The cab came out by the gate, and soon having reached the Cours, **trotted** quietly beneath the elm-trees. The coachman **wiped** his **brow**, put his **leather** hat between his **knees**, and drove his **carriage** beyond the side **alley** by the **meadow** to the **margin** of the **waters**.

It went along by the river, along the towing-path **paved** with sharp pebbles, and for a long while in the direction of Oyssel, beyond the isles.

But suddenly it turned with a **dash** across Quatremares, Sotteville, La Grande-Chaussee, the Rue d'Elbeuf, and made its third **halt** in front of the Jardin des Plantes.

"Get on, will you?" cried the voice more **furiously**.

And at once **resuming** its course, it passed by Saint-Sever, by the Quai'des Curandiers, the Quai aux Meules, once more over the **bridge**, by the Place **du** Champ de Mars, and behind the hospital gardens, where old men in black coats

Spanish

alley: callejón, calleja.
argument: argumento, discusión, el argumento.
beadle: bedel.
bridge: puente, el puente.
brow: ceja, frente.
cab: taxi, cabina, policía.
carriage: coche, carro, cureña.
clerk: empleado, dependiente, oficinista, secretario, el dependiente.
coachman: cochero.
crossed: cruzado.

dash: raya, guión, arremetida, corre.
du: diferencial de tensión, uranio empobrecido.
forcing: compulsión.
furiously: sañudo, reñidamente, rabiosamente, furiosamente.
gallop: galope, galopar.
halt: parar, parada, detener, apeadero, alto, interrupción.
irresistible: irresistible.
knees: rodillas.
leather: cuero, duro, el cuero, piel.

lumbering: maderaje.
machine: máquina.
margin: margen, cobertura.
meadow: prado, pradera.
paved: pavimentado.
resuming: reanudando.
station: estación.
statue: estatua, la estatua.
threshold: umbral.
trotted: Trotado.
waters: aguas.
wiped: limpiado, Enjugado.

were walking in the sun along the terrace all green with ivy. It went up the Boulevard Bouvreuil, along the Boulevard Cauchoise, then the whole of Mont-Riboudet to the Deville hills.

It came back; and then, without any fixed plan or direction, wandered about at hazard. The cab was seen at Saint-Pol, at Lescure, at Mont Gargan, at La Rougue-Marc and Place du Gaillardbois; in the Rue Maladrerie, Rue Dinanderie, before Saint-Romain, Saint-Vivien, Saint-Maclou, Saint-Nicaise--in front of the Customs, at the "Vieille Tour," the "Trois Pipes," and the Monumental Cemetery. From time to time the **coachman**, on his box cast **despairing** eyes at the public-houses. He could not understand what furious desire for **locomotion** urged these **individuals** never to wish to stop. He tried to now and then, and at once exclamations of anger burst forth behind him. Then he **lashed** his **perspiring** jades **afresh**, but indifferent to their **jolting**, running up against things here and there, not **caring** if he did, **demoralised**, and almost **weeping** with **thirst**, fatigue, and depression.

And on the harbour, in the midst of the drays and **casks**, and in the streets, at the corners, the good folk opened large wonder-stricken eyes at this sight, so extraordinary in the provinces, a cab with **blinds** drawn, and which appeared thus constantly shut more closely than a tomb, and **tossing** about like a **vessel**.

Once in the middle of the day, in the open country, just as the sun beat most **fiercely** against the old **plated** lanterns, a **bared** hand passed beneath the small blinds of yellow canvas, and threw out some **scraps** of paper that scattered in the wind, and farther off **lighted** like white butterflies on a **field** of red **clover** all in bloom.

At about six o'clock the carriage stopped in a back street of the Beauvoisine Quarter, and a woman got out, who walked with her **veil** down, and without turning her head.

Spanish

afresh: de nuevo, otra vez.
bared: descubierto.
blinds: deslumbra, persianas.
caring: aflicción, esmero, preocupación, afectuoso, asistencia, bondadoso, cargo, cuidado, atención, custodia, cuidar.
casks: toneles.
clover: trébol.
coachman: cochero.
demoralised: desmoralizado.
despairing: sin esperanza, desesperación, desesperado, desesperanza, desesperanzarse, desesperar.
field: campo, el campo, zona, cancha.
fiercely: violentamente, acaloradamente, encarnizadamente, fieramente, furiosamente.
individuals: personas.
jolting: sacudidas, traqueteo.
lashed: Azotado.
lighted: encendido.
locomotion: locomoción.
perspiring: sudando.
plated: chapado.
scraps: chicharrones, recortes, residuos.
thirst: sed, la sed.
tossing: tirar.
veil: velo.
vessel: vaso, embarcación, barco, estuche, recipiente, vasija, olla, buque, jarro, caja.
weeping: llorando, lloroso, llanto, llorón.

CHAPTER TWO

On reaching the **inn**, Madame Bovary was surprised not to see the **diligence**. Hivert, who had waited for her **fifty**-three minutes, had at last started.

Yet nothing forced her to go; but she had given her word that she would return that same evening. Moreover, Charles expected her, and in her heart she felt already that **cowardly docility** that is for some women at once the **chastisement** and **atonement** of **adultery**.

She **packed** her box quickly, paid her bill, took a **cab** in the yard, **hurrying** on the **driver**, **urging** him on, every moment **inquiring** about the time and the miles **traversed**. He succeeded in **catching** up the "Hirondelle" as it neared the first houses of Quincampoix.

Hardly was she **seated** in her corner than she closed her eyes, and opened them at the foot of the hill, when from **afar** she recognised Felicite, who was on the **lookout** in front of the farrier's shop. Hivert pulled in his horses and, the **servant**, **climbing** up to the window, said mysteriously--

"Madame, you must go at once to Monsieur Homais. It's for something important."

The village was silent as usual. At the corner of the streets were small pink **heaps** that **smoked** in the air, for this was the time for jam-making, and everyone at Yonville prepared his supply on the same day. But in front of the chemist's

Spanish

adultery: adulterio.
afar: lejos.
atonement: expiación.
cab: taxi, cabina, policía.
catching: cogiendo, contagioso, asiendo, acertando.
chastisement: castigo.
climbing: alpinismo, escalar.
cowardly: cobarde.
diligence: diligencia.
docility: docilidad.
driver: chófer, conductor, controlador,

chauffeur, mecánico.
fifty-three: cincuenta y tres, cinquenta y tres.
heaps: muchísimo.
hurrying: apurar.
inn: albergue, fonda, posada, mesón.
inquiring: inquiriendo, curioso, preguntando.
lookout: atalaya.
packed: guardado, empacado, embalado, comprimido, lleno, marcado, apuesto tendenciosamente,

aborrotado, abarrotado, hasta los topes.
seated: sentado.
servant: criado, criada, sirviente, servidor.
smoked: fumado, ahumado, humeado.
traversed: Atravesado.
urging: instar.

shop one might admire a far larger heap, and that **surpassed** the others with the **superiority** that a laboratory must have over ordinary **stores**, a general need over individual fancy.

She went in. The large arm-chair was upset, and even the "Fanal de Rouen" lay on the ground, outspread between two pestles. She pushed open the **lobby** door, and in the middle of the kitchen, amid brown jars full of picked **currants**, of powdered sugar and lump sugar, of the scales on the table, and of the **pans** on the fire, she saw all the Homais, small and large, with aprons reaching to their chins, and with forks in their hands. Justin was standing up with bowed head, and the chemist was screaming--

"Who told you to go and fetch it in the Capharnaum."

"What is it? What is the matter?"

"What is it?" replied the druggist. "We are making preserves; they are **simmering**; but they were about to **boil** over, because there is too much **juice**, and I ordered another pan. Then he, from indolence, from laziness, went and took, hanging on its nail in my laboratory, the key of the Capharnaum."

It was thus the druggist called a small room under the leads, full of the **utensils** and the goods of his trade. He often spent long hours there alone, **labelling, decanting,** and doing up again; and he looked upon it not as a simple store, but as a veritable **sanctuary,** whence there afterwards **issued, elaborated** by his hands, all sorts of pills, boluses, **infusions,** lotions, and potions, that would bear far and wide his celebrity. No one in the world set foot there, and he respected it so, that he **swept** it himself. Finally, if the pharmacy, open to all comers, was the spot where he displayed his pride, the Capharnaum was the refuge where, **egoistically concentrating** himself, Homais **delighted** in the exercise of his **predilections,** so that Justin's **thoughtlessness** seemed to him a monstrous piece of **irreverence,** and, redder than the currants, he repeated--

"Yes, from the Capharnaum! The key that locks up the **acids** and **caustic** alkalies! To go and get a **spare** pan! a pan with a **lid**! and that I shall perhaps never use! Everything is of importance in the delicate operations of our **art**! But, devil take it! one must make distinctions, and not **employ** for almost domestic

Spanish

acids: ácidos.
art: arte, el arte.
boil: hervir, furúnculo, bullir, cocer.
caustic: cáustico.
concentrating: concentrando.
currants: grosellas.
decanting: decantándose.
delighted: encantado, gozoso.
egoistically: egoístamente.
elaborated: elaborado.
employ: emplear, usar, hacer uso de.
infusions: infusiones.

irreverence: irreverencia.
issued: emitido.
juice: zumo, jugo, el jugo, joco.
labelling: etiquetado.
lid: tapa, la tapa, tapadera.
lobby: grupo de presión, vestíbulo, antecámara, cabildear.
pan: sartén, cacerola.
predilections: predilecciones.
sanctuary: santuario.
simmering: estofando, fermentando, hirviendo.

spare: sobrante, ahorrar, recambio, perdonar.
store: tienda, almacenar, almacén, la tienda, memoria, depósito.
stores: reservas.
superiority: superioridad.
surpassed: aventajado, sobrepujado.
swept: pret y pp de sweep, barrido.
thoughtlessness: irreflexión, inconsideración, inconsciencia, desconsideración.
utensils: los utensilios, utensilios.

purposes that which is meant for **pharmaceutical**! It is as if one were to carve a **fowl** with a **scalpel**; as if a magistrate--"

"Now be calm," said Madame Homais.

And Athalie, pulling at his coat, cried "Papa! papa!"

"No, let me alone," went on the **druggist** "let me alone, hang it! My word! One might as well set up for a **grocer**. That's it! go it! respect nothing! break, smash, let loose the **leeches**, burn the mallow-paste, **pickle** the **gherkins** in the window jars, tear up the bandages!"

"I thought you had--"said Emma.

"**Presently**! Do you know to what you **exposed** yourself? Didn't you see anything in the corner, on the left, on the third shelf? Speak, answer, **articulate** something."

"I--don't--know," **stammered** the young fellow.

"Ah! you **don't** know! Well, then, I do know! You saw a bottle of blue glass, sealed with yellow wax, that **contains** a white powder, on which I have even written 'Dangerous!' And do you know what is in it? **Arsenic**! And you go and touch it! You take a pan that was next to it!"

"Next to it!" cried Madame Hoinais, **clasping** her hands. "Arsenic! You might have **poisoned** us all."

And the children began howling as if they already had **frightful** pains in their **entrails**.

"Or poison a patient!" continued the druggist. "Do you want to see me in the prisoner's **dock** with criminals, in a court of **justice**? To see me dragged to the **scaffold**? Don't you know what care I take in **managing** things, although I am so thoroughly used to it? Often I am **horrified** myself when I think of my responsibility; for the Government **persecutes** us, and the absurd **legislation** that rules us is a veritable Damocles' sword over our heads."

Emma no longer dreamed of asking what they wanted her for, and the druggist went on in breathless phrases--

Spanish

arsenic: arsénico.
articulate: articulado, articular.
clasping: Agarrar.
contains: contiene.
dock: muelle, dique, dársena, reducir, atracar.
don't: no.
druggist: droguero.
entrails: entrañas.
exposed: expuesto.
fowl: gallina, aves, ave.
frightful: espantoso, horrible.

gherkins: pepinillos, pepinillos en vinagre, pepinillo.
grocer: tendero, almacenero, bodeguero, abacero.
horrified: horrorizado.
justice: justicia.
leeches: sanguijelas.
legislation: legislación.
managing: administrando, gestionando, manejando, gerente, dirigiendo.
persecutes: persigue.

pharmaceutical: medicamento, medicina, farmacéutico.
pickle: muchacho travieso, escabeche, el encurtido.
poison: veneno, envenenar, intoxicar.
poisoned: envenenado.
presently: por ahora.
scaffold: andamio.
scalpel: escalpelo, bisturí.
stammered: tartamudeó.

"That is your return for all the **kindness** we have **shown** you! That is how you **recompense** me for the really **paternal** care that I **lavish** on you! For without me where would you be? What would you be doing? Who **provides** you with **food**, education, clothes, and all the means of **figuring** one day with honour in the ranks of society? But you must pull hard at the **oar** if you're to do that, and get, as, people say, callosities upon your hands. Fabricando fit faber, age **quod** agis."

He was so **exasperated** he **quoted** Latin. He would have quoted Chinese or Greenlandish had he known those two **languages**, for he was in one of those crises in which the whole soul **shows indistinctly** what it contains, like the ocean, which, in the **storm, opens** itself from the seaweeds on its shores down to the **sands** of its abysses.

And he went on--

"I am beginning to **repent terribly** of having taken you up! I should certainly have done better to have left you to rot in your poverty and the **dirt** in which you were born. Oh, you'll never be fit for anything but to herd animals with horns! You have no **aptitude** for science! You hardly know how to stick on a label! And there you are, **dwelling** with me **snug** as a **parson**, living in **clover**, taking your ease!"

But Emma, turning to Madame Homais, "I was told to come here--"

"Oh, dear me!" interrupted the good woman, with a sad air, "how am I to tell you? It is a misfortune!"

She could not finish, the **druggist** was thundering--"Empty it! Clean it! Take it back! Be quick!"

And **seizing** Justin by the collar of his **blouse**, he shook a book out of his pocket. The lad **stooped**, but Homais was the quicker, and, having picked up the volume, **contemplated** it with staring eyes and open mouth.

"CONJUGAL--LOVE!" he said, slowly separating the two words. "Ah! very good! very good! very pretty! And illustrations! Oh, this is too much!"

Madame Homais came forward.

Spanish

aptitude: aptitud, capacidad, disposición, talento.
blouse: blusa, la blusa.
clover: trébol.
contemplated: Contemplado.
dirt: suciedad, mugre.
druggist: droguero.
dwelling: morando, vivienda, morada.
exasperated: exasperado.
figuring: figurar, computación.
food: comida, alimento, comestibles, alimentos, plato.

indistinctly: indistintamente.
kindness: amabilidad, la bondad.
languages: las lenguas.
lavish: pródigo.
oar: remo, el remo.
opens: abre.
parson: sacerdote, cura, párroco.
paternal: paterno, paternal.
provides: suministra, provee, proporciona.
quod: cárcel, chirona, encarcelar, poner a la sombra.

quoted: cotizado, citado.
recompense: recompensa.
repent: arrepentirse.
sands: banco de arena, playa.
seizing: agarrando, asiendo.
shown: mostrado.
shows: muestra.
snug: acogedor, cómodo.
stooped: rebajado.
storm: tormenta, tempestad, la tormenta, borrasca, tomar por asalto.
terribly: terriblemente.

"No, do not touch it!"

The children wanted to look at the pictures.

"Leave the room," he said **imperiously**; and they went out.

First he walked up and down with the open volume in his hand, rolling his eyes, choking, **tumid**, apoplectic. Then he came straight to his pupil, and, planting himself in front of him with crossed arms--

"Have you every **vice**, then, little **wretch**? Take care! you are on a **downward** path. Did not you reflect that this **infamous** book might fall in the hands of my children, **kindle** a spark in their minds, **tarnish** the purity of Athalie, corrupt Napoleon. He is already formed like a man. Are you quite sure, anyhow, that they have not read it? Can you **certify** to me--"

"But really, sir," said Emma, "you wished to tell me--"

"Ah, yes! madame. Your father-in-law is dead."

In fact, Monsieur Bovary senior had **expired** the evening before suddenly from an attack of apoplexy as he got up from table, and by way of greater precaution, on account of Emma's **sensibility**, Charles had begged Homais to break the horrible news to her gradually. Homais had thought over his speech; he had rounded, polished it, made it **rhythmical**; it was a masterpiece of prudence and **transitions**, of subtle turns and delicacy; but anger had got the better of **rhetoric**.

Emma, giving up all chance of **hearing** any details, left the pharmacy; for Monsieur Homais had taken up the thread of his vituperations. However, he was growing calmer, and was now grumbling in a paternal tone whilst he fanned himself with his skull-cap.

"It is not that I **entirely disapprove** of the work. Its **author** was a doctor! There are certain **scientific points** in it that it is not ill a man should know, and I would even venture to say that a man must know. But later--later! At any rate, not till you are man yourself and your temperament is formed."

When Emma knocked at the door. Charles, who was waiting for her, came forward with open arms and said to her with tears in his voice--

Spanish

author: autor, artífice, el autor, escritor.
certify: certificar, certifica, certifiquen, certifico, certificas, certifican, certificamos, certificáis, certificad, certifique, acreditar.
disapprove: desaprobar, desaprobas, desaprobo, desaprobe, desaproban, desaprobamos, desaprobáis, desaprobad, desaproba, desaproben, reprobar.
downward: descendente, hacia abajo,
de arriba hacia abajo.
entirely: enteramente, completamente, totalmente.
expired: expirado, caducado.
hearing: oyendo, oído, audiencia, vista, audición.
imperiously: imperiosamente, autoritariamente.
infamous: infame.
kindle: encender, encienda, enciendo, enciendan, encendéis, encendemos, encended, enciende, enciendes,
encienden, inflamar.
points: puntos, aguja.
rhetoric: retórica.
rhythmical: rítmico.
scientific: científico.
sensibility: sensibilidad.
tarnish: manchar, deslustrar, empañadura, deslustre.
transitions: transiciones.
tumid: protuberante, túmido.
vice: vicio, virtud, tornillo de banco.
wretch: desgraciado.

"Ah! my dear!"

And he **bent** over her gently to **kiss** her. But at the contact of his lips the memory of the other **seized** her, and she passed her hand over her face shuddering.

But she made answer, "Yes, I know, I know!"

He showed her the letter in which his mother told the event without any **sentimental hypocrisy**. She only **regretted** her husband had not received the consolations of religion, as he had died at Daudeville, in the street, at the door of a **cafe** after a **patriotic** dinner with some ex-officers.

Emma gave him back the letter; then at dinner, for appearance's sake, she affected a certain **repugnance**. But as he **urged** her to try, she **resolutely** began **eating**, while Charles opposite her sat **motionless** in a **dejected attitude**.

Now and then he raised his head and gave her a long look full of **distress**. Once he **sighed**, "I should have liked to see him again!"

She was silent. At last, understanding that she must say something, "How old was your father?" she asked.

"Fifty-eight."

"Ah!"

And that was all.

A quarter of an hour after he added, "My poor mother! what will become of her now?"

She made a **gesture** that **signified** she did not know. Seeing her so **taciturn**, Charles **imagined** her much affected, and forced himself to say nothing, not to reawaken this **sorrow** which moved him. And, **shaking** off his own--

"Did you enjoy yourself yesterday?" he asked.

"Yes."

When the **cloth** was removed, Bovary did not **rise**, nor did Emma; and as she looked at him, the **monotony** of the **spectacle** drove little by little all **pity** from her heart. He seemed to her **paltry**, weak, a cipher--in a word, a poor thing in

Spanish

attitude: actitud, posición, postura.
bent: inclinación, torcido.
cafe: café, cafés.
cloth: tela, trapo, paño, la tela, mantel, tejido.
dejected: abatido, desanimado.
distress: afligir, indigencia, entristecer, acongojar, dolor.
eating: comiendo.
emma: Ema.
gesture: gesto, ademán, acción.
hypocrisy: hipocresía.

imagined: imaginado.
kiss: besar, beso, besarse.
monotony: monotonía.
motionless: inmóvil, estático.
paltry: vil, mezquino, ínfimo, despreciable, ruin, miserable.
patriotic: patriótico.
pity: dolerse por, piedad, compadecer a, lástima, compasión.
regretted: Lamentado.
repugnance: repugnancia.
resolutely: determinadamente,

resueltamente.
rise: subir, levantarse, aumento, levantamiento, alza, subida.
seized: agarrado, asido.
sentimental: sentimental.
shaking: sacudiendo, sacudida.
sighed: suspirado.
signified: significado.
sorrow: tristeza, pena, dolor.
spectacle: espectáculo.
taciturn: taciturno, taciturna.
urged: Instado.

every way. How to get rid of him? What an **interminable** evening! Something **stupefying** like the fumes of **opium** seized her.

They heard in the passage the sharp noise of a wooden leg on the boards. It was Hippolyte bringing back Emma's luggage. In order to put it down he **described painfully** a quarter of a circle with his **stump**.

"He doesn't even remember any more about it," she thought, looking at the poor devil, whose coarse red hair was wet with **perspiration**.

Bovary was searching at the bottom of his purse for a **centime**, and without **appearing** to understand all there was of humiliation for him in the mere presence of this man, who stood there like a **personified reproach** to his **incurable incapacity**.

"**Hallo**! you've a pretty **bouquet**," he said, noticing Leon's **violets** on the chimney.

"Yes," she replied **indifferently**; "it's a bouquet I bought just now from a beggar."

Charles picked up the flowers, and **freshening** his eyes, red with tears, against them, smelt them delicately.

She took them quickly from his hand and put them in a glass of water.

The next day Madame Bovary senior arrived. She and her son **wept** much. Emma, on the **pretext** of **giving** orders, disappeared. The following day they had a talk over the **mourning**. They went and sat down with their workboxes by the **waterside** under the **arbour**.

Charles was thinking of his father, and was surprised to feel so much affection for this man, whom till then he had thought he **cared** little about. Madame Bovary senior was thinking of her husband. The worst days of the past seemed **enviable** to her. All was forgotten beneath the **instinctive** regret of such a long habit, and from time to time whilst she **sewed**, a big tear rolled along her nose and hung suspended there a moment. Emma was thinking that it was scarcely **forty**-eight hours since they had been together, far from the world, all in a **frenzy** of joy, and not having eyes enough to **gaze** upon each other. She tried to

Spanish

appearing: apareciendo, compareciendo.
arbour: cenador, emparrado.
bouquet: ramillete.
cared: Cuidado.
centime: céntimo.
described: descrito.
enviable: envidiable.
forty-eight: cuarenta y ocho.
frenzy: frenesí.
freshening: refrescando.
gaze: mirada.

giving: dando.
hallo: hola.
incapacity: incapacidad.
incurable: incurable.
indifferently: indiferentemente.
instinctive: instintivo.
interminable: incabable.
mourning: luto, deplorando, duelo.
opium: opio.
painfully: dolorosamente.
personified: personificado.
perspiration: sudor, transpiración.

pretext: pretexto.
reproach: reproche, censurar, reprender, reprobar, desaprobar, reprochar.
sewed: pret de sew, cosido.
son: hijo, el hijo.
stump: tocón, muñón, esfumino.
stupefying: aturdiendo, entorpeciendo.
violets: huevas de mar.
waterside: ribera.
wept: Llorado.

recall the slightest **details** of that past day. But the presence of her husband and mother-in-law worried her. She would have liked to hear nothing, to see nothing, so as not to disturb the meditation on her love, that, do what she would, became lost in **external** sensations.

She was **unpicking** the lining of a dress, and the **strips** were scattered around her. Madame Bovary senior was **plying** her **scissor** without looking up, and Charles, in his **list** slippers and his old brown surtout that he used as a **dressing-gown**, sat with both hands in his pockets, and did not speak either; near them Berthe, in a little white **pinafore**, was **raking** sand in the walks with her **spade**. Suddenly she saw Monsieur Lheureux, the linendraper, come in through the gate.

He came to **offer** his services "under the sad circumstances." Emma answered that she thought she could do without. The **shopkeeper** was not to be **beaten**.

"I beg your pardon," he said, "but I should like to have a private talk with you." Then in a low voice, "It's about that affair--you know."

Charles crimsoned to his ears. "Oh, yes! certainly." And in his confusion, turning to his wife, "Couldn't you, my darling?"

She seemed to understand him, for she rose; and Charles said to his mother, "It is nothing particular. No doubt, some household trifle." He did not want her to know the story of the bill, **fearing** her reproaches.

As soon as they were alone, Monsieur Lheureux in sufficiently clear terms began to congratulate Emma on the **inheritance**, then to talk of indifferent matters, of the **espaliers**, of the harvest, and of his own health, which was always so-so, always having **ups** and downs. In fact, he had to work **devilish** hard, although he didn't make enough, in **spite** of all people said, to find **butter** for his bread.

Emma let him talk on. She had bored herself so **prodigiously** the last two days.

"And so you're quite well again?" he went on. "Ma foi! I saw your husband in a sad state. He's a good fellow, though we did have a little misunderstanding."

Spanish

beaten: vencido.
butter: mantequilla, la mantequilla, manteca, untar con mantequilla.
details: orden del día, entresijos, detalles.
devilish: diabólico.
dressing-gown: camarera.
espaliers: espalda.
external: externo, exterior.
fearing: por miedo a, por temor a, temer.
inheritance: herencia.

list: lista, listar, la lista, listado, minuta.
offer: oferta, ofrecer, ofrecimiento, proposición, presentar, proponer, pretensión, retratar, reproducir.
pinafore: falda con peto, pichi, delantal.
plying: ejerciendo, recorriendo, manejando, trabajando, enrollando.
prodigiously: portentosamente, prodigiosamente.
raking: rastrillaje, rastro, atizar,

rastrear, rasguear, rastrillar, rastrillo.
recall: recordar, llamada, hacer volver, recuerdo.
scissor: cortar con tijeras, tijeras, tijera.
shopkeeper: tendero.
so-so: así así, regular.
spade: cavar, pala, laya.
spite: rencor.
strips: tiritas.
unpicking: descoser.
ups: ARRIBA, altos.

She asked what **misunderstanding**, for Charles had said nothing of the **dispute** about the goods supplied to her.

"Why, you know well enough," cried Lheureux. "It was about your little fancies--the **travelling** trunks."

He had drawn his hat over his **eyes**, and, with his hands behind his back, smiling and **whistling**, he looked straight at her in an **unbearable** manner. Did he suspect anything?

She was lost in all kinds of apprehensions. At last, however, he went on--

"We made it up, all the same, and **I've** come again to **propose** another arrangement."

This was to **renew** the bill Bovary had signed. The doctor, of course, would do as he pleased; he was not to trouble himself, **especially** just now, when he would have a lot of worry. "And he would do better to give it over to someone else--to you, for example. With a power of **attorney** it could be easily managed, and then we (you and I) would have our little business **transactions** together."

She did not understand. He was silent. Then, passing to his trade, Lheureux declared that **madame** must require something. He would send her a black barege, twelve yards, just enough to make a **gown**.

"The one you've on is good enough for the house, but you want another for calls. I saw that the very moment that I came in. I've the eye of an American!"

He did not send the stuff; he brought it. Then he came again to **measure** it; he came again on other pretexts, always trying to make himself **agreeable**, **useful**, "enfeoffing himself," as Homais would have said, and always **dropping** some **hint** to Emma about the power of attorney. He never **mentioned** the bill; she did not think of it. Charles, at the beginning of her **convalescence**, had certainly said something about it to her, but so many emotions had passed through her head that she no longer remembered it. Besides, she took care not to talk of any money questions. Madame Bovary seemed surprised at this, and **attributed** the change in her ways to the **religious** sentiments she had **contracted** during her illness.

Spanish

agreeable: agradable, conforme, grato.
attorney: abogado, procurador, apoderado.
attributed: adscrito, Atribuido.
contracted: contraído, contratado.
convalescence: convalecencia.
dispute: disputa.
dropping: goteante.
especially: sobre todo, principalmente, especialmente, sobretodo.
eye: ojo, el ojo, ojear, mirar.
gown: vestido, toga.

hint: indirecta.
i've: he, Tengo.
madame: señora.
measure: medida, medir.
mentioned: acotado, Mencionado.
misunderstanding: malentendido, equivocación.
propose: proponer, propon, proponed, propongo, propongan, propones, proponen, proponéis, propone, proponemos, proponga.
religious: religioso.

renew: renovar, renueve, renueven, renuevas, renuevan, renueva, renovamos, renovad, renuevo, renováis, reanudar.
transactions: actas, memorias.
travelling: corredizo, de viaje, ambulante, el viajar, itinerante, viajar, viajes.
unbearable: insufrible, insoportable.
useful: útil.
whistling: silbido.

But as soon as she was gone, Emma **greatly astounded** Bovary by her **practical** good sense. It would be necessary to make inquiries, to look into mortgages, and see if there were any occasion for a **sale** by **auction** or a **liquidation**. She quoted technical terms **casually**, pronounced the grand words of order, the future, **foresight**, and constantly exaggerated the difficulties of **settling** his father's affairs so much, that at last one day she showed him the rough **draft** of a power of attorney to manage and **administer** his business, arrange all **loans**, sign and **endorse** all bills, pay all sums, **etc**. She had **profited** by Lheureux's lessons. Charles **naively** asked her where this paper came from.

"Monsieur Guillaumin"; and with the utmost coolness she added, "I don't trust him **overmuch**. Notaries have such a bad reputation. Perhaps we ought to consult--we only know--no one."

"Unless Leon--" replied Charles, who was reflecting. But it was difficult to explain matters by letter. Then she offered to make the journey, but he thanked her. She insisted. It was quite a **contest** of **mutual** consideration. At last she cried with affected waywardness--

"No, I will go!"

"How good you are!" he said, kissing her forehead.

The next morning she set out in the "Hirondelle" to go to Rouen to consult Monsieur Leon, and she stayed there three days.

CHAPTER THREE

They were three full, exquisite days--a true honeymoon. They were at the Hotel-de-Boulogne, on the harbour; and they lived there, with drawn **blinds** and closed doors, with flowers on the floor, and **iced** syrups were brought them early in the morning.

Towards evening they took a covered boat and went to **dine** on one of the **islands**. It was the time when one **hears** by the side of the **dockyard** the caulking-mallets sounding against the **hull** of **vessels**. The smoke of the **tar** rose up between the trees; there were large **fatty** drops on the water, **undulating** in the **purple** colour of the sun, like floating plaques of Florentine bronze.

They **rowed** down in the midst of **moored** boats, whose long **oblique** cables **grazed** lightly against the bottom of the boat. The din of the town gradually grew distant; the rolling of carriages, the **tumult** of voices, the **yelping** of dogs on the **decks** of vessels. She took off her **bonnet**, and they **landed** on their island.

They sat down in the low-ceilinged room of a **tavern**, at whose door hung black nets. They ate **fried smelts**, **cream** and **cherries**. They lay down upon the grass; they kissed behind the poplars; and they would **fain**, like two Robinsons, have lived for ever in this little place, which seemed to them in their **beatitude** the most magnificent on earth. It was not the first time that they had seen trees, a blue sky, meadows; that they had heard the water flowing and the wind blowing in the leaves; but, no doubt, they had never admired all this, as if Nature had not

Spanish

beatitude: beatitud.
blinds: deslumbra, persianas.
bonnet: capot, capó, gorro, capota.
cherries: cerezas.
cream: crema, nata, flan, desnatar, la crema.
decks: engalana.
din: ruido, fragor.
dine: cenar, cenáis, ceno, cenen, cenas, cenamos, cenad, cenan, cena, cene.
dockyard: arsenal.
fain: dispuesto.

fatty: graso, gordo, grueso, adiposo.
fried: frito.
grazed: apacentado.
hears: oye.
hull: casco, cáscara.
iced: escarchado.
island: isla, la isla.
landed: puesto, posado, pescado, obtenido, logrado, llegado, hecho, hacendado, ganado, conseguido, dado.
moored: amarrado.

oblique: oblicuo, inclinado.
purple: morado, púrpura, purpúreo, lila.
rowed: remado.
smelts: amalgama, funde.
tar: alquitrán, alquitranar, brea, pez.
tavern: taberna.
tumult: tumulto, ruido.
undulating: Ondular, ondeo.
vessels: embarcaciones.
yelping: gañir, gañido, gañendo, gritar.

existed before, or had only begun to be beautiful since the **gratification** of their desires.

At night they returned. The boat **glided** along the shores of the islands. They sat at the bottom, both hidden by the shade, in silence. The square **oars** rang in the iron **thwarts**, and, in the **stillness**, seemed to **mark** time, like the beating of a **metronome**, while at the **stern** the **rudder** that **trailed** behind never ceased its gentle **splash** against the water.

Once the moon rose; they did not fail to make fine phrases, finding the **orb** **melancholy** and full of poetry. She even began to sing--

"One night, do you remember, we were sailing," etc.

Her **musical** but weak voice died away along the waves, and the winds carried off the **trills** that Leon heard pass like the **flapping** of wings about him.

She was opposite him, leaning against the **partition** of the **shallop**, through one of whose raised **blinds** the moon **streamed** in. Her black dress, whose **drapery** spread out like a fan, made her seem more slender, **taller**. Her head was raised, her hands **clasped**, her eyes turned towards heaven. At times the shadow of the willows hid her completely; then she **reappeared** suddenly, like a **vision** in the **moonlight**.

Leon, on the floor by her side, found under his hand a ribbon of scarlet silk. The **boatman** looked at it, and at last said--

"Perhaps it belongs to the party I took out the other day. A lot of jolly folk, gentlemen and ladies, with cakes, **champagne**, cornets--everything in style! There was one especially, a tall handsome man with small **moustaches**, who was that **funny**! And they all kept saying, 'Now tell us something, Adolphe--Dolpe,' I think."

She **shivered**.

"You are in pain?" asked Leon, coming closer to her.

"Oh, it's nothing! No doubt, it is only the night air."

Spanish

blinds: deslumbra, persianas.
boatman: barquero.
champagne: champaña, champán.
clasped: apretado, abrochado.
drapery: pañería.
flapping: batir, aleteo, aleteador.
funny: cómico, divertido, chistoso, gracioso.
glided: deslizado.
gratification: satisfacción, gratificación.
mark: señal, seña, marca, nota, marcar,

sellar, signo, timbrar, señalar, marcos, marco.
melancholy: melancolía, melancólico.
metronome: metrónomo.
moonlight: luz de la luna.
moustaches: los bigotes.
musical: musical.
oars: remos.
orb: orbe.
partition: separación, partición, tabique, división.
reappeared: reaparecido.

rudder: timón, volante.
shallop: chalupa.
shivered: tiritado.
splash: salpicar, salpicadura.
stern: popa, severo.
stillness: quietud.
streamed: corrido.
tall: alto.
thwarts: dificulta, frustra.
trailed: Arrastrado.
trills: gorjea, trina.
vision: visión.

"And who doesn't want for women, either," **softly added** the **sailor, thinking** he was **paying** the **stranger** a compliment.

Then, **spitting** on his **hands**, he took the **oars** again.

Yet they had to part. The adieux were **sad**. He was to **send** his **letters** to Mere Rollet, and she gave him such **precise instructions** about a **double envelope** that he **admired greatly** her **amorous astuteness**.

"So you can **assure** me it is all right?" she said with her last **kiss**.

"Yes, certainly."

"But why," he thought **afterwards** as he came back through the **streets alone**, "is she so very **anxious** to get this power of attorney?"

Spanish

added: sumado, agregado, añadido.
admired: admirado.
afterwards: después, luego, más adelante.
alone: solo, único, solamente, sólo.
amorous: amoroso.
anxious: inquieto, ansioso.
assure: asegurar, asegura, aseguren, aseguras, aseguran, aseguramos, aseguráis, asegurad, aseguro, asegure, garantizar.
astuteness: astucia.

double: doble, doblar, doblado.
envelope: sobre, el sobre, envolvente, ampolla.
greatly: muy, grandemente.
hands: las manos.
instructions: instrucciones.
kiss: besar, beso, besarse.
letters: letras.
oars: remos.
paying: pagando, pagar.
precise: preciso.
sad: triste, afligido.

sailor: marinero, navegante, el marinero, marino.
send: enviar, envío, envía, envíe, enviad, enviáis, enviamos, envían, envías, envíen, mandar.
softly: suavemente.
spitting: escupiendo.
stranger: forastero, extraño, desconocido.
streets: calles, las calles.
thinking: pensando, reflexionando, pensamiento, pensante.

CHAPTER FOUR

Leon soon put on an air of **superiority** before his comrades, **avoided** their company, and completely **neglected** his work.

He waited for her letters; he re-read them; he wrote to her. He called her to mind with all the strength of his desires and of his **memories**. Instead of **lessening** with absence, this **longing** to see her again grew, so that at last on Saturday morning he **escaped** from his office.

When, from the **summit** of the hill, he saw in the valley below the church-spire with its **tin flag swinging** in the wind, he felt that **delight mingled** with **triumphant vanity** and **egoistic tenderness** that millionaires must experience when they come back to their **native** village.

He went **rambling** round her house. A light was **burning** in the kitchen. He watched for her shadow behind the **curtains**, but nothing appeared.

Mere Lefrancois, when she saw him, **uttered** many exclamations. She thought he "had grown and was thinner," while Artemise, on the **contrary**, thought him stouter and darker.

He **dined** in the little room as of **yore**, but alone, without the tax-gatherer; for Binet, tired of waiting for the "Hirondelle," had **definitely** put forward his **meal** one hour, and now he dined **punctually** at five, and yet he declared usually the **rickety** old **concern** "was late."

Spanish

avoided: Evitado, eludido, rehuido.
burning: quemadura, ardiente.
concern: concernir, cuidado, preocupación, importancia.
contrary: contrario.
curtains: las cortinas.
definitely: definitivamente.
delight: deleitar, delicia, encantar.
dined: cenado.
egoistic: egoísta.
escaped: escapado.
flag: bandera, la bandera, estandarte,
indicador.
lessening: achicando, minorando.
longing: anhelo, anhelante.
meal: comida, harina, la comida.
memories: memorias, recuerdos.
mere: mero.
mingled: mezclado, triscado.
native: indígena, nativo, innato.
neglected: abandonado, descuidado.
punctually: puntualmente.
rambling: vagaroso.
rickety: raquítico, decrépito,
desvencijado.
summit: punta, cumbre, superficie, cima, cúspide.
superiority: superioridad.
swinging: balanceo.
tenderness: ternura.
tin: lata, estaño, hojalata, estañar, bote.
triumphant: triunfante.
uttered: pronunciado.
vanity: vanidad.
yore: antaño, de antaño, hace tiempo, tiempos pasados.

Leon, however, made up his mind, and knocked at the doctor's door. Madame was in her room, and did not come down for a quarter of an hour. The doctor seemed delighted to see him, but he never **stirred** out that evening, nor all the next day.

He saw her alone in the evening, very late, behind the garden in the lane; in the lane, as she had the other one! It was a **stormy** night, and they talked under an umbrella by **lightning flashes**.

Their separation was becoming **intolerable**. "I would rather die!" said Emma. She was **writhing** in his arms, **weeping**. "**Adieu**! adieu! When shall I see you again?"

They came back again to embrace once more, and it was then that she promised him to find soon, by no matter what means, a regular opportunity for seeing one another in freedom at least once a week. Emma never **doubted** she should be able to do this. Besides, she was full of hope. Some money was coming to her.

On the strength of it she bought a pair of yellow curtains with large stripes for her room, whose **cheapness** Monsieur Lheureux had **commended**; she **dreamed** of getting a carpet, and Lheureux, **declaring** that it wasn't "drinking the sea," politely **undertook** to **supply** her with one. She could no longer do without his services. Twenty times a day she sent for him, and he at once put by his business without a **murmur**. People could not understand either why Mere Rollet **breakfasted** with her every day, and even paid her **private** visits.

It was about this time, that is to say, the beginning of winter, that she seemed seized with great musical **fervour**.

One evening when Charles was listening to her, she began the same piece four times over, each time with much **vexation**, while he, not **noticing** any difference, cried--

"Bravo! very good You are wrong to stop. Go on!"

"Oh, no; it is **execrable**! My fingers are quite rusty."

The next day he **begged** her to **play** him something again.

Spanish

adieu: adiós.
begged: Mendigado.
breakfasted: desayunado.
cheapness: baratura.
commended: alabado.
declaring: declarando.
doubted: dudado.
dreamed: soñado.
execrable: condenable, maldito, execrable.
fervour: celo.
flashes: bocadillos, intermitentes.

intolerable: intolerable.
lightning: relámpago, rayo, el relámpago.
murmur: murmurar, murmullo.
noticing: notando.
play: jugar, jueguen, juega, juegan, juegue, jugad, jugáis, jugamos, juegas, juego, tocar.
private: privado, soldado raso.
stirred: batido.
stormy: tempestuoso, tormentoso.
supply: suministro,

aprovisionamiento, abastecimiento, entregar, suministrar, proveer, oferta, abastecer, provisión.
undertook: pret de undertake, Emprendió.
vexation: vejación, zaherimiento, molestia, sinsabor, disgusto, atufamiento, animosidad, mal trato.
weeping: llorando, lloroso, llanto, llorón.
writhing: retorcer, retorcimiento, retorciendo.

"Very well; to please you!"

And Charles **confessed** she had gone off a little. She played wrong notes and **blundered**; then, **stopping** short--

"Ah! it is no use. I ought to take some lessons; but--" She bit her lips and added, "Twenty **francs** a lesson, that's too dear!"

"Yes, so it is--rather," said Charles, giggling **stupidly**. "But it seems to me that one might be able to do it for less; for there are artists of no reputation, and who are often better than the celebrities."

"Find them!" said Emma.

The next day when he came home he looked at her **shyly**, and at last could no longer keep back the words.

"How **obstinate** you are sometimes! I went to Barfucheres **to**-day. Well, Madame Liegard **assured** me that her three young ladies who are at La Misericorde have lessons at fifty sous **apiece**, and that from an excellent mistress!"

She shrugged her shoulders and did not open her piano again. But when she passed by it (if Bovary were there), she sighed--

"Ah! my poor piano!"

And when anyone came to see her, she did not fail to **inform** them she had given up music, and could not begin again now for important **reasons**. Then people **commiserated** her--

"What a **pity**! she had so much talent!"

They even spoke to Bovary about it. They put him to **shame**, and especially the **chemist**.

"You are wrong. One should never let any of the faculties of **nature lie fallow**. Besides, just think, my good friend, that by **inducing madame** to study; you are **economising** on the **subsequent** musical education of your child. For my own part, I think that mothers ought themselves to **instruct** their children. That is

---

Spanish

apiece: cada uno, por cabeza.
assured: asegurado.
blundered: Pifiado.
chemist: químico, farmacéutico, boticario.
commiserated: compadecido.
confessed: confesado, reconocido.
economising: economizar.
fallow: barbecho.
francs: francos.
inducing: induciendo.
inform: informar, informe, informen,

informo, informa, informad, informáis, informamos, informas, informan, enterar.
instruct: notificar, dar instrucciones, enseñar, instruir, notificad, notifica, notifiquen, notifique, notifico, notificas, notifican.
lie: mentir, mentira, yacer, estar tendido, embuste, echarse.
madame: señora.
nature: naturaleza, índole, carácter.
obstinate: obstinado, contumaz,

tozudo.
pity: dolerse por, piedad, compadecer a, lástima, compasión.
reasons: razona.
shame: vergüenza, verguenza, pudor, oprobio, avergonzar.
shyly: tímidamente.
stopping: parando, deteniendo.
stupidly: estúpidamente, estupidez, necedad, torpeza.
subsequent: subsiguiente.
to-day: hoy.

an idea of Rousseau's, still rather new perhaps, but that will end by **triumphing,** I am certain of it, like **mothers nursing** their own children and vaccination."

So Charles **returned** once more to this question of the **piano. Emma replied bitterly** that it would be better to **sell** it. This **poor** piano, that had given her **vanity** so much satisfaction--to see it go was to Bovary like the **indefinable suicide** of a part of herself.

"If you liked," he said, "a **lesson** from time to time, that wouldn't after all be very ruinous."

"But lessons," she replied, "are only of use when **followed** up."

And thus it was she set about **obtaining** her husband's **permission** to go to **town** once a week to see her **lover.** At the end of a **month** she was even **considered** to have made **considerable progress.**

Spanish

bitterly: amargamente.
considerable: notable, considerable.
considered: considerado.
emma: Ema.
followed: seguido.
indefinable: indefinible.
lesson: lección.
lover: querido, amante, novio.
month: mes, el mes.
mothers: las madres.
nursing: lactancia.
obtaining: obteniendo, obtención.

permission: permiso, autorización, declaración, el permiso.
piano: el piano, piano.
poor: pobre, malo, deplorable, indigente, miserable.
progress: progreso.
replied: Contestado.
returned: devuelto.
sell: vender, venda, vended, vendo, vendes, venden, vendéis, vende, vendan, vendemos.
suicide: suicidio.

town: ciudad, pueblo, población, el pueblo.
triumphing: Triunfar.
vanity: vanidad.

CHAPTER FIVE

She went on Thursdays. She got up and dressed **silently**, in order not to **awaken** Charles, who would have made remarks about her getting ready too early. Next she walked up and down, went to the windows, and looked out at the Place. The early dawn was **broadening** between the **pillars** of the market, and the chemist's shop, with the **shutters** still up, showed in the pale light of the dawn the large letters of his **signboard**.

When the clock pointed to a quarter past **seven**, she went off to the "Lion d'Or," whose door Artemise opened **yawning**. The girl then made up the coals covered by the **cinders**, and **Emma** remained alone in the kitchen. Now and again she went out. Hivert was **leisurely harnessing** his horses, listening, moreover, to Mere Lefrancois, who, passing her head and **nightcap** through a **grating**, was **charging** him with commissions and giving him explanations that would have **confused** anyone else. Emma kept **beating** the soles of her boots against the **pavement** of the yard.

At last, when he had **eaten** his **soup**, put on his **cloak**, **lighted** his pipe, and **grasped** his **whip**, he **calmly installed** himself on his seat.

The "Hirondelle" started at a slow **trot**, and for about a mile stopped here and there to **pick** up **passengers** who waited for it, standing at the border of the road, in front of their yard gates.

Spanish

awaken: despertar.
beating: paliza, pulsación, latido.
broadening: ensanchando.
calmly: calmadamente, serenamente.
charging: tasación, tarificación, cargar, carga.
cinders: cenizas.
cloak: abrigo, capa.
confused: confuso, confundido.
eaten: comido.
emma: Ema.
grasped: agarrado.

grating: reja, emparrillado, verja, parrilla, enrejado, irritante.
harnessing: movilización, enjaezar, captación, arreo.
installed: instalado.
leisurely: pausadamente.
lighted: encendido.
nightcap: gorro de dormir, sosiega, bebida.
passengers: pasajeros.
pavement: acera, pavimento.
pick: picar, piquen, pican, picamos,

picáis, picad, picas, pique, pica, pico, arrancar.
pillars: pilar.
seven: siete.
shutters: obturadores, obturador.
signboard: letrero.
silently: silenciosamente, silencioso.
soup: sopa, la sopa.
trot: trote, trotar.
whip: látigo, zurriago, azotar, fustigar, fusta, azote.
yawning: bostezante, bostezando.

Those who had **secured** seats the evening before kept it waiting; some even were still in bed in their houses. Hivert called, shouted, swore; then he got down from his seat and went and knocked loudly at the doors. The wind blew through the cracked windows.

The four seats, however, filled up. The carriage rolled off; rows of apple-trees followed one upon another, and the road between its two long ditches, full of yellow water, rose, constantly **narrowing** towards the horizon.

Emma knew it from end to end; she knew that after a meadow there was a sign-post, next an elm, a **barn**, or the hut of a lime-kiln tender. Sometimes even, in the hope of getting some surprise, she shut her eyes, but she never lost the clear perception of the distance to be **traversed**.

At last the brick houses began to follow one another more closely, the earth **resounded** beneath the wheels, the "Hirondelle" **glided** between the gardens, where through an opening one saw statues, a **periwinkle plant**, **clipped** yews, and a swing. Then on a sudden the town appeared. Sloping down like an **amphitheatre**, and drowned in the fog, it widened out beyond the bridges **confusedly**. Then the open country spread away with a monotonous movement till it touched in the distance the vague line of the pale sky. Seen thus from above, the whole landscape looked **immovable** as a picture; the **anchored** ships were massed in one corner, the river curved round the foot of the green hills, and the isles, oblique in **shape**, lay on the water, like large, motionless, black fishes. The **factory** chimneys **belched** forth immense brown fumes that were blown away at the top. One heard the **rumbling** of the foundries, together with the clear chimes of the churches that stood out in the mist. The **leafless** trees on the boulevards made violet thickets in the midst of the houses, and the roofs, all shining with the rain, threw back unequal reflections, **according** to the height of the quarters in which they were. Sometimes a **gust** of wind drove the clouds towards the Saint Catherine hills, like **aerial** waves that broke silently against a **cliff**.

A **giddiness** seemed to her to **detach** itself from this mass of existence, and her heart **swelled** as if the hundred and twenty thousand souls that palpitated

Spanish

according: conforme, de acuerdo con.
aerial: antena, aéreo.
amphitheatre: anfiteatro.
anchored: anclado.
barn: granero, cobertizo, puesto, barraca, cabina, el troje, barnio.
belched: Eructado.
cliff: acantilado, precipicio, el acantilado.
clipped: sujetado, cortado.
confusedly: confusamente.
detach: destacar, destaquen, destacad, destacamos, destacan, destacas, destaco, destaque, destaca, destacáis, desprender.
factory: fábrica, factoría.
giddiness: mareo.
glided: deslizado.
gust: ráfaga, racha.
immovable: inconmovible, inamovible, que no se puede mover, inmovible, inmoble, inmobiliario, inmóvil, fijo, inalterable.
leafless: deshojado.
narrowing: estrechamiento, estrechando.
periwinkle: vincapervinca.
plant: planta, plantar, cultivar, fábrica, instalación.
resounded: Resonado.
rumbling: retumbar.
secured: fijado, asegurado, afianzado.
shape: forma, formar, figura, amoldar, horma, la forma, perfil, conformar.
swelled: hinchado.
traversed: Atravesado.

there had all at once sent into it the vapour of the passions she fancied theirs. Her love grew in the presence of this **vastness**, and expanded with **tumult** to the vague murmurings that rose towards her. She poured it out upon the square, on the walks, on the streets, and the old Norman city **outspread** before her eyes as an enormous capital, as a Babylon into which she was entering. She leant with both hands against the window, drinking in the breeze; the three horses **galloped**, the stones grated in the mud, the diligence rocked, and Hivert, from **afar**, **hailed** the **carts** on the road, while the bourgeois who had spent the night at the Guillaume woods came quietly down the hill in their little family carriages.

They stopped at the **barrier**; Emma **undid** her **overshoes**, put on other gloves, **rearranged** her **shawl**, and some twenty paces farther she got down from the "Hirondelle."

The town was then **awakening**. Shop-boys in caps were **cleaning** up the shop-fronts, and women with baskets against their hips, at intervals uttered **sonorous** cries at the corners of streets. She walked with **downcast** eyes, **close** to the walls, and smiling with pleasure under her lowered black veil.

For fear of being seen, she did not usually take the most **direct** road. She plunged into dark **alleys**, and, all **perspiring**, reached the bottom of the Rue Nationale, near the fountain that **stands** there. It, is the quarter for theatres, public-houses, and whores. Often a cart would pass near her, bearing some shaking scenery. Waiters in **aprons** were **sprinkling** sand on the flagstones between green shrubs. It all smelt of **absinthe**, **cigars**, and **oysters**.

She turned down a street; she recognised him by his **curling** hair that escaped from beneath his hat.

Leon walked along the pavement. She followed him to the **hotel**. He went up, opened the door, entered--What an embrace!

Then, after the kisses, the words gushed forth. They told each other the sorrows of the week, the presentiments, the anxiety for the letters; but now everything was forgotten; they gazed into each **other's** faces with **voluptuous** laughs, and tender **names**.

Spanish

absinthe: ajenjo, absenta.
afar: lejos.
alleys: paseos.
aprons: sendero.
awakening: despertar.
barrier: barrera, reja, obstrucción.
carts: carretillas.
cigars: los puros.
cleaning: limpiando, limpia, limpieza, limpiar.
close: cerrar, cierras, cierra, cierren, cerráis, cerrad, cerramos, cierro,

cierre, cierran, cerca.
curling: rizado, ensortijamiento.
direct: directo, mandar, guiar, derecho, dirigir.
downcast: abatido.
galloped: galopado.
hailed: granizado.
hotel: hotel, el hotel, hotelero.
names: nombres, Michael.
other's: otro.
outspread: desplegado, extendido, extensión.

overshoes: botas protectoras.
oysters: Ostiones.
perspiring: sudando.
rearranged: reorganizado.
shawl: chal.
sonorous: sonoro.
sprinkling: rociadura.
stands: tenderetes, jaulas.
tumult: tumulto, ruido.
undid: Deshizo, pret de undo.
vastness: vastedad, inmensidad.
voluptuous: voluptuoso.

The bed was large, of mahogany, in the shape of a boat. The curtains were in red **levantine**, that hung from the ceiling and **bulged** out too much towards the **bell**-shaped bedside; and nothing in the world was so lovely as her brown head and white skin standing out against this purple colour, when, with a movement of shame, she crossed her bare arms, hiding her face in her hands.

The warm room, with its discreet carpet, its gay ornaments, and its calm light, seemed made for the intimacies of passion. The curtain-rods, ending in arrows, their brass pegs, and the great balls of the fire-dogs shone suddenly when the sun came in. On the chimney between the **candelabra** there were two of those pink **shells** in which one hears the murmur of the **sea** if one holds them to the ear.

How they loved that dear room, so full of **gaiety**, despite its rather faded splendour! They always found the furniture in the same place, and sometimes hairpins, that she had forgotten the Thursday before, under the **pedestal** of the clock. They **lunched** by the **fireside** on a little round table, **inlaid** with **rosewood**. Emma carved, put bits on his plate with all sorts of **coquettish** ways, and she **laughed** with a **sonorous** and **libertine** laugh when the **froth** of the champagne ran over from the glass to the rings on her fingers. They were so completely lost in the possession of each other that they thought themselves in their own house, and that they would live there till death, like two spouses **eternally** young. They said "our room," "our carpet," she even said "my slippers," a **gift** of Leon's, a whim she had had. They were pink satin, bordered with swansdown. When she sat on his knees, her leg, then too short, hung in the air, and the **dainty** shoe, that had no back to it, was held only by the toes to her bare foot.

He for the first time enjoyed the **inexpressible** delicacy of feminine refinements. He had never met this grace of language, this reserve of **clothing**, these poses of the weary dove. He admired the **exaltation** of her soul and the lace on her **petticoat**. Besides, was she not "a lady" and a married woman--a real mistress, in fine?

By the **diversity** of her humour, in turn **mystical** or **mirthful**, **talkative**, **taciturn**, passionate, careless, she **awakened** in him a thousand desires, called up

Spanish

awakened: despertado.
bell-shaped: aboquillado, encampanado, campanudo, campaniforme, acampanado.
bulged: Sobresalido.
candelabra: candelabro.
clothing: ropa, vistiendo, la ropa.
coquettish: coqueta.
dainty: fino, amable, delicado, poquita.
diversity: diversidad.
eternally: eternamente.

exaltation: exaltación.
fireside: hogar, chimenea.
froth: espuma.
gaiety: alegría.
gift: regalo, donación, el regalo, don, talento.
inexpressible: inexpresable.
inlaid: pret y pp de inlay, incrustado, embutido.
laughed: Reído.
levantine: levantino.
libertine: libertino.

lunched: Almorzado.
mirthful: alegre.
mystical: místico.
pedestal: pedestal.
petticoat: enaguas.
rosewood: palisandro, palosanto, palo de rosa.
sea: mar, el mar.
shells: cáscaras.
sonorous: sonoro.
taciturn: taciturno, taciturna.
talkative: hablador, locuaz.

instincts or memories. She was the mistress of all the novels, the **heroine** of all the dramas, the vague "she" of all the volumes of verse. He found again on her shoulder the **amber colouring** of the "Odalisque Bathing"; she had the long waist of **feudal** chatelaines, and she **resembled** the "Pale Woman of Barcelona." But above all she was the Angel!

Often looking at her, it seemed to him that his soul, **escaping** towards her, spread like a wave about the outline of her head, and **descended** drawn down into the **whiteness** of her breast. He **knelt** on the ground before her, and with both elbows on her knees looked at her with a smile, his face upturned.

She bent over him, and murmured, as if **choking** with intoxication--

"Oh, do not **move**! do not speak! look at me! Something so sweet **comes** from your eyes that **helps** me so much!"

She called him "child." "Child, do you love me?"

And she did not listen for his answer in the **haste** of her lips that **fastened** to his mouth.

On the clock there was a bronze **cupid**, who smirked as he bent his arm beneath a golden **garland**. They had laughed at it many a time, but when they had to part everything seemed serious to them.

Motionless in front of each other, they kept repeating, "Till Thursday, till Thursday."

Suddenly she seized his head between her hands, kissed him **hurriedly** on the forehead, crying, "Adieu!" and rushed down the stairs.

She went to a hairdresser's in the Rue de la Comedie to have her hair arranged. Night fell; the **gas** was **lighted** in the shop. She heard the bell at the theatre calling the mummers to the performance, and she saw, passing opposite, men with white faces and women in faded gowns going in at the stage-door.

It was hot in the room, small, and too low where the **stove** was **hissing** in the midst of wigs and pomades. The smell of the **tongs**, together with the **greasy** hands that **handled** her head, soon stunned her, and she **dozed** a little in her **wrapper**. Often, as he did her hair, the man offered her tickets for a **masked** ball.

Spanish

amber: ámbar, ámbar amarillo, ambarino.
choking: la obstrucción aérea, estrangular, atragantamiento, ahogarse.
colouring: colorar, colorido, colorante.
comes: Viene.
cupid: Cupido.
descended: descendido, bajado.
dozed: dormitado.
escaping: escapar.
fastened: fijado, sujetado, atado.

feudal: feudal.
garland: guirnalda.
gas: gas.
greasy: grasiento, gordo, grueso, untuoso.
handled: manejado.
haste: prisa, precipitación.
helps: ayuda defensiva.
heroine: heroína.
hissing: silbar, silbido, sisteo.
hurriedly: precipitadamente, apresuradamente.

knelt: pret y pp de kneel, Arrodillado.
lighted: encendido.
masked: enmascarado.
motionless: inmóvil, estático.
move: mover, conmover, moverse, mudar, mudanza, movimiento, trasladar, traslado, mudarse, jugada.
resembled: Parecido.
stove: estufa, la estufa, hornillo.
tongs: tenazas.
whiteness: albura.
wrapper: envoltorio, envoltura.

Then she went away. She went up the streets; reached the Croix-Rouge, put on her **overshoes**, that she had hidden in the morning under the seat, and sank into her place among the impatient passengers. Some got out at the foot of the hill. She remained alone in the carriage. At every turning all the lights of the town were seen more and more completely, making a great luminous vapour about the dim houses. Emma knelt on the **cushions** and her eyes wandered over the dazzling light. She sobbed; called on Leon, sent him tender words and kisses lost in the wind.

On the **hillside** a poor devil wandered about with his stick in the midst of the diligences. A mass of rags covered his shoulders, and an old staved-in beaver, turned out like a basin, hid his face; but when he took it off he discovered in the place of eyelids empty and **bloody orbits**. The flesh hung in red **shreds**, and there flowed from it liquids that **congealed** into green **scale** down to the nose, whose black nostrils **sniffed convulsively**. To speak to you he threw back his head with an idiotic laugh; then his bluish eyeballs, rolling constantly, at the temples beat against the edge of the open **wound**. He sang a little **song** as he followed the carriages--

"Maids an the warmth of a summer day Dream of love, and of love always"

And all the **rest** was about birds and sunshine and green leaves.

Sometimes he appeared suddenly behind Emma, **bareheaded**, and she drew back with a cry. Hivert made fun of him. He would **advise** him to get a booth at the Saint Romain fair, or else ask him, laughing, how his young woman was.

Often they had started when, with a sudden movement, his hat entered the diligence through the small window, while he clung with his other arm to the **footboard**, between the wheels splashing mud. His voice, **feeble** at first and **quavering**, grew sharp; it resounded in the night like the **indistinct moan** of a vague distress; and through the ringing of the bells, the murmur of the trees, and the rumbling of the empty **vehicle**, it had a far-off sound that disturbed Emma. It went to the bottom of her soul, like a whirlwind in an abyss, and carried her away into the distances of a **boundless** melancholy. But Hivert, noticing a weight behind, gave the blind man sharp **cuts** with his whip. The **thong** lashed his

Spanish

advise: aconsejar, aconsejan, aconsejen, aconsejas, aconsejo, aconsejamos, aconsejáis, aconsejad, aconseja, aconseje, anunciar.
bareheaded: descubierto.
bloody: sangriento, sanguinario, cruento.
boundless: ilimitado.
congealed: helado, cuajado, cuajarse, coagulado, helar, cuajar, congelarse, congelar, congelado, helarse.
convulsively: convulsivamente.

cushions: cojines.
cuts: reducciones, recortes, corta, cortes.
feeble: débil.
footboard: plancha de vuelo, estribo, pie de la cama, plataforma, campo de pie.
hillside: ladera, cuesta.
indistinct: indistinto.
moan: gemir, gemido.
orbits: gira, orbita, órbitas.
overshoes: botas protectoras.

quavering: trinar, tembloroso.
rest: descansar, descanso, resto, detrito, desechos, reposar, reposo.
scale: escama, escala, incrustación, balanza, ascender, escalar, báscula, subir a.
shreds: desbrizna, despedaza.
sniffed: olido.
song: canción, canto.
thong: correa.
vehicle: vehículo.
wound: herida, herir, la herida, lesión.

wounds, and he fell back into the mud with a **yell**. Then the, passengers in the "Hirondelle" ended by falling asleep, some with open mouths, others with lowered chins, leaning against their neighbour's shoulder, or with their arm passed through the strap, **oscillating** regularly with the **jolting** of the carriage; and the **reflection** of the lantern swinging without, on the **crupper** of the **wheeler**; penetrating into the **interior** through the **chocolate calico** curtains, threw **sanguineous** shadows over all these motionless people. Emma, drunk with grief, shivered in her clothes, feeling her feet grow colder and colder, and death in her soul.

Charles at home was waiting for her; the "Hirondelle" was always late on Thursdays. Madame arrived at last, and scarcely kissed the child. The dinner was not ready. No matter! She excused the servant. This girl now seemed **allowed** to do just as she liked.

Often her husband, **noting** her pallor, asked if she were **unwell**.

"No," said Emma.

"But," he replied, "you seem so strange this evening."

"Oh, it's nothing! nothing!"

There were even days when she had no sooner come in than she went up to her room; and Justin, **happening** to be there, moved about **noiselessly**, quicker at helping her than the best of maids. He put the **matches** ready, the **candlestick**, a book, arranged her **nightgown**, turned back the **bedclothes**.

"Come!" said she, "that will do. Now you can go."

For he stood there, his hands hanging down and his eyes wide open, as if enmeshed in the innumerable threads of a sudden reverie.

The following day was frightful, and those that came after still more unbearable, because of her impatience to once again seize her happiness; an ardent **lust**, **inflamed** by the **images** of past experience, and that burst forth **freely** on the **seventh** day beneath Leon's **caresses**. His ardours were hidden beneath outbursts of wonder and gratitude. Emma tasted this love in a discreet,

---

Spanish

allowed: permitido, dejado.
bedclothes: ropa de cama.
calico: calicó.
candlestick: candelero.
caresses: caricias.
chocolate: chocolate, el chocolate, bombón, de chocolate.
crupper: baticola, grupa.
freely: libremente.
happening: pasando, aconteciendo, ocurriendo, sucediendo, suceso, acaeciendo, acontecimiento.

images: imágenes.
inflamed: inflamado.
interior: interno, de hogar, de interiores, hogar, casa.
jolting: sacudidas, traqueteo.
lust: lujuria.
matches: cerillas.
nightgown: camisa de dormir, camisón, camisón de dormir.
noiselessly: calladamente, silenciosamente, tranquilamente.
noting: detección, levantamiento del

protesto, Notar.
oscillating: oscilando, oscilante, fluctuando.
reflection: reflexión, reflejo.
sanguineous: sanguinario, sanguíneo, sangriento, de color rojo sangre.
seventh: séptimo, séptima.
unwell: enfermo.
wheeler: girador, vehículo, Vapor De Ruedas, motociclista, ciclista, buque de ruedas, rodador.
yell: grito, gritar, aullar, chillar.

absorbed fashion, maintained it by all the artifices of her tenderness, and **trembled** a little lest it should be lost later on.

She often said to him, with her sweet, **melancholy** voice--

"Ah! you too, you will leave me! You will **marry**! You will be like all the others."

He asked, "What others?"

"Why, like all men," she replied. Then added, **repulsing** him with a **languid** movement--

"You are all evil!"

One day, as they were talking **philosophically** of earthly **disillusions**, to experiment on his jealousy, or **yielding**, perhaps, to an over-strong need to **pour** out her heart, she told him that formerly, before him, she had loved someone.

"Not like you," she went on quickly, protesting by the head of her child that "nothing had passed between them."

The young man believed her, but none the less questioned her to find out what he was.

"He was a ship's captain, my dear."

Was this not **preventing** any **inquiry**, and, at the same time, assuming a higher ground through this pretended fascination **exercised** over a man who must have been of **warlike** nature and accustomed to **receive** homage?

The clerk then felt the **lowliness** of his position; he longed for **epaulettes**, crosses, titles. All that would please her--he gathered that from her **spendthrift** habits.

Emma nevertheless concealed many of these extravagant **fancies**, such as her wish to have a blue tilbury to drive into Rouen, drawn by an English horse and driven by a groom in top-boots. It was Justin who had inspired her with this **whim**, by begging her to take him into her service as valet-de-chambre, and if the **privation** of it did not **lessen** the pleasure of her arrival at each rendezvous, it certainly augmented the bitterness of the return.

Spanish

disillusions: desilusiona.
epaulettes: charreteras.
exercised: ejercitado.
fancies: extravagante.
inquiry: encuesta, pregunta, investigación, interrogación, demanda.
languid: lánguido.
lessen: minorar, achicar, disminuir, minora, minore, minoras, minoran, minoramos, achicas, minoráis, minoro.

lowliness: humildad, bajeza.
marry: casarse, casar, cásese, se casan, se casa, nos casamos, me caso, te casas, cásense, cásate, cásados.
melancholy: melancolía, melancólico.
philosophically: filosóficamente.
pour: derramar, verter, lluvia intensa, servir.
preventing: impidiendo, previniendo.
privation: apuro, derrame, estrechez, miseria, pérdida, privación, Privación .

receive: recibir, reciben, recibís, recibimos, recibes, recibe, reciban, recibid, reciba, recibo, tomar.
repulsing: Repelando.
spendthrift: derrochador.
trembled: Temblado, tembló.
warlike: belicoso.
whim: capricho, antojo.
yielding: cediendo, rindiendo, rentando.

Often, when they **talked** together of Paris, she **ended** by **murmuring,** "Ah! how **happy** we should be there!"

"Are we not happy?" **gently answered** the young man **passing** his hands over her hair.

"Yes, that is true," she said. "I am **mad. Kiss** me!"

To her husband she was more **charming** than ever. She made him pistachio-creams, and played him waltzes after dinner. So he thought himself the most **fortunate** of men and Emma was without **uneasiness,** when, one evening suddenly he said--

"It is Mademoiselle Lempereur, isn't it, who gives you lessons?"

"Yes."

"Well, I saw her just now," Charles went on, "at Madame Liegeard's. I spoke to her about you, and she doesn't know you."

This was like a **thunderclap.** However, she **replied** quite naturally--

"Ah! no **doubt** she **forgot** my name."

"But perhaps," said the doctor, "there are several Demoiselles Lempereur at Rouen who are music-mistresses."

"Possibly!" Then quickly--"But I have my **receipts** here. See!"

And she went to the writing-table, **ransacked** all the **drawers, rummaged** the papers, and at last lost her head so completely that Charles **earnestly begged** her not to take so much trouble about those **wretched** receipts.

"Oh, I will find them," she said.

And, in fact, on the following Friday, as Charles was putting on one of his **boots** in the dark **cabinet** where his clothes were kept, he felt a piece of paper between the **leather** and his **sock.** He took it out and read--

"Received, for three months' lessons and several **pieces** of music, the **sum** of **sixty**-three francs.--Felicie Lempereur, **professor** of music."

"How the **devil** did it get into my boots?"

Spanish

answered: contesta, Contestado.
begged: Mendigado.
boots: botas.
cabinet: armario, gabinete.
charming: encantador, simpático, lindo, bonito, coquetón, amable.
devil: diablo, el diablo.
doubt: dudar, duda.
drawers: calzoncillos.
earnestly: seriamente.
ended: finalizó, terminado.
forgot: olvidado, pret de forget.

fortunate: afortunado.
gently: suavemente.
happy: feliz, alegre, contento.
kiss: besar, beso, besarse.
leather: cuero, duro, el cuero, piel.
mad: loco, enojado, chiflado, majara, majareta, demente, enfadado.
murmuring: murmurar.
passing: paso.
pieces: material de artillería.
professor: catedrático, profesor.
ransacked: saqueado.

receipts: ingresos, recibos.
replied: Contestado.
rummaged: registró.
sixty-three: sesenta y tres.
sock: calcetín.
sum: suma, importe, cantidad.
talked: Hablado, charlado.
thunderclap: tronido.
uneasiness: malestar.
wretched: miserable, menesteroso, pobre, infeliz, necesitado, desdichado.

"It must," she replied, "have fallen from the old box of bills that is on the edge of the shelf."

From that moment her existence was but one long tissue of lies, in which she **enveloped** her love as in veils to hide it. It was a want, a **mania**, a pleasure carried to such an extent that if she said she had the day before walked on the right side of a road, one might know she had taken the left.

One morning, when she had gone, as usual, rather lightly **clothed**, it suddenly began to snow, and as Charles was watching the weather from the window, he caught sight of Monsieur Bournisien in the **chaise** of Monsieur Tuvache, who was driving him to Rouen. Then he went down to give the priest a thick **shawl** that he was to hand over to Emma as soon as he reached the "Croix-Rouge." When he got to the inn, Monsieur Bournisien asked for the wife of the Yonville doctor. The **landlady** replied that she very **rarely** came to her establishment. So that evening, when he recognised Madame Bovary in the "Hirondelle," the cure told her his **dilemma**, without, however, appearing to **attach** much importance to it, for he began **praising** a **preacher** who was doing wonders at the Cathedral, and whom all the ladies were **rushing** to hear.

Still, if he did not ask for any **explanation**, others, later on, might **prove** less **discreet**. So she thought well to get down each time at the "Croix-Rouge," so that the good folk of her village who saw her on the stairs should suspect nothing.

One day, however, Monsieur Lheureux met her coming out of the Hotel de Boulogne on Leon's arm; and she was frightened, thinking he would **gossip**. He was not such a fool. But three days after he came to her room, shut the door, and said, "I must have some money."

She declared she could not give him any. Lheureux burst into lamentations and reminded her of all the kindnesses he had shown her.

In fact, of the two bills signed by Charles, Emma up to the present had paid only one. As to the second, the **shopkeeper**, at her **request**, had **consented** to **replace** it by another, which again had been renewed for a long **date**. Then he drew from his pocket a list of goods not paid for; to wit, the curtains, the carpet,

Spanish

attach: adjuntar, fijar, adjunte, fijamos, fija, fijáis, fijan, fijo, fijas, fijad, adjuntáis.
chaise: coche postal.
clothed: vestido.
consented: Consentido.
date: fecha, dátil, cita, la fecha, data.
dilemma: dilema.
discreet: discreto.
enveloped: enrollado, envuelto.
explanation: explicación.
gossip: cotillear, cotilleo, chismear, chismes, los chismes, chismorreo.
landlady: arrendadora, casera, dueña, patrona, propietaria, propietaria de una vivienda, ama.
mania: manía.
praising: alabar.
preacher: predicador.
prove: probar, probad, prueban, pruebas, pruebo, probamos, probáis, prueben, prueba, pruebe, verificar.
rarely: raramente, rara vez.
replace: sustituir, sustituyen,
sustituyo, sustituid, sustituimos, sustituís, sustituya, sustituye, sustituyes, sustituyan, reemplazar.
request: petición, pedir, solicitar, solicitud, demandar, solicitación, requerimiento, ruego, rogar, demanda.
rushing: apresurar.
shawl: chal.
shopkeeper: tendero.

the **material** for the armchairs, several **dresses**, and **divers** articles of dress, the bills for which **amounted** to about two thousand **francs**.

She **bowed** her head. He went on--

"But if you **haven't** any ready money, you have an estate." And he reminded her of a **miserable** little **hovel** situated at Barneville, near Aumale, that brought in almost nothing. It had formerly been part of a small farm sold by Monsieur Bovary senior; for Lheureux knew everything, even to the number of acres and the names of the neighbours.

"If I were in your place," he said, "I should clear myself of my debts, and have money left over."

She pointed out the difficulty of getting a **purchaser**. He held out the hope of finding one; but she asked him how she should manage to sell it.

"Haven't you your power of attorney?" he replied.

The phrase came to her like a breath of fresh air. "Leave me the bill," said Emma.

"Oh, it isn't worth while," answered Lheureux.

He came back the following week and **boasted** of having, after much trouble, at last discovered a certain Langlois, who, for a long time, had had an eye on the **property**, but without **mentioning** his price.

"Never mind the price!" she cried.

But they would, on the **contrary**, have to wait, to sound the fellow. The thing was worth a journey, and, as she could not **undertake** it, he offered to go to the place to have an **interview** with Langlois. On his return he **announced** that the purchaser proposed four thousand francs.

Emma was **radiant** at this news.

"Frankly," he added, "that's a good price."

She drew half the sum at once, and when she was about to pay her account the **shopkeeper** said--

Spanish

amounted: Sumó.
announced: anunciado.
boasted: Jactado.
bowed: agobiado, arqueado, cabizbajo, encorvado, inclinado.
contrary: contrario.
divers: varios, diversos.
dresses: los vestidos.
francs: francos.
haven't: no tener.
hovel: cabaña, cuchitril, tugurio.
interview: entrevista, entrevistar, la entrevista.
material: tela, material.
mentioning: mencionar.
miserable: pobre, deplorable, malo, triste, indigente, menesteroso, afligido, necesitado, desgraciado, miserable.
property: propiedad, bienes, finca, calidad, granja, ralea, característica, tenencia.
purchaser: comprador, cliente.
radiant: resplandeciente, radiante, brillante.
shopkeeper: tendero.
undertake: emprender, emprenda, emprenden, emprended, emprendo, emprendes, emprendéis, emprendan, emprende, emprendemos, encargarse de.

"It really grieves me, on my word! to see you **depriving** yourself all at once of such a big sum as that."

Then she looked at the bank-notes, and dreaming of the **unlimited** number of rendezvous represented by those two thousand francs, she stammered--

"What! what!"

"Oh!" he went on, laughing good-naturedly, "one **puts** anything one **likes** on **receipts**. **Don't** you think I know what household affairs are?" And he looked at her fixedly, while in his hand he held two long papers that he **slid** between his nails. At last, opening his pocket-book, he spread out on the table four bills to order, each for a thousand francs.

"Sign these," he said, "and keep it all!"

She cried out, scandalised.

"But if I give you the surplus," replied Monsieur Lheureux **impudently**, "is that not helping you?"

And taking a pen he wrote at the bottom of the **account**, "Received of Madame Bovary four thousand francs."

"Now who can trouble you, since in six months you'll draw the **arrears** for your **cottage**, and I don't make the last bill **due** till after you've been paid?"

Emma grew rather confused in her calculations, and her ears tingled as if gold pieces, **bursting** from their **bags**, rang all round her on the floor. At last Lheureux explained that he had a very good friend, Vincart, a **broker** at Rouen, who would **discount** these four bills. Then he himself would hand over to madame the remainder after the actual **debt** was paid.

But instead of two thousand francs he brought only eighteen hundred, for the friend Vincart (which was only fair) had **deducted** two hundred francs for **commission** and discount. Then he carelessly asked for a receipt.

"You understand--in business--sometimes. And with the date, if you please, with the date."

Spanish

account: cuenta, considerar, comunicación, creer, contemplar, lugar, tomar en consideración, motivo, noticia, explicación, información.
arrears: atrasos.
bags: bolsas.
broker: corredor, agente, intermediario.
bursting: muy lleno, estallido, a rebosar, desbordándose, estallar, explosión, haz de explosión, ráfaga,

reventar, reventón.
commission: comisión, encargar, encargo, comisionar.
cottage: cabaña, casa de campo.
debt: deuda.
deducted: deducido.
depriving: privando.
discount: descuento, rebaja, bajar, reducción, descontar.
don't: no.
due: debido.
impudently: atrevidamente,

descaradamente, impúdicamente, impudentemente, insolentemente.
likes: aprecia, inclinaciones, hechizos, gustos, entendimientos, ensalmos, encantos, efusiones, cariños, simpatías, arreglos.
puts: pone, mete, coloca.
receipt: recibo, recepción, comprobante, talón, el recibo, acuse de recibo.
slid: pret y pp de slide.
unlimited: ilimitado.

A horizon of **realisable** whims opened out before Emma. She was **prudent** enough to lay by a thousand crowns, with which the first three bills were paid when they fell due; but the fourth, by chance, came to the house on a Thursday, and Charles, quite upset, **patiently** awaited his wife's return for an explanation.

If she had not told him about this bill, it was only to spare him such **domestic** worries; she sat on his knees, caressed him, **cooed** to him, gave him a long **enumeration** of all the indispensable things that had been got on **credit**.

"Really, you must confess, considering the quantity, it isn't too dear."

Charles, at his wit's end, soon had recourse to the eternal Lheureux, who swore he would arrange matters if the doctor would sign him two bills, one of which was for seven hundred francs, **payable** in three months. In order to arrange for this he wrote his mother a **pathetic** letter. Instead of sending a **reply** she came herself; and when Emma wanted to know whether he had got anything out of her, "Yes," he replied; "but she **wants** to see the account." The next morning at daybreak Emma ran to Lheureux to beg him to make out another account for not more than a thousand francs, for to show the one for four thousand it would be **necessary** to say that she had paid two-thirds, and confess, **consequently**, the sale of the estate--a **negotiation admirably** carried out by the shopkeeper, and which, in fact, was only actually known later on.

Despite the low **price** of each article, Madame Bovary senior, of course, thought the **expenditure** extravagant.

"**Couldn't** you do without a carpet? Why have recovered the **arm**-chairs? In my time there was a single arm-chair in a house, for **elderly** persons--at any **rate** it was so at my mother's, who was a good woman, I can tell you. Everybody can't be **rich**! No fortune can **hold** out against waste! I should be **ashamed** to **coddle** myself as you do! And yet I am old. I need looking after. And there! there! **fitting** up gowns! **fallals**! What! silk for lining at two francs, when you can get jaconet for ten sous, or even for eight, that would do well enough!"

Emma, lying on a **lounge**, replied as quietly as possible--"Ah! Madame, enough! enough!"

Spanish

admirably: admirablemente.
arm-chair: sillón, butaca.
ashamed: avergonzado, vergonzoso.
coddle: consentir.
consequently: por consiguiente.
cooed: Arrullado.
couldn't: no fue posible.
credit: crédito, haber, acreditar.
domestic: indígena, doméstico, nacional.
elderly: mayor, anciano.
enumeration: enumeración.

expenditure: gasto, desembolso, gastos.
fallals: adorno.
fitting: conveniente, adecuado, apropiado.
hold: tener, sujetar, continuar, retención, sostener, contener, mantener, retenido, presa, bodega.
lounge: salón, sala.
necessary: necesario.
negotiation: negociación.
pathetic: patético.

patiently: pacientemente.
payable: pagadero, pagable.
price: precio, el precio, costo.
prudent: prudente.
rate: tasa, fila, estimar, tipo, velocidad, tarifa, cadencia, valorar, proporción, ritmo, arancel.
realisable: factible.
reply: respuesta, responder, contestación, contestar.
rich: rico.
wants: quiere, desea.

The other went on lecturing her, **predicting** they would end in the **workhouse**. But it was Bovary's fault. **Luckily** he had promised to **destroy** that power of **attorney**.

"What?"

"Ah! he **swore** he would," went on the good woman.

Emma opened the window, called Charles, and the poor fellow was **obliged** to **confess** the promise torn from him by his mother.

Emma disappeared, then came back quickly, and **majestically** handed her a thick piece of paper.

"Thank you," said the old woman. And she threw the power of attorney into the fire.

Emma began to laugh, a **strident**, **piercing**, continuous laugh; she had an **attack** of **hysterics**.

"Oh, my God!" cried Charles. "Ah! you really are wrong! You come here and make scenes with her!"

His mother, shrugging her shoulders, declared it was "all put on."

But Charles, **rebelling** for the first time, took his wife's part, so that Madame Bovary, senior, said she would leave. She went the very next day, and on the **threshold**, as he was trying to **detain** her, she replied--

"No, no! You love her better than me, and you are right. It is natural. For the rest, so much the **worse**! You will see. Good day--for I am not likely to come soon again, as you say, to make scenes."

Charles nevertheless was very **crestfallen** before Emma, who did not hide the **resentment** she still felt at his want of confidence, and it **needed** many **prayers** before she would consent to have another power of attorney. He even accompanied her to Monsieur Guillaumin to have a second one, just like the other, drawn up.

"I understand," said the **notary**; "a man of science **can't** be worried with the practical details of life."

Spanish

attack: atacar, ataque, acometer, acometida, agresión, acceso.
attorney: abogado, procurador, apoderado.
can't: no puede.
confess: confesar, confiesan, confiesen, confieso, confiesas, confesamos, confesad, confesáis, confiesa, confiese, declarar.
crestfallen: alicaído.
destroy: destruir, destruid, destruimos, destruís, destruyan, destruye, destruyen, destruyes, destruyo, destruya.
detain: retener, retengo, retienes, retiene, retengan, retenemos, retenéis, retened, reten, retienen, retenga.
emma: Ema.
hysterics: ataque de nervios.
luckily: afortunadamente, por suerte.
majestically: majestuosamente.
needed: necesario, necesitado.
notary: notario, escribano.
obliged: obligado.
piercing: penetrante, agujereando.
prayers: ruegos, rezos, oraciones.
predicting: prediciendo.
rebelling: rebelar.
resentment: resentimiento.
strident: estridente.
swore: pret de swear, Juró.
threshold: umbral.
torn: roto.
workhouse: asilo de pobres.
worse: peor.

And Charles felt relieved by this **comfortable** reflection, which gave his weakness the **flattering** appearance of **higher** pre-occupation.

And what an **outburst** the next Thursday at the hotel in their room with Leon! She laughed, cried, sang, sent for sherbets, wanted to smoke **cigarettes**, seemed to him wild and **extravagant**, but **adorable**, superb.

He did not know what recreation of her whole being drove her more and more to **plunge** into the pleasures of life. She was becoming **irritable**, **greedy**, **voluptuous**; and she walked about the streets with him carrying her head high, without fear, so she said, of **compromising** herself. At times, however, Emma **shuddered** at the sudden thought of meeting Rodolphe, for it seemed to her that, although they were separated forever, she was not completely free from her **subjugation** to him.

One night she did not return to Yonville at all. Charles lost his head with anxiety, and little Berthe would not go to bed without her **mamma**, and **sobbed** enough to break her heart. Justin had gone out searching the road at **random**. Monsieur Homais even had left his **pharmacy**.

At last, at eleven o'clock, able to bear it no longer, Charles **harnessed** his **chaise**, jumped in, **whipped** up his horse, and reached the "Croix-Rouge" about two o'clock in the morning. No one there! He thought that the clerk had perhaps seen her; but where did he live? **Happily**, Charles remembered his employer's address, and rushed off there.

Day was breaking, and he could distinguish the escutcheons over the door, and knocked. Someone, without opening the door, shouted out the **required** information, adding a few insults to those who **disturb** people in the middle of the night.

The house **inhabited** by the clerk had neither bell, **knocker**, nor **porter**. Charles knocked loudly at the **shutters** with his hands. A **policeman** happened to pass by. Then he was frightened, and went away.

"I am mad," he said; "no doubt they kept her to dinner at Monsieur Lormeaux'." But the Lormeaux no longer lived at Rouen.

Spanish

adorable: cute, adorable.
chaise: coche postal.
cigarettes: los cigarros.
comfortable: cómodo, agradable.
compromising: comprometido, comprometedor.
disturb: molestar, moleste, molestad, molestáis, molestamos, molestan, molestas, molesta, molesto, molesten, incomodar.
extravagant: extravagante.
flattering: adulando, adulador.

greedy: codicioso, ávido, goloso.
happily: alegremente, felizmente, afortunadamente.
harnessed: enjaezado.
higher: superior.
inhabited: habitado, poblado.
irritable: irritable.
knocker: aldaba.
mamma: mama.
outburst: explosión.
pharmacy: farmacia.
plunge: bucear, zambullida,

zambullirse.
policeman: policía, guardia.
porter: portero, mozo, conserje.
random: aleatorio, al azar, azar.
required: necesitado, exigido, necesario, requerido.
shuddered: estremecido.
shutters: obturadores, obturador.
sobbed: sollozado.
subjugation: dominación.
voluptuous: voluptuoso.
whipped: batido, Azotado.

"She probably stayed to look after Madame Dubreuil. Why, Madame Dubreuil has been dead these ten months! Where can she be?"

An idea occurred to him. At a **cafe** he asked for a Directory, and **hurriedly** looked for the name of Mademoiselle Lempereur, who lived at No. 74 Rue de la Renelle-des-Maroquiniers.

As he was turning into the street, Emma **herself** appeared at the other end of it. He **threw** himself upon her rather than **embraced** her, crying--

"What kept you yesterday?"

"I was not well."

"What was it? Where? How?"

She passed her hand over her **forehead** and **answered**, "At Mademoiselle Lempereur's."

"I was sure of it! I was going there."

"Oh, it isn't worth while," said Emma. "She went out just now; but for the future **don't** worry. I do not feel free, you see, if I know that the least **delay** upsets you like this."

This was a sort of permission that she gave herself, so as to get perfect freedom in her escapades. And she **profited** by it **freely**, fully. When she was **seized** with the desire to see Leon, she set out upon any **pretext**; and as he was not **expecting** her on that day, she went to **fetch** him at his office.

It was a great **delight** at first, but soon he no longer **concealed** the truth, which was, that his master **complained** very much about these interruptions.

"**Pshaw**! come along," she said.

And he **slipped** out.

She wanted him to dress all in black, and grow a pointed **beard**, to look like the portraits of Louis XIII. She wanted to see his **lodgings**; thought them poor. He **blushed** at them, but she did not notice this, then **advised** him to buy some **curtains** like hers, and as he **objected** to the expense--

"Ah! ah! you care for your money," she said **laughing**.

Spanish

advised: aconsejado.
answered: contesta, Contestado.
beard: barba, la barba, arista.
blushed: enrojecido.
cafe: café, cafés.
complained: regañado, se quejado, lamentado, demandado, reclamado, se querellado, Quejado.
concealed: ocultado, disimulado.
curtains: las cortinas.
delay: retraso, retardo, demora, retrasar, demorar, retardar.

delight: deleitar, delicia, encantar.
don't: no.
embraced: abrazado.
expecting: esperando.
fetch: traer, traemos, traed, trae, traéis, traes, traigo, traigan, traen, traiga, coger.
forehead: frente, la frente.
freely: libremente.
hers: suyo.
hurriedly: precipitadamente, apresuradamente.

laughing: riendo.
lodgings: alojamiento, apartamento alquilado, habitación, pensión.
objected: objetado.
pretext: pretexto.
profited: ganado.
pshaw: bah.
seized: agarrado, asido.
slipped: resbalado.
threw: pret de throw, Tiró, tiro.

Each time Leon had to tell her **everything** that he had done since their last **meeting**. She asked him for some **verses**--some verses "for herself," a "love **poem**" in **honour** of her. But he never **succeeded** in getting a **rhyme** for the second verse; and at last **ended** by **copying** a **sonnet** in a "Keepsake." This was less from **vanity** than from the one **desire** of **pleasing** her. He did not question her ideas; he **accepted** all her **tastes**; he was rather **becoming** her **mistress** than she his. She had **tender** words and **kisses** that **thrilled** his **soul**. Where could she have **learnt** this **corruption** almost **incorporeal** in the **strength** of its **profanity** and **dissimulation**?

Spanish

accepted: aceptado, admitido.
becoming: conveniente, aconteciendo.
copying: copia, duplicación.
corruption: corrupción, deterioración, putrefacción.
desire: desear, deseo, tener, querer, gana, codiciar.
dissimulation: disimulación.
ended: finalizó, terminado.
everything: todo.
honour: honor, homenaje.
incorporeal: incorpóreo.

kisses: besos.
learnt: pret de learn.
meeting: encontrando, reunión, encuentro, hallando, sesión, entrevista, cita, asamblea.
mistress: señora.
pleasing: agradable.
poem: poema, el poema.
profanity: profanidad.
rhyme: rima, rimar.
sonnet: soneto.
soul: alma, espíritu, ánimo.

strength: fuerza, resistencia, virtud, potencia, fortaleza.
succeeded: conseguido.
tastes: gustos.
tender: tierno, oferta, dulce, subasta, proposición, ofrecer, destajo, licitación, presentar, reproducir, retratar.
thrilled: estremecido.
vanity: vanidad.
verse: verso, estrofa, copla, versículo.

CHAPTER SIX

During the journeys he made to see her, Leon had often **dined** at the chemist's, and he felt obliged from **politeness** to invite him in turn.

"With pleasure!" Monsieur Homais replied; "besides, I must **invigorate** my mind, for I am getting **rusty** here. **We'll** go to the theatre, to the **restaurant**; we'll make a night of it."

"Oh, my dear!" **tenderly** murmured Madame Homais, **alarmed** at the vague perils he was **preparing** to **brave**.

"Well, what? Do you think I'm not sufficiently **ruining** my health living here **amid** the **continual** emanations of the **pharmacy**? But there! that is the way with women! They are **jealous** of science, and then are opposed to our taking the most **legitimate** distractions. No matter! Count upon me. One of these days I shall turn up at Rouen, and we'll go the pace together."

The **druggist** would formerly have taken good care not to use such an expression, but he was **cultivating** a gay Parisian style, which he thought in the best taste; and, like his neighbour, Madame Bovary, he questioned the clerk **curiously** about the customs of the capital; he even talked **slang** to **dazzle** the **bourgeois**, saying **bender**, **crummy**, **dandy**, **macaroni**, the cheese, cut my stick and "I'll hook it," for "I am going."

Spanish

alarmed: alarmado.
amid: en medio de, entre.
bender: dobladora, juerga, mierda.
bourgeois: burgués.
brave: valiente, bravo, animoso.
continual: continuo.
crummy: lo de calidad baja, de calidad inferior, despreciable, miserable, sucio.
cultivating: cultivando.
curiously: curiosamente.
dandy: Estupendo, Excelente, Mono, Paquete, pisaverde, Maravilloso, Raro, Soledad, elegante, de Primera, dandi.
dazzle: deslumbrar, deslumbramiento.
dined: cenado.
druggist: droguero.
invigorate: vigorizar, vigorizamos, vigorizo, vigorizas, vigorizan, vigoricen, vigorizad, vigoriza, vigorizáis, vigorice.
jealous: celoso.
legitimate: legítimo.
macaroni: macarrones.
pharmacy: farmacia.
politeness: cortesía, educación, atenciones.
preparing: preparando.
restaurant: restaurante, el restaurante.
ruining: arruinar.
rusty: mohoso, oxidado, herrumbroso.
slang: jerga, argot.
tenderly: con ternura, tiernamente, endeblemente, delicado.
we'll: Haremos.

So one Thursday Emma was surprised to meet Monsieur Homais in the kitchen of the "Lion d'Or," wearing a traveller's **costume**, that is to say, wrapped in an old cloak which no one knew he had, while he carried a **valise** in one hand and the **foot**-warmer of his establishment in the other. He had confided his intentions to no one, for fear of **causing** the public anxiety by his absence.

The idea of seeing again the place where his youth had been spent no doubt excited him, for during the whole journey he never ceased talking, and as soon as he had arrived, he jumped quickly out of the diligence to go in **search** of Leon. In vain the clerk tried to get rid of him. Monsieur Homais dragged him off to the large Cafe de la Normandie, which he entered **majestically**, not raising his hat, thinking it very provincial to **uncover** in any public place.

Emma waited for Leon three quarters of an hour. At last she ran to his office; and, lost in all sorts of **conjectures**, **accusing** him of indifference, and **reproaching** herself for her weakness, she spent the afternoon, her face pressed against the window-panes.

At two o'clock they were still at a table opposite each other. The large room was emptying; the stove-pipe, in the shape of a **palm**-tree, spread its gilt leaves over the white ceiling, and near them, **outside** the window, in the bright sunshine, a little fountain gurgled in a white basin, where; in the midst of **watercress** and **asparagus**, three **torpid lobsters** stretched across to some quails that lay **heaped** up in a pile on their **sides**.

Homais was **enjoying** himself. Although he was even more **intoxicated** with the luxury than the rich **fare**, the Pommard wine all the same rather excited his faculties; and when the **omelette** au rhum appeared, he began **propounding** immoral **theories** about women. What seduced him above all else was **chic**. He admired an elegant **toilette** in a well-furnished apartment, and as to **bodily** qualities, he didn't dislike a young girl.

Leon watched the clock in despair. The **druggist** went on drinking, eating, and talking.

"You must be very lonely," he said suddenly, "here at Rouen. To be sure your lady-love doesn't live far away."

Spanish

accusing: acusando.
asparagus: espárrago.
bodily: corporal.
causing: causante, causar.
chic: elegante.
conjectures: supone.
costume: traje.
druggist: droguero.
enjoying: disfrutando, gozando.
fare: tarifa, pasaje.
foot-warmer: calientapiés.
heaped: amontonado.

intoxicated: ebrio, intoxicado, borracho, aturdido.
lobsters: las langostas.
majestically: majestuosamente.
omelette: tortilla, la tortilla.
outside: afuera, fuera de, fuera, exterior, externo.
palm-tree: palma.
propounding: proponiendo, proponer.
reproaching: Reprochar.
search: buscar, búsqueda, busca, registro, investigación.

sides: costados, Lados.
theories: teorías.
toilette: wáter, de tocador, inodoro, lavabo, retrete, sanitario, servicios, tocado, vestido, atavío, baño.
torpid: torpe.
uncover: descubrir, descubre, descubrís, descubrimos, descubrid, descubro, descubren, descubran, descubra, descubres, destapar.
valise: maleta, maleta de mano.
watercress: berro.

And the other blushed--

"Come now, be **frank**. Can you **deny** that at Yonville--"

The young man **stammered** something.

"At Madame Bovary's, you're not making love to--"

"To whom?"

"The servant!"

He was not **joking**; but **vanity** getting the better of all **prudence**, Leon, in **spite** of himself protested. Besides, he only liked dark women.

"I approve of that," said the **chemist**; "they have more passion."

And **whispering** into his friend's ear, he pointed out the symptoms by which one could find out if a woman had passion. He even launched into an **ethnographic digression**: the German was **vapourish**, the French woman **licentious**, the Italian passionate.

"And negresses?" asked the clerk.

"They are an artistic taste!" said Homais. "**Waiter**! two cups of coffee!"

"Are we going?" at last asked Leon **impatiently**.

"Ja!"

But before leaving he wanted to see the **proprietor** of the establishment and made him a few compliments. Then the young man, to be alone, **alleged** he had some business **engagement**.

"Ah! I will **escort** you," said Homais.

And all the while he was walking through the streets with him he talked of his wife, his children; of their future, and of his business; told him in what a **decayed** condition it had formerly been, and to what a **degree** of **perfection** he had raised it.

Arrived in front of the Hotel de Boulogne, Leon left him abruptly, ran up the stairs, and found his mistress in great **excitement**. At **mention** of the chemist she flew into a passion. He, however, **piled** up good reasons; it wasn't his fault;

Spanish

alleged: alegado, presunto, pretendido.
chemist: químico, farmacéutico, boticario.
decayed: decrépito.
degree: grado, título, licencia.
deny: negar, negad, niego, niegas, niegan, negáis, negamos, nieguen, niega, niegue, desmentir.
digression: digresión.
engagement: obligación, compromiso, contrato, contratación.
escort: acompañamiento, escoltar, acompañar, acompañante, escolta.
ethnographic: etnográfico.
excitement: excitación, agitación.
frank: franco, franquear.
impatiently: impacientemente, con impaciencia.
joking: bromeando.
licentious: licencioso, libertino, desenfrenado.
mention: mencionar, mención.
perfection: perfección.
piled: amontonado.
proprietor: propietario.
prudence: prudencia.
spite: rencor.
stammered: tartamudeó.
vanity: vanidad.
vapourish: vaporoso.
waiter: camarero, el camarero, el mozo, mozo.
whispering: chismes, chismografía, con eco, cuchicheo, de difamación, rumores, susurro, de rumores.

didn't she know Homais--did she believe that he would **prefer** his company? But she turned away; he drew her back, and, sinking on his knees, **clasped** her waist with his arms in a **languorous** pose, full of **concupiscence** and supplication.

She was standing; up, her large **flashing** eyes looked at him seriously, almost terribly. Then tears **obscured** them, her red eyelids were lowered, she gave him her hands, and Leon was pressing them to his lips when a servant appeared to tell the gentleman that he was wanted.

"You will come back?" she said.

"Yes."

"But when?"

"Immediately."

"It's a trick," said the chemist, when he saw Leon. "I wanted to **interrupt** this **visit**, that seemed to me to **annoy** you. Let's go and have a glass of gaurs at Bridoux'."

Leon **vowed** that he must get back to his office. Then the **druggist joked** him about quill-drivers and the law.

"Leave Cujas and Barthole alone a bit. Who the devil prevents you? Be a man! Let's go to Bridoux'. You'll see his dog. It's very interesting."

And as the clerk still insisted--

"I'll go with you. I'll read a paper while I wait for you, or turn over the leaves of a 'Code.'"

Leon, **bewildered** by Emma's anger, Monsieur Homais' **chatter**, and, perhaps, by the **heaviness** of the **luncheon**, was **undecided**, and, as it were, fascinated by the chemist, who kept repeating--

"Let's go to Bridoux'. It's just by here, in the Rue Malpalu."

Then, through **cowardice**, through **stupidity**, through that **indefinable** feeling that **drags** us into the most **distasteful acts**, he allowed himself to be led off to Bridoux', whom they found in his small yard, **superintending** three workmen, who **panted** as they turned the large **wheel** of a machine for making

Spanish

acts: hechos.
annoy: molestar, molestad, molestáis, molestamos, molestan, molestas, molesten, moleste, molesto, molesta, enfadar.
bewildered: descarriado, desconcertado.
chatter: charlar, charla, castañetear, parlotear.
clasped: apretado, abrochado.
concupiscence: concupiscencia.
cowardice: cobardía.

distasteful: desagradable.
drags: arrastra, remolca.
druggist: droguero.
flashing: destello.
heaviness: pesadez.
indefinable: indefinible.
interrupt: interrumpir, interrupción.
joked: Bromeó.
languorous: apático, lánguido.
luncheon: almuerzo.
obscured: disimulado.
panted: jadeado.

prefer: preferir, prefiero, prefieres, prefieren, prefiere, prefieran, preferís, preferimos, preferid, prefiera.
stupidity: estupidez.
superintending: dirigiendo, supervisando, vigilando, supervisar.
undecided: indeciso.
visit: visitar, visita, visitad, visiten, visitan, visitas, visito, visitamos, visitáis, visite.
vowed: Prometido.
wheel: rueda, la rueda.

seltzer-water. Homais gave them some good advice. He embraced Bridoux; they took some garus. Twenty times Leon tried to escape, but the other seized him by the arm saying--

"Presently! **I'm** coming! We'll go to the 'Fanal de Rouen' to see the fellows there. I'll **introduce** you to Thornassin."

At last he managed to get rid of him, and rushed straight to the hotel. Emma was no longer there. She had just gone in a fit of anger. She detested him now. This **failing** to keep their rendezvous seemed to her an insult, and she tried to rake up other reasons to **separate** herself from him. He was incapable of heroism, weak, **banal**, more **spiritless** than a woman, **avaricious** too, and cowardly.

Then, growing calmer, she at length discovered that she had, no doubt, **calumniated** him. But the **disparaging** of those we love always **alienates** us from them to some extent. We must not touch our idols; the gilt sticks to our fingers.

They gradually came to talking more **frequently** of matters outside their love, and in the letters that Emma wrote him she spoke of flowers, verses, the moon and the stars, naive **resources** of a **waning** passion striving to keep itself alive by all external aids. She was constantly **promising** herself a profound felicity on her next journey. Then she confessed to herself that she felt nothing extraordinary. This disappointment quickly gave way to a new hope, and Emma returned to him more inflamed, more **eager** than ever. She undressed **brutally**, **tearing** off the thin laces of her **corset** that nestled around her hips like a gliding **snake**. She went on tiptoe, **barefooted**, to see once more that the door was closed, then, pale, serious, and, without speaking, with one movement, she threw herself upon his breast with a long shudder.

Yet there was upon that brow covered with cold drops, on those quivering lips, in those wild eyes, in the **strain** of those arms, something vague and dreary that seemed to Leon to glide between them **subtly** as if to separate them.

He did not dare to question her; but, seeing her so **skilled**, she must have passed, he thought, through every experience of suffering and of pleasure. What had once charmed now frightened him a little. Besides, he rebelled against his **absorption**, daily more marked, by her **personality**. He **begrudged** Emma this

Spanish

absorption: absorción.
alienates: aliena, enajena.
avaricious: avaro.
banal: trivial, banal.
barefooted: descalzo.
begrudged: deplorado.
brutally: brutalmente.
calumniated: calumniado.
corset: corsé.
disparaging: desacreditando.
eager: ansioso, ávido, codicioso.
failing: fracaso, falta.

frequently: a menudo, frecuentemente.
i'm: soy.
introduce: presentar, presente, presento, presenta, presentad, presentáis, presentamos, presentan, presenten, presentas, introducir.
personality: personalidad, índole, naturaleza.
promising: prometiendo, prometedor.
resources: medio, recursos.
separate: separado, separar, apartar,

aparte, particular, dividir, separarse, segregar, independiente, compartir.
skilled: hábil, experto, experimentado, especializado.
snake: serpiente, la serpiente.
spiritless: exánime.
strain: colar, esfuerzo, deformación, cepa, tensión, torcedura.
subtly: disimuladamente, sutilmente.
tearing: romper, desgarramiento, efecto bandera, ruptura.
waning: menguando.

constant **victory**. He even **strove** not to love her; then, when he heard the **creaking** of her boots, he turned **coward**, like drunkards at the sight of **strong** drinks.

She did not fail, in **truth**, to lavish all sorts of attentions upon him, from the **delicacies** of food to the coquettries of dress and **languishing** looks. She brought roses to her breast from Yonville, which she threw into his face; was anxious about his health, gave him advice as to his **conduct**; and, in order the more **surely** to keep her hold on him, hoping perhaps that heaven would take her part, she tied a medal of the Virgin round his neck. She **inquired** like a **virtuous** mother about his companions. She said to him--

"Don't see them; **don't** go out; think only of ourselves; love me!"

She would have liked to be able to watch over his life; and the idea occurred to her of having him followed in the streets. Near the hotel there was always a kind of **loafer** who **accosted** travellers, and who would not **refuse**. But her pride **revolted** at this.

"Bah! so much the worse. Let him **deceive** me! What does it matter to me? As If I cared for him!"

One day, when they had parted early and she was returning alone along the **boulevard**, she saw the walls of her convent; then she sat down on a form in the shade of the elm-trees. How calm that time had been! How she longed for the **ineffable** sentiments of love that she had tried to figure to herself out of books! The first month of her marriage, her rides in the wood, the **viscount** that waltzed, and Lagardy singing, all repassed before her eyes. And Leon suddenly appeared to her as far off as the others.

"Yet I love him," she said to herself.

No matter! She was not happy--she never had been. **Whence** came this **insufficiency** in life--this **instantaneous** turning to **decay** of everything on which she leant? But if there were somewhere a being strong and beautiful, a **valiant** nature, full at once of **exaltation** and refinement, a poet's heart in an angel's form, a **lyre** with sounding chords ringing out **elegiac** epithalamia to heaven, why,

Spanish

accosted: abordado.
boulevard: bulevar.
conduct: conducir, guiar, dirigir, conducta, comportamiento.
coward: cobarde, el cobarde.
creaking: crujido, chirriando.
decay: decadencia, decaimiento, putrefacción, baja, deterioración, descomposición.
deceive: engañar, engaño, engañe, engaña, engañamos, engañen, engañan, engañáis, engañad,

engañas, embaucar.
delicacies: comestibles finos.
don't: no.
elegiac: elegíaco.
exaltation: exaltación.
ineffable: inefable.
inquired: inquirido, preguntado.
instantaneous: instantáneo.
insufficiency: insuficiencia.
languishing: languideciendo.
loafer: holgazán.
lyre: lira.

refuse: rehusar, rechazar, denegar, desecho, desechos, detrito, negar.
revolted: rebelado, rebelde.
strong: fuerte, intenso, marcado.
strove: pret de strive.
surely: seguramente, ciertamente.
truth: verdad, veras, la verdad.
valiant: bravo, valiente.
victory: victoria.
virtuous: virtuoso.
viscount: vizconde.
whence: de dónde.

perchance, should she not find him? Ah! how impossible! Besides, nothing was worth the trouble of seeking it; everything was a lie. Every smile **hid** a **yawn** of **boredom**, every joy a **curse**, all pleasure **satiety**, and the sweetest **kisses** left upon your lips only the **unattainable** desire for a greater delight.

A **metallic clang droned** through the air, and four strokes were heard from the convent-clock. Four o'clock! And it seemed to her that she had been there on that form an **eternity**. But an **infinity** of passions may be contained in a minute, like a crowd in a small space.

Emma lived all absorbed in hers, and troubled no more about money matters than an **archduchess**.

Once, however, a wretched-looking man, **rubicund** and **bald**, came to her house, saying he had been sent by Monsieur Vincart of Rouen. He took out the **pins** that held together the side-pockets of his long green **overcoat**, stuck them into his sleeve, and **politely** handed her a paper.

It was a bill for seven hundred **francs**, signed by her, and which Lheureux, in **spite** of all his professions, had paid away to Vincart. She sent her servant for him. He could not come. Then the stranger, who had remained standing, **casting** right and left curious glances, that his thick, fair eyebrows hid, asked with a **naive** air--

"What answer am I to take Monsieur Vincart?"

"Oh," said Emma, "tell him that I **haven't** it. I will send next week; he must wait; yes, till next week."

And the fellow went without another word.

But the next day at twelve o'clock she received a **summons**, and the sight of the **stamped** paper, on which appeared several times in large letters, "Maitre Hareng, **bailiff** at Buchy," so frightened her that she rushed in hot **haste** to the linendraper's. She found him in his shop, doing up a **parcel**.

"Your obedient!" he said; "I am at your service."

Spanish

archduchess: archiduquesa.
bailiff: alguacil, administrador.
bald: calvo, pelado.
boredom: fastidio, aburrimiento.
casting: fundición, colada, vaciado.
clang: sonar, sonido metálico, sonido metálico resonante, resonar, estruendo, hacer sonar, hacer estruendo.
curse: maldecir, maldición, jurar.
droned: zumbó.
eternity: eternidad.

francs: francos.
haste: prisa, precipitación.
haven't: no tener.
hid: escondió, pret de hide.
infinity: infinidad, infinito.
kisses: besos.
metallic: metálico.
naive: ingenuo.
overcoat: abrigo, el abrigo.
parcel: paquete, parcela.
perchance: quizás, tal vez.
pins: pines, patas.

politely: comedidamente, cortésmente, educadamente, refinadamente.
rubicund: rubicundo, rubicunda, rubeo.
satiety: saciedad.
spite: rencor.
stamped: estampillado.
summons: citación, emplazamiento.
unattainable: inasequible.
yawn: bostezo, bostezar, el bostezo.

But Lheureux, all the same, went on with his work, **helped** by a young girl of about thirteen, somewhat hunch-backed, who was at once his clerk and his servant.

Then, his **clogs** clattering on the shop-boards, he went up in front of Madame Bovary to the first door, and introduced her into a narrow **closet**, where, in a large bureau in sapon-wood, lay some ledgers, **protected** by a horizontal padlocked iron **bar**. Against the wall, under some **remnants** of **calico**, one **glimpsed** a safe, but of such **dimensions** that it must **contain** something besides bills and money. Monsieur Lheureux, in fact, went in for **pawnbroking**, and it was there that he had put Madame Bovary's gold chain, together with the **earrings** of poor old Tellier, who, at last forced to sell out, had bought a **meagre** store of **grocery** at Quincampoix, where he was dying of **catarrh** amongst his candles, that were less yellow than his face.

Lheureux sat down in a large **cane arm**-chair, saying: "What news?"

"See!"

And she showed him the paper.

"Well how can I help it?"

Then she grew angry, **reminding** him of the promise he had given not to pay away her bills. He **acknowledged** it.

"But I was pressed myself; the knife was at my own throat."

"And what will **happen** now?" she went on.

"Oh, it's very simple; a judgment and then a distraint--that's about it!"

Emma kept down a desire to strike him, and asked gently if there was no way of **quieting** Monsieur Vincart.

"I dare say! **Quiet** Vincart! You **don't** know him; he's more **ferocious** than an Arab!"

Still Monsieur Lheureux must interfere.

"Well, listen. It seems to me so far I've been very good to you." And opening one of his ledgers, "See," he said. Then running up the **page** with his finger, "Let's see! let's see! August 3d, two hundred **francs**; June 17th, a hundred and fifty; March 23d, **forty**-six. In April—"

He stopped, as if afraid of making some mistake.

"Not to speak of the bills signed by Monsieur Bovary, one for seven hundred francs, and another for three hundred. As to your little **installments**, with the interest, why, there's no end to 'em; one **gets** quite **muddled** over 'em. I'll have nothing more to do with it."

She **wept**; she even called him "her good Monsieur Lheureux." But he always fell back upon "that **rascal** Vincart." **Besides**, he **hadn't** a **brass farthing**; no one was paying him now-a-days; they were eating his coat off his back; a poor **shopkeeper** like him **couldn't** advance money.

Emma was silent, and Monsieur Lheureux, who was **biting** the feathers of a **quill**, no doubt became **uneasy** at her silence, for he went on--

"Unless one of these days I have something coming in, I might—"

"Besides," said she, "as soon as the balance of Barneville--"

"What!"

And on hearing that Langlois had not yet paid he seemed much surprised. Then in a honied voice--

"And we **agree**, you say?"

"Oh! to anything you like."

On this he closed his eyes to reflect, wrote down a few figures, and **declaring** it would be very difficult for him, that the affair was **shady**, and that he was being **bled**, he wrote out four bills for two hundred and fifty francs each, to fall due month by month.

"**Provided** that Vincart will listen to me! However, it's settled. I **don't** play the **fool**; I'm straight enough."

Next he **carelessly** showed her several new goods, not one of which, however, was in his opinion **worthy** of **madame**.

Spanish

agree: acordar, acordáis, acuerde, acuerdas, acuerden, acuerdan, acordad, acuerda, acordamos, acuerdo, convenir.
besides: además, demás, además de, amén de.
biting: mordaz, punzante, penetrante.
bled: Sangrado.
brass: latón, metal.
carelessly: descuidadamente, sin cuidado.
couldn't: no fue posible.

declaring: declarando.
don't: no.
emma: Ema.
farthing: comino.
fool: engañar, necio, tonto.
forty-six: cuanrenta y seis, cuarenta y seis, quarenta y seis.
francs: francos.
gets: obtiene.
hadn't: no ha.
installments: reembolso a plazos, plazos.

madame: señora.
muddled: desordenó.
provided: suministrado, proporcionado, provisto, siempre que, con tal que.
quill: pluma.
rascal: bribón.
shady: umbrío, sombreado.
shopkeeper: tendero.
uneasy: inquieto, intranquilo.
wept: Llorado.
worthy: digno.

"When I think that there's a dress at threepence-halfpenny a yard, and **warranted** fast colours! And yet they actually swallow it! Of course you understand one doesn't tell them what it really is!" He hoped by this confession of **dishonesty** to others to quite **convince** her of his **probity** to her.

Then he called her back to show her three yards of guipure that he had lately picked up "at a sale."

"Isn't it lovely?" said Lheureux. "It is very much used now for the backs of arm-chairs. It's quite the rage."

And, more ready than a **juggler**, he wrapped up the guipure in some blue paper and put it in Emma's hands.

"But at least let me know--"

"Yes, another time," he replied, turning on his heel.

That same evening she urged Bovary to write to his mother, to ask her to send as quickly as possible the whole of the balance due from the father's **estate**. The mother-in-law replied that she had nothing more, the winding up was over, and there was due to them besides Barneville an income of six hundred francs, that she would pay them **punctually**.

Then Madame Bovary sent in **accounts** to two or three patients, and she made large use of this **method**, which was very **successful**. She was always careful to **add** a **postscript**: "Do not mention this to my husband; you know how **proud** he is. Excuse me. Yours obediently." There were some complaints; she **intercepted** them.

To get money she began selling her old gloves, her old hats, the old **odds** and ends, and she **bargained rapaciously**, her peasant blood standing her in good **stead**. Then on her journey to town she picked up nick-nacks **secondhand**, that, in **default** of anyone else, Monsieur Lheureux would certainly take off her hands. She bought **ostrich** feathers, Chinese **porcelain**, and **trunks**; she borrowed from Felicite, from Madame Lefrancois, from the landlady at the Croix-Rouge, from everybody, no matter where.

Spanish

accounts: cuentas.
add: sumar, sumad, sumáis, sumamos, suman, sumas, sume, sumen, suma, sumo, agregar.
bargained: Negociado.
convince: convencer, convenza, convencen, convences, convenzo, convenzan, convencéis, convenced, convence, convencemos.
default: predeterminado, incumplimiento, defecto, por omisión, por defecto.

dishonesty: deshonestidad.
estate: finca, granja, propiedad, herencia, hacienda, patrimonio.
intercepted: interceptado.
juggler: malabarista.
method: método, procedimiento.
odds: posibilidades.
ostrich: avestruz.
porcelain: porcelana.
postscript: posdata, postdata.
probity: probidad.
proud: orgulloso.

punctually: puntualmente.
rapaciously: rapazmente.
secondhand: de segunda mano.
stead: lugar.
successful: exitoso, afortunado.
trunks: traje de baño, bañador, mampara encerradora de la escotilla, pantaloneta, pantalón de baño.
warranted: justificado, garantizado.

With the money she at last received from Barneville she paid two bills; the other fifteen hundred **francs** fell due. She renewed the bills, and thus it was continually.

Sometimes, it is true, she tried to make a **calculation**, but she discovered things so **exorbitant** that she could not believe them possible. Then she recommenced, soon got confused, gave it all up, and thought no more about it.

The house was very **dreary** now. **Tradesmen** were seen leaving it with angry faces. Handkerchiefs were lying about on the **stoves**, and little Berthe, to the great **scandal** of Madame Homais, wore **stockings** with holes in them. If Charles **timidly ventured** a remark, she answered roughly that it wasn't her fault.

What was the meaning of all these fits of **temper**? She explained everything through her old nervous illness, and **reproaching** himself with having taken her infirmities for **faults**, **accused** himself of **egotism**, and longed to go and take her in his arms.

"Ah, no!" he said to himself; "I should worry her."

And he did not **stir**.

After dinner he walked about alone in the garden; he took little Berthe on his knees, and **unfolding** his medical journal, tried to teach her to read. But the child, who never had any lessons, soon looked up with large, sad eyes and began to cry. Then he **comforted** her; went to **fetch** water in her can to make rivers on the sand path, or broke off branches from the **privet** hedges to plant trees in the beds. This did not **spoil** the garden much, all **choked** now with long **weeds**. They owed Lestiboudois for so many days. Then the child grew cold and asked for her mother.

"Call the servant," said Charles. "You know, dearie, that **mamma** does not like to be disturbed."

Autumn was setting in, and the leaves were already falling, as they did two years ago when she was ill. Where would it all end? And he walked up and down, his hands behind his back.

Spanish

accused: acusado.
calculation: cálculo, cuenta.
choked: estrangulado.
comforted: aliviado.
dreary: triste, lúgubre, árido, horroroso, horrible, afligido.
egotism: egotismo.
exorbitant: exorbitante.
faults: desperfecto, fallas.
fetch: traer, traemos, traed, trae, traéis, traes, traigo, traigan, traen, traiga, coger.

francs: francos.
mamma: mama.
privet: alheña.
reproaching: Reprochar.
scandal: escándalo.
spoil: mimar, deteriorar, echar a perder, corromper, consentir, despojo, estropear.
stir: conmover, revolver, remover, agitar.
stockings: las medias.
stoves: estufas.

temper: humor, genio, templar, temperamento.
timidly: temerosamente, temeroso, tímidamente, encogidamente, apocadamente.
tradesmen: trabajadores especializados.
unfolding: desplegando.
ventured: Aventurado.
weeds: malas hierbas, hierbajos.

Madame was in her room, which no one entered. She stayed there all day long, **torpid**, half dressed, and from time to time burning Turkish pastilles which she had bought at Rouen in an Algerian's shop. In order not to have at night this sleeping man stretched at her side, by dint of **manoeuvring**, she at last succeeded in banishing him to the second floor, while she read till morning extravagant books, full of pictures of orgies and **thrilling** situations. Often, seized with fear, she cried out, and Charles hurried to her.

"Oh, go away!" she would say.

Or at other times, **consumed** more **ardently** than ever by that inner flame to which adultery added **fuel**, panting, **tremulous**, all desire, she threw open her window, breathed in the cold air, shook loose in the wind her masses of hair, too heavy, and, gazing upon the stars, longed for some **princely** love. She thought of him, of Leon. She would then have given anything for a single one of those **meetings** that **surfeited** her.

These were her **gala** days. She wanted them to be **sumptuous**, and when he alone could not pay the expenses, she made up the **deficit liberally**, which happened pretty well every time. He tried to make her understand that they would be quite as comfortable somewhere else, in a **smaller** hotel, but she always found some objection.

One day she drew six small silver-gilt spoons from her **bag** (they were old Roualt's wedding present), begging him to **pawn** them at once for her, and Leon obeyed, though the **proceeding** annoyed him. He was afraid of compromising himself.

Then, on, reflection, he began to think his mistress's ways were growing odd, and that they were perhaps not wrong in **wishing** to separate him from her.

In fact someone had sent his mother a long anonymous letter to **warn** her that he was "ruining himself with a married woman," and the good lady at once **conjuring** up the eternal **bugbear** of **families** the vague pernicious creature, the **siren**, the monster, who **dwells fantastically** in depths of love, wrote to Lawyer Dubocage, his employer, who **behaved** perfectly in the affair. He kept him for three quarters of an hour trying to open his eyes, to warn him of the abyss into

Spanish

ardently: ardientemente.
bag: bolso, bolsa, saco.
behaved: se comportado, portado, funcionado, conducido, educado, Comportado, comportarse bien, comportar.
bugbear: coco, espantajo, pesadilla.
conjuring: conjurando, prestidigitación.
consumed: consumido.
deficit: déficit.
dwells: mora.

families: familias.
fantastically: fantásticamente.
fuel: combustible, carburante.
gala: gala.
liberally: libremente, liberalmente, a manos llenas.
manoeuvring: maniobra.
meetings: reuniones, encuentros.
pawn: empeñar, peón, prenda, pignorar.
princely: magnífico, regio, principesco, príncipe.

proceeding: procedimiento, proceder.
siren: sirena.
smaller: menor.
sumptuous: suntuoso, rumboso.
surfeited: sació.
thrilling: emocionante.
torpid: torpe.
tremulous: trémulo.
warn: avisar, aviso, avisa, avise, avisas, avisan, avisamos, avisen, avisad, avisáis, advertir.
wishing: desear.

which he was falling. Such an intrigue would **damage** him later on, when he set up for himself. He implored him to break with her, and, if he would not make this sacrifice in his own interest, to do it at least for his, Dubocage's sake.

At last Leon swore he would not see Emma again, and he reproached himself with not having kept his word, considering all the worry and lectures this woman might still draw down upon him, without **reckoning** the jokes made by his companions as they sat round the stove in the morning. Besides, he was soon to be head clerk; it was time to **settle** down. So he gave up his flute, exalted sentiments, and **poetry**; for every bourgeois in the **flush** of his youth, were it but for a day, a moment, has believed himself capable of immense passions, of lofty enterprises. The most mediocre libertine has dreamed of **sultanas**; every notary bears within him the **debris** of a poet.

He was bored now when Emma suddenly began to sob on his breast, and his heart, like the people who can only **stand** a certain **amount** of music, dozed to the sound of a love whose delicacies he no longer **noted**.

They knew one another too well for any of those surprises of possession that **increase** its joys a hundred-fold. She was as sick of him as he was weary of her. Emma found again in adultery all the **platitudes** of marriage.

But how to get rid of him? Then, though she might feel humiliated at the **baseness** of such enjoyment, she clung to it from habit or from corruption, and each day she hungered after them the more, **exhausting** all felicity in wishing for too much of it. She accused Leon of her **baffled** hopes, as if he had **betrayed** her; and she even longed for some catastrophe that would bring about their separation, since she had not the courage to make up her mind to it herself.

She none the less went on writing him love letters, in virtue of the **notion** that a woman must **write** to her lover.

But whilst she wrote it was another man she saw, a **phantom fashioned** out of her most ardent memories, of her finest reading, her strongest lusts, and at last he became so real, so **tangible**, that she **palpitated wondering**, without, however, the power to imagine him **clearly**, so lost was he, like a **god**, beneath the abundance of his attributes. He dwelt in that azure land where silk ladders

Spanish

amount: cantidad, importe, suma, número, monto, monta.
baffled: confundido.
baseness: bajeza.
betrayed: traicionado.
clearly: claramente.
damage: daño, avería, deterioro, deteriorar, perjuicio, defecto.
debris: detrito, desechos, ruinas, escombros.
exhausting: agotador.
fashioned: ideado.

flush: rubor, enjuagar.
god: Dios.
increase: aumentar, ampliación, acrecentar, incremento, aumento.
noted: nombrado.
notion: noción, idea, inteligencia.
palpitated: Palpitado.
phantom: fantasma.
platitudes: tópicos.
poet: poeta, el poeta.
reckoning: cuenta, cálculo.
settle: despachar, despacha, despacho,

despachas, despachan, despachamos, despacháis, despachad, despachen, despache, establecer.
stand: estar de pie, puesto, levantarse, granero, posición, cabina, soporte, base, estante, caseta, pararse.
sultanas: pasas de Esmirna.
tangible: tangible, palpable.
wondering: preguntar.
write: escribir, escriba, escriban, escribo, escribís, escribimos, escribid, escribes, escribe, escriben.

hang from **balconies** under the breath of flowers, in the light of the moon. She felt him near her; he was coming, and would carry her right away in a kiss.

Then she fell back exhausted, for these transports of vague love wearied her more than great **debauchery**.

She now felt constant **ache** all over her. Often she even received **summonses**, **stamped** paper that she barely looked at. She would have liked not to be alive, or to be always asleep.

On Mid-Lent she did not return to Yonville, but in the evening went to a **masked** ball. She wore velvet **breeches**, red **stockings**, a **club wig**, and three-cornered hat **cocked** on one side. She **danced** all night to the wild tones of the trombones; people gathered round her, and in the morning she found herself on the steps of the theatre together with five or six **masks**, debardeuses and sailors, Leon's comrades, who were talking about having supper.

The neighbouring cafes were full. They caught sight of one on the harbour, a very indifferent restaurant, whose **proprietor** showed them to a little room on the fourth floor.

The men were **whispering** in a corner, no doubt consorting about expenses. There were a clerk, two medical **students**, and a shopman--what company for her! As to the women, Emma soon perceived from the tone of their voices that they must almost belong to the lowest **class**. Then she was frightened, pushed back her chair, and cast down her eyes.

The others began to eat; she ate nothing. Her head was on fire, her eyes smarted, and her skin was **ice**-cold. In her head she seemed to feel the floor of the ball-room **rebounding** again beneath the **rhythmical pulsation** of the **thousands** of dancing feet. And now the smell of the punch, the smoke of the **cigars**, made her **giddy**. She **fainted**, and they carried her to the window.

Day was breaking, and a great **stain** of purple colour **broadened** out in the pale horizon over the St. Catherine hills. The **livid** river was **shivering** in the wind; there was no one on the bridges; the street **lamps** were going out.

Spanish

ache: doler, dolor, desear.
balconies: voladizos.
breeches: calzones, pantalones.
broadened: Ensanchado.
cigars: los puros.
class: clase, curso, cursillo, la clase, promoción, categoría.
club: garrote, club.
cocked: Montado, de tres picos, tres picos.
danced: bailo.
debauchery: libertinaje.

fainted: pasmado, desfallecido, amortecido, desmayado.
giddy: mareado.
ice-cold: helado.
lamps: lámparas.
livid: lívido.
masked: enmascarado.
masks: máscaras.
proprietor: propietario.
pulsation: pulsación.
rebounding: rebotar.
rhythmical: rítmico.

shivering: tiritar.
stain: manchar, mancha, mancilla, teñir, tintura, la mancha.
stamped: estampillado.
stockings: las medias.
students: estudiantes, alumnos.
summonses: citaciones.
thousands: miles.
whispering: chismes, chismografía, con eco, cuchicheo, de difamación, rumores, susurro, de rumores.
wig: peluca.

She revived, and began thinking of Berthe asleep **yonder** in the servant's room. Then a cart filled with long strips of iron passed by, and made a **deafening metallic** vibration against the walls of the houses.

She slipped away suddenly, threw off her costume, told Leon she must get back, and at last was alone at the Hotel de Boulogne. Everything, even herself, was now **unbearable** to her. She wished that, taking **wing** like a bird, she could fly somewhere, far away to regions of purity, and there grow young again.

She went out, crossed the Boulevard, the Place Cauchoise, and the Faubourg, as far as an open street that overlooked some gardens. She walked rapidly; the fresh air **calming** her; and, little by little, the faces of the crowd, the **masks**, the quadrilles, the lights, the supper, those women, all disappeared like mists **fading** away. Then, reaching the "Croix-Rouge," she threw herself on the bed in her little room on the second floor, where there were pictures of the "Tour de Nesle." At four o'clock Hivert **awoke** her.

When she got home, Felicite showed her behind the clock a grey paper. She read--

"In virtue of the **seizure** in execution of a judgment."

What judgment? As a matter of fact, the evening before another paper had been brought that she had not yet seen, and she was stunned by these words--

"By order of the king, law, and justice, to Madame Bovary." Then, **skipping** several lines, she read, "Within twenty-four hours, without fail--" But what? "To pay the sum of eight thousand francs." And there was even at the bottom, "She will be **constrained thereto** by every form of law, and **notably** by a **writ** of **distraint** on her furniture and effects."

What was to be done? In twenty-four hours--tomorrow. Lheureux, she thought, wanted to **frighten** her again; for she saw through all his **devices**, the object of his kindnesses. What **reassured** her was the very **magnitude** of the sum.

However, by **dint** of **buying** and not paying, of **borrowing**, signing bills, and **renewing** these bills that grew at each new falling-in, she had ended by

Spanish

awoke: pret y pp de awake.
borrowing: préstamo.
buying: comprar.
calming: calmante.
constrained: encogido.
deafening: ensordecedor, ensordeciendo.
devices: artefactos, dispositivos, divisas.
dint: esfuerzo grande, abolladura, abollar, abollarse, chichón, golpe, mellar, mella, fuerza, fuerza de.

distraint: traba de ejecución, detención, embargo, secuestro, secuestro de bienes.
fading: desvanecimiento.
frighten: espantar, espantad, espanta, espantáis, espantamos, espantan, espantas, espanten, asustar, espante, espanto.
magnitude: magnitud.
masks: máscaras.
metallic: metálico.
notably: notablemente.

reassured: tranquilizado.
renewing: renovando.
seizure: toma, embargo, apoplejía, captura, incautación, ataque, convulsión, gripado, secuestro.
skipping: saltar, salto a la comba.
thereto: a eso.
unbearable: insufrible, insoportable.
wing: ala, el ala, guardabarros, la ala.
writ: escritura, orden, escrito, orden por escrito.
yonder: allí, ahí, aquel.

preparing a capital for Monsieur Lheureux which he was **impatiently awaiting** for his speculations.

She presented herself at his place with an **offhand** air.

"You know what has happened to me? No doubt it's a joke!"

"How so?"

He turned away slowly, and, **folding** his arms, said to her--

"My good lady, did you think I should go on to all **eternity** being your **purveyor** and **banker**, for the love of God? Now be just. I must get back what I've **laid** out. Now be just."

She **cried** out against the debt.

"Ah! so much the worse. The court has **admitted** it. There's a **judgment**. It's been **notified** to you. **Besides**, it isn't my fault. It's Vincart's."

"Could you not--?"

"Oh, nothing whatever."

"But still, now talk it over."

And she began **beating** about the **bush**; she had known nothing about it; it was a surprise.

"Whose fault is that?" said Lheureux, **bowing ironically**. "While I'm **slaving** like a **nigger**, you go **gallivanting** about."

"Ah! no lecturing."

"It never does any harm," he replied.

She turned **coward**; she **implored** him; she even **pressed** her pretty white and **slender** hand against the shopkeeper's **knee**.

"There, that'll do! Anyone'd think you wanted to **seduce** me!"

"You are a wretch!" she cried.

"Oh, oh! go it! go it!"

"I will show you up. I shall tell my husband."

Spanish

admitted: confesado, admitido.
awaiting: esperando, aguardando.
banker: banquero, el banquero.
beating: paliza, pulsación, latido.
besides: además, demás, además de, amén de.
bowing: reverencia, toque con el arco, inclinar, golpes de arco.
bush: arbusto, matorral, casquillo, el arbusto, buje, mata.
coward: cobarde, el cobarde.
cried: Lloró.

eternity: eternidad.
folding: plegable.
gallivanting: vagando, callejeando.
impatiently: impacientemente, con impaciencia.
implored: implorado, suplicado.
ironically: irónicamente.
judgment: juicio, fallo, sentencia, criterio.
knee: rodilla, la rodilla.
laid: puesto, colocado, recostado, acostado.

nigger: negro.
notified: Notificado.
offhand: de improviso.
preparing: preparando.
pressed: prensado, apretado, planchado, plegado a presión.
purveyor: abastecedor, proveedor.
seduce: seducir, seduzca, seduzco, seduzcan, seducen, seducís, seduces, seduce, seducid, seducimos.
slaving: esclavizar.
slender: fino, esbelto.

"All right! I too. I'll show your husband something."

And Lheureux drew from his strong box the **receipt** for **eighteen** hundred **francs** that she had given him when Vincart had **discounted** the bills.

"Do you think," he added, "that he'll not understand your little **theft**, the poor dear man?"

She **collapsed**, more **overcome** than if **felled** by the **blow** of a **pole**-axe. He was walking up and down from the window to the **bureau, repeating** all the while--

"Ah! I'll show him! I'll show him!" Then he **approached** her, and in a soft voice said--

"It isn't **pleasant**, I know; but, after all, no **bones** are broken, and, since that is the only way that is left for you paying back my money--"

"But where am I to get any?" said **Emma, wringing** her hands.

"Bah! when one has friends like you!"

And he looked at her in so keen, so terrible a fashion, that she **shuddered** to her very heart.

"I **promise** you," she said, "to sign--"

"**I've** enough of your signatures."

"I will sell something."

"Get along!" he said, shrugging his shoulders; "you've not got anything."

And he called through the **peep**-hole that looked down into the shop--

"Annette, **don't** forget the three coupons of No. 14."

The **servant** appeared. Emma understood, and asked how much money would be wanted to put a stop to the proceedings.

"It is too late."

"But if I brought you several thousand francs--a quarter of the sum--a third-- perhaps the whole?"

"No; it's no use!"

Spanish

approached: Acercado.
blow: soplar, golpe.
bones: huesos, los huesos.
bureau: oficina, mesa, escritorio, agencia.
collapsed: desplomado.
discounted: descontado.
don't: no.
eighteen: dieciocho, diez y ocho.
emma: Ema.
felled: truncado, derribado, desanimado, cortado.

francs: francos.
i've: he, Tengo.
overcome: superar, superen, supera, superad, superado, superáis, superamos, superan, supere, supero, superas.
peep-hole: trampilla, ventanillo.
pleasant: agradable, simpático, placentero, grato.
pole-axe: desnuque.
promise: prometer, prometéis, prometemos, prometen, prometo,

promete, prometan, prometa, prometes, prometed, promesa.
receipt: recibo, recepción, comprobante, talón, el recibo, acuse de recibo.
repeating: repitiendo, repetidor.
servant: criado, criada, sirviente, servidor.
shuddered: estremecido.
theft: robo, hurto, el robo, latrocinio.
wringing: arrancando, retorciendo.

And he **pushed** her **gently** towards the staircase.

"I **implore** you, Monsieur Lheureux, just a **few** days more!" She was **sobbing**.

"There! **tears** now!"

"You are **driving** me to despair!"

"What do I care?" said he, **shutting** the door.

Spanish

driving: conduciendo, manejando, conducción, conducir.
few: pocos.
gently: suavemente.
implore: implorar, implorad, imploráis, imploramos, imploran, imploras, implore, imploren, imploro, implora, suplicar.
pushed: empujado.
shutting: cerrar.
sobbing: sollozar.
tears: desgarra, rasga.

CHAPTER SEVEN

She was **stoical** the next day when Maitre Hareng, the **bailiff**, with two assistants, presented himself at her house to draw up the **inventory** for the distraint.

They began with Bovary's consulting-room, and did not write down the phrenological head, which was considered an "instrument of his profession"; but in the kitchen they **counted** the plates; the **saucepans**, the chairs, the **candlesticks**, and in the bedroom all the nick-nacks on the **whatnot**. They examined her **dresses**, the **linen**, the **dressing**-room; and her whole existence to its most intimate details, was, like a **corpse** on whom a **post**-mortem is made, **outspread** before the eyes of these three men.

Maitre Hareng, **buttoned** up in his thin black coat, wearing a white **choker** and very tight foot-straps, repeated from time to time--"Allow me, **madame**. You **allow** me?" Often he **uttered** exclamations. "Charming! very pretty." Then he began writing again, **dipping** his pen into the **horn inkstand** in his left hand.

When they had done with the **rooms** they went up to the **attic**. She kept a **desk** there in which Rodolphe's letters were **locked**. It had to be opened.

"Ah! a correspondence," said Maitre Hareng, with a **discreet** smile. "But allow me, for I must make sure the box contains nothing else." And he **tipped** up the papers lightly, as if to shake out napoleons. Then she grew **angered** to see this

Spanish

allow: permitir, permitan, permitid, permiten, permites, permitimos, permite, permito, permitís, permita, dejar.
angered: enojado.
attic: desván, ático, buhardilla.
bailiff: alguacil, administrador.
buttoned: abotonado, abrochado.
candlesticks: candelabros.
choker: gargantilla.
corpse: cadáver.
counted: contado.

desk: pupitre, escritorio, el escritorio, mostrador, mesa de trabajo.
dipping: mojar, mojadura, lavado, inmersión.
discreet: discreto.
dresses: los vestidos.
dressing-room: camerino, camarino, camarín.
horn: cuerno, bocina, claxon, trompa.
inkstand: escribanía, tintero.
inventory: inventario, existencias.
linen: lino, lencería, ropa blanca.

locked: estén aseguradas, cerrado, bloqueado, protegido.
madame: señora.
outspread: desplegado, extendido, extensión.
post-mortem: después de la muerte.
rooms: salas.
saucepans: cacerolas.
stoical: estoico.
tipped: volcado.
uttered: pronunciado.
whatnot: estante, cualquier cosa.

coarse hand, with fingers red and **pulpy** like slugs, **touching** these pages against which her heart had beaten.

They went at last. Felicite came back. Emma had sent her out to watch for Bovary in order to keep him off, and they **hurriedly** installed the man in possession under the roof, where he **swore** he would **remain**.

During the evening Charles seemed to her **careworn**. Emma watched him with a look of **anguish**, fancying she saw an **accusation** in every line of his face. Then, when her eyes **wandered** over the chimney-piece ornamented with Chinese **screens**, over the large curtains, the armchairs, all those things, in a word, that had, **softened** the **bitterness** of her life, **remorse** seized her or rather an immense regret, that, far from **crushing, irritated** her passion. Charles **placidly poked** the fire, both his feet on the fire-dogs.

Once the man, no doubt bored in his **hiding**-place, made a slight noise.

"Is anyone walking upstairs?" said Charles.

"No," she replied; "it is a window that has been left open, and is **rattling** in the wind."

The next day, Sunday, she went to Rouen to **call** on all the brokers whose names she knew. They were at their country-places or on journeys. She was not **discouraged**; and those whom she did manage to see she asked for money, **declaring** she must have some, and that she would pay it back. Some laughed in her face; all refused.

At two o'clock she hurried to Leon, and knocked at the door. No one answered. At length he appeared.

"What brings you here?"

"Do I **disturb** you?"

"No; but--" And he admitted that his landlord didn't like his having "women" there.

"I must speak to you," she went on.

Then he took down the key, but she stopped him.

Spanish

accusation: acusación, denuncia, cargo, imputación.
anguish: angustia, miedo, angustiar.
bitterness: amargura, rencor, amargor.
call: llamada, llamar, llaman, llamen, llamad, llamas, llamo, llamamos, llamáis, llame, llama.
careworn: agobiado por los cuidados.
coarse: áspero, desigual, tosco, grosero, basto.
crushing: aplastante, aplastar, estrujado, trituración.

declaring: declarando.
discouraged: espantado, desanimado.
disturb: molestar, moleste, molestad, molestáis, molestamos, molestan, molestas, molesta, molesto, molesten, incomodar.
hiding-place: escondite.
hurriedly: precipitadamente, apresuradamente.
irritated: irritado.
placidly: plácidamente.
poked: metido.

pulpy: carnoso, pastoso, pulposo.
rattling: zumbar, muy, rápido, vaivén, realmente, estupendo.
remain: quedarse, restar, permanecer, restas, resto, reste, restan, restamos, restáis, restad, resta.
remorse: remordimiento.
screens: mallas.
softened: ablandado.
swore: pret de swear, Juró.
touching: conmovedor.
wandered: Vagado.

"No, no! Down there, in our home!"

And they went to their room at the Hotel de Boulogne.

On **arriving** she **drank** off a large glass of water. She was very **pale**. She said to him--

"Leon, you will do me a service?"

And, **shaking** him by both hands that she **grasped tightly**, she added

"Listen, I want eight thousand **francs**."

"But you are mad!"

"Not yet."

And **thereupon**, telling him the story of the **distraint**, she explained her **distress** to him; for Charles knew nothing of it; her **mother-in-law detested** her; old Rouault could do nothing; but he, Leon, he would set about finding this **indispensable sum**.

"How on earth can I?"

"What a **coward** you are!" she **cried**.

Then he said **stupidly**, "You are **exaggerating** the difficulty. Perhaps, with a thousand **crowns** or so the **fellow** could be stopped."

All the greater reason to try and do something; it was impossible that they could not find three thousand francs. **Besides**, Leon, could be security instead of her.

"Go, try, try! I will love you so!"

He went out, and came back at the end of an hour, saying, with **solemn** face--

"I have been to three people with no success."

Then they remained sitting face to face at the two **chimney** corners, **motionless**, in silence. **Emma** shrugged her **shoulders** as she **stamped** her feet. He heard her murmuring--

"If I were in your place *I* should soon get some."

"But where?"

Spanish

arriving: llegando.
besides: además, demás, además de, amén de.
chimney: chimenea, la chimenea.
coward: cobarde, el cobarde.
cried: Lloró.
crowns: coronas.
detested: detestado.
distraint: traba de ejecución, detención, embargo, secuestro, secuestro de bienes.
distress: afligir, indigencia, entristecer,

acongojar, dolor.
drank: pret de drink, bebió.
emma: Ema.
exaggerating: exagerando.
fellow: compañero, hombre, socio, tipo, becario.
francs: francos.
grasped: agarrado.
indispensable: imprescindible, necesario, indispensable.
mother-in-law: suegra.
motionless: inmóvil, estático.

pale: pálido, palidecer, descolorido.
shaking: sacudiendo, sacudida.
shoulders: espalda, hombros.
solemn: solemne.
stamped: estampillado.
stupidly: estúpidamente, estupidez, necedad, torpeza.
sum: suma, importe, cantidad.
thereupon: luego, por eso, por tanto, en eso.
tightly: apretadamente, herméticamente.

"At your office." And she looked at him.

An **infernal boldness** looked out from her burning eyes, and their **lids** drew close together with a **lascivious** and **encouraging** look, so that the young man felt himself growing weak beneath the **mute** will of this woman who was urging him to a crime. Then he was afraid, and to **avoid** any explanation he **smote** his forehead, crying--

"Morel is to come back to-night; he will not refuse me, I hope" (this was one of his **friends**, the son of a very rich merchant); "and I will bring it you to-morrow," he added.

Emma did not seem to **welcome** this hope with all the joy he had expected. Did she suspect the lie? He went on, blushing--

"However, if you **don't** see me by three o'clock do not wait for me, my darling. I must be off now; forgive me! Goodbye!"

He pressed her hand, but it felt quite **lifeless**. Emma had no strength left for any **sentiment**.

Four o'clock struck, and she rose to return to Yonville, **mechanically obeying** the force of old habits.

The weather was fine. It was one of those March days, clear and sharp, when the sun **shines** in a perfectly white sky. The Rouen folk, in Sunday-clothes, were walking about with happy looks. She reached the Place du Parvis. People were coming out after **vespers**; the crowd **flowed** out through the three doors like a stream through the three arches of a bridge, and in the middle one, more **motionless** than a rock, stood the **beadle**.

Then she remembered the day when, all anxious and full of hope, she had entered beneath this large **nave**, that had opened out before her, less profound than her love; and she walked on **weeping** beneath her **veil**, **giddy**, **staggering**, almost **fainting**.

"Take care!" cried a voice **issuing** from the gate of a courtyard that was thrown open.

She stopped to let pass a black horse, pawing the ground between the **shafts** of a tilbury, driven by a gentleman in **sable furs**. Who was it? She knew him. The carriage darted by and disappeared.

Why, it was he--the Viscount. She turned away; the street was empty. She was so overwhelmed, so sad, that she had to lean against a wall to keep herself from falling.

Then she thought she had been mistaken. **Anyhow**, she did not know. All within her and around her was **abandoning** her. She felt lost, sinking at random into **indefinable abysses**, and it was almost with joy that, on reaching the "Croix-Rouge," she saw the good Homais, who was watching a large box full of pharmaceutical stores being **hoisted** on to the "Hirondelle." In his hand he held tied in a silk handkerchief six cheminots for his wife.

Madame Homais was very fond of these small, heavy turban-shaped loaves, that are eaten in Lent with salt butter; a last **vestige** of Gothic food that **goes** back, perhaps, to the time of the Crusades, and with which the robust Normans gorged themselves of **yore**, fancying they saw on the table, in the light of the yellow **torches**, between tankards of hippocras and huge boars' heads, the heads of Saracens to be **devoured**. The druggist's wife **crunched** them up as they had done--heroically, despite her wretched teeth. And so whenever Homais **journeyed** to town, he never **failed** to bring her home some that he bought at the great **baker's** in the Rue Massacre.

"**Charmed** to see you," he said, **offering** Emma a hand to help her into the "Hirondelle." Then he hung up his cheminots to the **cords** of the **netting,** and remained bare-headed in an attitude **pensive** and Napoleonic.

But when the blind man appeared as usual at the foot of the hill he exclaimed--

"I **can't** understand why the **authorities tolerate** such **culpable** industries. Such unfortunates should be locked up and forced to work. Progress, my word! **creeps** at a snail's pace. We are floundering about in mere barbarism."

Spanish

abandoning: abandonando, desamparando, abandono.
abysses: abismos.
anyhow: sin embargo.
authorities: autoridades, magistratura.
baker's: panadería.
can't: no puede.
charmed: encantado.
cords: cuerdas.
creeps: arrastra.
crunched: roznado, crujido, tascado, ronzado.

culpable: culposo.
devoured: devorado.
failed: fracasado, no satisfactorio, fallado.
furs: pieles.
goes: va, marcha.
hoisted: Levantado.
indefinable: indefinible.
journeyed: Viajado.
netting: coger con red, producir una ganancia neta, precio neto, neto, Coger, red, red de pesca, redes,

enredar, Internet, compensación.
offering: ofrenda, oferta, ofrecer.
pensive: pensativo.
sable: marta cebellina, negro, marta.
shafts: ejes.
tolerate: tolerar, tolere, tolera, tolerad, toleráis, toleramos, toleran, toleras, toleren, tolero, aguantar.
torches: antorchas.
vestige: vestigio.
yore: antaño, de antaño, hace tiempo, tiempos pasados.

The blind man held out his hat, that **flapped** about at the door, as if it were a bag in the **lining** that had come unnailed.

"This," said the **chemist**, "is a **scrofulous** affection."

And though he knew the poor devil, he **pretended** to see him for the first time, murmured something about "cornea," "**opaque** cornea," "sclerotic," "facies," then asked him in a **paternal** tone--

"My friend, have you long had this terrible **infirmity**? Instead of getting drunk at the public, you'd do better to die yourself."

He advised him to take good wine, good beer, and good joints. The blind man went on with his song; he seemed, moreover, almost **idiotic**. At last Monsieur Homais opened his purse--

"Now there's a sou; give me back two lairds, and **don't** forget my advice: you'll be the better for it."

Hivert openly cast some doubt on the **efficacy** of it. But the **druggist** said that he would cure himself with an **antiphlogistic pomade** of his own **composition**, and he gave his address--"Monsieur Homais, near the market, pretty well known."

"Now," said Hivert, "for all this trouble you'll give us your performance."

The blind man sank down on his haunches, with his head thrown back, whilst he rolled his **greenish** eyes, **lolled** out his tongue, and rubbed his stomach with both hands as he **uttered** a kind of **hollow yell** like a **famished** dog. Emma, filled with **disgust**, threw him over her shoulder a five-franc piece. It was all her fortune. It seemed to her very fine thus to throw it away.

The coach had gone on again when suddenly Monsieur Homais **leant** out through the window, crying--

"No **farinaceous** or milk food, wear wool next the skin, and **expose** the **diseased** parts to the smoke of **juniper** berries."

Spanish

antiphlogistic: antiflogístico.
chemist: químico, farmacéutico, boticario.
composition: composición.
diseased: enfermo.
disgust: aversión, repugnancia, asquear.
don't: no.
druggist: droguero.
efficacy: eficacia.
expose: exponer, exponen, expongo, expongan, expones, exponemos, exponéis, exponed, expon, expone, exponga.
famished: hambriento.
farinaceous: farináceo.
flapped: batido.
greenish: verdoso.
hollow: hueco, cavidad, hondonada, vacuo.
idiotic: idiota, tonto.
infirmity: enfermedad, debilidad.
juniper: enebro, junípero.
leant: pret y pp de lean.
lining: forro, revestimiento.
lolled: Repantigado, colgado, pendido.
opaque: opaco.
paternal: paterno, paternal.
pomade: pomada.
pretended: fingido, pretendido.
scrofulous: escrofuloso.
uttered: pronunciado.
yell: grito, gritar, aullar, chillar.

The sight of the **well**-known **objects** that **defiled** before her eyes gradually **diverted** Emma from her **present** trouble. An **intolerable fatigue overwhelmed** her, and she reached her home **stupefied, discouraged**, almost asleep.

"Come what may come!" she said to herself. "And then, who **knows**? Why, at any moment could not some extraordinary event **occur**? Lheureux even might die!"

At nine o'clock in the morning she was **awakened** by the sound of voices in the Place. There was a crowd round the market reading a large bill fixed to one of the posts, and she saw Justin, who was climbing on to a stone and **tearing** down the bill. But at this moment the rural guard seized him by the collar. Monsieur Homais came out of his shop, and Mere Lefrangois, in the **midst** of the crowd, seemed to be perorating.

"**Madame**! madame!" cried Felicite, running in, "it's abominable!"

And the poor girl, **deeply** moved, handed her a yellow paper that she had just torn off the door. Emma read with a glance that all her furniture was for sale.

Then they looked at one another silently. The servant and **mistress** had no **secret** one from the other. At last Felicite sighed--

"If I were you, madame, I should go to Monsieur Guillaumin."

"Do you think--"

And this question meant to say--

"You who know the house through the servant, has the master spoken sometimes of me?"

"Yes, you'd do well to go there."

She dressed, put on her black **gown**, and her **hood** with **jet beads**, and that she might not be seen (there was still a crowd on the Place), she took the path by the river, outside the village.

She reached the notary's gate quite **breathless**. The sky was **sombre**, and a little snow was falling. At the sound of the bell, Theodore in a red waistcoat

---

Spanish

awakened: despertado.
beads: perlas.
breathless: jadeante, sin aliento.
deeply: profundamente.
defiled: manchado, mancillado, desfilado, deshonrado, profanado, ensuciado.
discouraged: espantado, desanimado.
diverted: desviado.
fatigue: fatiga, fatigar.
gown: vestido, toga.
hood: capucha, tapa, capot, campana,

capota, capó.
intolerable: intolerable.
jet: chorro, azabache, avión de reacción, avión a reacción, surtidor.
knows: sabe, conoce.
madame: señora.
midst: medio.
mistress: señora.
objects: objetos.
occur: ocurrir, ocurrimos, ocurrís, ocurro, ocurres, ocurren, ocurran, ocurrid, acontecer, ocurra, ocurre.

overwhelmed: enterrado.
present: presente, actual, presentar, regalo, contemporáneo, ofrecer, reproducir, retratar.
secret: secreto, el secreto, arcano, clandestino.
sombre: sombrío.
stupefied: aturdido, entorpecido.
tearing: romper, desgarramiento, efecto bandera, ruptura.
well-known: conocido, sabido, notorio.

appeared on the steps; he came to open the door almost **familiarly**, as to an acquaintance, and showed her into the dining-room.

A large porcelain stove **crackled** beneath a **cactus** that filled up the **niche** in the wall, and in black wood frames against the oak-stained paper hung Steuben's "Esmeralda" and Schopin's "Potiphar." The ready-laid table, the two silver chafing-dishes, the crystal door-knobs, the **parquet** and the furniture, all shone with a **scrupulous**, English **cleanliness**; the windows were ornamented at each corner with stained glass.

"Now this," thought Emma, "is the dining-room I ought to have."

The **notary** came in pressing his palm-leaf dressing-gown to his breast with his left arm, while with the other hand he raised and quickly put on again his brown velvet cap, **pretentiously cocked** on the right side, **whence** looked out the ends of three fair curls drawn from the back of the head, following the line of his bald **skull**.

After he had offered her a seat he sat down to **breakfast**, **apologising profusely** for his **rudeness**.

"I have come," she said, "to beg you, sir--"

"What, madame? I am listening."

And she began explaining her position to him. Monsieur Guillaumin knew it, being secretly **associated** with the linendraper, from whom he always got capital for the loans on mortgages that he was asked to make.

So he knew (and better than she herself) the long story of the bills, small at first, bearing different names as endorsers, made out at long **dates**, and constantly renewed up to the day, when, **gathering** together all the protested bills, the **shopkeeper** had **bidden** his friend Vincart take in his own name all the necessary **proceedings**, not wishing to pass for a **tiger** with his fellow-citizens.

She **mingled** her story with recriminations against Lheureux, to which the notary replied from time to time with some **insignificant** word. Eating his **cutlet** and drinking his **tea**, he buried his chin in his **sky**-blue **cravat**, into which were thrust two **diamond** pins, held together by a small gold chain; and he smiled a

Spanish

apologising: disculpar.
associated: asociado.
bidden: pp de bid.
breakfast: desayuno, el desayuno, desayunar.
cactus: cacto, el cacto.
cleanliness: limpieza.
cocked: Montado, de tres picos, tres picos.
crackled: abertal, crujido.
cravat: corbata.
cutlet: chuleta, escalope.

dates: dátiles, citas.
diamond: diamante, el diamante, rombo.
familiarly: conocidamente, con demasiada confianza, familiarmente.
gathering: recolección, reunión.
insignificant: insignificante.
mingled: mezclado, triscado.
niche: nicho, hornacina.
notary: notario, escribano.
parquet: platea.
pretentiously: pretensiosamente,

vanidosamente.
proceedings: actas.
profusely: abundantemente, pródigamente, profusamente.
rudeness: rudeza.
scrupulous: escrupuloso, meticuloso.
shopkeeper: tendero.
skull: cráneo, calavera.
sky-blue: azul celeste.
tea: té, te.
tiger: tigre, el tigre.
whence: de dónde.

singular smile, in a **sugary**, **ambiguous** fashion. But noticing that her feet were damp, he said--

"Do get closer to the stove; put your feet up against the porcelain."

She was afraid of **dirtying** it. The **notary** replied in a **gallant** tone--

"Beautiful things spoil nothing."

Then she tried to move him, and, growing moved herself, she began telling him about the **poorness** of her home, her worries, her wants. He could understand that; an elegant woman! and, without leaving off eating, he had turned completely round towards her, so that his knee brushed against her boot, whose sole curled round as it smoked against the stove.

But when she asked for a thousand sous, he closed his lips, and declared he was very **sorry** he had not had the management of her fortune before, for there were **hundreds** of ways very convenient, even for a lady, of turning her money to account. **They** might, either in the turf-peats of Grumesnil or building-ground at Havre, almost without **risk**, have **ventured** on some excellent **speculations**; and he let her **consume** herself with rage at the thought of the **fabulous** sums that she would certainly have made.

"How was it," he went on, "that you didn't come to me?"

"I hardly know," she said.

"Why, hey? Did I frighten you so much? It is I, on the contrary, who ought to **complain**. We hardly know one another; yet I am very **devoted** to you. You do not doubt that, I hope?"

He held out his hand, took hers, covered it with a greedy kiss, then held it on his knee; and he played **delicately** with her fingers whilst he murmured a thousand **blandishments**. His **insipid** voice murmured like a running **brook**; a light **shone** in his eyes through the **glimmering** of his spectacles, and his hand was **advancing** up Emma's sleeve to press her arm. She felt against her cheek his **panting** breath. This man **oppressed** her **horribly**.

She sprang up and said to him--

Spanish

advancing: avanzar, movimiento hacia adelante.
ambiguous: ambiguo.
blandishments: halagos.
brook: arroyo.
complain: quejarse.
consume: consumir, consuman, consumimos, consumid, consumes, consumen, consumís, consume, consumo, consuma.
delicately: delicadamente.
devoted: afectuoso, consagrado, dedicado, adicto, fiel.
dirtying: ensuciando.
fabulous: fabuloso, fantástico.
gallant: galante, galán, valeroso.
glimmering: resplandor, alborear, brillar, luz ténue, vislumbre.
hey: eh, hola.
horribly: horriblemente.
hundreds: centena.
insipid: insípido, soso.
notary: notario, escribano.
oppressed: apretado.
panting: jadeante, palpitación.
poorness: pobreza, mala calidad.
risk: riesgo, arriesgar.
shone: brillado, pret y pp de shine.
singular: original, excepcional, único, individual, raro, singularísimo, solo, extraño.
sorry: afligido, arrepentido, pesaroso, siento, triste.
speculations: especulaciones.
sugary: azucarado.
ventured: Aventurado.

"Sir, I am waiting."

"For what?" said the **notary**, who suddenly became very pale.

"This money."

"But--" Then, **yielding** to the outburst of too **powerful** a desire, "Well, yes!"

He dragged himself towards her on his knees, **regardless** of his dressing-gown.

"For pity's sake, stay. I love you!"

He seized her by her waist. Madame Bovary's face flushed purple. She recoiled with a terrible look, crying--

"You are taking a **shameless** advantage of my distress, sir! I am to be pitied--not to be sold."

And she went out.

The notary remained quite **stupefied**, his eyes fixed on his fine **embroidered** slippers. They were a love gift, and the sight of them at last **consoled** him. Besides, he reflected that such an adventure might have carried him too far.

"What a **wretch**! what a **scoundrel**! what an infamy!" she said to herself, as she fled with nervous steps beneath the aspens of the path. The disappointment of her **failure increased** the **indignation** of her outraged **modesty**; it seemed to her that Providence **pursued** her **implacably**, and, **strengthening** herself in her pride, she had never felt so much esteem for herself nor so much contempt for others. A spirit of **warfare** transformed her. She would have liked to strike all men, to **spit** in their faces, to crush them, and she walked rapidly straight on, pale, **quivering**, **maddened**, searching the empty horizon with tear-dimmed eyes, and as it were **rejoicing** in the hate that was **choking** her.

When she saw her house a **numbness** came over her. She could not go on; and yet she must. Besides, **whither** could she flee?

Felicite was waiting for her at the door. "Well?"

"No!" said Emma.

Spanish

choking: la obstrucción aérea, estrangular, atragantamiento, ahogarse.
consoled: Consolado.
embroidered: bordado.
failure: fallo, fracaso, bancarrota quiebra, avería, falla, aborto, falta.
implacably: implacablemente.
increased: aumentado.
indignation: indignación.
maddened: enloquecido.
modesty: modestia, pudor.

notary: notario, escribano.
numbness: entumecimiento.
powerful: poderoso, potente, fuerte.
pursued: perseguido.
quivering: estremecimiento, vibrante, vibración, tembloroso, vibrar, temblor, parpadeante, estremecerse, carcaj, aljaba, temblador.
regardless: negligente, pese a quien pese, insensible, indiferente, desatento, a rajatabla, a pesar de todo, que no merece la pena.

rejoicing: regocijo.
scoundrel: bribón, sinvergüenza, canalla.
shameless: desvergonzado.
spit: escupir, asador, saliva, salivar.
strengthening: fortaleciendo.
stupefied: aturdido, entorpecido.
warfare: guerra.
whither: adónde, adonde.
wretch: desgraciado.
yielding: cediendo, rindiendo, rentando.

And for a quarter of an hour the two of them went over the **various** persons in Yonville who might perhaps be inclined to help her. But each time that Felicite **named** someone Emma replied--

"Impossible! they will not!"

"And the master'll soon be in."

"I know that well enough. Leave me alone."

She had tried everything; there was nothing more to be done now; and when Charles came in she would have to say to him--

"Go away! This carpet on which you are walking is no longer ours. In your own house you do not possess a chair, a pin, a straw, and it is I, poor man, who have ruined you."

Then there would be a great **sob**; next he would **weep abundantly**, and at last, the surprise past, he would forgive her.

"Yes," she murmured, **grinding** her teeth, "he will forgive me, he who would give a million if I would forgive him for having known me! Never! never!"

This thought of Bovary's **superiority** to her **exasperated** her. Then, whether she **confessed** or did not confess, presently, immediately, **to**-morrow, he would know the **catastrophe** all the same; so she must wait for this horrible scene, and bear the weight of his **magnanimity**. The desire to return to Lheureux's seized her--what would be the use? To write to her father--it was too late; and perhaps, she began to **repent** now that she had not **yielded** to that other, when she heard the **trot** of a horse in the **alley**. It was he; he was opening the gate; he was whiter than the **plaster** wall. **Rushing** to the stairs, she ran out quickly to the square; and the wife of the mayor, who was talking to Lestiboudois in front of the church, saw her go in to the tax-collector's.

She hurried off to tell Madame Caron, and the two ladies went up to the **attic**, and, hidden by some linen spread across **props**, **stationed** themselves comfortably for **overlooking** the whole of Binet's room.

He was alone in his **garret**, busy **imitating** in wood one of those **indescribable** bits of **ivory**, composed of crescents, of **spheres hollowed** out one

Spanish

abundantly: abundantemente.
alley: callejón, calleja.
attic: desván, ático, buhardilla.
catastrophe: catástrofe.
confess: confesar, confiesan, confiesen, confieso, confiesas, confesamos, confesad, confesáis, confiesa, confiese, declarar.
confessed: confesado, reconocido.
exasperated: exasperado.
garret: buhardilla, desván.
grinding: molienda, molturación.

hollowed: ahuecado.
imitating: imitando.
indescribable: indescriptible.
ivory: marfil, de marfil.
magnanimity: magnanimidad, magnanimosidad.
named: denominado.
overlooking: con vista a.
plaster: esparadrapo, yeso, emplasto, enlucido.
props: attrezzo, propiedades, encargado del atrezo, accesorios.

repent: arrepentirse.
rushing: apresurar.
sob: sollozar, sollozo.
spheres: esferos.
stationed: estacionado.
superiority: superioridad.
to-morrow: mañana.
trot: trote, trotar.
various: varios, varias, diferente.
weep: llorar, llore, lloren, llora, lloro, lloras, lloran, lloramos, lloráis, llorad.
yielded: cedido, Rendido, rentado.

within the other, the whole as straight as an **obelisk**, and of no use whatever; and he was beginning on the last piece--he was nearing his goal. In the **twilight** of the **workshop** the white dust was flying from his **tools** like a shower of **sparks** under the hoofs of a **galloping** horse; the two wheels were turning, **droning**; Binet smiled, his chin lowered, his nostrils **distended**, and, in a word, seemed lost in one of those complete happinesses that, no doubt, belong only to **commonplace** occupations, which **amuse** the mind with **facile** difficulties, and satisfy by a **realisation** of that beyond which such minds have not a dream.

"Ah! there she is!" exclaimed Madame Tuvache.

But it was impossible because of the **lathe** to hear what she was saying.

At last these ladies thought they made out the word "francs," and Madame Tuvache whispered in a low voice--

"She is **begging** him to give her time for paying her taxes."

"Apparently!" replied the other.

They saw her walking up and down, examining the napkin-rings, the **candlesticks**, the **banister rails** against the walls, while Binet **stroked** his beard with satisfaction.

"Do you think she wants to order something of him?" said Madame Tuvache.

"Why, he doesn't sell anything," objected her neighbour.

The **tax**-collector seemed to be listening with wide-open eyes, as if he did not understand. She went on in a tender, **suppliant** manner. She came nearer to him, her breast **heaving**; they no longer spoke.

"Is she making him advances?" said Madame Tuvache. Binet was scarlet to his very ears. She took hold of his hands.

"Oh, it's too much!"

And no doubt she was **suggesting** something **abominable** to him; for the tax-collector--yet he was brave, had **fought** at Bautzen and at Lutzen, had been through the French campaign, and had even been recommended for the cross--

---

Spanish

abominable: abominable, horrible, horroroso.
amuse: divertir, diviértete, diviértase, diviértanse, divértidos, me divierto, nos divertimos, os divertís, se divierte, se divierten, te diviertes.
banister: pasamano.
begging: mendicidad, mendigando, mendigar.
candlesticks: candelabros.
commonplace: común, trivial, trivialidad.

distended: distendido, estirado, dilatado.
droning: zumbando.
facile: fácil, vivo.
fought: luchado.
galloping: galopante, galope, galopando, galopar.
heaving: tirar, movimiento vertical del buque, dislocación.
lathe: torno.
obelisk: obelisco.
rails: valores de ferrocarriles, vertical

de barras.
realisation: realización.
sparks: telegrafista, moscas, iluminista.
stroked: alisarse.
suggesting: sugiriendo, designando.
suppliant: suplicante.
tax-collector: exactor.
tools: herramientas.
twilight: crepúsculo, anochecer.
workshop: taller, seminario.

suddenly, as at the sight of a **serpent**, recoiled as far as he could from her, crying--

"Madame! what do you mean?"

"Women like that ought to be whipped," said Madame Tuvache.

"But where is she?" continued Madame Caron, for she had disappeared whilst they spoke; then catching sight of her going up the Grande Rue, and turning to the right as if making for the **cemetery**, they were lost in **conjectures**.

"Nurse Rollet," she said on reaching the nurse's, "I am **choking; unlace** me!" She fell on the bed **sobbing**. Nurse Rollet covered her with a **petticoat** and remained standing by her side. Then, as she did not answer, the good woman **withdrew**, took her wheel and began **spinning flax**.

"Oh, leave off!" she murmured, fancying she heard Binet's **lathe**.

"What's **bothering** her?" said the nurse to herself. "Why has she come here?"

She had rushed **thither; impelled** by a kind of **horror** that drove her from her home.

Lying on her back, **motionless**, and with staring eyes, she saw things but **vaguely**, although she tried to with **idiotic persistence**. She looked at the scales on the walls, two brands smoking end to end, and a long **spider crawling** over her head in a rent in the **beam**. At last she began to collect her thoughts. She remembered--one day--Leon--Oh! how long ago that was--the sun was **shining** on the river, and the **clematis** were **perfuming** the air. Then, carried away as by a **rushing torrent**, she soon began to recall the day before.

"What time is it?" she asked.

Mere Rollet went out, raised the fingers of her right hand to that side of the sky that was brightest, and came back slowly, saying--

"Nearly three."

"Ahl thanks, thanks!"

Spanish

beam: viga, rayo, haz, plegador, radio, haz de luz.
bothering: fastidioso, Molestar, molesto.
cemetery: cementerio, el cementerio, campo santo.
choking: la obstrucción aérea, estrangular, atragantamiento, ahogarse.
clematis: clemátide.
conjectures: supone.
crawling: arrastre.

flax: lino.
horror: horror, aversión.
idiotic: idiota, tonto.
impelled: impulsado, espoleado.
lathe: torno.
motionless: inmóvil, estático.
perfuming: perfumar, aromatizante.
persistence: persistencia.
petticoat: enaguas.
rushing: apresurar.
serpent: serpiente.
shining: brillante, luminoso.

sobbing: sollozar.
spider: araña, cuerpo, estrella, arana.
spinning: hilado, giro.
thither: allá.
torrent: torrente.
unlace: desenlace, desenlazar.
vaguely: vagamente.
withdrew: pret de withdraw, secretar, retiró.

For he would come; he would have found some money. But he would, perhaps, go down **yonder**, not **guessing** she was here, and she told the nurse to run to her house to fetch him.

"Be quick!"

"But, my dear lady, I'm going, I'm going!"

She wondered now that she had not thought of him from the first. **Yesterday** he had given his word; he would not break it. And she already saw herself at Lheureux's spreading out her three bank-notes on his bureau. Then she would have to **invent** some story to explain matters to Bovary. What should it be?

The nurse, however, was a long while gone. But, as there was no clock in the **cot**, Emma feared she was perhaps **exaggerating** the length of time. She began walking round the garden, step by step; she went into the path by the hedge, and returned quickly, hoping that the woman would have come back by another road. At last, **weary** of waiting, **assailed** by fears that she thrust from her, no longer conscious whether she had been here a **century** or a moment, she sat down in a corner, closed her eyes, and stopped her ears. The gate **grated**; she **sprang** up. Before she had spoken Mere Rollet said to her--

"There is no one at your house!"

"What?"

"Oh, no one! And the doctor is crying. He is calling for you; they're looking for you."

Emma answered nothing. She **gasped** as she turned her eyes about her, while the peasant woman, frightened at her face, drew back **instinctively**, thinking her mad. Suddenly she struck her brow and **uttered** a cry; for the thought of Rodolphe, like a **flash** of **lightning** in a dark night, had passed into her soul. He was so good, so delicate, so generous! And besides, should he **hesitate** to do her this service, she would know well enough how to **constrain** him to it by re-waking, in a single moment, their lost love. So she set out towards La Huchette, not seeing that she was **hastening** to offer herself to that which but a while **ago** had so **angered** her, not in the least conscious of her **prostitution**.

Spanish

ago: hace.
angered: enojado.
assailed: Asaltado.
century: siglo, el siglo, centuria.
constrain: restringir, apretar, restringir a, reprimir, obligar, fuerce, constreñido, constreñir, obligo, reprimes, reprimen.
cot: camita de niño, catre.
exaggerating: exagerando.
flash: destello, llamarada, centella, rebaba, fogonazo, relampaguear,

destellar.
gasped: jadeado.
grated: rallado.
guessing: tanteo, suponer, pensar, estimación, conjetura, adivinar, adivinación, suposición, creer.
hastening: acelerando, apresurando, acelerar.
hesitate: vacilar, vacile, vacilan, vacila, vacilad, vacilamos, vacilo, vacilas, vacilen, vaciláis, titubear.
instinctively: instintivamente.

invent: inventar, invente, invento, inventas, inventen, inventan, inventamos, inventáis, inventad, inventa.
lightning: relámpago, rayo, el relámpago.
prostitution: prostitución.
sprang: pret de spring, saltó.
uttered: pronunciado.
weary: cansado, fatigado.
yesterday: ayer.
yonder: allí, ahí, aquel.

CHAPTER EIGHT

She asked herself as she walked along, "What am I going to say? How shall I begin?" And as she went on she recognised the thickets, the trees, the sea-rushes on the hill, the **chateau yonder**. All the sensations of her first **tenderness** came back to her, and her poor **aching** heart opened out **amorously**. A warm wind **blew** in her face; the **melting** snow fell drop by drop **from** the buds to the grass.

She entered, as she used to, through the small park-gate. She reached the **avenue** bordered by a double row of **dense** lime-trees. They were **swaying** their long **whispering** branches to and fro. The dogs in their **kennels** all **barked**, and the noise of their voices **resounded**, but brought out no one.

She went up the large straight **staircase** with wooden **balusters** that led to the corridor **paved** with **dusty flags**, into which several doors in a row opened, as in a **monastery** or an **inn**. His was at the top, right at the end, on the left. When she placed her fingers on the lock her strength suddenly **deserted** her. She was afraid, almost wished he would not be there, though this was her only hope, her last chance of **salvation**. She collected her thoughts for one moment, and, **strengthening** herself by the feeling of present necessity, went in.

He was in front of the fire, both his feet on the **mantelpiece**, smoking a pipe.

"What! it is you!" he said, getting up **hurriedly**.

"Yes, it is I, Rodolphe. I should like to ask your advice."

Spanish

aching: dolor, que duele.
amorously: amorosamente, tiernamente.
avenue: avenida, la avenida.
balusters: barandilla.
barked: Ladrado.
blew: pret de blow, Sopló.
chateau: castillo.
dense: denso.
deserted: desierto.
dusty: polvoriento.
flags: banderas.

fro: atrás, allá.
hurriedly: precipitadamente, apresuradamente.
inn: albergue, fonda, posada, mesón.
kennels: perrera, residencia canina.
mantelpiece: repisa.
melting: deshielo, fusión, derretirse, fundición.
monastery: monasterio, convento.
paved: pavimentado.
resounded: Resonado.
salvation: salvación.

staircase: escalera, la escalera.
strengthening: fortaleciendo.
swaying: oscilación, oscilar, ladearse, tambalear, vaivén, que balancea, oscilante, mimbrear, influir en, inclinarse, inclinación lateral.
tenderness: ternura.
whispering: chismes, chismografía, con eco, cuchicheo, de difamación, rumores, susurro, de rumores.
yonder: allí, ahí, aquel.

And, despite all her efforts, it was impossible for her to open her lips.

"You have not changed; you are **charming** as ever!"

"Oh," she replied **bitterly**, "they are poor **charms** since you **disdained** them."

Then he began a long explanation of his conduct, **excusing** himself in vague **terms**, in **default** of being able to **invent** better.

She **yielded** to his words, still more to his voice and the sight of him, so that, she **pretended** to believe, or perhaps believed; in the **pretext** he gave for their **rupture**; this was a secret on which **depended** the honour, the very life of a third person.

"No matter!" she said, looking at him **sadly**. "I have suffered much."

He replied philosophically--

"Such is life!"

"Has life," **Emma** went on, "been good to you at least, since our separation?"

"Oh, neither good nor bad."

"Perhaps it would have been better never to have parted."

"Yes, perhaps."

"You think so?" she said, drawing nearer, and she sighed. "Oh, Rodolphe! if you but knew! I loved you so!"

It was then that she took his hand, and they remained some time, their fingers **intertwined**, like that first day at the Show. With a gesture of pride he **struggled** against this **emotion**. But **sinking** upon his **breast** she said to him--

"How did you think I could live without you? One **cannot** lose the habit of happiness. I was **desolate**. I thought I should die. I will tell you about all that and you will see. And you--you **fled** from me!"

For, all the three years, he had carefully avoided her in **consequence** of that natural **cowardice** that **characterises** the stronger sex. Emma went on, with **dainty** little nods, more **coaxing** than an **amorous** kitten--

Spanish

amorous: amoroso.
bitterly: amargamente.
breast: pecho, seno, pechuga, mama.
cannot: presente de no poder.
characterises: caracterizan.
charming: encantador, simpático, lindo, bonito, coquetón, amable.
charms: amuletos.
coaxing: halagando.
consequence: consecuencia, secuela.
cowardice: cobardía.
dainty: fino, amable, delicado,

poquita.
default: predeterminado, incumplimiento, defecto, por omisión, por defecto.
depended: dependido.
desolate: desolado, desolar.
disdained: desdeñado.
emma: Ema.
emotion: emoción.
excusing: dispensar.
fled: huido.
intertwined: entrelazado.

invent: inventar, invente, invento, inventas, inventen, inventan, inventamos, inventáis, inventad, inventa.
pretended: fingido, pretendido.
pretext: pretexto.
rupture: ruptura, rotura, quebradura.
sadly: tristemente.
sinking: hundimiento, sumidero.
struggled: luchado.
terms: condiciones, condición.
yielded: cedido, Rendido, rentado.

"You love others, **confess** it! Oh, I understand them, dear! I excuse them. You probably **seduced** them as you seduced me. You are **indeed** a man; you have everything to make one love you. But **we'll** begin again, won't we? We will love one another. See! I am laughing; I am happy! Oh, speak!"

And she was charming to see, with her eyes, in which **trembled** a **tear**, like the rain of a storm in a blue corolla.

He had drawn her upon his knees, and with the back of his hand was **caressing** her **smooth** hair, where in the **twilight** was **mirrored** like a golden arrow one last ray of the sun. She bent down her **brow**; at last he kissed her on the eyelids quite gently with the **tips** of his lips.

"Why, you have been crying! What for?"

She burst into tears. Rodolphe thought this was an **outburst** of her love. As she did not speak, he took this silence for a last **remnant** of **resistance**, and then he cried out--

"Oh, forgive me! You are the only one who **pleases** me. I was **imbecile** and cruel. I love you. I will love you always. What is it. Tell me!" He was **kneeling** by her.

"Well, I am **ruined**, Rodolphe! You must **lend** me three thousand **francs**."

"But--but--" said he, getting up slowly, while his face assumed a grave expression.

"You know," she went on quickly, "that my husband had placed his whole fortune at a notary's. He ran away. So we **borrowed**; the patients **don't** pay us. Moreover, the **settling** of the estate is not yet done; we shall have the money later on. But **to**-day, for want of three thousand francs, we are to be sold up. It is to be at once, this very moment, and, **counting** upon your friendship, I have come to you."

"Ah!" thought Rodolphe, turning very pale, "that was what she came for." At last he said with a calm air--

"Dear madame, I have not got them."

Spanish

borrowed: prestado.
brow: ceja, frente.
caressing: mimoso, zalamero.
confess: confesar, confiesan, confiesen, confieso, confiesas, confesamos, confesad, confesáis, confiesa, confiese, declarar.
counting: contar, cuenta.
don't: no.
francs: francos.
imbecile: imbécil.
indeed: verdaderamente, en efecto, de veras, en realidad, efectivamente.
kneeling: arrodillar, arrodillarse, estar de rodillas, arrodillado, de rodillas, arrodillando.
lend: prestar, presto, preste, presten, prestas, prestan, prestamos, prestáis, prestad, presta.
mirrored: reflejado.
outburst: explosión.
pleases: complace.
remnant: remanente.
resistance: resistencia.
ruined: arruinado.
seduced: seducido.
settling: despachando.
smooth: liso, plano, alisar, suavizar, suave.
tear: lágrima, desgarrar, rajar, romper, rasgar, desgarro.
tips: propinas.
to-day: hoy.
trembled: Temblado, tembló.
twilight: crepúsculo, anochecer.
we'll: Haremos.

He did not lie. If he had had them, he would, no doubt, have given them, although it is **generally disagreeable** to do such fine things: a **demand** for money being, of all the winds that blow upon love, the coldest and most destructive.

First she looked at him for some moments.

"You have not got them!" she repeated several times. "You have not got them! I ought to have **spared** myself this last shame. You never loved me. You are no **better** than the others."

She was **betraying, ruining** herself.

Rodolphe interrupted her, declaring he was "hard up" himself.

"Ah! I pity you," said Emma. "Yes--very much."

And **fixing** her eyes upon an **embossed carabine**, that **shone** against its **panoply**, "But when one is so poor one doesn't have silver on the **butt** of one's gun. One doesn't buy a clock **inlaid** with **tortoise** shell," she went on, pointing to a buhl **timepiece**, "nor silver-gilt whistles for one's whips," and she touched them, "nor **charms** for one's watch. Oh, he wants for nothing! even to a liqueur-stand in his room! For you love yourself; you live well. You have a **chateau**, farms, woods; you go hunting; you travel to Paris. Why, if it were but that," she cried, taking up two **studs** from the **mantelpiece**, "but the least of these **trifles**, one can get money for them. Oh, I do not want them, keep them!"

And she threw the two **links** away from her, their gold chain breaking as it struck against the wall.

"But I! I would have given you everything. I would have sold all, **worked** for you with my hands, I would have **begged** on the highroads for a smile, for a look, to hear you say 'Thanks!' And you sit there quietly in your **arm**-chair, as if you had not made me suffer enough already! But for you, and you know it, I might have lived happily. What made you do it? Was it a bet? Yet you loved me--you said so. And but a moment since--Ah! it would have been better to have driven me away. My hands are hot with your **kisses**, and there is the **spot** on the carpet where at my knees you swore an **eternity** of love! You made me believe you; for two years you held me in the most magnificent, the sweetest dream! Eh!

Spanish

arm-chair: sillón, butaca.
begged: Mendigado.
bet: apostar, apuesta.
betraying: traicionando.
butt: culata, colilla, extremo, tope.
carabine: fusil.
charms: amuletos.
chateau: castillo.
demand: exigir, demanda, deducción, salida, consumo, despacho, potencia, petición.
disagreeable: desagradable.

embossed: realzado, repujado, acuñado, abollonado, estampillado, abollado, realzar, abollonar, grabado en relieve.
eternity: eternidad.
fixing: fijando, reparando, fijación, accesorios.
generally: generalmente.
inlaid: pret y pp de inlay, incrustado, embutido.
kisses: besos.
links: enlaces.

mantelpiece: repisa.
panoply: panoplia.
ruining: arruinar.
shone: brillado, pret y pp de shine.
spared: libre de, reservado.
spot: mancha, punto, sitio, verrugato croca, manchar, mancilla, lugar.
studs: columnas, tacos.
timepiece: reloj.
tortoise: tortuga, jicotea.
trifles: zarandajas.
worked: trabajo.

Our **plans** for the journey, do you remember? Oh, your letter! your letter! it tore my heart! And then when I come back to him--to him, rich, happy, free--to **implore** the help the first stranger would give, a **suppliant**, and bringing back to him all my tenderness, he **repulses** me **because** it would **cost** him three thousand francs!"

"I **haven't** got them," replied Rodolphe, with that perfect calm with which resigned rage covers itself as with a shield.

She went out. The walls **trembled**, the ceiling was crushing her, and she passed back through the long alley, stumbling against the heaps of dead leaves scattered by the wind. At last she reached the ha-ha hedge in front of the gate; she broke her nails against the lock in her haste to open it. Then a hundred steps farther on, breathless, almost falling, she stopped. And now turning round, she once more saw the **impassive chateau**, with the **park**, the gardens, the three courts, and all the windows of the **facade**.

She remained lost in **stupor**, and having no more consciousness of herself than through the beating of her arteries, that she seemed to hear bursting forth like a **deafening** music filling all the fields. The earth beneath her feet was more yielding than the sea, and the furrows seemed to her immense brown waves breaking into foam. Everything in her head, of memories, ideas, went off at once like a thousand pieces of fireworks. She saw her father, Lheureux's **closet**, their room at home, another landscape. Madness was coming upon her; she grew afraid, and managed to **recover** herself, in a confused way, it is true, for she did not in the, least remember the cause of the terrible condition she was in, that is to say, the question of money. She suffered only in her love, and felt her soul passing from her in this memory; as wounded men, dying, feel their life **ebb** from their **bleeding** wounds.

Night was falling, crows were flying about.

Suddenly it seemed to her that **fiery** spheres were **exploding** in the air like **fulminating** balls when they strike, and were **whirling**, whirling, to **melt** at last upon the snow between the branches of the trees. In the midst of each of them appeared the face of Rodolphe. They multiplied and drew near her, penetrating,

Spanish

bleeding: sangrando, sangría, sangrante, sangrado, hemorragia.
cause: causa, causar, ocasionar, dar lugar a, instigar, producir, maquinar, provocar.
chateau: castillo.
closet: armario, gabinete, el armario, el clóset.
cost: costar, costo, coste, gastos.
deafening: ensordecedor, ensordeciendo.
ebb: menguar, reflujo.

exploding: estallando.
facade: fachada, frontón.
fiery: ardiente.
fulminating: fulminando.
haven't: no tener.
impassive: impasible.
implore: implorar, implorad, imploráis, imploramos, imploran, imploras, implore, imploren, imploro, implora, suplicar.
melt: derretirse, derretir, fundir, fusión.

park: parque, aparcar, el parque, estacionar.
plans: planes.
recover: recuperar, sanar, recupere, sanad, recuperad, recuperáis, recuperamos, recuperan, recuperas, recuperen, recupero.
repulses: repulsiones.
stupor: estupor.
suppliant: suplicante.
trembled: Temblado, tembló.
whirling: turbulencia.

her. It all disappeared; she recognised the lights of the houses that **shone** through the fog.

Now her situation, like an **abyss**, rose up before her. She was **panting** as if her heart would burst. Then in an **ecstasy** of **heroism**, that made her almost **joyous**, she ran down the hill, crossed the cow-plank, the foot-path, the **alley**, the market, and reached the chemist's shop. She was about to enter, but at the sound of the bell someone might come, and slipping in by the gate, holding her breath, feeling her way along the walls, she went as far as the door of the kitchen, where a **candle** stuck on the **stove** was burning. Justin in his shirt-sleeves was carrying out a dish.

"Ah! they are dining; I will wait."

He returned; she **tapped** at the window. He went out.

"The key! the one for upstairs where he **keeps** the--"

"What?"

And he looked at her, **astonished** at the **pallor** of her face, that stood out white against the black background of the night. She seemed to him **extraordinarily** beautiful and **majestic** as a **phantom**. Without understanding what she wanted, he had the **presentiment** of something terrible.

But she went on quickly in a love voice; in a sweet, **melting** voice, "I want it; give it to me."

As the **partition** wall was thin, they could hear the **clatter** of the **forks** on the plates in the dining-room.

She **pretended** that she wanted to **kill** the **rats** that kept her from sleeping.

"I must tell master."

"No, stay!" Then with an **indifferent** air, "Oh, it's not worth while; I'll tell him presently. Come, light me upstairs."

She entered the corridor into which the laboratory door opened. Against the wall was a key **labelled** Capharnaum.

"Justin!" called the **druggist impatiently**.

Spanish

abyss: abismo, despeñadero, precipicio.
alley: callejón, calleja.
astonished: asombrado, sorprendido, estupefacto.
candle: vela, la vela, bujía, candela, cirio.
clatter: martilleo.
druggist: droguero.
ecstasy: éxtasis.
extraordinarily: extraordinariamente.
forks: bifurcarse, horquillas, tenedor.

heroism: heroísmo.
impatiently: impacientemente, con impaciencia.
indifferent: indiferente.
joyous: jubiloso, gozoso, de jubiloso, alegre.
keeps: guarda, vigila, conserva, preserva.
kill: matar.
labelled: etiquetado, marcado.
majestic: majestuoso.
melting: deshielo, fusión, derretirse,

fundición.
pallor: palidez.
panting: jadeante, palpitación.
partition: separación, partición, tabique, división.
phantom: fantasma.
presentiment: presentimiento.
pretended: fingido, pretendido.
rats: rata.
shone: brillado, pret y pp de shine.
stove: estufa, la estufa, hornillo.
tapped: utilizado.

"Let us go up."

And he followed her. The key turned in the lock, and she went straight to the third **shelf**, so well did her memory guide her, seized the blue **jar, tore** out the **cork, plunged** in her hand, and **withdrawing** it full of a white **powder**, she began eating it.

"Stop!" he cried, **rushing** at her.

"**Hush**! someone will come."

He was in **despair**, was calling out.

"Say nothing, or all the blame will fall on your master."

Then she went home, suddenly **calmed**, and with something of the **serenity** of one that had **performed** a duty.

When Charles, **distracted** by the news of the **distraint**, returned home, Emma had just gone out. He cried **aloud, wept, fainted**, but she did not return. Where could she be? He sent Felicite to Homais, to Monsieur Tuvache, to Lheureux, to the "Lion d'Or," everywhere, and in the intervals of his **agony** he saw his reputation **destroyed**, their fortune lost, Berthe's future **ruined**. By what?--Not a word! He waited till six in the evening. At last, unable to bear it any longer, and fancying she had gone to Rouen, he set out along the **highroad**, walked a mile, met no one, again waited, and returned home. She had come back.

"What was the matter? Why? Explain to me."

She sat down at her writing-table and wrote a letter, which she **sealed** slowly, adding the date and the hour. Then she said in a **solemn** tone:

"You are to read it **to**-morrow; till then, I pray you, do not ask me a single question. No, not one!"

"But--"

"Oh, leave me!"

She lay down full length on her bed. A **bitter** taste that she felt in her mouth **awakened** her. She saw Charles, and again closed her eyes.

Spanish

agony: agonía, angustia, miedo.
aloud: en voz alta.
awakened: despertado.
bitter: amargo, agrio.
calmed: calmado.
cork: corcho, el corcho, tapón.
despair: desesperación.
destroyed: destruido.
distracted: distraído.
distraint: traba de ejecución, detención, embargo, secuestro, secuestro de bienes.

fainted: pasmado, desfallecido, amortecido, desmayado.
highroad: calle principal, carretera, carretera nacional, carretera principal.
hush: silencio, acallar.
jar: tarro, jarra, la jarra.
performed: hecho.
plunged: hundido.
powder: polvos, polvo, empolvar, pólvora, el polvo.
ruined: arruinado.

rushing: apresurar.
sealed: sellado, hermético, estanco.
serenity: serenidad.
shelf: estante, tabla, el estante, repisa, anaquel.
solemn: solemne.
to-morrow: mañana.
tore: pret de tear, rompió.
wept: Llorado.
withdrawing: retirando.

She was **studying** herself **curiously,** to see if she were not suffering. But no! nothing as yet. She heard the **ticking** of the clock, the **crackling** of the fire, and Charles **breathing** as he stood **upright** by her bed.

"Ah! it is but a little thing, death!" she thought. "I shall fall asleep and all will be over."

She **drank** a **mouthful** of water and turned to the wall. The **frightful** taste of **ink** continued.

"I am **thirsty**; oh! so thirsty," she sighed.

"What is it?" said Charles, who was **handing** her a glass.

"It is nothing! Open the window; I am choking."

She was **seized** with a **sickness** so sudden that she had hardly time to draw out her **handkerchief** from under the **pillow.**

"Take it away," she said quickly; "throw it away."

He spoke to her; she did not answer. She lay **motionless,** afraid that the slightest movement might make her **vomit.** But she felt an **icy** cold **creeping** from her feet to her heart.

"Ah! it is beginning," she **murmured**.

"What did you say?"

She turned her head from side to side with a gentle movement full of **agony,** while constantly opening her mouth as if something very heavy were **weighing** upon her tongue. At eight o'clock the **vomiting** began again.

Charles noticed that at the bottom of the **basin** there was a sort of white **sediment sticking** to the sides of the **porcelain.**

"This is extraordinary--very singular," he repeated.

But she said in a **firm** voice, "No, you are mistaken."

Then gently, and almost as **caressing** her, he passed his hand over her stomach. She **uttered** a sharp cry. He fell back terror-stricken.

Spanish

agony: agonía, angustia, miedo.
basin: cuenca, recipiente de agua, fuente, pelvis, tazón, dársena, jofaina, palangana.
breathing: respirando, respiración, respirar.
caressing: mimoso, zalamero.
crackling: crepitaciones.
creeping: arrastrando.
curiously: curiosamente.
drank: pret de drink, bebió.
firm: firma, firme, fijo, empresa, sólido, fuerte, compañía.
frightful: espantoso, horrible.
handing: entregar.
handkerchief: pañuelo.
icy: helado, álgido.
ink: tinta, la tinta, entintar.
motionless: inmóvil, estático.
mouthful: bocado.
murmured: Murmurado.
pillow: almohada, la almohada.
porcelain: porcelana.
sediment: sedimento, poso.
seized: agarrado, asido.
sickness: enfermedad.
sticking: pegajoso.
studying: estudiando.
thirsty: sediento.
ticking: terliz, tictac.
upright: vertical, montante, derecho.
uttered: pronunciado.
vomit: vomitar, vómito.
vomiting: vomitar.
weighing: pesando, peso, pesaje, pesar.

Then she began to **groan, faintly** at first. Her shoulders were **shaken** by a strong **shuddering,** and she was growing paler than the sheets in which her **clenched** fingers buried themselves. Her **unequal pulse** was now almost imperceptible.

Drops of **sweat oozed** from her **bluish** face, that seemed as if rigid in the exhalations of a **metallic vapour.** Her teeth **chattered,** her **dilated** eyes looked **vaguely** about her, and to all questions she replied only with a shake of the head; she even smiled once or **twice.** Gradually, her **moaning** grew louder; a **hollow shriek** burst from her; she **pretended** she was better and that she would get up **presently.** But she was seized with convulsions and cried out--

"Ah! my God! It is horrible!"

He threw himself on his knees by her bed.

"Tell me! what have you eaten? Answer, for heaven's sake!"

And he looked at her with a **tenderness** in his eyes such as she had never seen.

"Well, there--there!" she said in a faint voice. He flew to the writing-table, **tore** open the seal, and read **aloud:** "Accuse no one." He stopped, passed his hands across his eyes, and read it over again.

"What! help--help!"

He could only keep **repeating** the word: "Poisoned! poisoned!" Felicite ran to Homais, who **proclaimed** it in the market-place; Madame Lefrancois heard it at the "Lion d'Or"; some got up to go and tell their neighbours, and all night the village was on the **alert.**

Distraught, faltering, reeling, Charles **wandered** about the room. He knocked against the furniture, tore his hair, and the **chemist** had never believed that there could be so terrible a sight.

He went home to write to Monsieur Canivet and to Doctor Lariviere. He lost his head, and made more than fifteen rough copies. Hippolyte went to Neufchatel, and Justin so **spurred** Bovary's horse that he left it **foundered** and three parts dead by the hill at Bois-Guillaume.

Spanish

alert: alerta, alarma, alertar.
aloud: en voz alta.
bluish: azulado.
chattered: Parloteado.
chemist: químico, farmacéutico, boticario.
clenched: apretado.
dilated: dilatado.
distraught: aturrullado.
faintly: débilmente.
faltering: titubeando.
foundered: hundido.

groan: gemir, gemido.
hollow: hueco, cavidad, hondonada, vacuo.
metallic: metálico.
moaning: gemiendo.
oozed: rezumado.
presently: por ahora.
pretended: fingido, pretendido.
proclaimed: proclamado.
pulse: pulso, impulso, pulsación.
reeling: Tambalear.
repeating: repitiendo, repetidor.

shaken: sacudido.
shriek: chillido, chillar.
shuddering: estremecer.
spurred: espoleado.
sweat: sudor, sudar, transpirar.
tenderness: ternura.
tore: pret de tear, rompió.
twice: dos veces.
unequal: desigual.
vaguely: vagamente.
vapour: vapor, vaho.
wandered: Vagado.

Charles tried to look up his medical dictionary, but could not read it; the lines were dancing.

"Be calm," said the **druggist**; "we have only to **administer** a powerful **antidote**. What is the poison?"

Charles showed him the letter. It was **arsenic**.

"Very well," said Homais, "we must make an analysis."

For he knew that in cases of **poisoning** an analysis must be made; and the other, who did not understand, answered--

"Oh, do anything! save her!"

Then going back to her, he sank upon the carpet, and lay there with his head leaning against the edge of her bed, **sobbing**.

"**Don't** cry," she said to him. "Soon I shall not trouble you any more."

"Why was it? Who drove you to it?"

She replied. "It had to be, my dear!"

"Weren't you happy? Is it my fault? I did all I could!"

"Yes, that is true--you are good--you."

And she passed her hand slowly over his hair. The **sweetness** of this sensation **deepened** his sadness; he felt his whole being **dissolving** in despair at the thought that he must lose her, just when she was **confessing** more love for him than ever. And he could think of nothing; he did not know, he did not dare; the urgent need for some immediate resolution gave the finishing stroke to the **turmoil** of his mind.

So she had done, she thought, with all the **treachery**; and **meanness**, and **numberless** desires that had **tortured** her. She hated no one now; a **twilight dimness** was settling upon her thoughts, and, of all **earthly** noises, Emma heard none but the **intermittent** lamentations of this poor heart, sweet and **indistinct** like the echo of a **symphony** dying away.

"Bring me the child," she said, raising herself on her elbow.

Spanish

administer: administrar, administrad, administro, administren, administras, administran, administráis, administra, administramos, administre.
antidote: antídoto, contraveneno.
arsenic: arsénico.
confessing: confesando.
deepened: ahondado.
dimness: lo confuso, casi obscuridad, debilidad, lo lerdo, semioscuridad, lo débil, lo sombrío, lo turbio,

ofuscamiento, oscurecimiento, oscuridad.
dissolving: disolviendo.
don't: no.
druggist: droguero.
earthly: terrenal, terrestre.
indistinct: indistinto.
intermittent: intermitente.
meanness: bajeza, vileza, escasez, maldad, mezquindad, pobreza, tacañería, humildad.
numberless: innumerable.

poisoning: envenenamiento, intoxicación, envenenar, envenenando.
sobbing: sollozar.
sweetness: dulzura.
symphony: sinfonía.
tortured: torturado.
treachery: traición.
turmoil: tumulto.
twilight: crepúsculo, anochecer.

"You are not worse, are you?" asked Charles.

"No, no!"

The child, serious, and still **half**-asleep, was carried in on the servant's arm in her long white **nightgown**, from which her bare feet **peeped** out. She looked **wonderingly** at the **disordered** room, and **half**-closed her eyes, **dazzled** by the candles burning on the table. They reminded her, no doubt, of the morning of New Year's day and Mid-Lent, when thus **awakened** early by **candle**-light she came to her mother's bed to **fetch** her presents, for she began saying--

"But where is it, **mamma**?" And as everybody was silent, "But I **can't** see my little stocking."

Felicite held her over the bed while she still kept looking towards the **mantelpiece**.

"Has nurse taken it?" she asked.

And at this name, that carried her back to the memory of her adulteries and her **calamities**, Madame Bovary turned away her head, as at the **loathing** of another bitterer **poison** that rose to her mouth. But Berthe remained **perched** on the bed.

"Oh, how big your eyes are, mamma! How pale you are! how hot you are!"

Her mother looked at her. "I am frightened!" cried the child, **recoiling**.

Emma took her hand to kiss it; the child **struggled**.

"That will do. Take her away," cried Charles, who was **sobbing** in the **alcove**.

Then the symptoms **ceased** for a moment; she seemed less **agitated**; and at every **insignificant** word, at every **respiration** a little more easy, he **regained** hope. At last, when Canivet came in, he threw himself into his arms.

"Ah! it is you. Thanks! You are good! But she is better. See! look at her."

His colleague was by no means of this opinion, and, as he said of himself, "never **beating** about the bush," he **prescribed**, an **emetic** in order to empty the stomach completely.

Spanish

agitated: agitado, inquieto.
alcove: alcoba, nicho.
awakened: despertado.
beating: paliza, pulsación, latido.
calamities: calamidades.
candle-light: luz de una vela.
can't: no puede.
ceased: ceso, Cesado.
dazzled: deslumbrado.
disordered: desarreglado, desconcertado en algo, trastornado, desordenado.

emetic: emético, vomitivo.
emma: Ema.
fetch: traer, traemos, traed, trae, traéis, traes, traigo, traigan, traen, traiga, coger.
half-asleep: medio dormido.
half-closed: entreabierto.
insignificant: insignificante.
loathing: detestando, aversión, aborrecimiento.
mamma: mama.
mantelpiece: repisa.

nightgown: camisa de dormir, camisón, camisón de dormir.
peeped: pipió.
perched: encaramado, posado.
poison: veneno, envenenar, intoxicar.
prescribed: prescrito, recetado.
recoiling: retráctil.
regained: recobrado, recuperado.
respiration: respiración.
sobbing: sollozar.
struggled: luchado.
wonderingly: preguntar.

She soon began **vomiting** blood. Her lips became drawn. Her limbs were **convulsed**, her whole body covered with brown spots, and her pulse slipped beneath the fingers like a stretched thread, like a harp-string nearly breaking.

After this she began to scream horribly. She cursed the poison, railed at it, and **implored** it to be quick, and thrust away with her stiffened arms everything that Charles, in more agony than herself, tried to make her drink. He stood up, his handkerchief to his lips, with a rattling sound in his throat, weeping, and choked by **sobs** that shook his whole body. Felicite was running **hither** and **thither** in the room. Homais, motionless, uttered great sighs; and Monsieur Canivet, always **retaining** his **self**-command, nevertheless began to feel uneasy.

"The devil! yet she has been **purged**, and from the moment that the cause ceases--"

"The effect must cease," said Homais, "that is evident."

"Oh, save her!" cried Bovary.

And, without listening to the chemist, who was still **venturing** the **hypothesis**, "It is perhaps a **salutary** paroxysm," Canivet was about to administer some **theriac**, when they heard the **cracking** of a whip; all the windows rattled, and a **post**-chaise drawn by three horses **abreast**, up to their ears in mud, drove at a **gallop** round the corner of the market. It was Doctor Lariviere.

The **apparition** of a god would not have **caused** more **commotion**. Bovary raised his hands; Canivet stopped short; and Homais pulled off his skull-cap long before the doctor had come in.

He belonged to that great school of **surgery begotten** of Bichat, to that **generation**, now **extinct**, of philosophical practitioners, who, loving their art with a **fanatical** love, exercised it with enthusiasm and **wisdom**. Everyone in his hospital **trembled** when he was angry; and his students so **revered** him that they tried, as soon as they were themselves in practice, to imitate him as much as possible. So that in all the **towns** about they were found wearing his long **wadded merino** overcoat and black frock-coat, whose **buttoned** cuffs slightly covered his **brawny** hands--very beautiful hands, and that never knew gloves, as

Spanish

abreast: de frente, caminar cuatro de frente.
apparition: aparición.
begotten: engendrado.
brawny: musculoso.
buttoned: abotonado, abrochado.
caused: causado.
commotion: escándalo, conmoción, alboroto.
convulsed: Convulsionado.
cracking: agrietamiento.
extinct: extinguido, extinto.

fanatical: fanático.
gallop: galope, galopar.
generation: generación.
hither: acá.
hypothesis: hipótesis.
implored: implorado, suplicado.
merino: merino.
post-chaise: calesa.
purged: purgó.
retaining: reteniendo.
revered: reverenciado, acatado, venerado.

salutary: saludable.
self-command: dominio de sí mismo.
sobs: solloza.
surgery: cirugía.
theriac: tríaca.
thither: allá.
towns: pueblos.
trembled: Temblado, tembló.
venturing: Aventurar.
vomiting: vomitar.
wadded: apretado, guata de relleno.
wisdom: sabiduría, sapiencia.

though to be more ready to **plunge** into suffering. **Disdainful** of honours, of titles, and of **academies**, like one of the old Knight-Hospitallers, generous, **fatherly** to the poor, and **practising** virtue without believing in it, he would almost have passed for a **saint** if the **keenness** of his **intellect** had not caused him to be feared as a **demon**. His glance, more **penetrating** than his bistouries, looked straight into your soul, and **dissected** every lie **athwart** all assertions and all reticences. And thus he went along, full of that **debonair majesty** that is given by the consciousness of great **talent**, of fortune, and of forty years of a labourious and **irreproachable** life.

He frowned as soon as he had passed the door when he saw the **cadaverous** face of Emma stretched out on her back with her mouth open. Then, while **apparently** listening to Canivet, he **rubbed** his fingers up and down beneath his nostrils, and repeated--

"Good! good!"

But he made a slow gesture with his shoulders. Bovary watched him; they looked at one another; and this man, **accustomed** as he was to the sight of **pain**, could not keep back a **tear** that fell on his shirt-frill.

He tried to take Canivet into the next room. Charles followed him.

"She is very ill, isn't she? If we put on sinapisms? Anything! Oh, think of something, you who have **saved** so many!"

Charles caught him in both his arms, and **gazed** at him **wildly**, **imploringly**, half-fainting against his breast.

"Come, my poor fellow, courage! There is nothing more to be done."

And Doctor Lariviere turned away.

"You are going?"

"I will come back."

He went out only to give an order to the **coachman**, with Monsieur Canivet, who did not care either to have Emma die under his hands.

Spanish

academies: academias.
accustomed: acostumbrado.
apparently: evidentemente, al parecer, aparentemente.
athwart: a través de.
cadaverous: cadavérico.
coachman: cochero.
debonair: cortés.
demon: demonio.
disdainful: desdeñoso.
dissected: disecado.
fatherly: paternal, paternalmente.

gazed: mirado.
imploringly: suplicar, de modo suplicante.
intellect: intelecto.
irreproachable: irreprochable.
keenness: agudeza, viveza, sutileza, perspicacia, ansia, entusiasmo.
majesty: majestad.
pain: dolor, el dolor, pena, sufrimiento.
penetrating: penetrando, penetrante.
plunge: bucear, zambullida,

zambullirse.
practising: ejercicio, ejercicios, entrenamiento, práctica, practicante, practicar, que ejerce.
rubbed: frotado.
saint: santo, santa, san.
saved: guardado, salvado, ahorrado.
talent: talento, disposición, capacidad, habilidad.
tear: lágrima, desgarrar, rajar, romper, rasgar, desgarro.
wildly: ferozmente.

The **chemist rejoined** them on the Place. He could not by **temperament** keep away from celebrities, so he **begged** Monsieur Lariviere to do him the signal honour of **accepting** some breakfast.

He sent quickly to the "Lion d'Or" for some pigeons; to the **butcher's** for all the **cutlets** that were to be had; to Tuvache for cream; and to Lestiboudois for eggs; and the **druggist** himself **aided** in the **preparations**, while Madame Homais was saying as she pulled together the **strings** of her jacket--

"You must excuse us, sir, for in this poor place, when one hasn't been told the night before--"

"Wine glasses!" whispered Homais.

"If only we were in town, we could fall back upon **stuffed** trotters."

"Be quiet! Sit down, doctor!"

He thought fit, after the first few mouthfuls, to give some details as to the **catastrophe**.

"We first had a feeling of siccity in the **pharynx**, then **intolerable pains** at the **epigastrium**, **super purgation**, coma."

"But how did she **poison** herself?"

"I **don't** know, doctor, and I don't even know where she can have **procured** the **arsenious** acid."

Justin, who was just bringing in a pile of plates, began to **tremble**.

"What's the matter?" said the chemist.

At this question the young man dropped the whole lot on the ground with a crash.

"Imbecile!" cried Homais. "**awkward lout**! block-head! **confounded** ass!"

But suddenly **controlling** himself--

"I wished, doctor, to make an analysis, and **primo** I **delicately** introduced a tube--"

Spanish

accepting: aceptando, admitiendo.
aided: asistido, guiado, ayudado.
arsenious: arsenioso.
awkward: difícil.
begged: Mendigado.
butcher's: carnicería.
catastrophe: catástrofe.
chemist: químico, farmacéutico, boticario.
confounded: perplejo.
controlling: controlador, mayoritario.
cutlets: chuletas, milanesa.

delicately: delicadamente.
don't: no.
druggist: droguero.
epigastrium: epigastrio.
intolerable: intolerable.
lout: patán, gamberro.
pains: dolores del parto, esfuerzos, desvelos.
pharynx: faringe.
poison: veneno, envenenar, intoxicar.
preparations: preparativos.
primo: primero, Aventajado.

procured: procurado.
purgation: purgación.
rejoined: replicado, reunido.
strings: instrumentos de cuerda, cuerdas.
stuffed: disecado, ahíto, llenó.
super: fabuloso, alza, bárbaro, estupendo, excelente, guay, sobre, superintendente, superior, súper.
temperament: temperamento, genio.
tremble: temblar, temblor.

"You would have done better," said the physician, "to introduce your fingers into her throat."

His colleague was silent, having just before **privately** received a severe **lecture** about his **emetic**, so that this good Canivet, so **arrogant** and so **verbose** at the time of the **clubfoot**, was **to**-day very modest. He smiled without **ceasing** in an **approving** manner.

Homais **dilated** in Amphytrionic pride, and the **affecting** thought of Bovary vaguely contributed to his pleasure by a kind of **egotistic reflex** upon himself. Then the presence of the doctor transported him. He displayed his **erudition**, cited **pell**-mell **cantharides**, upas, the **manchineel**, **vipers**.

"I have even read that various persons have found themselves under **toxicological** symptoms, and, as it were, thunderstricken by black-pudding that had been **subjected** to a too **vehement fumigation**. At least, this was **stated** in a very fine report drawn up by one of our pharmaceutical chiefs, one of our masters, the **illustrious** Cadet de Gassicourt!"

Madame Homais **reappeared**, carrying one of those **shaky machines** that are **heated** with spirits of wine; for Homais liked to make his coffee at table, having, moreover, torrefied it, **pulverised** it, and mixed it himself.

"Saccharum, doctor?" said he, offering the sugar.

Then he had all his children brought down, anxious to have the physician's opinion on their **constitutions**.

At last Monsieur Lariviere was about to leave, when Madame Homais asked for a consultation about her husband. He was making his blood too thick by going to sleep every evening after dinner.

"Oh, it isn't his blood that's too thick," said the physician.

And, smiling a little at his **unnoticed** joke, the doctor opened the door. But the chemist's shop was full of people; he had the greatest difficulty in getting rid of Monsieur Tuvache, who feared his spouse would get inflammation of the lungs, because she was in the habit of **spitting** on the ashes; then of Monsieur Binet, who sometimes experienced sudden attacks of great **hunger**; and of

Spanish

affecting: afectando, conmovedor, conmoviendo.
approving: aprobando, aprobar, aprobatorio.
arrogant: arrogante, altanero.
cantharides: cantárida.
ceasing: cesación, parar, cesar, cese, acabar.
clubfoot: pata de palo.
constitutions: constituciones.
dilated: dilatado.
egotistic: egotístico.

emetic: emético, vomitivo.
erudition: erudición.
fumigation: fumigación.
heated: calentado.
hunger: hambre, la hambre.
illustrious: ilustre.
lecture: conferencia.
machines: máquinas.
manchineel: manzanillo, mancinella.
pell-mell: atropelladamente.
privately: privadamente.
pulverised: pulverizado.

reappeared: reaparecido.
reflex: reflejo.
shaky: inseguro.
spitting: escupiendo.
stated: escrito, expresado, fijado.
subjected: sometido, sujetado.
to-day: hoy.
toxicological: toxicológico.
unnoticed: inadvertido.
vehement: vehemente.
verbose: verboso.
vipers: víboras.

Madame Caron, who suffered from tinglings; of Lheureux, who had **vertigo**; of Lestiboudois, who had rheumatism; and of Madame Lefrancois, who had **heartburn**. At last the three horses started; and it was the general opinion that he had not shown himself at all obliging.

Public attention was distracted by the appearance of Monsieur Bournisien, who was going across the market with the holy oil.

Homais, as was due to his principles, compared priests to ravens attracted by the odour of death. The sight of an **ecclesiastic** was **personally** disagreeable to him, for the **cassock** made him think of the **shroud**, and he detested the one from some fear of the other.

Nevertheless, not **shrinking** from what he called his **mission**, he returned to Bovary's in company with Canivet whom Monsieur Lariviere, before leaving, had **strongly** urged to make this visit; and he would, but for his wife's **objections**, have taken his two sons with him, in order to **accustom** them to great occasions; that this might be a lesson, an example, a solemn **picture**, that should remain in their heads later on.

The room when they went in was full of **mournful** solemnity. On the **work-**table, **covered** over with a white cloth, there were five or six small balls of cotton in a silver dish, near a large **crucifix** between two lighted candles.

Emma, her chin sunken upon her breast, had her eyes **inordinately** wide open, and her poor hands wandered over the sheets with that hideous and soft movement of the dying, that seems as if they wanted already to cover themselves with the shroud. Pale as a statue and with eyes red as fire, Charles, not weeping, stood opposite her at the foot of the bed, while the priest, bending one knee, was muttering words in a low voice.

She turned her face slowly, and seemed filled with joy on seeing suddenly the violet **stole**, no doubt finding again, in the midst of a **temporary lull** in her pain, the lost **voluptuousness** of her first mystical transports, with the visions of eternal **beatitude** that were beginning.

Spanish

accustom: acostumbrar, acostumbren, acostumbran, acostumbro, acostumbras, acostumbráis, acostumbrad, acostumbra, acostumbramos, acostumbre, habituar.
beatitude: beatitud.
cassock: sotana.
cover: cubrir, tapa, cobertura, recorrer, tapar, forrar, cubierta, neumático, portada, forro, encuadernación.
crucifix: crucifijo.

ecclesiastic: eclesiástico.
heartburn: acedía, acidez de estómago, ardor de estómago, acidez.
inordinately: desmesuradamente, inmoderadamente.
lull: calma, arrullar.
mission: misión.
mournful: fúnebre.
objections: objeciones.
personally: personalmente.
picture: imagen, cuadro, grabado, pintura, retrato, el cuadro,

reproducción, ilustración, foto.
shrinking: contracción, encoger, encogimiento.
shroud: mortaja, obenque, protector, protector de contacto.
stole: estola.
strongly: fuertemente.
temporary: provisional, temporal, temporario.
vertigo: vértigo.
voluptuousness: voluptuosidad.
work-table: mesa de trabajo.

The priest rose to take the **crucifix**; then she stretched forward her neck as one who is **athirst**, and **glueing** her lips to the body of the Man-God, she pressed upon it with all her **expiring** strength the fullest kiss of love that she had ever given. Then he **recited** the Misereatur and the Indulgentiam, dipped his right **thumb** in the oil, and began to give extreme **unction**. First upon the eyes, that had so **coveted** all **worldly pomp**; then upon the nostrils, that had been greedy of the warm breeze and **amorous** odours; then upon the mouth, that had uttered lies, that had curled with pride and cried out in **lewdness**; then upon the hands that had delighted in sensual **touches**; and finally upon the soles of the feet, so swift of **yore**, when she was running to satisfy her desires, and that would now walk no more.

The cure wiped his fingers, threw the bit of cotton dipped in oil into the fire, and came and sat down by the dying woman, to tell her that she must now blend her sufferings with those of Jesus Christ and **abandon** herself to the divine mercy.

Finishing his **exhortations**, he tried to place in her hand a **blessed** candle, **symbol** of the **celestial** glory with which she was soon to be surrounded. Emma, too weak, could not close her fingers, and the **taper**, but for Monsieur Bournisien would have fallen to the ground.

However, she was not quite so pale, and her face had an expression of **serenity** as if the sacrament had cured her.

The priest did not fail to point this out; he even explained to Bovary that the Lord sometimes prolonged the life of persons when he thought it meet for their salvation; and Charles remembered the day when, so near death, she had received the communion. Perhaps there was no need to despair, he thought.

In fact, she looked around her slowly, as one **awakening** from a dream; then in a distinct voice she asked for her **looking**-glass, and remained some time bending over it, until the big tears fell from her eyes. Then she turned away her head with a sigh and fell back upon the pillows.

Her chest soon began panting rapidly; the whole of her tongue **protruded** from her mouth; her eyes, as they rolled, grew paler, like the two **globes** of a

Spanish

abandon: abandonar, abandonen, abandona, abandonad, abandonáis, abandonamos, abandonan, abandonas, abandone, abandono, desamparar.
amorous: amoroso.
athirst: sediento.
awakening: despertar.
blessed: bendecido, bendito, bienaventurado.
celestial: celeste, celestial.
coveted: codiciado.

crucifix: crucifijo.
exhortations: exhortaciones.
expiring: expirando, caducando.
finishing: acabando, terminando, acabado, concluyendo.
globes: GLOBOS.
glueing: pegar, encolado, encoladura.
lewdness: obscenidad, lascivia, liviandad.
looking-glass: espejo.
pomp: pompa.
protruded: sobresalido.

recited: recitado.
serenity: serenidad.
symbol: símbolo.
taper: manipulador, taladro cónico, conicidad.
thumb: pulgar, el pulgar, dedo pulgar.
touches: alcanza, toca, conmueve, palpa.
unction: unción.
worldly: mundano.
yore: antaño, de antaño, hace tiempo, tiempos pasados.

lamp that is going out, so that one might have thought her already dead but for the fearful **labouring** of her **ribs**, shaken by violent breathing, as if the soul were **struggling** to free itself. Felicite knelt down before the **crucifix**, and the **druggist** himself slightly bent his knees, while Monsieur Canivet looked out vaguely at the Place. Bournisien had again begun to pray, his face bowed against the edge of the bed, his long black **cassock** trailing behind him in the room. Charles was on the other side, on his knees, his arms outstretched towards Emma. He had taken her hands and pressed them, **shuddering** at every beat of her heart, as at the shaking of a falling ruin. As the death-rattle became stronger the priest prayed faster; his prayers **mingled** with the **stifled sobs** of Bovary, and sometimes all seemed lost in the **muffled** murmur of the Latin syllables that **tolled** like a passing bell.

Suddenly on the pavement was heard a loud noise of **clogs** and the clattering of a stick; and a voice rose--a **raucous** voice--that sang--

"Maids an the warmth of a summer day Dream of love and of love always"

Emma raised herself like a **galvanised** corpse, her hair **undone**, her eyes fixed, staring.

"Where the **sickle blades** have been, Nannette, gathering ears of corn, Passes bending down, my queen, To the earth where they were born."

"The blind man!" she cried. And Emma began to laugh, an **atrocious, frantic, despairing** laugh, thinking she saw the hideous face of the poor **wretch** that stood out against the eternal night like a **menace**.

"The wind is strong this summer day, Her **petticoat** has **flown** away."

She fell back upon the **mattress** in a **convulsion**. They all drew near. She was dead.

Spanish

atrocious: atroz.
blades: aspas, cuchillas.
cassock: sotana.
clogs: atasca.
convulsion: convulsión.
crucifix: crucifijo.
despairing: sin esperanza, desesperación, desesperado, desesperanza, desesperanzarse, desesperar.
druggist: droguero.
flown: volado.

frantic: frenético.
galvanised: galvanizado.
labouring: persona que trabaja, trabajante, trabajar, obrero.
mattress: colchón.
menace: amenaza, amenazar, conminación, conminar.
mingled: mezclado, triscado.
muffled: silenciador, sordo, silenciado, mufla, embozar, apagar, apagado, amortiguar, amortiguado.
petticoat: enaguas.

raucous: rauco, ronco, estridente.
ribs: costillas.
shuddering: estremecer.
sickle: hoz.
sobs: solloza.
stifled: se ahogado, sofocado, reprimido, callado, suprimido.
struggling: en apuros, luchar.
tolled: Tocado.
undone: deshecho.
wretch: desgraciado.

CHAPTER NINE

There is always after the death of anyone a kind of **stupefaction**; so difficult is it to **grasp** this **advent** of **nothingness** and to **resign** ourselves to believe in it. But still, when he saw that she did not move, Charles **threw** himself upon her, crying--

"Farewell! farewell!"

Homais and Canivet **dragged** him from the room.

"**Restrain** yourself!"

"Yes." said he, **struggling**, "I'll be quiet. I'll not do anything. But leave me alone. I want to see her. She is my wife!"

And he **wept**.

"Cry," said the **chemist**; "let nature take her course; that will **solace** you."

Weaker than a child, Charles let himself be led **downstairs** into the sitting-room, and Monsieur Homais soon went home. On the Place he was **accosted** by the **blind** man, who, having dragged himself as far as Yonville, in the hope of getting the **antiphlogistic pomade**, was asking every **passer**-by where the **druggist** lived.

"There now! as if I **hadn't** got other **fish** to fry. Well, so much the worse; you must come later on."

Spanish

accosted: abordado.
advent: advenimiento, adviento.
antiphlogistic: antiflogístico.
blind: ciego, persiana, deslumbrar, deslumbrad, deslumbre, deslumbras, deslumbran, deslumbro, deslumbramos, deslumbráis, deslumbren.
chemist: químico, farmacéutico, boticario.
downstairs: abajo, de abajo, en el fondo.

dragged: arrastrado, remolcado.
druggist: droguero.
fish: pez, pescado, pescar, el pescado, pescados, peces, el pez.
fry: freír.
grasp: agarrar, asir, coger, empuñar, asimiento, aferrar.
hadn't: no ha.
nothingness: nada.
passer-by: transeúnte, peregrino, turista, viandante, caminante.
pomade: pomada.

resign: dimitir, dimita, dimito, dimitís, dimitimos, dimitid, dimites, dimiten, dimite, dimitan, abdicar.
restrain: refrenar, contener, refrene, refrenas, refrena, contengo, refrenad, contiene, contienen, contienes, refrenen.
solace: solaz, consolar, consuelo.
struggling: en apuros, luchar.
stupefaction: estupefacción.
threw: pret de throw, Tiró, tiro.
wept: Llorado.

And he entered the shop hurriedly.

He had to write two letters, to **prepare** a **soothing potion** for Bovary, to invent some lie that would conceal the **poisoning,** and work it up into an article for the "Fanal," without counting the people who were waiting to get the news from him; and when the Yonvillers had all heard his story of the **arsenic** that she had mistaken for sugar in making a **vanilla** cream. Homais once more returned to Bovary's.

He found him alone (Monsieur Canivet had left), sitting in an **arm**-chair near the window, staring with an **idiotic** look at the flags of the floor.

"Now," said the chemist, "you ought yourself to **fix** the hour for the ceremony."

"Why? What ceremony?" Then, in a **stammering,** frightened voice, "Oh, no! not that. No! I want to see her here."

Homais, to keep himself in **countenance,** took up a **water**-bottle on the **whatnot** to water the geraniums.

"Ah! thanks," said Charles; "you are good."

But he did not finish, **choking** beneath the crowd of memories that this action of the **druggist** recalled to him.

Then to **distract** him, Homais thought fit to talk a little **horticulture: plants** wanted **humidity.** Charles bowed his head in sign of **approbation.**

"Besides, the fine days will soon be here again."

"Ah!" said Bovary.

The druggist, at his wit's end, began softly to draw aside the small window-curtain.

"**Hallo!** there's Monsieur Tuvache passing."

Charles repeated like a machine---

"Monsieur Tuvache passing!"

Spanish

approbation: aprobación.
arm-chair: sillón, butaca.
arsenic: arsénico.
choking: la obstrucción aérea, estrangular, atragantamiento, ahogarse.
countenance: semblante.
distract: distraer, distrae, distraed, distraéis, distraemos, distraen, distraes, distraigan, distraigo, distraiga, confundir.
druggist: droguero.

fix: fijar, fijad, fijáis, fijamos, fijan, fijas, fijen, fije, fijo, fija, reparar.
hallo: hola.
horticulture: horticultura.
humidity: humedad, la humedad.
idiotic: idiota, tonto.
plants: plantas.
poisoning: envenenamiento, intoxicación, envenenar, envenenando.
potion: poción.
prepare: preparar, preparas, prepare,

prepara, preparad, preparáis, preparan, preparo, preparen, preparamos, prepararse.
soothing: calmando, consolador, calmante, tranquilizador.
stammering: balbuceo, tartamudo, estropajoso, balbuciente, tartamudear, tartamudeo, tartamudez, tartamudeando.
vanilla: vainilla, la vainilla.
water-bottle: jarra.
whatnot: estante, cualquier cosa.

Homais did not dare to speak to him again about the funeral **arrangements**; it was the priest who succeeded in **reconciling** him to them.

He shut himself up in his consulting-room, took a pen, and after **sobbing** for some time, wrote--

"I wish her to be buried in her wedding-dress, with white shoes, and a **wreath**. Her hair is to be spread out over her shoulders. Three coffins, one of oak, one of **mahogany**, one of lead. Let no one say anything to me. I shall have strength. Over all there is to be placed a large piece of green **velvet**. This is my wish; see that it is done."

The two men were much surprised at Bovary's **romantic** ideas. The **chemist** at once went to him and said--

"This velvet seems to me a superfetation. Besides, the expense--"

"What's that to you?" cried Charles. "Leave me! You did not love her. Go!"

The priest took him by the arm for a turn in the garden. He discoursed on the **vanity** of **earthly** things. God was very great, was very good: one must **submit** to his **decrees** without a **murmur**; **nay**, must even **thank** him.

Charles burst out into blasphemies: "I hate your God!"

"The spirit of **rebellion** is still upon you," sighed the **ecclesiastic**.

Bovary was far away. He was walking with great **strides** along by the wall, near the **espalier**, and he ground his teeth; he raised to heaven looks of **malediction**, but not so much as a **leaf stirred**.

A fine rain was falling: Charles, whose chest was bare, at last began to **shiver**; he went in and sat down in the kitchen.

At six o'clock a noise like a **clatter** of old iron was heard on the Place; it was the "Hirondelle" coming in, and he remained with his forehead against the windowpane, watching all the passengers get out, one after the other. Felicite put down a **mattress** for him in the **drawing**-room. He threw himself upon it and fell asleep.

Spanish

arrangements: acuerdos.
chemist: químico, farmacéutico, boticario.
clatter: martilleo.
decrees: decreta.
drawing-room: estrado.
earthly: terrenal, terrestre.
ecclesiastic: eclesiástico.
espalier: espaldera.
leaf: hoja, la hoja.
mahogany: caoba.
malediction: maldición.

mattress: colchón.
murmur: murmurar, murmullo.
nay: más aún, más bien, voto negativo, voto en contra, no, negativa, mejor dicho.
rebellion: rebelión.
reconciling: reconciliándose, conciliándose.
romantic: romántico.
shiver: tiritar, temblar, escalofrío.
sobbing: sollozar.
stirred: batido.

strides: zancadas.
submit: someter, sometan, sometes, someto, someten, sometemos, sometéis, someted, somete, someta, presentar.
thank: agradecer, agradezco, agradeces, agradezcan, agradece, agradezca, agradecemos, agradeced, agradecen, agradecéis, dar gracias.
vanity: vanidad.
velvet: terciopelo, el terciopelo.
wreath: guirnalda, corona.

Although a **philosopher**, Monsieur Homais respected the dead. So bearing no **grudge** to poor Charles, he came back again in the evening to sit up with the body; bringing with him three volumes and a pocket-book for taking notes.

Monsieur Bournisien was there, and two large candles were burning at the head of the bed, that had been taken out of the **alcove**. The **druggist**, on whom the silence **weighed**, was not long before he began **formulating** some **regrets** about this "unfortunate young woman." and the priest replied that there was nothing to do now but pray for her.

"Yet," Homais went on, "one of two things; either she died in a state of grace (as the Church has it), and then she has no need of our prayers; or else she **departed impertinent** (that is, I believe, the **ecclesiastical** expression), and then--"

Bournisien interrupted him, **replying testily** that it was none the less necessary to pray.

"But," **objected** the **chemist**, "since God knows all our needs, what can be the good of prayer?"

"What!" cried the ecclesiastic, "prayer! Why, aren't you a Christian?"

"Excuse me," said Homais; "I admire Christianity. To begin with, it **enfranchised** the slaves, introduced into the world a morality--"

"That isn't the question. All the **texts**-"

"Oh! oh! As to texts, look at history; it, is known that all the texts have been **falsified** by the Jesuits."

Charles came in, and **advancing** towards the bed, slowly drew the curtains.

Emma's head was turned towards her right shoulder, the corner of her mouth, which was open, seemed like a black **hole** at the lower part of her face; her two thumbs were bent into the palms of her hands; a kind of white dust **besprinkled** her lashes, and her eyes were beginning to disappear in that **viscous pallor** that looks like a thin **web**, as if **spiders** had **spun** it over. The sheet sunk in from her breast to her knees, and then rose at the tips of her toes, and it seemed to Charles that infinite masses, an enormous **load**, were **weighing** upon her.

Spanish

advancing: avanzar, movimiento hacia adelante.
alcove: alcoba, nicho.
besprinkled: Salpicado.
chemist: químico, farmacéutico, boticario.
departed: salido, partido.
druggist: droguero.
ecclesiastic: eclesiástico.
ecclesiastical: eclesiástico.
enfranchised: emancipado, franqueado, liberado, manumitido.

falsified: falsificado.
formulating: formulando.
grudge: rencor.
hole: agujero, zanja, hueco, orificio, cavidad.
impertinent: impertinente.
load: carga, cargar, la carga, cargo.
objected: objetado.
pallor: palidez.
philosopher: filósofo.
regrets: lamenta, excusas.
replying: Contestar.

spiders: hilar.
spun: hilado.
testily: malhumoradamente, irritadamente, irritablemente.
texts: textos.
viscous: viscoso.
web: telaraña, red, tejido tela telaraña enredo red trama.
weighed: Pesado.
weighing: pesando, peso, pesaje, pesar.

The church clock struck two. They could hear the loud **murmur** of the river **flowing** in the darkness at the foot of the terrace. Monsieur Bournisien from time to time blew his nose **noisily**, and Homais' pen was **scratching** over the paper.

"Come, my good friend," he said, "withdraw; this **spectacle** is **tearing** you to pieces."

Charles once gone, the **chemist** and the cure recommenced their discussions.

"Read Voltaire," said the one, "read D'Holbach, read the 'Encyclopaedia'!"

"Read the 'Letters of some Portuguese Jews,'" said the other; "read 'The Meaning of Christianity,' by Nicolas, formerly a magistrate."

They grew warm, they grew red, they both talked at once without listening to each other. Bournisien was **scandalized** at such **audacity**; Homais **marvelled** at such **stupidity**; and they were on the point of **insulting** one another when Charles suddenly **reappeared**. A **fascination** drew him. He was **continually** coming upstairs.

He stood opposite her, the better to see her, and he lost himself in a **contemplation** so deep that it was no longer painful.

He recalled stories of **catalepsy**, the marvels of **magnetism**, and he said to himself that by **willing** it with all his force he might perhaps succeed in **reviving** her. Once he even bent towards he, and cried in a low voice, "Emma! Emma!" His strong breathing made the flames of the candles **tremble** against the wall.

At **daybreak** Madame Bovary senior arrived. Charles as he **embraced** her burst into another **flood** of tears. She tried, as the chemist had done, to make some remarks to him on the expenses of the funeral. He became so angry that she was silent, and he even **commissioned** her to go to town at once and buy what was necessary.

Charles remained alone the whole afternoon; they had taken Berthe to Madame Homais'; Felicite was in the room upstairs with Madame Lefrancois.

In the evening he had some visitors. He rose, pressed their hands, **unable** to speak. Then they sat down near one another, and formed a large **semicircle** in front of the fire. With **lowered** faces, and **swinging** one leg crossed over the other

Spanish

audacity: audacia.
catalepsy: catalepsia.
chemist: químico, farmacéutico, boticario.
commissioned: comisionado.
contemplation: contemplación.
continually: continuamente, siempre.
daybreak: amanecer, alba.
embraced: abrazado.
fascination: fascinación.
flood: diluvio, inundación, enterrar, pleamar, inundar.

flowing: fluido, corriente.
insulting: insultante, insultar.
lowered: bajado, arriado.
magnetism: magnetismo.
marvelled: Maravillado.
murmur: murmurar, murmullo.
noisily: ruidosamente, clamorosamente, alborotadamente.
reappeared: reaparecido.
reviving: reavivando.
scandalized: escandalizado.
scratching: arañar, arañazo,

improvisado, rasguño, rasguñar, raspamiento, rayadura, rascadura, rascar.
semicircle: semicírculo.
spectacle: espectáculo.
stupidity: estupidez.
swinging: balanceo.
tearing: romper, desgarramiento, efecto bandera, ruptura.
tremble: temblar, temblor.
unable: incapaz.
willing: dispuesto, deseoso.

knee, they uttered deep sighs at intervals; each one was **inordinately** bored, and yet none would be the first to go.

Homais, when he returned at nine o'clock (for the last two days only Homais seemed to have been on the Place), was laden with a **stock** of **camphor**, of **benzine**, and aromatic **herbs**. He also carried a large jar full of **chlorine** water, to keep off all miasmata. Just then the servant, Madame Lefrancois, and Madame Bovary senior were busy about Emma, finishing dressing her, and they were drawing down the long stiff veil that covered her to her satin shoes.

Felicite was sobbing--"Ah! my poor mistress! my poor mistress!"

"Look at her," said the landlady, sighing; "how pretty she still is! Now, **couldn't** you swear she was going to get up in a minute?"

Then they bent over her to put on her wreath. They had to **raise** the head a little, and a rush of black liquid issued, as if she were vomiting, from her mouth.

"Oh, goodness! The dress; take care!" cried Madame Lefrancois. "Now, just come and help," she said to the chemist. "Perhaps you're afraid?"

"I afraid?" replied he, shrugging his shoulders. "I dare say! **I've** seen all sorts of things at the hospital when I was studying **pharmacy**. We used to make punch in the **dissecting** room! **Nothingness** does not **terrify** a philosopher; and, as I often say, I even **intend** to leave my body to the hospitals, in order, later on, to **serve** science."

The cure on his arrival inquired how Monsieur Bovary was, and, on the reply of the **druggist**, went on--"The blow, you see, is still too recent."

Then Homais congratulated him on not being exposed, like other people, to the **loss** of a beloved companion; whence there followed a **discussion** on the **celibacy** of priests.

"For," said the chemist, "it is **unnatural** that a man should do without women! There have been crimes--"

"But, good heaven!" cried the **ecclesiastic**, "how do you **expect** an individual who is married to keep the **secrets** of the **confessional**, for example?"

Spanish

benzine: bencina.
camphor: alcanfor.
celibacy: celibato.
chlorine: cloro.
confessional: confesionario.
couldn't: no fue posible.
discussion: discusión.
dissecting: disecando.
druggist: droguero.
ecclesiastic: eclesiástico.
expect: esperar, esperad, espero, esperen, esperáis, esperamos,

esperas, esperan, espera, espere.
herbs: hierbas.
inordinately: desmesuradamente, inmoderadamente.
intend: querer decir, tener el propósito.
i've: he, Tengo.
loss: pérdida, perdida, pérdidas, siniestro, atenuación.
nothingness: nada.
pharmacy: farmacia.
raise: levantar, entonar, criar, subir,

alzar, elevar, alza, izar, aumento.
secrets: misterios, partes pudendas.
serve: servir, sirva, sirvo, servimos, servid, servís, sirvan, sirve, sirven, sirves.
stock: acciones, existencias, existencia, almacenar, acción, mango, proveer, reserva, ganado, valores.
terrify: aterrar, aterre, aterrad, aterráis, aterramos, aterro, aterran, aterras, aterren, aterra, terroriza.
unnatural: innatural, antinatural.

Homais fell **foul** of the **confessional**. Bournisien **defended** it; he enlarged on the acts of **restitution** that it brought about. He cited various anecdotes about thieves who had suddenly become **honest**. Military men on approaching the **tribunal** of **penitence** had felt the scales fall from their eyes. At Fribourg there was a minister--

His companion was asleep. Then he felt somewhat **stifled** by the over-heavy atmosphere of the room; he opened the window; this **awoke** the chemist.

"Come, take a **pinch** of snuff," he said to him. "Take it; it'll relieve you."

A continual **barking** was heard in the distance. "Do you hear that dog howling?" said the chemist.

"They smell the dead," replied the priest. "It's like bees; they leave their **hives** on the **decease** of any person."

Homais made no remark upon these prejudices, for he had again dropped asleep. Monsieur Bournisien, stronger than he, went on moving his lips gently for some time, then **insensibly** his chin sank down, he let fall his big black boot, and began to **snore**.

They sat opposite one another, with **protruding** stomachs, puffed-up faces, and **frowning** looks, after so much **disagreement uniting** at last in the same human weakness, and they moved no more than the corpse by their side, that seemed to be sleeping.

Charles coming in did not wake them. It was the last time; he came to bid her farewell.

The **aromatic** herbs were still smoking, and spirals of **bluish vapour blended** at the window-sash with the fog that was coming in. There were few stars, and the night was warm. The **wax** of the candles fell in great drops upon the sheets of the bed. Charles watched them burn, **tiring** his eyes against the **glare** of their yellow flame.

The **watering** on the **satin** gown **shimmered** white as **moonlight**. Emma was lost beneath it; and it seemed to him that, spreading beyond her own **self**, she

Spanish

aromatic: aromático.
awoke: pret y pp de awake.
barking: ladrar, ladrido.
blended: mezclado.
bluish: azulado.
confessional: confesionario.
decease: defunción.
defended: defendido.
disagreement: desacuerdo.
foul: falta, asqueroso, sucio.
frowning: ceñudo.
glare: deslumbramiento, deslumbrar.

hives: urticaria.
honest: honrado, sincero, honesto.
insensibly: insensiblemente.
moonlight: luz de la luna.
penitence: penitencia.
pinch: pizca, apuro, pizcar, pellizco, pellizcar.
protruding: sobresaliendo, sobresaliente.
restitution: restitución, devolución.
satin: raso, satén.
self: mismo.

shimmered: brilló.
snore: roncar, ronquido.
stifled: se ahogado, sofocado, reprimido, callado, suprimido.
tiring: fatigoso.
tribunal: juzgado, tribunal.
uniting: reuniendo, uniendo.
vapour: vapor, vaho.
watering: riego.
wax: cera, crema para zapatos, cerumen, crecer, la cera.

blended confusedly with everything around her-- the silence, the night, the passing wind, the damp odours rising from the ground.

Then suddenly he saw her in the garden at Tostes, on a **bench** against the **thorn** hedge, or else at Rouen in the streets, on the threshold of their house, in the yard at Bertaux. He again heard the laughter of the happy boys beneath the apple-trees: the room was filled with the **perfume** of her hair; and her dress **rustled** in his arms with a noise like **electricity**. The dress was still the same.

For a long while he thus recalled all his lost joys, her attitudes, her movements, the sound of her voice. Upon one fit of despair followed another, and even others, **inexhaustible** as the waves of an **overflowing** sea.

A terrible curiosity seized him. Slowly, with the tips of his fingers, **palpitating**, he lifted her **veil**. But he **uttered** a cry of horror that **awoke** the other two.

They dragged him down into the sitting-room. Then Felicite came up to say that he wanted some of her hair.

"Cut some off," replied the **druggist**.

And as she did not dare to, he himself stepped forward, **scissors** in hand. He **trembled** so that he **pierced** the skin of the **temple** in several places. At last, **stiffening** himself against emotion, Homais gave two or three great cuts at random that left white patches amongst that beautiful black hair.

The chemist and the cure plunged **anew** into their occupations, not without sleeping from time to time, of which they accused each other **reciprocally** at each fresh **awakening**. Then Monsieur Bournisien **sprinkled** the room with holy water and Homais threw a little **chlorine** water on the floor.

Felicite had taken care to put on the chest of drawers, for each of them, a bottle of brandy, some cheese, and a large roll. And the druggist, who could not hold out any longer, about four in the morning sighed--

"My word! I should like to take some sustenance."

The priest did not need any **persuading**; he went out to go and say mass, came back, and then they ate and **hobnobbed**, giggling a little without knowing

Spanish

anew: otra vez, de nuevo, nuevamente.
awakening: despertar.
awoke: pret y pp de awake.
bench: banco, estrado, banquillo, escaño.
blended: mezclado.
chlorine: cloro.
confusedly: confusamente.
druggist: droguero.
electricity: electricidad, la electricidad.
hobnobbed: codeado.

inexhaustible: inagotable.
overflowing: desbordamiento, desbordante.
palpitating: palpitando.
perfume: perfume, el perfume, perfumar.
persuading: convenciendo, persuadiendo.
pierced: agujereado.
reciprocally: recíprocamente.
rustled: susurrado.
scissors: tijeras, las tijeras.

sprinkled: rociado.
stiffening: endureciendo, agarrotándose, atiesando, agarrotamiento, espesar, engomado, endurecimiento, endurecerse, endurecer, atiesarse, atiesar.
temple: templo, sien, el templo.
thorn: espina.
trembled: Temblado, tembló.
uttered: pronunciado.
veil: velo.

why, **stimulated** by that **vague gaiety** that comes upon us after times of **sadness**, and at the last glass the **priest** said to the **druggist**, as he **clapped** him on the shoulder--

"We shall end by understanding one another."

In the passage **downstairs** they met the undertaker's men, who were coming in. Then Charles for two hours had to suffer the **torture** of hearing the **hammer resound** against the wood. Next day they **lowered** her into her **oak coffin**, that was **fitted** into the other two; but as the **bier** was too large, they had to fill up the gaps with the **wool** of a **mattress**. At last, when the three **lids** had been **planed** down, **nailed**, **soldered**, it was placed outside in front of the door; the house was **thrown** open, and the people of Yonville began to **flock** round.

Old Rouault arrived, and **fainted** on the Place when he saw the black **cloth**!

Spanish

bier: féretro, andas.
clapped: Aplaudido.
cloth: tela, trapo, paño, la tela, mantel, tejido.
coffin: ataúd.
downstairs: abajo, de abajo, en el fondo.
druggist: droguero.
fainted: pasmado, desfallecido, amortecido, desmayado.
fitted: en buen salud, ajustarse, conveniente, capacitado, ataque, apto, convulsión, capaz, encajar, entallar, instalada.
flock: bandada, rebaño, manada.
gaiety: alegría.
hammer: martillo, el martillo, martillar.
lids: cubiertas.
lowered: bajado, arriado.
mattress: colchón.
nailed: clavado, remachado.
oak: roble.
planed: planeado.
priest: sacerdote, cura, preste.
resound: resonar, resuene, resuena, resueno, resuenen, resuenan, resonamos, resonáis, resonad, resuenas.
sadness: tristeza.
soldered: soldó.
stimulated: estimulado.
thrown: tirado, pp de throw.
torture: tortura, tormento, torturar.
vague: vago.
wool: lana, la lana.

CHAPTER TEN

He had only received the chemist's letter **thirty**-six hours after the event; and, from consideration for his feelings, Homais had so worded it that it was impossible to make out what it was all about.

First, the old fellow had fallen as if struck by **apoplexy**. Next, he understood that she was not dead, but she might be. At last, he had put on his **blouse**, taken his hat, **fastened** his **spurs** to his boots, and set out at full **speed**; and the whole of the way old Rouault, **panting**, was **torn** by **anguish**. Once even he was **obliged** to **dismount**. He was **dizzy**; he heard voices round about him; he felt himself going mad.

Day broke. He saw three black hens asleep in a tree. He **shuddered**, **horrified** at this **omen**. Then he promised the Holy Virgin three chasubles for the church, and that he would go **barefooted** from the **cemetery** at Bertaux to the chapel of Vassonville.

He entered Maromme **shouting** for the people of the **inn**, burst open the door with a thrust of his shoulder, made for a **sack** of **oats**, **emptied** a bottle of sweet **cider** into the **manger**, and again **mounted** his **nag**, whose feet struck fire as it **dashed** along.

He said to himself that no doubt they would save her; the doctors would discover some **remedy** surely. He remembered all the **miraculous** cures he had

Spanish

anguish: angustia, miedo, angustiar.
apoplexy: apoplejía.
barefooted: descalzo.
blouse: blusa, la blusa.
cemetery: cementerio, el cementerio, campo santo.
cider: sidra, la sidra.
dashed: quebrado.
dismount: apearse, desmontar, desmontad, desmonta, desmonto, desmonten, desmonte, desmontáis, desmontamos, desmontan,

desmontas.
dizzy: mareado, vertiginoso.
emptied: desocupado, vaciado.
fastened: fijado, sujetado, atado.
horrified: horrorizado.
inn: albergue, fonda, posada, mesón.
manger: pesebre.
miraculous: milagroso.
mounted: montado.
nag: rocín, jaca.
oats: avena.
obliged: obligado.

omen: agüero, augurio, presagio.
panting: jadeante, palpitación.
remedy: curar, remedio, recurso, medio, remediar.
sack: saco, despedir, bolso.
shouting: griterío.
shuddered: estremecido.
speed: velocidad, prisa, rapidez, la velocidad, prontitud.
spurs: espuelas.
thirty-six: treinta y seis.
torn: roto.

been **told** about. Then she appeared to him dead. She was there; before his eyes, lying on her back in the middle of the road. He **reined** up, and the **hallucination** disappeared.

At Quincampoix, to give himself heart, he drank three cups of coffee one after the other. He **fancied** they had made a **mistake** in the name in writing. He looked for the letter in his pocket, felt it there, but did not dare to open it.

At last he began to think it was all a joke; someone's **spite**, the **jest** of some **wag**; and besides, if she were dead, one would have known it. But no! There was nothing extraordinary about the country; the sky was blue, the trees **swayed**; a **flock** of sheep passed. He saw the village; he was seen coming **bending** forward upon his horse, **belabouring** it with great **blows**, the girths **dripping** with blood.

When he had recovered consciousness, he fell, **weeping**, into Bovary's arms: "My girl! Emma! my child! tell me--"

The other replied, **sobbing**, "I **don't** know! I don't know! It's a curse!"

The **druggist** separated them. "These horrible details are useless. I will tell this gentleman all about it. Here are the people coming. Dignity! Come now! Philosophy!"

The poor fellow tried to show himself brave, and repeated several times. "Yes! courage!"

"Oh," cried the old man, "so I will have, by God! I'll go along o' her to the end!"

The bell began **tolling**. All was ready; they had to start. And **seated** in a **stall** of the **choir**, side by side, they saw pass and **repass** in front of them continually the three **chanting** choristers.

The serpent-player was **blowing** with all his might. Monsieur Bournisien, in full **vestments**, was singing in a **shrill** voice. He **bowed** before the **tabernacle**, raising his hands, stretched out his arms. Lestiboudois went about the church with his **whalebone** stick. The **bier** stood near the **lectern**, between four rows of candles. Charles felt inclined to get up and put them out.

Spanish

belabouring: apaleando.
bending: flexión, torcimiento.
bier: féretro, andas.
blowing: soplado, sopladura, soplar, silbido, soplo.
blows: golpes.
bowed: agobiado, arqueado, cabizbajo, encorvado, inclinado.
chanting: cantar.
choir: coro.
don't: no.
dripping: goteo.

druggist: droguero.
fancied: preferido, imaginario.
flock: bandada, rebaño, manada.
hallucination: alucinación.
jest: bromear, broma.
lectern: atril, facistol.
mistake: error, equivocación, yerro, la falta.
o: oxígeno.
reined: Contenido.
repass: repasar.
seated: sentado.

shrill: chillón.
sobbing: sollozar.
spite: rencor.
stall: establo, cuadra, puesto, casilla.
swayed: Oscilado.
tabernacle: tabernáculo.
tolling: tañido, gravamen, Tocar.
vestments: vestiduras.
wag: menear, meneo, mover.
weeping: llorando, lloroso, llanto, llorón.
whalebone: ballena.

Yet he tried to **stir** himself to a feeling of **devotion**, to throw himself into the hope of a future life in which he should see her again. He imagined to himself she had gone on a long journey, far away, for along time. But when he thought of her lying there, and that all was over, that they would lay her in the earth, he was seized with a fierce, **gloomy**, despairful **rage**. At times he thought he felt nothing more, and he enjoyed this **lull** in his pain, whilst at the same time he **reproached** himself for being a wretch.

The sharp noise of an iron-ferruled stick was heard on the stones, striking them at **irregular** intervals. It came from the end of the church, and stopped short at the lower **aisles**. A man in a **coarse** brown jacket **knelt** down **painfully**. It was Hippolyte, the stable-boy at the "Lion d'Or." He had put on his new leg.

One of the choristers went round the **nave** making a **collection**, and the coppers chinked one after the other on the silver plate.

"Oh, make **haste**! I am in pain!" cried Bovary, **angrily** throwing him a five-franc piece. The **churchman thanked** him with a deep bow.

They sang, they knelt, they stood up; it was **endless**! He remembered that once, in the early times, they had been to mass together, and they had sat down on the other side, on the right, by the wall. The bell began again. There was a great moving of chairs; the **bearers** slipped their three **staves** under the coffin, and everyone left the church.

Then Justin appeared at the door of the shop. He suddenly went in again, pale, **staggering**.

People were at the windows to see the **procession** pass. Charles at the head walked **erect**. He affected a brave air, and **saluted** with a **nod** those who, coming out from the lanes or from their doors, stood **amidst** the crowd.

The six men, three on either side, walked slowly, **panting** a little. The priests, the choristers, and the two choirboys **recited** the De profundis, and their voices **echoed** over the fields, rising and falling with their undulations. Sometimes they disappeared in the **windings** of the path; but the great silver cross rose always before the trees.

Spanish

aisles: pasillos.
amidst: en medio de, entre.
angrily: con enojo, enconadamente, airadamente, enojadamente.
bearers: apoyos.
churchman: clérigo.
coarse: áspero, desigual, tosco, grosero, basto.
collection: colección, colecta, cobro, grupo, recopilación, recaudación, recogida.
devotion: devoción.

echoed: resonado.
endless: interminable, sin fin.
erect: edificar, erguido, erecto, fundar.
gloomy: oscuro, tenebroso, lóbrego.
haste: prisa, precipitación.
irregular: irregular.
knelt: pret y pp de kneel, Arrodillado.
lull: calma, arrullar.
nave: carrete de rueda.
nod: inclinación, cabecear.
painfully: dolorosamente.
panting: jadeante, palpitación.

procession: comitiva, procesión, desfile.
rage: rabia, furia, furor, ira.
recited: recitado.
reproached: Reprochado.
saluted: saludado.
staggering: asombroso.
staves: estrofas.
stir: conmover, revolver, remover, agitar.
thanked: agradecido.
windings: bobinado.

The women followed in black cloaks with **turned**-down hoods; each of them carried in her hands a large lighted candle, and Charles felt himself growing weaker at this continual repetition of prayers and **torches**, beneath this **oppressive** odour of wax and of cassocks. A fresh breeze was blowing; the **rye** and **colza** were **sprouting**, little dewdrops trembled at the roadsides and on the **hawthorn** hedges. All sorts of **joyous** sounds filled the air; the **jolting** of a cart rolling **afar** off in the **ruts**, the crowing of a cock, repeated again and again, or the **gambling** of a **foal** running away under the apple-trees: The pure sky was **fretted** with rosy clouds; a **bluish haze** rested upon the cots covered with **iris**. Charles as he passed recognised each courtyard. He remembered mornings like this, when, after visiting some patient, he came out from one and returned to her.

The black cloth bestrewn with white beads blew up from time to time, laying bare the coffin. The tired **bearers** walked more slowly, and it advanced with constant jerks, like a boat that **pitches** with every wave.

They reached the cemetery. The men went right down to a place in the grass where a grave was dug. They ranged themselves all round; and while the priest spoke, the red soil thrown up at the sides kept **noiselessly** slipping down at the corners.

Then when the four ropes were arranged the coffin was placed upon them. He watched it descend; it seemed descending for ever. At last a **thud** was heard; the ropes **creaked** as they were drawn up. Then Bournisien took the spade handed to him by Lestiboudois; with his left hand all the time **sprinkling** water, with the right he **vigorously** threw in a large **spadeful**; and the wood of the coffin, struck by the pebbles, gave forth that dread sound that seems to us the **reverberation** of eternity.

The **ecclesiastic** passed the holy water **sprinkler** to his neighbour. This was Homais. He swung it **gravely**, then handed it to Charles, who sank to his knees in the earth and threw in handfuls of it, crying, "Adieu!" He sent her kisses; he dragged himself towards the grave, to **engulf** himself with her. They led him

Spanish

afar: lejos.
bearers: apoyos.
bluish: azulado.
colza: colza.
creaked: chirriado.
ecclesiastic: eclesiástico.
engulf: tragar, traguen, tragad, tragáis, tragamos, tragan, tragas, trague, traga, trago, tomar.
foal: potro, potra.
fretted: preocupado.
gambling: juego, juego con apuestas.

gravely: gravemente.
hawthorn: espino, espino blanco, majuelo.
haze: bruma, calina, neblina, la bruma.
iris: lirio.
jolting: sacudidas, traqueteo.
joyous: jubiloso, gozoso, de jubiloso, alegre.
noiselessly: calladamente, silenciosamente, tranquilamente.
oppressive: oprimido, opresivo.
pitches: argumentos de venta.

reverberation: reverberación.
ruts: carriles.
rye: centeno.
spadeful: pala.
sprinkler: rociador, regadera, aspersor.
sprinkling: rociadura.
sprouting: brotante, brotar, brote.
thud: porrazo.
torches: antorchas.
turned-down: deterioro.
vigorously: vigorosamente.

away, and he soon grew calmer, feeling perhaps, like the others, a **vague satisfaction** that it was all over.

Old Rouault on his way back began quietly **smoking** a **pipe**, which Homais in his **innermost conscience** thought not quite the thing. He also noticed that Monsieur Binet had not been present, and that Tuvache had "made off" after mass, and that Theodore, the notary's **servant** wore a blue coat, "as if one could not have got a black coat, since that is the **custom**, by Jove!" And to **share** his **observations** with others he went from group to group. They were **deploring** Emma's death, especially Lheureux, who had not failed to come to the funeral.

"Poor little woman! What a trouble for her husband!"

The **druggist** continued, "Do you know that but for me he would have committed some **fatal** attempt upon himself?"

"Such a good woman! To think that I saw her only last Saturday in my shop."

"I **haven't** had leisure," said Homais, "to prepare a few words that I would have cast upon her tomb."

Charles on getting home **undressed**, and old Rouault put on his blue **blouse**. It was a new one, and as he had often during the journey **wiped** his eyes on the **sleeves**, the **dye** had **stained** his face, and the **traces** of tears made lines in the **layer** of **dust** that covered it.

Madame Bovary senior was with them. All three were silent. At last the old fellow sighed--

"Do you remember, my friend, that I went to Tostes once when you had just lost your first **deceased**? I **consoled** you at that time. I thought of something to say then, but now--" Then, with a **loud groan** that shook his whole chest, "Ah! this is the end for me, do you see! I saw my wife go, then my son, and now **to-day** it's my daughter."

He wanted to go back at once to Bertaux, saying that he could not sleep in this house. He even refused to see his **granddaughter**.

Spanish

blouse: blusa, la blusa.
conscience: conciencia.
consoled: Consolado.
custom: costumbre, usanza.
deceased: difunto, fallecido.
deploring: deplorando.
druggist: droguero.
dust: polvo, quitar el polvo, quitar el polvo a.
dye: teñir, color, pintura, tinte, tintura, colorante.
fatal: mortal.

granddaughter: nieta, la nieta.
groan: gemir, gemido.
haven't: no tener.
innermost: más profundo.
layer: capa, estrato.
loud: alto, fuerte, ruidoso, chillón.
madame: señora.
observations: observaciones.
pipe: pipa, cañería, tubo, tubería, conducto, la pipa.
satisfaction: satisfacción.
servant: criado, criada, sirviente,

servidor.
share: compartir, acción, parte, dividir, ración, cuota, lote.
sleeves: manguitos, mangas.
smoking: fumando, humeando, fumar, ahumar.
stained: manchado.
to-day: hoy.
traces: trazas.
undressed: sin curtir.
vague: vago.
wiped: limpiado, Enjugado.

"No, no! It would **grieve** me too much. Only you'll kiss her many times for me. **Good**-bye! you're a good fellow! And then I shall never forget that," he said, **slapping** his **thigh**. "Never fear, you shall always have your turkey."

But when he reached the top of the hill he turned back, as he had turned once before on the road of Saint-Victor when he had **parted** from her. The windows of the village were all on fire beneath the **slanting** rays of the sun **sinking** behind the field. He put his hand over his eyes, and saw in the horizon an **enclosure** of walls, where trees here and there formed black clusters between white stones; then he went on his way at a gentle **trot**, for his **nag** had gone lame.

Despite their **fatigue**, Charles and his mother stayed very long that evening talking together. They spoke of the days of the past and of the future. She would come to live at Yonville; she would keep house for him; they would never part again. She was **ingenious** and **caressing, rejoicing** in her heart at **gaining** once more an affection that had **wandered** from her for so many years. Midnight struck. The village as usual was silent, and Charles, awake, thought always of her.

Rodolphe, who, to **distract** himself, had been **rambling** about the wood all day, was sleeping quietly in his **chateau**, and Leon, down **yonder**, always slept.

There was another who at that hour was not asleep.

On the grave between the pine-trees a child was on his knees **weeping**, and his heart, rent by **sobs**, was beating in the shadow beneath the load of an immense regret, sweeter than the moon and **fathomless** as the night. The gate suddenly **grated**. It was Lestiboudois; he came to fetch his **spade**, that he had forgotten. He recognised Justin climbing over the wall, and at last knew who was the **culprit** who **stole** his **potatoes**.

Spanish

caressing: mimoso, zalamero.
chateau: castillo.
culprit: culpable, delincuente.
distract: distraer, distrae, distraed, distraéis, distraemos, distraen, distraes, distraigan, distraigo, distraiga, confundir.
enclosure: cercado, envolvente, vallado, recinto, caja.
fathomless: insondable.
fatigue: fatiga, fatigar.
gaining: ganar.

good-bye: despedida, adiós.
grated: rallado.
grieve: afligir, afligís, aflijo, aflija, afligimos, afligid, afliges, aflige, aflijan, afligen, entristecer.
ingenious: ingenioso.
nag: rocín, jaca.
parted: despedido.
potatoes: patatas.
rambling: vagaroso.
rejoicing: regocijo.
sinking: hundimiento, sumidero.

slanting: inclinado, sesgo.
slapping: rápido, abofeteamiento, abofetear, batiente.
sobs: solloza.
spade: cavar, pala, laya.
stole: estola.
thigh: muslo, el muslo.
trot: trote, trotar.
wandered: Vagado.
weeping: llorando, lloroso, llanto, llorón.
yonder: allí, ahí, aquel.

CHAPTER ELEVEN

The next day Charles had the child brought back. She asked for her **mamma**. They told her she was away; that she would bring her back some playthings. Berthe spoke of her again several times, then at last thought no more of her. The child's **gaiety** broke Bovary's heart, and he had to bear **besides** the **intolerable** consolations of the chemist.

Money **troubles** soon began again, Monsieur Lheureux **urging** on **anew** his friend Vincart, and Charles **pledged** himself for **exorbitant** sums; for he would never **consent** to let the **smallest** of the things that had **belonged** to HER be sold. His mother was **exasperated** with him; he **grew** even more **angry** than she did. He had **altogether** changed. She left the house.

Then everyone began "taking advantage" of him. **Mademoiselle** Lempereur presented a bill for six months' **teaching**, although Emma had never taken a **lesson** (despite the receipted bill she had shown Bovary); it was an **arrangement** between the two women. The man at the **circulating** library **demanded** three years' subscriptions; Mere Rollet claimed the **postage** due for some twenty letters, and when Charles asked for an **explanation**, she had the **delicacy** to reply--

"Oh, I **don't** know. It was for her business affairs."

Spanish

altogether: todo, en conjunto.
anew: otra vez, de nuevo, nuevamente.
angry: enojado, enfadado, furioso.
arrangement: arreglo, acuerdo, construcción, disposición, orden, combinación.
belonged: Pertenecido.
besides: además, demás, además de, amén de.
circulating: circulando, circulante.
consent: aprobación, acordar, declaración, declarar, consentimiento, autorización.
delicacy: manjar, dulce, delicadeza.
demanded: demandado, exigido.
don't: no.
exasperated: exasperado.
exorbitant: exorbitante.
explanation: explicación.
gaiety: alegría.
grew: creció, pret de grow, crecida.
intolerable: intolerable.
lesson: lección.
mademoiselle: señorita.
mamma: mama.
pledged: pignorado, prometido.
postage: franqueo, porte.
smallest: menor.
teaching: enseñando, enseñanza, instruyendo, desacostumbrando.
troubles: nubes.
urging: instar.

With every debt he paid Charles thought he had come to the end of them. But others followed **ceaselessly**. He sent in accounts for **professional attendance**. He was shown the letters his wife had written. Then he had to apologise.

Felicite now wore Madame Bovary's gowns; not all, for he had kept some of them, and he went to look at them in her **dressing**-room, **locking** himself up there; she was about her height, and often Charles, seeing her from behind, was seized with an **illusion**, and cried out--

"Oh, stay, stay!"

But at Whitsuntide she ran away from Yonville, carried off by Theodore, **stealing** all that was left of the **wardrobe**.

It was about this time that the widow Dupuis had the honour to inform him of the "marriage of Monsieur Leon Dupuis her son, **notary** at Yvetot, to Mademoiselle Leocadie Leboeuf of Bondeville." Charles, among the other **congratulations** he sent him, wrote this sentence--

"How glad my poor wife would have been!"

One day when, **wandering aimlessly** about the house, he had gone up to the **attic**, he felt a **pellet** of fine paper under his **slipper**. He opened it and read: "Courage, Emma, courage. I would not bring misery into your life." It was Rodolphe's letter, fallen to the ground between the boxes, where it had remained, and that the wind from the **dormer** window had just **blown** towards the door. And Charles stood, **motionless** and staring, in the very same place where, long ago, Emma, in **despair**, and paler even than he, had thought of dying. At last he discovered a small R at the bottom of the second page. What did this mean? He remembered Rodolphe's attentions, his sudden, **disappearance**, his **constrained** air when they had met two or three times since. But the **respectful** tone of the letter **deceived** him.

"Perhaps they loved one another platonically," he said to himself.

Besides, Charles was not of those who go to the bottom of things; he **shrank** from the **proofs**, and his vague **jealousy** was lost in the **immensity** of his **woe**.

Spanish

aimlessly: sin objeto, sin propósito fijo.
attendance: asistencia, servicio.
attic: desván, ático, buhardilla.
blown: soplado, hinchado, estropeado, jadeante, insípido, pp de blow.
ceaselessly: continuamente.
congratulations: enhorabuena, felicidades.
constrained: encogido.
deceived: engañado.

despair: desesperación.
disappearance: desaparición.
dormer: claraboya, dormitorio, buhardilla.
dressing-room: camerino, camarino, camarín.
illusion: ilusión, espejismo.
immensity: inmensidad.
jealousy: celos.
locking: bloqueo.
motionless: inmóvil, estático.
notary: notario, escribano.

pellet: pelotilla, bolita, perdigón, píldora.
professional: profesional.
proofs: testigos.
respectful: respetuoso.
shrank: pret de shrink.
slipper: zapatilla, pantufla.
stealing: hurto, taking, robando.
wandering: errante, vagando.
wardrobe: armario, guardarropa, armario ropero, ropero, vestuario.
woe: ay, penas.

Everyone, he thought, must have **adored** her; all men **assuredly** must have **coveted** her. She seemed but the more beautiful to him for this; he was seized with a lasting, furious desire for her, that **inflamed** his despair, and that was **boundless**, because it was now unrealisable.

To please her, as if she were still living, he **adopted** her **predilections**, her ideas; he bought patent leather boots and took to wearing white cravats. He put **cosmetics** on his moustache, and, like her, signed notes of hand. She **corrupted** him from beyond the grave.

He was obliged to sell his silver piece by piece; next he sold the drawing-room furniture. All the rooms were **stripped**; but the bedroom, her own room, remained as before. After his dinner Charles went up there. He pushed the round table in front of the fire, and drew up her armchair. He sat down opposite it. A candle burnt in one of the **gilt candlesticks**. Berthe by his side was **painting prints**.

He suffered, poor man, at seeing her so **badly** dressed, with laceless boots, and the arm-holes of her **pinafore** torn down to the hips; for the **charwoman** took no care of her. But she was so sweet, so pretty, and her little head bent forward so **gracefully**, letting the dear fair hair fall over her rosy cheeks, that an infinite joy came upon him, a happiness **mingled** with bitterness, like those ill-made wines that taste of **resin**. He **mended** her **toys**, made her puppets from cardboard, or **sewed** up half-torn dolls. Then, if his eyes fell upon the workbox, a ribbon lying about, or even a pin left in a crack of the table, he began to dream, and looked so sad that she became as sad as he.

No one now came to see them, for Justin had run away to Rouen, where he was a grocer's **assistant**, and the **druggist's** children saw less and less of the child, Monsieur Homais not caring, seeing the difference of their social position, to **continue** the intimacy.

The blind man, whom he had not been able to cure with the **pomade**, had gone back to the hill of Bois-Guillaume, where he told the travellers of the vain attempt of the druggist, to such an extent, that Homais when he went to town hid himself behind the curtains of the "Hirondelle" to avoid meeting him. He

Spanish

adopted: adoptado, adoptivo, prohijado.
adored: adorado.
assistant: asistente, ayudante, auxiliar.
assuredly: ciertamente.
badly: mal, malamente.
boundless: ilimitado.
candlesticks: candelabros.
charwoman: asistenta.
continue: continuar, continúe, continuad, continuáis, continuamos, continúan, continúas, continúen,

continúo, continúa, durar.
corrupted: corrompido.
cosmetics: cosméticos.
coveted: codiciado.
druggist: droguero.
gilt: dorado.
gracefully: graciosamente, desenvueltamente, elegantemente, gallardamente, airosamente.
inflamed: inflamado.
mended: Mejorado.
mingled: mezclado, triscado.

painting: pintura, cuadro, la pintura, pintar.
pinafore: falda con peto, pichi, delantal.
pomade: pomada.
predilections: predilecciones.
prints: huellas dactilares.
resin: resina.
sewed: pret de sew, cosido.
stripped: pelado, desarmado, desencofrado.
toys: juguetes.

detested him, and wishing, in the interests of his own reputation, to get rid of him at all costs, he **directed** against him a secret **battery**, that betrayed the depth of his intellect and the baseness of his vanity. Thus, for six consecutive months, one could read in the "Fanal de Rouen" **editorials** such as these--

"All who bend their steps towards the fertile plains of Picardy have, no doubt, remarked, by the Bois-Guillaume hill, a wretch suffering from a horrible **facial** wound. He **importunes**, persecutes one, and levies a regular tax on all travellers. Are we still living in the monstrous times of the Middle Ages, when vagabonds were permitted to **display** in our public places **leprosy** and scrofulas they had brought back from the Crusades?"

Or--

"In spite of the laws against **vagabondage**, the approaches to our great towns continue to be **infected** by bands of beggars. Some are seen going about alone, and these are not, perhaps, the least dangerous. What are our ediles about?"

Then Homais invented anecdotes--

"Yesterday, by the Bois-Guillaume hill, a **skittish** horse--" And then followed the story of an accident caused by the presence of the blind man.

He managed so well that the fellow was locked up. But he was **released**. He began again, and Homais began again. It was a struggle. Homais won it, for his **foe** was condemned to life-long confinement in an **asylum**.

This success **emboldened** him, and henceforth there was no longer a dog run over, a barn burnt down, a woman beaten in the parish, of which he did not immediately inform the public, guided always by the love of progress and the hate of priests. He **instituted** comparisons between the **elementary** and **clerical** schools to the **detriment** of the latter; called to mind the **massacre** of St. **Bartholomew** a **propos** of a grant of one hundred francs to the church, and **denounced abuses**, aired new **views**. That was his phrase. Homais was **digging** and **delving**; he was becoming dangerous.

However, he was stifling in the narrow **limits** of **journalism**, and soon a book, a work was necessary to him. Then he composed "General Statistics of the

---

Spanish

abuses: abusa.
asylum: asilo, refugio.
bartholomew: Bartolomé.
battery: batería, pila, acumulador.
clerical: de eclesiástico, clerical, concerniente a tareas administrativas o de oficina, de clérigo, de clero, de oficina, oficinista, oficinesco.
delving: cavando, cavar.
denounced: denunciado, delatado.
detriment: detrimento, perjuicio.
digging: cavando.
directed: dirigido.
display: pantalla, exhibición, visualización, exponer, exposición, desplegar.
editorials: artículo de fondo.
elementary: elemental.
emboldened: animado.
facial: facial.
foe: enemigo.
importunes: importuna.
infected: infectado, inficionado, contagiado.
instituted: instituido.
journalism: periodismo.
leprosy: lepra.
limits: límites.
massacre: masacre, matanza.
propos: propósito.
released: liberado.
skittish: caprichoso, frívolo, nervioso, asustadizo.
vagabondage: bordoneria, vagabundeo, vagabundaje.
views: Vistas, puntos de vista.

Canton of Yonville, followed by Climatological Remarks." The statistics drove him to philosophy. He busied himself with great questions: the social problem: moralisation of the poorer classes, **pisciculture, caoutchouc, railways,** etc. He even began to **blush** at being a bourgeois. He affected the artistic style, he smoked. He bought two chic Pompadour statuettes to **adorn** his drawing-room.

He by no means gave up his shop. On the contrary, he kept well abreast of new discoveries. He followed the great movement of **chocolates**; he was the first to introduce "cocoa" and "revalenta" into the Seine-Inferieure. He was **enthusiastic** about the **hydro**-electric Pulvermacher chains; he wore one himself, and when at night he took off his flannel vest, Madame Homais stood quite **dazzled** before the golden spiral beneath which he was hidden, and felt her **ardour redouble** for this man more **bandaged** than a Scythian, and splendid as one of the Magi.

He had fine ideas about Emma's tomb. First he proposed a broken **column** with some **drapery**, next a pyramid, then a Temple of Vesta, a sort of **rotunda**, or else a "mass of ruins." And in all his plans Homais always stuck to the weeping **willow**, which he looked upon as the indispensable symbol of sorrow.

Charles and he made a journey to Rouen together to look at some tombs at a funeral furnisher's, accompanied by an artist, one Vaufrylard, a friend of Bridoux's, who made puns all the time. At last, after having examined some hundred **designs**, having ordered an **estimate** and made another journey to Rouen, Charles decided in **favour** of a **mausoleum**, which on the two principal sides was to have a "spirit bearing an **extinguished** torch."

As to the inscription, Homais could think of nothing so fine as Sta viator, and he got no further; he **racked** his brain, he constantly repeated Sta viator. At last he hit upon Amabilen conjugem calcas, which was adopted.

A strange thing was that Bovary, while continually thinking of Emma, was forgetting her. He grew desperate as he felt this image fading from his memory in spite of all efforts to **retain** it. Yet every night he dreamt of her; it was always the same dream. He drew near her, but when he was about to clasp her she fell into decay in his arms.

Spanish

adorn: decorar, decora, decoren, decore, decoras, decoran, decoramos, decoráis, decoro, decorad, adornar.
ardour: exaltación, vehemencia, entusiasmo, ardor.
bandaged: vendado, venda.
blush: ruborizarse, rubor.
caoutchouc: caucho, logro de caucho.
chocolates: bombones.
column: columna.
dazzled: deslumbrado.
designs: diseños.

drapery: pañería.
enthusiastic: entusiasmado, entusiasta.
estimate: estimar, estiman, estimen, estimad, estimas, estimamos, estimáis, estimo, estime, estima, presupuesto.
extinguished: apagado, extinguido.
favour: favor, favorecer.
hydro-electric: Hidroeléctrico.
mausoleum: mausoleo.
pisciculture: piscicultura.

racked: atormentado.
railways: ferrocarriles, valores de ferrocarriles.
redouble: redoblar, redoble, redoblad, redoblo, redoblen, redoblas, redoblan, redobláis, redobla, redoblamos, reduplicar.
retain: retener, retenga, retenéis, retengo, retienes, retienen, retiene, retenemos, reten, retened, retengan.
rotunda: rotonda.
willow: sauce.

For a week he was seen going to church in the evening. Monsieur Bournisien even paid him two or three visits, then gave him up. Moreover, the old fellow was growing **intolerant, fanatic**, said Homais. He **thundered** against the spirit of the age, and never failed, every other week, in his sermon, to **recount** the death agony of Voltaire, who died **devouring** his excrements, as everyone knows.

In spite of the **economy** with which Bovary lived, he was far from being able to pay off his old debts. Lheureux refused to renew any more bills. A **distraint** became **imminent**. Then he **appealed** to his mother, who consented to let him take a **mortgage** on her property, but with a great many recriminations against Emma; and in return for her sacrifice she asked for a shawl that had escaped the **depredations** of Felicite. Charles refused to give it her; they **quarrelled**.

She made the first overtures of **reconciliation** by offering to have the little girl, who could help her in the house, to live with her. Charles consented to this, but when the time for parting came, all his courage failed him. Then there was a **final**, complete **rupture**.

As his affections vanished, he clung more closely to the love of his child. She made him anxious, however, for she **coughed** sometimes, and had red spots on her cheeks.

Opposite his house, flourishing and merry, was the family of the chemist, with whom everything was **prospering**. **Napoleon** helped him in the laboratory, Athalie embroidered him a **skullcap**, Irma cut out rounds of paper to cover the preserves, and Franklin **recited** Pythagoras' table in a breath. He was the happiest of fathers, the most fortunate of men.

Not so! A secret ambition **devoured** him. Homais **hankered** after the cross of the Legion of Honour. He had **plenty** of **claims** to it.

"First, having at the time of the cholera distinguished myself by a **boundless** devotion; second, by having **published**, at my expense, various works of public **utility**, such as" (and he recalled his **pamphlet** entitled, "Cider, its **manufacture** and effects," besides observation on the lanigerous plant-louse, sent to the Academy; his volume of statistics, and down to his pharmaceutical thesis);

Spanish

appealed: Apelado.
boundless: ilimitado.
claims: concesiones, demandas, reivindicaciones.
coughed: Tosido.
depredations: estragos.
devoured: devorado.
devouring: devorando.
distraint: traba de ejecución, detención, embargo, secuestro, secuestro de bienes.
economy: economía.

fanatic: fanático, el fanático.
final: final, último.
hankered: ansiado.
imminent: inminente.
intolerant: intolerante.
manufacture: fabricar, fabrique, fabrico, fabricas, fabricáis, fabriquen, fabricad, fabrica, fabrican, fabricamos, fabricación.
mortgage: hipoteca, hipotecar.
napoleon: Napoleón.
pamphlet: folleto, panfleto.

plenty: lleno.
prospering: prosperando.
published: publicado.
quarrelled: peleado.
recited: recitado.
reconciliation: conciliación, reconciliación.
recount: recuento.
rupture: ruptura, rotura, quebradura.
skullcap: solideo, casquete, gorro.
thundered: Tronado.
utility: utilidad.

"without counting that I am a **member** of several **learned** societies" (he was member of a single one).

"In short!" he cried, making a **pirouette**, "if it were only for **distinguishing** myself at fires!"

Then Homais inclined towards the Government. He secretly did the **prefect** great service during the **elections**. He sold himself--in a word, **prostituted** himself. He even addressed a **petition** to the sovereign in which he **implored** him to "do him justice"; he called him "our good king," and compared him to Henri IV.

And every morning the **druggist** rushed for the paper to see if his **nomination** were in it. It was never there. At last, unable to bear it any longer, he had a grass **plot** in his garden **designed** to **represent** the Star of the Cross of Honour with two little strips of grass running from the top to **imitate** the ribband. He walked round it with folded arms, **meditating** on the folly of the Government and the **ingratitude** of men.

From respect, or from a sort of **sensuality** that made him carry on his investigations slowly, Charles had not yet opened the secret drawer of a **rosewood** desk which Emma had generally used. One day, however, he sat down before it, turned the key, and pressed the spring. All Leon's letters were there. There could be no doubt this time. He **devoured** them to the very last, **ransacked** every corner, all the furniture, all the drawers, behind the walls, sobbing, crying aloud, distraught, mad. He found a box and broke it open with a **kick**. Rodolphe's portrait flew full in his face in the midst of the overturned love-letters.

People wondered at his **despondency**. He never went out, saw no one, refused even to visit his patients. Then they said "he shut himself up to drink."

Sometimes, however, some curious person **climbed** on to the garden hedge, and saw with amazement this long-bearded, **shabbily clothed**, wild man, who wept aloud as he walked up and down.

Spanish

climbed: Subido.
clothed: vestido.
designed: diseñado, demostrado.
despondency: desaliento.
devoured: devorado.
distinguishing: distinguiendo.
druggist: droguero.
elections: elecciones.
imitate: imitar, imite, imito, imitamos, imitas, imitáis, imitan, imitad, imita, imiten.
implored: implorado, suplicado.

ingratitude: ingratitud.
kick: patada, patear, puntapié, cocear, dar patadas, coz.
learned: aprendido, estudiado, docto, erudito, sabio.
meditating: meditando.
member: miembro, partidario, socio.
nomination: nominación.
petition: petición.
pirouette: pirueta.
plot: parcela, trama, argumento, complot, gráfico, solar, trazar.

prefect: monitor, prefecto.
prostituted: prostituido.
ransacked: saqueado.
represent: representar, represente, representad, representáis, representamos, representan, representas, representen, represento, representa, reproducir.
rosewood: palisandro, palosanto, palo de rosa.
sensuality: sensualidad.
shabbily: andrajosamente.

In the evening in summer he took his little girl with him and led her to the cemetery. They came back at **nightfall**, when the only light left in the Place was that in Binet's window.

The **voluptuousness** of his grief was, however, **incomplete**, for he had no one near him to share it, and he paid visits to Madame Lefrancois to be able to speak of her.

But the **landlady** only listened with half an ear, having troubles like himself. For Lheureux had at last **established** the "Favorites du Commerce," and Hivert, who enjoyed a great reputation for doing errands, insisted on a rise of **wages**, and was threatening to go over "to the **opposition** shop."

One day when he had gone to the market at Argueil to sell his horse--his last resource--he met Rodolphe.

They both turned pale when they caught sight of one another. Rodolphe, who had only sent his **card**, first **stammered** some **apologies**, then grew bolder, and even pushed his **assurance** (it was in the month of August and very hot) to the length of **inviting** him to have a bottle of **beer** at the public-house.

Leaning on the table opposite him, he **chewed** his **cigar** as he talked, and Charles was lost in **reverie** at this face that she had loved. He seemed to see again something of her in it. It was a **marvel** to him. He would have liked to have been this man.

The other went on talking agriculture, cattle, **pasturage**, filling out with **banal** phrases all the gaps where an **allusion** might slip in. Charles was not listening to him; Rodolphe noticed it, and he followed the succession of memories that crossed his face. This gradually grew redder; the nostrils **throbbed** fast, the lips **quivered**. There was at last a moment when Charles, full of a **sombre** fury, fixed his eyes on Rodolphe, who, in something of fear, stopped talking. But soon the same look of weary **lassitude** came back to his face.

"I **don't blame** you," he said.

Rodolphe was dumb. And Charles, his head in his hands, went on in a broken voice, and with the resigned **accent** of infinite sorrow--

Spanish

accent: acento, acentuar, acentúan, acentúas, acentúo, acentúen, acentuáis, acentuad, acentúa, acentúe, acentuamos.
allusion: alusión.
apologies: disculpas aceptadas, disculpas.
assurance: garantía, convicción, aseguramiento.
banal: trivial, banal.
beer: cerveza, la cerveza.
blame: culpa, reprender, valorar en,

reprobar, culpar.
card: tarjeta, carta, ficha.
chewed: masticado.
cigar: cigarro, puro, el puro, el cigarro, cigarro puro.
don't: no.
established: establecido, edificado.
incomplete: incompleto.
inviting: invitando.
landlady: arrendadora, casera, dueña, patrona, propietaria, propietaria de una vivienda, ama.

lassitude: lasitud.
marvel: maravilla, asombrarse.
nightfall: anochecer.
opposition: oposición.
pasturage: pasto, pastoreo.
quivered: temblado.
reverie: ensueño.
sombre: sombrío.
stammered: tartamudeó.
throbbed: Latido.
voluptuousness: voluptuosidad.
wages: salario.

"No, I **don't** blame you now."

He even added a fine phrase, the only one he ever made--

"It is the fault of **fatality**!"

Rodolphe, who had managed the fatality, thought the **remark** very **offhand** from a man in his position, **comic** even, and a little mean.

The next day Charles went to sit down on the seat in the **arbour**. Rays of light were **straying** through the **trellis**, the **vine** leaves threw their shadows on the sand, the **jasmines perfumed** the air, the **heavens** were blue, Spanish **flies buzzed** round the lilies in **bloom**, and Charles was **suffocating** like a youth beneath the vague love influences that filled his **aching** heart.

At seven o'clock little Berthe, who had not seen him all the afternoon, went to **fetch** him to dinner.

His head was thrown back against the wall, his eyes closed, his mouth open, and in his hand was a long **tress** of black hair.

"Come along, papa," she said.

And thinking he wanted to play; she pushed him gently. He fell to the ground. He was dead.

Thirty-six hours after, at the druggist's request, Monsieur Canivet came **thither**. He made a **post**-mortem and found nothing.

When everything had been sold, twelve **francs seventy**-five centimes remained, that served to pay for Mademoiselle Bovary's going to her **grandmother**. The good woman died the same year; old Rouault was **paralysed**, and it was an **aunt** who took charge of her. She is poor, and **sends** her to a cotton-factory to earn a living.

Since Bovary's death three doctors have followed one another at Yonville without any success, so **severely** did Homais attack them. He has an enormous practice; the authorities **treat** him with consideration, and public opinion **protects** him.

He has just received the cross of the Legion of Honour.

Spanish

aching: dolor, que duele.
arbour: cenador, emparrado.
aunt: tía.
bloom: flor, florecer, veladura, floración, florecimiento.
buzzed: Zumbado.
comic: cómico, comer.
don't: no.
fatality: fatalidad.
fetch: traer, traemos, traed, trae, traéis, traes, traigo, traigan, traen, traiga, coger.

flies: vuela.
francs: francos.
grandmother: abuela, la abuela.
heavens: cielo, cielos.
jasmines: jazmines.
offhand: de improviso.
paralysed: encadenado, paralizado.
perfumed: perfumado.
post-mortem: después de la muerte.
protects: protégé.
remark: comentario, observación, reparo, censura, nota, notar.

sends: envía, manda, despacha.
seventy-five: setenta y cinco.
severely: severamente.
straying: extravío, desviar.
suffocating: sofocando, sofocante, ahogándose, asfixiar.
thirty-six: treinta y seis.
thither: allá.
treat: tratar, curar, obsequio.
trellis: caballete, espaldera, enrejado.
tress: trenza.
vine: parra, viña, vid.

GLOSSARY

abbe: abate
abominable: abominable, horrible, horroroso
abominably: abominablemente
abreast: de frente, caminar cuatro de frente
abscess: absceso
absent-minded: distraído
absents: ausentes
absinthe: ajenjo, absenta
abstained: se abstenido, abstinente
abundantly: abundantemente
abuses: abusa
abyss: abismo, despeñadero, precipicio
abysses: abismos
acacia: acacia
academies: academias
accede: acceder, accedéis, accedes, accedo, accedemos, accede, accedan, acceden, acceded, acceda, acordar
accomplish: realizar, realizad, realizo, realizáis, realice, realicen, realizan, realiza, realizamos, realizas, lograr
accomplishes: realiza
accomplishments: triunfos
according: conforme, de acuerdo con
accosted: abordado
accuse: acusar, acusamos, acuso, acusen, acusan, acusáis, acusad, acusa, acusas, acuse, denunciar
accustom: acostumbrar, acostumbren, acostumbran, acostumbro, acostumbras, acostumbráis, acostumbrad, acostumbra, acostumbramos, acostumbre, habituar
accustomed: acostumbrado
ache: doler, dolor, desear
achilles: Aquiles
aching: dolor, que duele
acorns: bellotas
acquaintances: conocidos
actresses: actrices
adapting: adaptando
addled: podrido, zote

adieu: adiós
adjudicator: juez
administering: administrando
admirably: admirablemente
admiring: admirando
ado: ruido
adorable: cute, adorable
adore: adorar, adoran, adoren, adore, adoro, adoras, adoramos, adoráis, adora, adorad
adored: adorado
adorn: decorar, decora, decoren, decore, decoras, decoran, decoramos, decoráis, decoro, decorad, adornar
adorned: adornado, decorado
adorning: decorando
adulterous: adúltero
adultery: adulterio
afar: lejos
affectionate: afectuoso, zalamero, mimoso, cariñoso, amante
affinities: n - afinidades -f
affirm: afirmar, confirmar, confirmad, afirmamos, confirme, confirmas, confirman, confirmen, confirmamos, confirmo, confirmáis
affirmative: afirmativo
afflict: afligir, afligís, aflijan, afligimos, afligid, afliges, afligen, aflige, aflijo, aflija, entristecer
afflicted: afligido
affords: produce
afresh: de nuevo, otra vez
agitated: agitado, inquieto
agriculturist: agricultor
aimless: sin objeto
aimlessly: sin objeto, sin propósito fijo
airs: aires
aisles: pasillos
alcove: alcoba, nicho
algerian: argelino
alienated: alienado, enajenado
alienates: aliena, enajena
alighted: Bajado
alleging: alegando

all-embracing: global, omnímodo
alleviate: aliviar, aliviáis, alivias, alivien, aliviamos, alivia, alivian, aliviad, alivio, alivie
alleviation: alivio
alleys: paseos
alluded: Aludido
allusion: alusión
almonds: almendras
almond-shaped: almendrado
aloof: apartado
alternated: polarización alternada
alternately: por rotación, alternadamente, alternamente, alternantemente, alternativamente, eventualmente
amadou: yesca
amber: ámbar, ámbar amarillo, ambarino
ambled: Andado
ambrose: ambrosio
ambush: emboscada, acecho
amelioration: mejora
amiable: amistoso, amable
amiably: amablemente
amicably: amistosamente, amigablemente
ammonia: amoníaco, amoniaco
amorous: amoroso
amorously: amorosamente, tiernamente
amphitheatre: anfiteatro
amputated: amputado
amputation: amputación
amuse: divertir, diviértete, diviértase, diviértanse, divértidos, me divierto, nos divertimos, os divertís, se divierte, se divierten, te diviertes
amuses: se divierte, entretiene
anchored: anclado
ancients: antiguo
andalusian: andaluz
anecdote: anécdota
anew: otra vez, de nuevo, nuevamente
angelica: angélica
angelus: ángelus

angered: enojado
annihilated: aniquilado, anonadado
annoy: molestar, molestad, molestáis, molestamos, molestan, molestas, molesten, moleste, molesto, molesta, enfadar
anodyne: anodino
anomalies: Anomalías
anterior: anterior, anterior a, previo
ante-room: antesala, antecámara, vestíbulo
antidote: antídoto, contraveneno
antipathetic: antagónico, antipático, contrario, opuesto
antipathy: antipatía
antiphlogistic: antiflogístico
aphrodisiac: afrodisíaco
apiece: cada uno, por cabeza
aplomb: aplomo
apologised: disculpado
apologising: disculpar
apoplectic: apoplético
apoplexy: apoplejía
apotheosis: apoteosis
apparition: aparición
applauded: Aplaudido
approbation: aprobación
approving: aprobando, aprobar, aprobatorio
aprons: sendero
aptitude: aptitud, capacidad, disposición, talento
aqueous: acuoso
aquiline: aquilino, aguileño
arabesque: arabesco
arabian: árabe
arbour: cenador, emparrado
arbours: enramadas
arbutus: madroño
archduchess: archiduquesa
ardent: ardiente
ardently: ardientemente
ardour: exaltación, vehemencia, entusiasmo, ardor
arm-chair: sillón, butaca
aroma: olor, aroma
aromatic: aromático
aromatics: aromático
arrogantly: atorrantemente, altaneramente, altivo, altivamente, arrogantemente
arrondissement: distrito
arsenic: arsénico
arsenious: arsenioso
arteries: las arterias
artery: arteria
articulated: articulado
ascending: ascendiendo, subiendo, ascendente, escalando
ascension: ascensión
asparagus: espárrago
aspen: Álamo

asphalt: asfalto, asfaltar
aspired: ambicionado, Aspirado
assailed: Asaltado
assassinated: asesinado
assiduously: asiduamente
assizes: Tribunal de Justicia en los Condados de Inglaterra, sesión judicial
assuredly: ciertamente
assuring: asegurando
astonish: asombrar, asombramos, asombren, asombran, asombras, asombra, asombrad, asombráis, sorprender, asombro, asombre
astounded: pasmado, pasmar, aturdir, asombrado, sorprender
astray: desencaminado
astride: a horcajadas
astuteness: astucia
asunder: separadamente
athirst: sediento
athwart: a través de
atonement: expiación
atrocious: atroz
attentive: atento
attentively: atentamente
attenuated: se atenuado
au: unidad administrativa
audaciously: atrevidamente, audazmente, osadamente
audacity: audacia
augmented: aumentado
aureole: aureola
authenticity: autenticidad
avarice: avaricia
avaricious: avaro
awaited: esperado, aguardado
awaken: despertar
awakened: despertado
awakening: despertar
awaking: Despertar
awning: toldo
awnings: toldos, entoldado
awoke: pret y pp de awake
azure: azul celeste, azur
babylon: babel, Babilonia
bacchic: báquico
baffled: confundido
baffling: confundiendo
bagpipes: gaitas, gaita
bailiff: alguacil, administrador
baker's: panadería
balconies: voladizos
bald-headed: calvo
ballads: baladas
ballroom: salón de baile
balusters: barandilla
balustrade: balaustrada, barandilla
balustrades: barandillas
banal: trivial, banal
bandage: vendaje, venda, la venda, vendar

bandaged: vendado, venda
bandaging: vendaje
bandbox: sombrerera
banish: desterrar, destierran, destierras, destierra, desterramos, desterráis, desterrad, destierren, destierre, destierro
banishing: desterrando
banister: pasamano
banisters: balaustrada
banquet: banquete, banquetear, festín
baptized: bautizado
baptizing: bautizando
barbarism: barbarismo
barcarolle: barcarola
bared: descubierto
barefoot: descalzo
barefooted: descalzo
bareheaded: descubierto
bargained: Negociado
barked: Ladrado
barking: ladrar, ladrido
barometer: barómetro
bartholomew: Bartolomé
baseness: bajeza
baskets: las cestas
basque: vasco, vascuence
bathed: se bañado
battalion: batallón
beadle: bedel
beaming: radiante, brillante
bearable: soportable
beardless: imberbe
bearer: portador
bearers: apoyos
bearskin: piel de oso
beasts: ganado
beatitude: beatitud
beautifying: embelleciendo
beaver: castor
bedclothes: ropa de cama
bed-clothes: ropa de la cama
bedstead: camita, armadura de la cama
beehive: colmena
beggar: mendigo, pordiosero
begging: mendicidad, mendigando, mendigar
begotten: engendrado
begrudged: deplorado
behold: tenga
belabouring: apaleando
belated: tardío
belched: Eructado
belfry: campanario
bellowing: bramar
bellows: fuelle, fuelles
bell-shaped: aboquillado, encampanado, campanudo, campaniforme, acampanado
belongings: pertenencias
bender: dobladora, juerga, mierda

benefactions: donaciones
benefactor: bienhechor
bengal: Bengala
benignity: benignidad
benumbed: embotado, congelado,
  entumecido
benzine: bencina
berries: bayas
besotted: atontado, embriagado,
  entontecido
bespoken: indicado, pp de bespeak
besprinkled: Salpicado
betraying: traicionando
betrothed: desposado, prometido
bewailed: Lamentado
bewildering: desconcertando,
  desconcierto
bewitching: embrujando, fascinante
bidden: pp de bid
bier: féretro, andas
bigot: intolerante, fanático
bigoted: intolerante
bilious: bilioso
billiard: billar
billycock: hongo
bindings: enlaces, vinculaciones
birdlike: como un pajarito, pajaril
bisque: Biscocho, bizcocho, sopa de
  mariscos, helado de avellana,
  ventajas, porcelana blanca
blackberries: zarzamoras
blandishments: halagos
bleating: Balando
bled: Sangrado
bleed: sangrar, sangras, sangrad,
  sangráis, sangran, sangra, sangren,
  sangro, sangramos, sangre
blended: mezclado
blending: mezcla
blinding: deslumbrante,
  deslumbrando, deslumbramiento,
  esparcido de gravilla
blindness: ceguera
blinds: deslumbra, persianas
blinking: intermitente, parpadear,
  parpadeo
bliss: beatitud
blockheads: tonto
blood-letting: sangría
bloodshot: encarnizado, inyectado en
  sangre, inyectado de sangre,
  sanguinolento
blossom: flor, florecer, lozanía
blotting: oreo, secar
blouses: blusas
bluish: azulado
blundered: Pifiado
blush: ruborizarse, rubor
blushed: enrojecido
blushing: ruborizado, rubor
boarded: Abordar
boarder: huésped, pupilo,

pensionista, interno
boarding: embarque, entablado,
  abordaje
boasted: Jactado
boatman: barquero
bodice: corpiño, cuerpo
boldly: audazmente
boldness: intrepidez
bonfires: fogatas
bonnes: niñeras
bonnet: capot, capó, gorro, capota
bonnets: cabezal, gorras
bony: óseo, huesudo
bookcase: librería, estante para libros,
  armario para libros, biblioteca, el
  estante de libros
bookseller: librero
boon: bendición, don
botany: botánica
bothering: fastidioso, Molestar,
  molesto
bottoms: producto de fondo
boudoir: tocador
boulevard: bulevar
boulogne: Bolonia
bounded: amordazado, saltado,
  definido, encerrado
bounding: saltar
boundless: ilimitado
bouquet: ramillete
bovine: bovino, bovina, vacuno
bowing: reverencia, toque con el
  arco, inclinar, golpes de arco
bracelets: esposas
braces: tirantes
braiding: trenzado, trenzando
branchless: sin ramas
brandished: Blandido
brat: mocoso
bravado: valentía
bravely: valientemente
bravery: valentía, el valor
bravo: bravo, olé
brawled: Peleado
brawny: musculoso
bray: rebuznar, rebuzno
brays: rebuznos
brazen: de latón, descarado
brazier: latonero, brasero
breakfasted: desayunado
breathes: respira
breathlessly: jadeantemente
breeches: calzones, pantalones
breviary: breviario
bribe: soborno, sobornar, cohecho,
  cohechar
bridal: nupcial, boda
bridle: brida, reprimir, contener,
  malleta, embridar, frenillo
briefs: braguitas
brightened: avivado, esclarecido,
  abrillantado, Aclarado

brilliance: brillo, brillantez
brim: borde, ala, baranda
broadened: Ensanchado
broadening: ensanchando
broadens: ensancha
broad-shouldered: ancho de espaldas
bronchitis: bronquitis
broomstick: palo de escoba
browsing: explorar, hojeada, examen
  rápido, examinar, navegador,
  navegar, ojear, vistazo, hojear,
  navegación, recorrido
brutality: brutalidad
brutally: brutalmente
bubbling: burbujeo
bucked: corcoveado
buckle: hebilla, abrochar, corchete
buckled: Abrochado
budge: mover, mueve, muevan,
  muevo, mueves, mueva, moved,
  movemos, movéis, mueven,
  moverse
bugbear: coco, espantajo, pesadilla
bulge: protuberancia
bulged: Sobresalido
bullied: intimidado
bumps: badén, irregularidades
bunches: coletas
buoy: boya, baliza, balizar
burnishing: bruñido, Bruñir
burrowing: excavación, hurgoneo
bursts: ráfagas
burying: enterrando
butcher's: carnicería
buttoned: abotonado, abrochado
buzzed: Zumbado
buzzing: zumbido
cabbages: coles
cackled: Cacareó
cactus: cacto, el cacto
cactuses: cactos
cadaverous: cadavérico
cadence: cadencia
cadet: cadete
cages: jaulas
calamities: calamidades
calico: calicó
calmed: calmado
calming: calmante
calumniated: calumniado
calumny: calumnia
cambric: batista
camphor: alcanfor
canary: canario
candelabra: candelabro
candid: franco, sincero
candidature: candidatura
candied: confitado, acaramelado
candle-light: luz de una vela
candlestick: candelero
candlesticks: candelabros
candour: sinceridad, franqueza,

candor
canes: bastones
cannibal: caníbal
cannot: presente de no poder
can't: no puede
cantharides: cantárida
canton: cantón
caoutchouc: caucho, logro de caucho
capers: alcaparras
capillarity: capilaridad
capricious: caprichoso
captivated: cautivado
captive: cautivo
capuchin: capucho, gestos de
capucho, capuchino, aspecto de
capucho, acciones de capucho,
hombre capucho, persona capucha
carabine: fusil
carabineer: carabinero, soldado de
fusil, soldado con fusil
carbine: carabina
carcass: cadáver, canal
carelessly: descuidadamente, sin
cuidado
carelessness: descuido
caress: acariciar, caricia
caressed: Cariciado
caresses: caricias
caressing: mimoso, zalamero
careworn: agobiado por los cuidados
carp: carpa
carts: carretillas
carve: tallar, tallad, talláis, tallamos,
tallan, tallas, tallen, tallo, labrar,
talle, talla
cascades: cascadas
cashmere: cachemira
cask: tonel, barrica, barril, cofre de
plomo
casks: toneles
cassock: sotana
cast-iron: hierro colado
catacomb: catacumba
catalepsy: catalepsia
cataria: gatera
catarrh: catarro
catastrophe: catástrofe
catechism: catecismo
caustic: cáustico
cavalier: caballero
ceaselessly: continuamente
ceasing: cesación, parar, cesar, cese,
acabar
celebrity: celebridad
celestial: celeste, celestial
celibacy: celibato
censure: censurar, reprobación,
criticar, desaprobación
cent: centavo, céntimo, centésima, el
centavo
centered: centrado
centime: céntimo

certify: certificar, certifica,
certifiquen, certifico, certificas,
certifican, certificamos, certificáis,
certificad, certifique, acreditar
cessation: cese
chaff: barcia, paja menuda, paja, lo
barcia, hollejo, granzas, de barcia,
cortar, cascabillo, burlar, bagazo
chaise: coche postal
champ: mordisquear
chancel: presbiterio
chanting: cantar
chapels: iglesias
chaps: rajar, resquebrajar, quijada,
muchacho, grieta, carrillo, agrietar,
zajones
characterises: caracterizan
chariot: carro
charlatan: charlatán
charmed: encantado
charms: amuletos
charwoman: asistenta
chaser: perseguidor
chasm: abismo, precipicio,
despeñadero
chaste: casto
chastisement: castigo
chateau: castillo
chatted: charló
chatter: charlar, charla, castañetear,
parlotear
chattered: Parloteado
chattering: parlotear, castañetear los
dientes, charlar, parloteo, vibrar,
charla, vibración
cheapness: baratura
chemise: camisa
chemises: camisas
chemisette: camiseta
cherish: querer, quered, quieran,
quiero, quieres, quiere, quiera,
queremos, queréis, quieren, apreciar
cherished: querido
cherries: cerezas
cherry-tree: cerezo
chevalier: Caballero
chewed: masticado
chewing: masticando
chic: elegante
chicks: pollito
chickweed: pamplina
chignon: moño
childbed: parto, cama para niños
childishness: puerilidad
childlike: infantil
chilly: frío, friolero, friolento
chiming: Tocar, repique
chimneys: chimeneas
chink: grieta
chintz: zaraza
chipped: astillado
chiselled: escopleado, timado,

cincelado
chitterlings: menudos de cerdo,
mondongo
chlorine: cloro
chloroform: cloroformo
chocolates: bombones
choked: estrangulado
choker: gargantilla
choking: la obstrucción aérea,
estrangular, atragantamiento,
ahogarse
cholera: cólera
churchman: clérigo
cider: sidra, la sidra
cigar-case: cigarrera
cigars: los puros
cinders: cenizas
circulating: circulando, circulante
circumference: perímetro,
circunferencia, la circunferencia
citing: citando, mencionando
citron: cidra
clad: vestido, pret y pp de clothe
clambering: trepando, Gatear,
trepanación
clang: sonar, sonido metálico, sonido
metálico resonante, resonar,
estruendo, hacer sonar, hacer
estruendo
clapped: Aplaudido
clapper: badajo, palmoteador
clapping: aplauso, palmada,
aplausos, aplaudir, cerrar de golpe
clasp: broche
clasped: apretado, abrochado
clasping: Agarrar
clatter: martilleo
claw: garra, arañar
claws: garras
cleanliness: limpieza
clearness: claridad
clematis: clemátide
cleverly: hábilmente
climatological: climatológico
clink: tintín
clinked: Tintineado
clipped: sujetado, cortado
clod: terrón, bola
clogging: traba, obstructor, estorbar,
zueco, obstrucción, obstáculo,
estorbo, atrancar, atasco, obstruir,
atascamiento
clogs: atasca
closet: armario, gabinete, el armario,
el clóset
clothe: vestir, vestid, vistes, visten,
viste, vistan, vestís, vestimos, visto,
vista
clothed: vestido
clotted: grumoso
clover: trébol
clubfoot: pata de palo

clucking: cloqueo, cloquear
clung: pret y pp de cling
clustering: clasificación, arracimar, conglomeración
coachman: cochero
coarseness: grosería
coated: chaqueta, cuché, cubrir, cubierta, cubierto de pintura, dar una capa, grageado, mano de pintura, revistió, saburral, saco
coaxing: halagando
cob: avellano, cisne, cisne macho, cisne mancho, comer pan redondo, elote, mazorca, jaca, zuro, tusa, panoja
cocked: Montado, de tres picos, tres picos
cocoanut: coco, fruta de coco, de coco
coddle: consentir
coddled: consentido, mimado
coiffure: peinado
coliseum: coliseo
collated: intercalado
colonnade: columnata
colossal: colosal
colza: colza
coma: coma
comb: peine, peinar, el peine
combed: peinado
comets: cometas
comforted: aliviado
commended: alabado
commingled: Mezclada
commiserated: compadecido
commoner: plebeyo
commotion: escándalo, conmoción, alboroto
communicated: Comunicado
companionship: compañerismo, compañía
complexion: cutis, tez
complication: complicación
compose: componer, compongan, compongo, compones, componen, componéis, componed, compone, compon, componemos, componga
compress: comprimir, oprimir, compresa
compromised: Cedido
compromising: comprometido, comprometedor
computed: estimado, calculado, computado
conceivable: concebible
concourse: concurso
concubine: concubina
concupiscence: concupiscencia
condescended: condescendido, se dignado, Dignado
condescension: condescendencia
cones: conos
confectioner: pastelero, confitero,

repostero
confessing: confesando
confessional: confesionario
confide: confiar, confiamos, confío, confíen, confían, confiáis, confiad, confía, confías, confíe
confided: Confiado
confiding: confiando, crédulo
confinement: encierro
confines: fronteras
confounded: perplejo
confusedly: confusamente
congealed: helado, cuajado, cuajarse, coagulado, helar, cuajar, congelarse, congelar, congelado, helarse
congratulated: Felicitado, congratulado
congratulating: felicitando, congratulando
conjectures: supone
conjugate: conjugado, conjugar, conjugad, conjuguen, conjugo, conjugas, conjugan, conjugáis, conjuga, conjugamos, conjugue
conjured: conjurado
conjuring: conjurando, prestidigitación
conscientiously: escrupulosamente
conscription: alistamiento
consecrate: consagrar
consecutively: sucesivamente, consecutivamente
consented: Consentido
console: consolar, consola
consoled: Consolado
consoling: confortar, consolador, consolar, despenar, puesto de control, consola
consort: consorte
constantinople: Constantinopla
constitutions: constituciones
constrain: restringir, apretar, restringir a, reprimir, obligar, fuerce, constreñido, constreñir, obligo, reprimes, reprimen
contemplating: contemplando, meditando
contemplation: contemplación
contemptuous: despectivo, despreciativo
contemptuously: desdeñosamente
contended: Contendido
contented: contento, satisfecho
convalescence: convalecencia
conventionality: convencionalismo
convex: convexo
convulsed: Convulsionado
convulsion: convulsión
convulsively: convulsivamente
cooed: Arrullado
cooled: refrescado
coolness: frescura, calma, desapego,

frescor, frialdad, igualdad, serenidad, indiferencia
cooped: Encerrado
copiously: copiosamente
coppice: matorral
copying: copia, duplicación
coquettish: coqueta
corded: cortado, con cuerda
cordial: cordial
cordiality: cordialidad
cords: cuerdas
corduroy: pana, la pana
corking: estupendo, corcho, de primera, excelente, encorchar, taponar
cornelian: cornalina
cornfield: sembrado, maizal, campo de granos, milpa
corolla: corola
corpulence: corpulencia
corrosive: corrosivo
corrupted: corrompido
corset: corsé
coryza: rinitis
cosmetics: cosméticos
cotillion: cotillón
coughed: Tosido
coughing: tos
couldn't: no fue posible
countenance: semblante
coursing: caza de liebres
courtesan: cortesana
coveted: codiciado
coward: cobarde, el cobarde
cowardice: cobardía
cowardly: cobarde
cowered: se acurrucado, se agachado
cowherd: vaquero
crabbed: malhumorado, indescifrable, apretado
cracker: galleta salada, petardo
cracking: agrietamiento
crackled: abertal, crujido
crackling: crepitaciones
cradle: cuna, patria, horquilla, plataforma
cram: atestar, empollar, apretura, abarrotado, repaso de última hora, rellenar con, hartarse de comer, emborrar, cebar, atiborrar, atiborramiento
crammed: Atracado, hasta los topes
cramped: estrecho
cramps: grampillones, obstáculo
crape: crespón
cravat: corbata
crawled: Arrastrado, Repelado
crawling: arrastre
crayfish: cangrejo, cangrejo de río
crayon: lápiz de cera
creak: chirriar, chirrido, crujir, chirriad, chirrio, chirrien, chirrie,

chirrias, chirrian, chirriáis, chirria
creaked: chirriado
creaking: crujido, chirriando
creeps: arrastra
crescendo: crescendo
crestfallen: alicaído
crevices: grieta
crinoline: miriñaque
criticize: criticar, critique, critiquen, criticad, criticáis, criticamos, critican, critico, critica, criticas, censurar
crow: el cuervo, corneja, cuervo
crowding: hacinamiento, apiñamiento, amontonar, apiñadura, amontonamiento
crowns: coronas
crucifix: crucifijo
crumb: miga, migaja, la miga
crumble: desmoronarse, desmenuzar, derruirse
crumbled: desmenuzado, se desmoronado
crummy: lo de calidad baja, de calidad inferior, despreciable, miserable, sucio
crunched: roznado, crujido, tascado, ronzado
crupper: baticola, grupa
crushing: aplastante, aplastar, estrujado, trituración
crystalline: cristalino
cud: rumiada, bolo alimenticio, Rumia
cuirass: coraza
culpable: culposo
culprit: culpable, delincuente
cultivating: cultivando
cunning: astucia, astuto, hábil
cupid: Cupido
curate: coadjutor, cura
curbs: limita
cured: curado
curie: curio
curing: curación, curado
curiosities: curiosidades
curl: rizo, bucle, rizar, rizarse, rotacional, encrespar
curling: rizado, ensortijamiento
currants: grosellas
cursed: maldito
cursing: maldecir
curtsey: bravura, cortesía, reverencia, hacer con cortesía
cushions: cojines
cuteness: monería, gracia
cutlet: chuleta, escalope
cutlets: chuletas, milanesa
dab: lenguado, untar, palmada, toba, dar palmadas, golpecito
dabs: manos, verbos dactilares, huellas dactilares
daguerreotypes: daguerrotipos

dahlia: dalia
dainty: fino, amable, delicado, poquita
dallying: tardando
damocles: Damocles
dandy: Estupendo, Excelente, Mono, Paquete, pisaverde, Maravilloso, Raro, Soledad, elegante, de Primera, dandi
dangled: balanceado, pendido, se bamboleado, colgado
dangling: balancear, colgado, balanceando, bamboleándose, colgando, pendiendo
daresay: dicho atrevido
darken: oscurecer, oscurezca, oscurecen, oscurezco, oscurece, oscureced, oscurecéis, oscurecemos, oscurezcan, oscureces
darkening: oscureciendo
darning: zurcido
darns: zurce
dart: dardo
darting: rápido
daughter-in-law: nuera
dawdler: ocioso
daybreak: amanecer, alba
dazzle: deslumbrar, deslumbramiento
dazzled: deslumbrado
dazzling: deslumbrante
deadened: amortiguado, amortizado
deafening: ensordecedor, ensordeciendo
dearly: amorosamente
debauch: distracción, exceso, libertinaje, orgía, seducir, entregarse al vicio, divertirse por completo, corrupción, corromper, corrompa
debauchery: libertinaje
debonair: cortés
decamped: decampado
decanter: garrafa
decanting: decantándose
decayed: decrépito
decease: defunción
deceive: engañar, engaño, engañe, engaña, engañamos, engañen, engañan, engañáis, engañad, engañas, embaucar
deceived: engañado
decency: decencia
decently: como es debido
decks: engalana
declaimed: declamado, proclamado
decoction: decocción
decreed: decretado
decrees: decreta
deducted: deducido
deepened: ahondado
deerskin: piel de ciervo, de gamuza
deference: deferencia
defiled: manchado, mancillado,

desfilado, deshonrado, profanado, ensuciado
defray: costear, costeas, costead, costeen, costee, costeo, costeáis, costea, costeamos, costean, sufragar
defy: desafiar, desafiáis, desafío, desafíen, desafías, desafiamos, desafiad, desafía, desafían, desafíe
dejected: abatido, desanimado
deleterious: deletéreo
delicacies: comestibles finos
delicacy: manjar, dulce, delicadeza
delicately: delicadamente
delightfully: deleitablemente, deleitosamente, deliciosamente, encantadamente, encantado
delighting: deleitar
delirious: delirante
delirium: delirio
delving: cavando, cavar
demon: demonio
demoralised: desmoralizado
denunciations: denuncias de convenios
deplorable: lamentable, lastimoso
deploring: deplorando
depraved: depravado
depreciated: desvalorado, depreciado
depredations: estragos
depriving: privando
descending: descendiendo, bajando, descendente, descender, descendiente
deserting: desertar
desertion: deserción
desolate: desolado, desolar
despaired: desesperado
despairing: sin esperanza, desesperación, desesperado, desesperanza, desesperanzarse, desesperar
despising: despreciando
despondency: desaliento
dessert: postre, el postre
destinies: destinos
destitute: destituir, indigente
detach: destacar, destaquen, destacad, destacamos, destacan, destacas, destaco, destaque, destaca, destacáis, desprender
detain: retener, retengo, retienes, retiene, retengan, retenemos, retenéis, retened, reten, retienen, retenga
detest: detestar, detesto, detesta, detestad, detestáis, detestamos, detestan, detestas, detesten, deteste, aborrecer
detested: detestado
detesting: detestando
detriment: detrimento, perjuicio
deuce: diablo

devilish: diabólico
devotions: oraciones
devoured: devorado
devouring: devorando
devout: devoto
devoutly: devotamente, beatamente
devoutness: devoción
dew: rocío
diagonally: diagonalmente, diagonal
dictionaries: diccionarios
diffused: difundido, EXTENSIVO
diffusion: difusión
digesting: digerir
dignified: dignificado, digno
digression: digresión
dilapidated: decrépito, ruinoso
dilated: dilatado
dilettante: diletante, aficionado
diligence: diligencia
dimity: bombasí
dimmed: atenuado
dimness: lo confuso, casi obscuridad,
  debilidad, lo lerdo, semioscuridad,
  lo débil, lo sombrío, lo turbio,
  ofuscamiento, oscurecimiento,
  oscuridad
din: ruido, fragor
dine: cenar, cenáis, ceno, cenen,
  cenas, cenamos, cenad, cenan, cena,
  cene
dined: cenado
dint: esfuerzo grande, abolladura,
  abollar, abollarse, chichón, golpe,
  mellar, mella, fuerza, fuerza de
diplomatist: diplomático
dipped: mojado
dipping: mojar, mojadura, lavado,
  inmersión
directs: dirige
dirtying: ensuciando
disagreeable: desagradable
disapprove: desaprobar, desaprobas,
  desaprobo, desaprobe, desaproban,
  desaprobamos, desaprobáis,
  desaprobad, desaproba, desaproben,
  reprobar
disbursed: desembolsado
disconsolate: desconsolado
discontinued: terminado, acabado,
  anulado, discontinuado,
  discontinuado ir a, fuera de
  producción, interrumpido,
  suspendido
discord: discordia, disonancia
discounted: descontado
discouraged: espantado, desanimado
discouragement: desaliento
discreetly: discreta, discretamente,
  recatadamente
disdained: desdeñado
disdainful: desdeñoso
disdainfully: desdeñosamente,

altaneramente
diseased: enfermo
disengage: separar, desembragar
disengaged: desembarazado
disfigured: desfigurado
disgusted: inspirado aversión a,
  asqueado, disgustado, repugnado
dishonesty: deshonestidad
dishonoured: deshonrado
disillusioned: desilusionado
disillusions: desilusiona
disjointedly: desarticuladamente,
  descoyuntadamente, inconexamente
dismount: apearse, desmontar,
  desmontad, desmonta, desmonto,
  desmonten, desmonte, desmontáis,
  desmontamos, desmontan,
  desmontas
dismounted: desmontado
disordered: desarreglado,
  desconcertado en algo, trastornado,
  desordenado
disparaging: desacreditando
displeased: desagradado, disgustado
displeasing: desagradando,
  desagradable
dissected: disecado
dissecting: disecando
dissimulation: disimulación
dissolute: disoluto
dissolving: disolviendo
distasteful: desagradable
distended: distendido, estirado,
  dilatado
distract: distraer, distrae, distraed,
  distraéis, distraemos, distraen,
  distraes, distraigan, distraigo,
  distraiga, confundir
distracted: distraído
distraction: distracción
distraint: traba de ejecución,
  detención, embargo, secuestro,
  secuestro de bienes
distraught: aturrullado
dithyrambic: ditirámbico
divers: varios, diversos
divides: divide, separa, aparta,
  comparte, segrega
dizzy: mareado, vertiginoso
docile: dócil
docility: docilidad
dockyard: arsenal
dog-days: canícula
doleful: triste
domes: domos
domestics: doméstico
dominating: dominando
dominoes: el dominó
don't: no
dormer: claraboya, dormitorio,
  buhardilla
dormer-window: buharda

dormitory: dormitorio, la residencia
  universitaria
dotted: punteado
double-breasted: cruzado
doubles: juego de dobles, dobles
doublet: jubón, doblete
doublets: jubones
dove: pichón, paloma, la palomita
doves: las palomitas
downcast: abatido
dowry: dote
doze: dormitar, dormita, dormitas,
  dormito, dormiten, dormite,
  dormitamos, dormitáis, dormitad,
  dormitan, echar la siesta
dozed: dormitado
drags: arrastra, remolca
draped: cubierto, entapizado,
  tapizado, drapeado
draper: lencero, pañero
drapery: pañería
draughts: damas, juego de damas
dreaded: temido
dreamt: pret y pp de dream
dreary: triste, lúgubre, árido,
  horroroso, horrible, afligido
dregs: heces
dressing-gown: camarera
dressing-room: camerino, camarino,
  camarín
dribbled: goteado
drilled: taladró
drip: gotear, gota, goteo, gota a gota
dripping: goteo
drone: zumbido, zángano
droned: zumbó
droning: zumbando
drowning: ahogándose, el
  ahogamiento, ahogar, ahogo,
  ahogamiento
drowsy: soñoliento
druggist: droguero
drummer: tambor
drumming: envasado en bidones
drunkenness: embriaguez, ebriedad,
  borrachera
duel: duelo
duet: dúo
dumbness: mudez, tonterías
  comprensibles, estupidez
dumfounded: confundido
dung: estiércol
dungeon: mazmorra
dunghill: muladar
dupery: engaño
dwell: morar, morad, moren, moras,
  moráis, moran, moramos, mora,
  more, moro, habitar
dwells: mora
dwelt: pret de dwell, pp de dwell
dye: teñir, color, pintura, tinte,
  tintura, colorante

dyed: colorado, teñido
dyspnoea: disnea
eagerness: deseo, ansia, avidez
earnestly: seriamente
earrings: aretes, los aros, pendientes
earthly: terrenal, terrestre
eater: tener siempre buen apetito, comedero, comedor, manzana, agua
ebb: menguar, reflujo
ecchymosis: equimosis
ecclesiastic: eclesiástico
echoing: resonar
economise: economizar, guardar, economice, ahorrar, reservar
economising: economizar
editorials: artículo de fondo
effaced: borrado
effeminate: afeminado
effusion: derrame, efusión
egoistic: egoísta
egoistically: egoístamente
egotism: egotismo
egotistic: egotístico
elaborated: elaborado
elation: júbilo
elegiac: elegíaco
elevates: eleva
elm: olmo
em: ingeniero de mineras
emanated: emanado
embalmed: embalsamado
embellish: embellecer, embellezco, embellezcan, embelleces, embellecen, embellecéis, embelleced, embellece, embellecemos, embellezca, hermosear
embellished: embellecido
embers: rescoldo, ascuas, ascua
emboldened: animado
embossed: realzado, repujado, acuñado, abollonado, estampillado, abollado, realzar, abollonar, grabado en relieve
embraced: abrazado
embrasure: alféizar, Apertura, cañonera
embroider: bordar, bordad, borden, bordas, bordan, bordáis, bordamos, borda, borde, bordo
embroidered: bordado
embroidering: bordando
embroidery: bordado
emetic: emético, vomitivo
empiricism: empirismo
emptying: vaciado
encased: encajonado
encircled: rodeado
encircling: rodeando
encompassed: rodeado
encroachment: invasión, intrusión, usurpación

encrusted: incrustó
endurance: resistencia, aguante, endurancia
endured: durado, soportado
enfranchised: emancipado, franqueado, liberado, manumitido
engender: engendrar, engendran, engendramos, engendráis, engendrad, engendras, engendra, engendren, engendro, engendre, criar
engraving: grabado, grabando
engrossed: acaparado, copiado, absorbido, absorto
engulf: tragar, traguen, tragad, tragáis, tragamos, tragan, tragas, trague, traga, trago, tomar
engulfed: tragado
enlarge: ampliar, amplíe, amplía, amplíen, amplías, amplían, ampliamos, ampliáis, ampliad, amplío, agrandar
enlighten: iluminar, iluminas, ilumino, ilumine, iluminan, ilumináis, iluminad, ilumina, iluminamos, iluminen
enlightenment: esclarecimiento, ilustración
ennui: saciedad, tedio, aburrimiento, cansancio, hastío, fastido, desgano
enrage: enfurecer, enfurecerse
enrich: enriquecer, enriquecen, enriquezco, enriqueces, enriquecemos, enriquecéis, enriqueced, enriquece, enriquezcan, enriquecerse, enriquezca
enshrine: encerrar, encierran, encierren, encierre, encierras, encerramos, encerráis, encerrad, encierro, encierra
ensue: suceder, suceda, sucedes, suceden, sucedemos, sucedéis, suceded, sucede, sucedan, sucedo
entombed: sepultó
entrails: entrañas
entwined: entrelazado
enumerate: enumerar, enumerad, enumeráis, enumeramos, enumeran, enumeras, enumeren, enumero, enumera, enumere
enumerated: enumerado
enumerating: enumerando
enumeration: enumeración
envelop: enrollar, enrollad, enrolle, enrollas, enrollo, enrollan, enrollamos, enrolláis, enrolla, enrollen, envolver
enveloped: enrollado, envuelto
enviable: envidiable
envied: envidiado
epaulettes: charreteras
epigastrium: epigastrio

episcopal: episcopal
equalised: igualado
equine: equino
equipage: equipaje, equipo
ermine: armiño
erudition: erudición
espalier: espaldera
espaliered: espaldó
espaliers: espalda
esteem: estima, estimar, estimación, considerar, contemplar, aprecio, tomar en consideración, respectar, estimado
esteemed: estimado
estimation: estimación
estranged: alejado, extrañado, enajenado
eternally: eternamente
eternity: eternidad
ethereal: etéreo
ethnographic: etnográfico
eugene: Eugenio
eulogy: elogio
everlasting: eterno
evoked: evocado
exaggerating: exagerando
exaltation: exaltación
exalted: exaltado
exasperated: exasperado
exasperates: exaspera
exasperation: exasperación
excel: sobresalir, aventajar
excelled: sobrevenido, aventajado, descollado, sobresalido
excepting: excepto
exchanging: cambiar
excommunicate: excomulgar, excomulgad, excomulguen, excomulgo, excomulgas, excomulgar, excomulgáis, excomulga, excomulgamos, excomulgue
excused: excusado, dispensado
excusing: dispensar
execrable: condenable, maldito, execrable
execrated: execrado
exemplary: ejemplar
exerted: ejercido
exhalation: exhalación
exhale: exhalar, exhala, exhalen, exhale, exhalas, exhalan, exhalamos, exhalo, exhalad, exhaláis, respirar
exhaled: exhalado, espirado
exhausting: agotador
exhortations: exhortaciones
exhorted: exhortado
exhorting: exhortando
exigencies: exigencias
exorbitant: exorbitante
expands: se expande
expanse: extensión

expansive: expansivo
expatiated: explayado, espaciado
expedients: conveniente, material de circunstancias
expel: expulsar, expulsa, expulsad, expulso, expulsen, expulsas, expulsan, expulsamos, expulsáis, expulse
expired: expirado, caducado
expiring: expirando, caducando
exploding: estallando
exposition: exposición
expounding: comentando, exponiendo
extinguished: apagado, extinguido
extravagance: extravagancia, derroche
extravagant: extravagante
extremities: extremidades
extremity: extremidad, extremo, extremidades
eyeglass: ocular
eyeglasses: anteojos, ojos
eyelashes: las pestañas, pestañas
facade: fachada, frontón
facetious: jocoso, gracioso, chistoso
facets: facetas
facile: fácil, vivo
facings: vueltas, paramentos
fain: dispuesto
fainted: pasmado, desfallecido, amortecido, desmayado
fainting: desmayo, desvanecimiento
faintness: debilidad
fallals: adorno
fallow: barbecho
falseness: falsedad
falsified: falsificado
faltering: titubeando
familiarly: conocidamente, con demasiada confianza, familiarmente
famished: hambriento
fanatic: fanático, el fanático
fanatical: fanático
fanaticism: fanatismo, el fanatacismo
fancies: extravagante
fanfare: fanfarria
fanned: ventilado
fantastically: fantásticamente
far-away: lejano
farce: farsa
farewells: adiós
farinaceous: farináceo
farmed: cultivado
farmyard: corral
far-off: remoto
farrier: herrador
farthest: más lejanamente, a distancia, a lo lejos, a lo más, lejano, lejos, a la mayor distancia, más, más lejano, más lejos, remotamente
farthing: comino

fashioned: ideado
fashion-plate: figurín
fashions: modas
fasten: fijar, fije, fijas, fijan, fijamos, fijáis, fijad, fija, fijen, fijo, atar
fastened: fijado, sujetado, atado
fastidious: descontentadizo, esquilimoso, delicado, exigente, fastidioso, melindroso, de rapidez
fatality: fatalidad
fatherly: paternal, paternalmente
fathomless: insondable
fatigued: fatigado, rendido
fatten: engordar, engordan, engordo, engorden, engordas, engordamos, engordáis, engordad, engorda, engorde
fattened: engordado
fattens: engorda
fatter: más gordo
fatty: graso, gordo, grueso, adiposo
favorite: favorito, preferido
fawn: cervato
fearing: por miedo a, por temor a, temer
fearless: intrépido, arrojado
feathered: emplumado
feebly: blandenguemente, enfermizamente, enclenquemente, débilmente
felicity: felicidad
feline: felino
felled: truncado, derribado, desanimado, cortado
fenced: cercado
fender: guardabarros, parachoques
fermentation: fermentación
ferocious: feroz
fervour: celo
festivity: festividad
fete: celebración, festejar, festejo, fiesta
fetes: fiestas
fetuses: fetos
feuilleton: folletín
feverish: febril, afiebrado
fichu: pañuelo
fiddle: violín
fiddler: violinista
fidget: estar inquieto, agitarse
fidgeting: manoseando, meneando
fifty-eight: cincuenta y ocho, cincuenta y ocho
fifty-four: cincuenta y cuatro, cincuenta y cuatro
fifty-three: cincuenta y tres, cincuenta y tres
figuring: figurar, computación
fineness: ley, fineza, finura
fingering: tecleo, digitación, tocar
fir: abeto
fireside: hogar, chimenea

fireworks: fuegos artificiales, pirotecnia
firmness: firmeza
fisherman: pescador, el pescador
fishmonger: pescadero
fissure: hendidura, fisura, grieta
fitfully: irregularmente, espasmódicamente
fixedly: fijamente
flabby: flojo, flácido, fláccido
flanders: Flandes
flanked: flanqueado
flannel: franela, la franela
flannels: pantalones de franela
flapped: batido
flapping: batir, aleteo, aleteador
flared: acampanado
flaring: abocinado
flashes: bocadillos, intermitentes
flatly: terminantemente, sosamente, aplastadamente, categóricamente, chatamente, desentonadamente, desinfladamente, lisamente, llanamente, planamente, rotundamente
flattened: aplanado
flattered: adulado
flattering: adulando, adulador
flax: lino
fleeces: vellones
fleeing: huyendo
flemish: flamenco
fleshly: carnudo, carna, carnal, carnoso
fleshy: carnoso
flickered: parpadeó
fling: arrojado, tiro, tirar, lanzar, lanzamiento, lanza, lance, echar al suelo, echar, echada, aventura amorosa
flip: capirotazo, poco serio, invertir, echar de un capirotazo, arrojar, Voltear, tablero flipchart, girar
flitted: aleteado, revoloteado, revoloteó
flocking: flocado, congregar
flooring: embaldosar, puesto, enlosar, fondo del mar, material para pisos, pavimentación, embaldosado, enladrillar, revestimiento del suelo, plan, pisos
florentine: florentino
florid: florido
flounce: salir enfadado, volante, moverse torpemente, sacudida
flounced: sacudido
flounces: sacudidas
flourished: florecido
flourishing: floreciendo, floreciente
flowed: fluido
flute: flauta
flutter: aletear, vibración, centelleo

fluttered: revoloteado
fluttering: revolotear
foal: potro, potra
foals: potrillos
foe: enemigo
folding: plegable
folks: gente
fonts: fuentes
footbath: baño de pies
footboard: plancha de vuelo, estribo, pie de la cama, plataforma, campo de pie
footstool: escabel
foot-warmer: calientapiés
fops: petimetres
foraging: adentrándose
forbade: pret de forbid, entredicho, prohibió
forbid: prohibir, prohibid, prohiban, prohibo, prohibimos, prohibes, prohiben, prohibe, prohibís, prohiba
forbidding: prohibiendo, prohibitivo
fore: frente, delantero
foresaw: pret de foresee, previo
foreseeing: previendo
foresight: previsión
forge: forjar, falsificar, forja, fraguar, inventar
forges: falsifica
forks: bifurcarse, horquillas, tenedor
forlorn: abandonado, desamparado
formulating: formulando
forty-six: cuanrenta y seis, cuarenta y seis, quarenta y seis
forty-three: cuarenta y tres, curenta y tres
foundered: hundido
fowl: gallina, aves, ave
fracture: fractura, fracturar
fractures: fracturas, las fracturas
fragrant: fragante, oloroso
frankness: franqueza
fraternal: fraternal
fraternise: fraternice
frayed: raído
frenzy: frenesí
frequented: frecuentado, asendereado
freshening: refrescando
fresher: estudiante de primer año, fresco, mechón, novato, nuevo, puro, tierno
freshness: frescura
fretted: preocupado
friable: friable
fribourg: Friburgo
fried: frito
frightful: espantoso, horrible
frilled: volado
frills: adornos, volantes
frivolous: frívolo, hueco
fro: atrás, allá

frock: vestido, hábito
froth: espuma
frothed: espumar
frowning: ceñudo
frowningly: ceñudamente
full-blown: episodio completo
fullness: plenitud
fulminating: fulminando
fumigation: fumigación
fuming: fumante, humear, humo
funnel: embudo
furnish: amueblar, amueblas, amueblen, amueblo, amueble, amueblamos, amuebláis, amuebla, amueblan, amueblad, suministrar
furnishes: amuebla
furs: pieles
fussed: agitado
fussing: agitar
gable: aguilón, gablete
gaiety: alegría
gallant: galante, galán, valeroso
gallantry: galantería, gallardía
gallic: galo
gallivanting: vagando, callejeando
gallop: galope, galopar
galloped: galopado
galloping: galopante, galope, galopando, galopar
galvanised: galvanizado
gambling: juego, juego con apuestas
game-bag: escarcela
gamekeeper: guardabosque
gamin: Pilluelo, Gamín, golfillo
gangrene: gangrena
gaping: abertura, hueco, abrir la boca, abrir boquete en, boquete, vacío, boquiabierto, bostezar, intervalo, abrir brecha en, bostezo
garb: vestido
gargoyle: gárgola
garland: guirnalda
garlands: guirnaldas
garnet: granate
garnished: aderezó, con guarnición de
garret: buhardilla, desván
garter: liga
garters: ligas
gascon: gascón
gauze: gasa
geese: gansos
gelatine: gelatina
genie: genio
genoa: Génova
gentleness: apacibilidad, suavidad
genuflexion: genuflexión
geranium: geranio
germinated: germinado
gesticulating: gesticulando
gherkins: pepinillos, pepinillos en vinagre, pepinillo

giddiness: mareo
giddy: mareado
gigantic: gigantesco
gilding: dorado, dorando
gilt: dorado
gimlet: barrena, barrena de mano
gingerly: cauteloso, cautelosamente
gipsy: gitano
girdle: cinto, cinturón, pretina, faja
gleam: destello ·——
gleamed: brillado
gleefully: gozosamente, alegremente
glide: deslizarse, planeo
glided: deslizado
gliding: deslizar, planeación
glimmering: resplandor, alborear, brillar, luz ténue, vislumbre
glimpsed: vislumbrado
glittered: brillado
glitters: brilla
globes: GLOBOS
glorified: glorificado
glueing: pegar, encolado, encoladura
goblets: copas
godfather: padrino, compadre
godmother: madrina
goldfinch: jilguero
good-bye: despedida, adiós
good-naturedly: amablemente, bondadosamente
gracefully: graciosamente, desenvueltamente, elegantemente, gallardamente, airosamente
grafted: injertó
granary: granero
granddaughter: nieta, la nieta
grand-daughter: nieta
grandeur: grandeza
grandly: grandiosamente, grandemente
grasshopper: saltamontes, el saltamontes
grated: rallado
gratification: satisfacción, gratificación
grating: reja, emparrillado, verja, parrilla, enrejado, irritante
gratings: mallas reticulares, rejillas, rejillas de parrilla
gravedigger: sepulturero, enterrador
gravely: gravemente
gravy: salsa, jugo
grazed: apacentado
grazing: pasto
grease: grasa, engrasar, la grasa
greased: engrasado
greedily: vorazmente
greenish: verdoso
greenness: verdura
greyhound: galgo
greyish: grisáceo
grieve: afligir, afligís, aflijo, aflija,

afligimos, afligid, afliges, aflige, aflijan, afligen, entristecer
grieves: aflige, apena
grinding: molienda, molturación
groan: gemir, gemido
grocer: tendero, almacenero, bodeguero, abacero
grocery: almacén, tienda de comestibles
grooves: surcos, ranuras
grotesquely: grotescamente
ground-floor: piso bajo
growled: gruñido
grudge: rencor
gruel: gachas
grumbled: quejado
grumbling: barboteo, quejar, quejumbre, refunfuñadura
guelder: geldre
guessing: tanteo, suponer, pensar, estimación, conjetura, adivinar, adivinación, suposición, creer
gunshot: disparo
gurgling: borbotón, borboteo, murmullo, gorjeo, gorjear, gluglú, borbotar
gust: ráfaga, racha
haberdashery: mercería, camisería
habitually: habitualmente
habitue: asiduo, parroquiano
hadn't: no ha
haggard: ojeroso, macilento, demacrado
hail: granizo, granizar, alabar, pedrisco
half-a-dozen: media docena
half-asleep: medio dormido
half-closed: entreabierto
half-finished: semi-acabado
half-open: entreabran, entreabro, entreabrís, entreabrimos, entreabrid, entreabres, entreabre, entreabra, entreabren, entreabierto, a medio abrir
half-opened: entreabierto
hallo: hola
hallucination: alucinación
halos: aureolas
halter: cabestro
halting: parar, detenerse, hacer alto, renqueante, parada, interrupción, interrumpir, claudicante, vacilante, alto, detener
hamper: dificultar, cesta, canasta
hampered: estorbado
hangings: papel pintado
hangs: continúa, cuelga
hankered: ansiado
happiest: happy
harass: acosar, acosa, acosad, acosáis, acosamos, acosan, acosas, acosen, acoso, acose, atormentar

harassed: acosado, atormentado, acosada
hardened: endurecido
hardily: apenas, robustamente, audazmente, mal, bravamente, difícilmente, duramente, fuertemente, intrépidamente, nada de eso, resistentemente
hardness: dureza
harmonised: armonizado
harnessed: enjaezado
harnesses: marcos
harnessing: movilización, enjaezar, captación, arreo
harness-maker: guarnicionero
harridan: anciana, bruja, vieja, vieja bruja
haste: prisa, precipitación
hasten: acelerar, apresurar
hastening: acelerando, apresurando, acelerar
hatchet: hacha de mano, hacha
hatless: descubierto
haughty: orgulloso, altivo, altanero
haunting: espantar, frecuentar, guarida, inolvidable, obsesionante, obsesionar, perseguir, persistente, rondar
haven't: no tener
hawthorn: espino, espino blanco, majuelo
haymaking: henificación
haze: bruma, calina, neblina, la bruma
hazy: brumoso, neblinoso
headdress: tocado
heaped: amontonado
heaps: muchísimo
heartaches: penas
heartburn: acedía, acidez de estómago, ardor de estómago, acidez
hearth: hogar, chimenea, crisol
heartily: sinceramente
heaved: tirado
heavenly: celestial, celeste
heaviness: pesadez
heaving: tirar, movimiento vertical del buque, dislocación
hedgehog: erizo
hedgerow: seto, seto vivo
heed: atención
heedless: distraído, desatento
heiresses: herederas
hem: dobladillo
henceforth: de aquí en adelante
henceforward: de aquí en adelante
heresy: herejía
heretofore: hasta aquí, hasta ahora
heroine: heroína
heroism: heroísmo
herrings: arenque

hiding-place: escondite
highroad: calle principal, carretera, carretera nacional, carretera principal
hinges: goznes, bisagras
hippocrates: Hipócrates
hiring: alquilando, arrendando, contratando
hissing: silbar, silbido, sisteo
hitched: Atado
hither: acá
hives: urticaria
hoar-frost: escarcha
hoarse: ronco
hobnobbed: codeado
hoc: éste
hoisted: Levantado
hollowed: ahuecado
hollows: ahueca
homages: homenajes
homewards: hacia la tierra natal, hacia casa, hacia la patria, hacia el país natal
homicidal: homicida
honeysuckle: madreselva
hoof: pezuña, casco
hooks: ganchos, manos, garfios
horny: córneo, corneo
horribly: horriblemente
horseback: a caballo
horsemanship: equitación
horticulture: horticultura
hosier: calcetero
hostess: anfitriona, azafata
hovel: cabaña, cuchitril, tugurio
hovered: Cernido, flotado, revoloteado, rondado
howitzer: obús
howled: Rugido
howling: aullido, lamentarse, clamoroso, aullador, alarido, aullar, lamento, gritar, rugir, grito, dar alaridos
hubbub: alboroto
huddled: apiñado
hugely: enormemente, inmensamente, muy
humid: húmedo
humidity: humedad, la humedad
humiliated: humillado
humility: humildad
humming: zumbador
humus: humus
hunchback: jorobado
hurled: arrojado, lanzado, tirado
hurrying: apurar
hush: silencio, acallar
hustled: Apresurado
hustling: buscarse la vida, Apresurar
hydro-electric: Hidroeléctrico
hygienic: higiénico
hypocrisy: hipocresía

hysterics: ataque de nervios
ice-cold: helado
iced: escarchado
i'd: Hago
idiotic: idiota, tonto
idleness: ociosidad
idol: ídolo
ignominy: ignominia
ill-tempered: de mal genio, mal genio
illumine: poner luminarias, ilumine,
  iluminar, dar focos, aclarar
illumined: iluminado
illustrious: ilustre
i'm: soy
imagining: imaginando
imbecile: imbécil
imbeciles: imbéciles
imitate: imitar, imite, imito,
  imitamos, imitas, imitáis, imitan,
  imitad, imita, imiten
imitating: imitando
immensity: inmensidad
immobile: inmóvil
immodest: inmodesto
immolation: inmolación
immoral: inmoral
immortal: inmortal, imperecedero
immovable: inconmovible,
  inamovible, que no se puede mover,
  inmovible, inmoble, inmobiliario,
  inmóvil, fijo, inalterable
impassive: impasible
impelled: impulsado, espoleado
imperceptible: imperceptible
imperceptibly: imperceptiblemente
imperiously: imperiosamente,
  autoritariamente
impertinent: impertinente
impetuously: impetuosamente
implacably: implacablemente
implements: útiles, instrumental,
  menesteres, implementos,
  implementa
implore: implorar, implorad,
  imploráis, imploramos, imploran,
  imploras, implore, imploren,
  imploro, implora, suplicar
implored: implorado, suplicado
imploringly: suplicar, de modo
  suplicante
importunes: importuna
impossibility: imposibilidad
impotence: impotencia
impropriety: impropiedad
impudently: atrevidamente,
  descaradamente, impúdicamente,
  impudentemente, insolentemente
impure: impuro
inaccessible: inaccesible
inaugurating: inaugurando
inauguration: inauguración
inborn: innato

incapacity: incapacidad
incarnation: encarnación, renacer
incendiary: incendiario
incense: incienso, encolerizar
incessant: incesante
incline: inclinar, propender, cuesta
incomprehensible: incomprensible
incongruity: incongruidad,
  incoherencia, incongruencia
incorporeal: incorpóreo
incurable: incurable
indecency: indecencia
indecision: indecisión
indefatigable: infatigable
indefinable: indefinible
indefinite: indefinido
indescribable: indescriptible
indifferently: indiferentemente
indigestion: indigestión, empacho
indignant: indignado
indignantly: con indignación,
  indignadamente
indigo: índigo, añil
indiscreet: indiscreto
indissolubly: indisolublemente
indistinct: indistinto
indistinctly: indistintamente
indolence: indolencia
indolent: indolente
inducing: induciendo
indulgence: indulgencia, bula
ineffable: inefable
inert: inerte
inexhaustible: inagotable
inexpressible: inexpresable
inexpressive: inexpresivo
infallible: infalible
infamous: infame
infernal: de infierno, infernal
infested: infestado
infidel: infiel
infinity: infinidad, infinito
infirmity: enfermedad, debilidad
inflamed: inflamado
infringed: infringido
infringing: infringiendo
infusions: infusiones
ingenuousness: ingenuidad
ingratitude: ingratitud
inhabited: habitado, poblado
initials: iniciales
injuring: hiriendo
inkstand: escribanía, tintero
inlaid: pret y pp de inlay, incrustado,
  embutido
innermost: más profundo
innkeeper: posadero
innumerable: innumerable
inoffensive: inofensivo, cándido,
  ingenuo, inofensiva
inordinately: desmesuradamente,
  inmoderadamente

inquire: preguntar, inquirís,
  inquieran, inquiere, inquieren,
  inquieres, inquiero, inquirid,
  inquirimos, inquiera, inquirir
inquired: inquirido, preguntado
inquiring: inquiriendo, curioso,
  preguntando
insalubrious: insalubre
inscription: inscripción
insensibly: insensiblemente
insides: tripas
insignificant: insignificante
insinuates: insinúa
insipid: insípido, soso
insolent: insolente, procaz
inspire: inspirar, animar, inspiráis,
  inspiro, inspiren, inspire, inspiras,
  inspiramos, inspirad, inspira,
  inspiran
inspires: inspira
installments: reembolso a plazos,
  plazos
instantaneous: instantáneo
instep: empeine
instituted: instituido
instruct: notificar, dar instrucciones,
  enseñar, instruir, notificad, notifica,
  notifiquen, notifique, notifico,
  notificas, notifican
insufficiency: insuficiencia
insulting: insultante, insultar
intellect: intelecto
intercepted: interceptado
interdict: quitar, vetar, prohibir,
  prohibición, privar, oponer,
  obstaculizar, no proponer,
  interdecir, entredecir, vedar
interfered: intervenido, interpuesto,
  obstruido, perturbado, introducido,
  entrometido, injerido, entremetido,
  inmiscuido, interferido
interlacing: enlazamiento,
  entrelazado, enlace, encruzamiento,
  entrelazando, concatenando
interminable: incabable
intermittent: intermitente
interrupting: interrumpir
interruption: interrupción
interspersed: esparcido
intertwined: entrelazado
interwoven: entretejido
intimidated: intimidado
intolerant: intolerante
intoning: entonando
intoxicated: ebrio, intoxicado,
  borracho, aturdido
intoxication: intoxicación,
  embriaguez, envenenamiento
intrigue: intrigar, intriga
intruded: impuesto, estorbado,
  molestado, metido, intervenido,
  incursionado

intrusted: Fiado, se encargado, confiado, encomendado
inveighed: vituperado
invent: inventar, invente, invento, inventas, inventen, inventan, inventamos, inventáis, inventad, inventa
inventing: inventando
inveteracy: costumbre arraigada
invigorate: vigorizar, vigorizamos, vigorizo, vigorizas, vigorizan, vigoricen, vigorizad, vigoriza, vigorizáis, vigorice
invincible: invencible
invites: invita
involuntarily: involuntariamente
inwardly: interiormente
inwards: tripas, hacia el centro, hacia adentro
ionic: iónico
ironed: planchado
ironing: férreo, planchar, hierro, plancha, planchado, ferrizo, férrico
ironmonger: ferretero, ferretería, de ferretero
irregularly: irregularmente
irrepressible: irreprimible, incontrolable
irreproachable: irreprochable
irreverence: irreverencia
irreverent: irreverente
irrevocably: irrevocablemente
irritable: irritable
irritably: irasciblemente, coléricamente, irritablemente
irritate: irritar, irrite, irrito, irrita, irritad, irritáis, irritamos, irritan, irritas, irriten
irritated: irritado
i've: he, Tengo
jack-in-the-box: Caja De Resorte, el payaso sorpresa, caja de sorpresa, Caja Sorpresa
jars: paso
jasmine: jazmín
jasmines: jazmines
jeer: injuriar, burla, insultar, abuchear
jeering: mofándose
jest: bromear, broma
jesuit: jesuita
jesuits: jesuitas
jingling: tintineando, cascabeleo
joists: mordazas, eclisas
joked: Bromeó
jolt: traqueteo, empujar, sacudir
jolted: sacudido
jolting: sacudidas, traqueteo
journeyed: Viajado
jove: Júpiter
jovial: jovial
joyous: jubiloso, gozoso, de jubiloso,

alegre
jubilation: júbilo
juggler: malabarista
juggling: hacer malabares, hacer malabarismos, juglaria, malabar, malabarismo, malabares
jujube: pastilla, jinjolero, azufaifa, azufaifo
jujubes: jinjoles
juniper: enebro, junípero
jurisconsult: jurisconsulto
kaleidoscope: calidoscopio, caleidoscopio
keenness: agudeza, viveza, sutileza, perspicacia, ansia, entusiasmo
keepsake: recuerdo
kennels: perrera, residencia canina
keyhole: ojo de la cerradura
kindle: encender, encienda, enciendo, enciendan, encendéis, encendemos, encended, enciende, enciendes, encienden, inflamar
kingdoms: reinos
king's: inglés correcto
kneading-trough: amasadera
kneeling: arrodillar, arrodillarse, estar de rodillas, arrodillado, de rodillas, arrodillando
knocker: aldaba
knockers: tetas
knocks: Golpes
knotted: anudado
knotty: nudoso
labelling: etiquetado
laborious: laborioso, tabajoso
labouring: persona que trabaja, trabajante, trabajar, obrero
laces: cintas
ladders: las escaleras, escalas
laden: cargado, abrumado
lame: cojo
lamentation: lamento, lamentación
lamented: lamentado
lampshade: pantalla
lancet: lanceta
landau: landó
landlady: arrendadora, casera, dueña, patrona, propietaria, propietaria de una vivienda, ama
languid: lánguido
languished: Languidecido
languishing: languideciendo
languor: languidez
languorous: apático, lánguido
lantern: farol, linterna
lascivious: lascivo
lashed: Azotado
lassitude: lasitud
latch: pestillo, cerrojo
lathe: torno
latterly: últimamente, en nuestro tiempo, postreramente, en

actualidad
laughingly: reír, risueñamente
lavender: lavanda, espliego
lavished: Prodigó
lavishes: prodiga
laziness: flojedad, apoltronamiento, pigricia, poltronería, dejadez, haraganería, flojera, pereza, holgazanería
leaden: de plomo, plomizo
leafless: deshojado
leans: inclinación ficticia
leant: pret y pp de lean
leaping: saltar
lectern: atril, facistol
leeches: sanguijelas
leggings: polainas
leisurely: pausadamente
lemons: limones
lengthened: alargado
lengthening: alargando, alargamiento
leprosy: lepra
lessen: minorar, achicar, disminuir, minora, minore, minoras, minoran, minoramos, achicas, minoráis, minoro
lessened: achicado, minorado
lessening: achicando, minorando
lettuce: lechuga, la lechuga
levantine: levantino
lewd: lujurioso, obsceno, lascivo
lewdness: obscenidad, lascivia, liviandad
liberally: libremente, liberalmente, a manos llenas
libertine: libertino
libretto: libreto
licentious: licencioso, libertino, desenfrenado
lichen: liquen
licked: lamido
lids: cubiertas
lifeless: inanimado
ligature: ligadura
lighted: encendido
liking: afición, gusto
limitless: ilimitado
limped: Cojeado
limpid: límpido
limping: cojera, cojear
lingered: Demorado, quedado, durado, tardado, remoloneado, permanecido, pausado, persistido
lint: hilas
liqueur: licor
liqueurs: licores
liquorice: regaliz
liveries: Libreas
livery: librea
livid: lívido
loading: carga

loafer: holgazán
loathed: detestado
loathing: detestando, aversión, aborrecimiento
lobe: lóbulo
lobsters: las langostas
locking: bloqueo
locksmith: cerrajero, el cerrajero
loco: locomotora, Caracol comestible, Concholepas concholepas
locomotion: locomoción
lodges: cabañas
lodgings: alojamiento, apartamento alquilado, habitación, pensión
lofty: alto, encumbrado
logs: bloques, libros de control, troncos
loins: los lomos
loitered: Holgazaneado
lolled: Repantigado, colgado, pendido
looking-glass: espejo
lookout: atalaya
loomed: Asomado
lounging: repantigar
lout: patán, gamberro
lowliness: humildad, bajeza
lugubrious: lúgubre
lull: calma, arrullar
lullaby: arrullo, canción de cuna
lulled: Calmó
lumbar: lumbar
lumbering: maderaje
luminous: luminoso
lumps: amontona
lunched: Almorzado
luncheon: almuerzo
lust: lujuria
lustily: lozanamente, cachondo, lujuriosamente
lustre: brillantez
lymphatic: linfático
lyre: lira
lyric: texto
lyrical: lírico
macaroni: macarrones
maddened: enloquecido
mademoiselle: señorita
madonnas: Madonas
magi: los Reyes Magos
magnanimity: magnanimidad, magnanimosidad
magnetism: magnetismo
majestic: majestuoso
majestically: majestuosamente
malediction: maldición
malleable: maleable
malmsey: malvasía
mamma: mama
manchineel: manzanillo, mancinella
mane: melena, crin
manger: pesebre

mania: manía
manifested: Manifestado
manifold: múltiple, colector
manly: varonil
manoeuvring: maniobra
mantelpiece: repisa
manure: estiércol, abono, abonar, estercolar
maraschino: marrasquino
marbles: bolita, canica, mármol
marchioness: marquesa
marguerite: Margarita
marquis: marqués
marseilles: Marsella
marshmallow: malvavisco
marvel: maravilla, asombrarse
marvelled: Maravillado
masked: enmascarado
masks: máscaras
masterpiece: obra maestra
mausoleum: mausoleo
maxilla: maxilar superior
meandering: con meandros, incoherente, largo y confuso, meandro, serpenteante, serpentear, vagar
meanderings: meandros, divagaciones
meanness: bajeza, vileza, escasez, maldad, mezquindad, pobreza, tacañería, humildad
mechanically: mecánicamente
medallion: medallón
meddle: entrometerse
mediation: mediación
medically: médicamente, médico, facultativamente
mediocre: mediano, mediocre
mediocrity: mediocridad
meditating: meditando
meditative: meditativo
melancholy: melancolía, melancólico
mellow: maduro, suave
melodious: melodioso
melting: deshielo, fusión, derretirse, fundición
memoir: autobiografía, biografía, informe, memoria, memorias, nota biográfica
mend: remendar, enmendar, reparar, zurcir
mended: Mejorado
mending: remendón, reparar, zurcir, ropa de repaso, reparación, remiendo, remendar, ir mejorando, enmendarse, enmendar, apaño
merino: merino
merriment: alegría
messieurs: señores
messrs: Señores, Sres
metaphors: metáforas
metronome: metrónomo

mettlesome: brioso
michaelmas: Fiesta De San Miguel
midget: enano, en miniatura
midsummer: canícula
milestone: hito
milking: ordeñar, Ordeño
millinery: sombrerería
millionaire: millonario
minded: dispuesto
minerva: minerva
mingled: mezclado, triscado
mingles: mezcla, trisca
mingling: mezcladura, entremezclar, mezclar, mezclarse, mezclando, triscando
miraculous: milagroso
mire: fango
mirrored: reflejado
mirthful: alegre
misfortune: infortunio, desgracia, desdicha, desventura
misplaced: extraviado
missal: misal, devocionario
misunderstand: entender mal
mitre: mitra, inglete
moan: gemir, gemido
moaning: gemiendo
mockery: burla
mocking: burlarse, falso, imitar, burlas, burlador, burlón, burla, fingido, escarnecer, engañar, imitado
modesty: modestia, pudor
modulated: modulado
moiling: Bulliendo
moistened: Humedecido
moles: lunares
momentous: importante
monotone: monótono, monotonía
monotonous: monótono
monotony: monotonía
monsignor: monseñor
monstrosities: Monstruosidades
monstrous: monstruoso
mont: montana
monumental: monumental
moonlit: luz de la luna, iluminado por la luna
moored: amarrado
mopping: trapear
moralising: moralizar
morals: moral, moralidad
morel: colmenilla, hierba, tanaceto
morn: mañana
morrow: día siguiente
morsel: pedacito, bocado
mortals: mortales
mortification: mortificación
mortified: mortificado
motionless: inmóvil, estático
motley: abigarramiento, abigarrado, multicolor

mottled: moteado
motto: lema
moulded: amoldado, modelado,
Moldeado
mountainous: montañoso
mournful: fúnebre
mourning: luto, deplorando, duelo
moustaches: los bigotes
muddled: desordenó
muffled: silenciador, sordo,
silenciado, mufla, embozar, apagar,
apagado, amortiguar, amortiguado
muffler: silenciador, bufanda
muggy: húmedo, bochornoso
mulled: ponderado, vino hervido,
Reflexionó, vino caliente
multiplied: multiplicado
mummer: bufón, mimo, máscara
mummeries: Pantomimas
munched: mascado
munificence: munificencia
murmur: murmurar, murmullo
murmuring: murmurar
muslin: muselina
mute: mudo, muda, sordina
muttering: barboteo, mumurar,
murmullo, rezongo
mutton: carnero, carne de carnero
muzzled: Abozalado
mystic: místico
mysticism: misticismo
nag: rocín, jaca
nailed: clavado, remachado
naively: ingenuamente
nakedness: desnudez
nameless: anónimo
nankeen: nanquín, mahón
nape: nuca, cogote
napkin: servilleta, la servilleta
napkins: servilletas
napoleonic: napoleónico
narrated: narrado
narrowing: estrechamiento,
estrechando
narrows: Estrecha
nay: más aún, más bien, voto
negativo, voto en contra, no,
negativa, mejor dicho
necessities: artículos de primera
necesidad
necklaces: gargantillas
necktie: corbata, la corbata
needlewoman: costurera
neglecting: Descuidar
negligently: negligentemente
neighbor: vecino, el vecino, la vecina
neighboring: vecino
neighed: Relinchó
neighing: relinchos
nervousness: nerviosidad,
nerviosismo
nestled: se acurrucado, anidado

netting: coger con red, producir una
ganancia neta, precio neto, neto,
Coger, red, red de pesca, redes,
enredar, Internet, compensación
nettles: molesta, provoca, irrita,
Ortigas
newest: el mas nuevo
nibbling: corte, Mordiscar
niches: nichos
nicolas: Nicolás
nigger: negro
nightcap: gorro de dormir, sosiega,
bebida
nightfall: anochecer
nightgown: camisa de dormir,
camisón, camisón de dormir
nightingales: ruiseñores
night-light: luz nocturna
nipping: mordaz, pellizcante,
pellizcar
noiselessly: calladamente,
silenciosamente, tranquilamente
noisily: ruidosamente,
clamorosamente, alborotadamente
nonpareil: sin igual, cosa sin par,
persona sin pareja, sin par, persona
sin par
normandy: Normandía
notary: notario, escribano
nothingness: nada
nourish: alimentar, alimentáis,
alimento, alimenten, alimentas,
alimentamos, alimentad, alimenta,
alimentan, alimente, nutrir
nozzle: tobera, boquilla
numb: entumecido, entorpecer,
entorpece, entorpezco, entorpezcan,
entorpezca, entorpeces, entorpecen,
entorpecemos, entorpecéis,
entorpeced
numberless: innumerable
numbness: entumecimiento
nursed: cuidado
nurture: crianza
nutritive: nutritivo
nutshell: cáscara de nuez, avellana,
cascarón de nuez
oaks: robles
oar: remo, el remo
oars: remos
oats: avena
obediently: obedientemente
obelisk: obelisco
obeyed: Obedecido, obedeció
obeying: obedeciendo
oblige: obligar, obligad, obligo,
obligas, obligan, obliga, obligáis,
obliguen, obligamos, obligue,
compeler
obliging: obligando, complaciente,
servicial
oblique: oblicuo, inclinado

obliquely: oblicuamente
oblong: oblongo, apaisado,
rectangular
obscured: disimulado
obscurity: oscuridad
obsequious: obsequioso
obsequiousness: sumisión
obstinacy: obstinación
obstinate: obstinado, contumaz,
tozudo
obtuse: obtuso, embotado
odalisque: odalisca
odious: odioso
odorous: oloroso
oedema: edema
offend: ofender, ofendo, ofendan,
ofende, ofended, ofendéis,
ofendemos, ofenden, ofendes,
ofenda, injuriar
offhand: de improviso
oilcloth: hule
omelette: tortilla, la tortilla
omen: agüero, augurio, presagio
one-fourth: un cuarto
oozed: rezumado
oozing: rezumando
opaque: opaco
openings: oportunidad
open-mouthed: boquiabierto
opera-glasses: gemelos de teatro
operatic: operístico
opium: opio
oppressed: apretado
orangery: invernadero de naranjos
oranges: naranjas
orator: orador
orb: orbe
orbits: gira, orbita, órbitas
ornament: alhaja, decorar,
ornamento, adorno
ornamental: decorativo, ornamental
ornaments: adornos
orphan: huérfano
orphans: huérfanos
orthography: ortografía
oscillating: oscilando, oscilante,
fluctuando
ostrich: avestruz
other's: otro
ottoman: otomano
ounce: onza
oust: expulsar, expulsas, expulsen,
expulsan, expulsamos, expulsáis,
expulsad, expulsa, expulso, expulse
outburst: explosión
outraged: despavorido, ultrajado
outspread: desplegado, extendido,
extensión
outstretched: extendido
oval: ovalado, óvalo, aovado, elipse
overcoat: abrigo, el abrigo
over-filled: sature

overflow: desbordamiento, inundación, inundar, desbordar, rebosadero
overflowing: desbordamiento, desbordante
overhanging: saliente
overmuch: demasiado, en demasía, exceso
overshoes: botas protectoras
overspread: esparcir, cubrir
overturned: invertido, trastornado, volcado
ovine: ovino, Ovina
ox: buey
oxalic: oxálico
oxen: buey
oysters: Ostiones
pads: botón
pale-faced: caripálido
pallor: palidez
palm-tree: palma
palpitated: Palpitado
palpitating: palpitando
palpitations: palpitaciones
paltry: vil, mezquino, ínfimo, despreciable, ruin, miserable
pane: hoja de vidrio, panel, cristal
panoply: panoplia
pant: jadear
panted: jadeado
panting: jadeante, palpitación
pantry: despensa
paralysed: encadenado, paralizado
parched: se agostado, secado, resecado, abrasado, seco, tostado
pare: pelar, pelen, pelad, peláis, pelamos, pelan, pelas, pela, pelo, pele, mondar
parentheses: paréntesis
parisian: parisiense, parisino
parleyed: debatió
parleying: parlamentando, debatiendo
paroxysm: paroxismo, acceso
parquet: platea
parson: sacerdote, cura, párroco
partaken: compartido
partakes: comparte
parthian: parte
parting: separación
partisan: partidista, partisano
parvis: atrio
passably: bastante, pasablemente, tolerablemente
passer-by: transeúnte, peregrino, turista, viandante, caminante
passional: pasional, martirologio
passports: pasaportes
paste: pegar, masa, pasta, engrudo
pasteboard: cartón
pasturage: pasto, pastoreo
patchouli: pachulí, pachuli, patchuli

paternal: paterno, paternal
pathological: patológico
pathology: patología
patriotic: patriótico
patriotism: patriotismo
patronized: fomentado, patrocinado, favorecido, patrocinó
paved: pavimentado
pawn: empeñar, peón, prenda, pignorar
pawnbroking: préstamos pignoraticios
peaceable: pacífico
peach: melocotón, durazno
peacock: pavo real
peaked: cresta, alcanzar el máximo, cima, con visera, cúspide, cumbre, puntiagudo, punta, pico, máximo
pear: pera, la pera, peral
pearls: perlas
pedestal: pedestal
pediment: frontón
pedlar: vendedor ambulante, vendedor al detalle, buhonero
peeped: pipió
peep-hole: trampilla, ventanillo
peeping: pipiando
peevish: malhumorado
pellet: pelotilla, bolita, perdigón, píldora
pellmell: a la desbandada, a trochemoche, barahúnda, caótico, desordenado, en desorden, lío
pell-mell: atropelladamente
pendant: colgante, pendiente
pendulum: péndulo
penetrated: penetrado
penetrating: penetrando, penetrante
penitence: penitencia
penitent: penitente, arrepentido
penknife: cortaplumas
pensive: pensativo
pent: reprimido, encerrado
perchance: quizás, tal vez
perched: encaramado, posado
perfumed: perfumado
perfuming: perfumar, aromatizante
periodicals: publicaciones periódicas
peristyle: peristilo
periwinkle: vincapervinca
pernicious: pernicioso
perpendicular: perpendicular
perpendicularly: perpendicularmente
persecute: perseguir, persigue, perseguid, persigues, persiguen, persigan, perseguimos, perseguís, persigo, persiga
persecuted: perseguido
persecutes: persigue
persevere: perseverar, perseveramos, persevero, perseveren, persevere,

perseveran, perseveráis, perseverad, persevera, perseveras
persevered: perseverado
personified: personificado
perspicacity: perspicacia
perspiration: sudor, transpiración
perspiring: sudando
perturb: perturbar, perturba, perturbad, perturbo, perturben, perturbe, perturbas, perturban, perturbáis, perturbamos
perturbation: perturbación
perturbations: inquietudes
pestering: importunando
peter's: peter
petrified: petrificado
petted: acariciado
petticoat: enaguas
pew: banco de iglesia, banco, asiento de iglesia
phantasmagoria: fantasmagoría
phantom: fantasma
pharmacy: farmacia
pharynx: faringe
philanthropy: filantropía
philosophically: filosóficamente
phlebotomy: flebotomía
physic: medicamento, remedio
physiology: fisiología
pickle: muchacho travieso, escabeche, el encurtido
pickling: decapado
pierce: agujerear, agujerean, agujereo, agujereen, agujereas, agujereamos, agujereáis, agujeread, agujerea, agujeree
pierced: agujereado
piercing: penetrante, agujereando
pilfering: ratería
piling: acopio, apilamiento, amontonar, pilotaje
pillion: asiento de atrás, asiento trasero, grupera, silla ligera de montar
pimples: granos, pústulas
pinafore: falda con peto, pichi, delantal
pines: los pinos
pinnacle: pináculo, pico
pious: piadoso, pío, beato
piquant: picante
pirouette: pirueta
pisciculture: piscicultura
pitches: argumentos de venta
pitied: compadecido
pitying: compasión, compadecer, compasivo, de lástima, piedad, tener lástima de, apiadarse de
pivot: pivote
placard: cartel
placarded: pancarta, etiquetados
placidly: plácidamente

plaids: jugado
plained: afinado, fino
plaint: lamento, querella, demanda, reclamación
plaited: trenzado, fruncido, trenzó
plaits: trenzas
planed: planeado
plank: tabla, tablón
planks: vertical de desviadores, tablazón, poste con tablas
plated: chapado
platitude: tópico
platitudes: tópicos
playtime: hora de recreo
pleading: suplicando, alegato
pleases: complace
pleated: plisado
plenitude: plenitud, abundancia
ploughboy: mozo de labranza
ploughed: aró
ploughman: labrador, arador
ploughs: arados
plucking: punteo, desnudamiento, arrancar
plumage: plumaje
plume: pluma, penacho
plum-tree: ciruelo
plunder: pillaje, botín, saqueo
plunging: zambullir, hundir, muy bajo, sumergir, zambullida
plying: ejerciendo, recorriendo, manejando, trabajando, enrollando
pocket-handkerchief: pañuelo
poesy: poesía
poisoned: envenenado
poisoning: envenenamiento, intoxicación, envenenar, envenenando
poked: metido
poking: meter
pole-axe: desnuque
polemic: polémica, polémico
polemics: polémica, polémico
polishing: limpieza, pulido, satinado, pulidor, lucidatura
politeness: cortesía, educación, atenciones
polygon: polígono
pomade: pomada
pomegranate: granada
pomp: pompa
pompadour: copete
pompon: borla, rosa de pitiminí, variedad de crisantemo
pondered: ponderado
poniard: apuñalar, puñal
poodle: perro de lanas
poorness: pobreza, mala calidad
porcelain: porcelana
porcine: porcino
pores: poro, los poros
portals: portales

portrays: retrata
postage: franqueo, porte
post-chaise: calesa
postilion: postillón
posting: puesto, expedición, remitir, mostrar, poste, destino, pase de asientos, anunciar, mandar por correo, mandar, fijar
post-mortem: después de la muerte
postscript: posdata, postdata
potash: potasa
potion: poción
pot-luck: comida en la que cada uno trae un plato
poultry: aves, aves de corral, pollería
pounced: estarcido, precipitado, repujado, abalanzado
pouting: faneca
powdered: empolvar, empolvarse, en polvo, pólvora, polvo, polvorear, pulverizado, pulverizar
powdering: espolvoreado
practicing: que ejerce, practicante, ejercicio, práctica, entrenamiento, ejercicios
praising: alabar
prance: cabriola
prancing: escarceos, encabritar
prattle: cháchara, balbuceo, charlar, parlotear, parloteo, balbucear
prawns: gambas
prayer-book: devocionario
preached: predicado, sermoneado
preacher: predicador
precaution: precaución
precipice: precipicio, despeñadero, abismo, derrumbadero
precipices: precipicios
precipitated: precipitado
predicting: prediciendo
predilections: predilecciones
prefect: monitor, prefecto
prefecture: prefectura
prejudiced: predispuesto
prejudicial: perjudicial
presbytery: presbiterio, casa del cura
prescribe: prescribir, prescribo, prescribís, prescribimos, prescriben, prescribid, prescribe, prescriban, prescribes, prescriba, recetar
prescriptions: las recetas
presentiment: presentimiento
preserves: conservas
presses: Prensas, prensa
pretentious: pretencioso, engreído
pretentiously: pretensiosamente, vanidosamente
pretext: pretexto
prick: pinchar, punzada, polla
pricked: pinchado
pricking: pinchar, picor, punción, punzada, hormigueo, que pincha, el

pinchazo, punzante
prie-dieu: reclinatorio
prima: primero, primer
primo: primero, Aventajado
princely: magnífico, regio, principesco, príncipe
privation: apuro, derrame, estrechez, miseria, pérdida, privación, Privación
privet: alheña
probity: probidad
procrastinating: aplazando, dilatar
procured: procurado
procurer: alcahuete
prodigal: pródigo
prodigiously: portentosamente, prodigiosamente
prods: anima, pincha, pica, instiga, estimula
profanity: profanidad
profited: ganado
profuse: profuso
profusely: abundantemente, pródigamente, profusamente
prohibit: prohibir, prohiban, prohibís, prohibimos, prohibid, prohibes, prohiben, prohibe, prohibo, prohiba
projecting: sobresaliente, saliente, saledizo, proyectar
prolong: prolongar, prolongáis, prolonguen, prolongo, prolongas, prolongamos, prolongad, prolonga, prolongan, prolongue
promenade: paseo
pronouncing: pronunciando
proofs: testigos
propagate: propagar
propitious: propicio, favorable
propos: propósito
propounding: proponiendo, proponer
propped: sostenido
props: attrezzo, propiedades, encargado del atrezo, accesorios
proscribing: proscribiendo, proscribir
prosecute: procesar, procesáis, procesad, procesamos, procesen, procesan, procesas, procesa, proceso, procese, perseguir
prospectus: prospecto, prospecto de emisión
prospering: prosperando
prostituted: prostituido
prostration: postración
protects: protégé
protesting: protestar, protestador
protracted: prolongado
protruded: sobresalido
protruding: sobresaliendo, sobresaliente
providence: providencia

prudence: prudencia
prudently: prudentemente
pshaw: bah
puberty: pubertad
puckered: arrugado, fruncido
puckers: arruga, frunce, fruncidos
puddles: charcos
puff: bollo esponjado, bocanada, soplo
puffing: reclamo excesivo, soplar
puffy: hinchado
pulpy: carnoso, pastoso, pulposo
pulsation: pulsación
pulverised: pulverizado
pumps: bombas
punctuality: puntualidad
punctually: puntualmente
puny: endeble
purgation: purgación
purge: purga, limpiar, purgar, depuración, depurar, purgante
purged: purgó
pursing: cierre de la jareta, embolsamiento, embolsar
purveyor: abastecedor, proveedor
pyrotechnic: pirotécnico, sustancia pirotécnica
pythagoras: Pitágoras
pyx: píxide
quadrangular: cuadrangular
quadrille: cuadrilla
quadrupedal: cuadrúpedo
quaint: pintoresco
quarreled: Peleado
quarrelled: peleado
quavering: trinar, tembloroso
quay: muelle, andén
queer: raro
quelled: sofocado
quieting: calmante
quill: pluma
quivered: temblado
quivering: estremecimiento, vibrante, vibración, tembloroso, vibrar, temblor, parpadeante, estremecerse, carcaj, aljaba, temblador
quod: cárcel, chirona, encarcelar, poner a la sombra
racehorses: caballos de carreras
racked: atormentado
racket: raqueta
racking: trasiego
racks: cremalleras
radiant: resplandeciente, radiante, brillante
radiating: radiando
raged: rabiado
rags: los trapos
railing: barandilla, balaustrada, pasamano, baranda
railings: verja, cancela, reja, Enrejado
rained: llovido

rainy: lluvioso
raisins: las pasas, las pasas de uva, pasas
rake: rastrillo, rastro, rastrear
raking: rastrillaje, rastro, atizar, rastrear, rasguear, rastrillar, rastrillo
rambling: vagaroso
ramshackle: ruinoso
rancour: encono, ojeriza, rencor
ranged: recorrido
ransacked: saqueado
rapaciously: rapazmente
rapidity: rapidez
rapier: estoque
rapture: rapto
rascal: bribón
rash: sarpullido, erupción, precipitado, salpullido, erupción cutánea
rattled: zumbado
rattling: zumbar, muy, rápido, vaivén, realmente, estupendo
raucous: rauco, ronco, estridente
ravages: estragos
ravens: cuervos
ravishingly: encantar
realisable: factible
reappear: reaparecer, reaparecen, reaparezcan, reapareces, reaparezco, reaparecemos, reaparecéis, reaparece, reapareced, reaparezca
reappeared: reaparecido
reappearing: reapareciendo
reared: criado
rearranged: reorganizado
rearranging: reorganizando
reasoned: razonado
rebelled: rebelado
rebelling: rebelar
rebellious: rebelde
rebounding: rebotar
receded: retrocedido
reciprocally: recíprocamente
recitative: recitativo, recitado
recited: recitado
reckoning: cuenta, cálculo
reclining: reclinando
recluse: recluso
recoiling: retráctil
recollect: recordar
recommending: recomendando, encareciendo, ensalzando
recompense: recompensa
reconciling: reconciliándose, conciliándose
recount: recuento
rectitude: rectitud
recur: repetirse
reddened: enrojecido
red-hot: candente, salchicha, vigoroso
redolent: fragante
redouble: redoblar, redoble,

redoblad, redoblo, redoblen, redoblas, redoblan, redobláis, redobla, redoblamos, reduplicar
redoubled: redoblado
redoubtable: temible
reeds: Peines, totoral
reeking: apestando, oliendo
reeling: Tambalear
re-enter: reingresar en, reentre, volver a entrar en
re-established: restablecido, restableció
refectory: comedor universitario, comedor, refectorio
refinement: refinamiento, finura
reflex: reflejo
refrain: estribillo, abstenerse
refresh: refrescar, refresco, actualizar, refresque, refresca, refresquen, refrescas, refrescan, refrescamos, refrescad, refrescáis
refreshed: refrescado
refreshment: refresco
refulgence: refulgencia, brillantez
regimen: régimen
regrets: lamenta, excusas
regularity: regularidad
reigned: Reinado
reimbursement: reembolso, reintegro
reined: Contenido
rejoice: alegrarse, regocijarse, alegrar
rejoices: alboroza, alegra, deleita, jubila
rejoicing: regocijo
rejoin: reincorporarse a, reunir, reunirse con, reunirse, volver a juntarse con, replicar, replicas, reúnan, reunís, reunimos, reunid
rejoined: replicado, reunido
relapsed: reincidido
relight: volver a arder
reliquary: relicario
remembrance: recuerdo
remnant: remanente
remnants: remanentes
remonstrances: protestas
remorse: remordimiento
rendezvous: cita
renewing: renovando
renouncing: renunciando
renunciation: renuncia
repainted: repintado
repass: repasar
repast: comida
repent: arrepentirse
repented: Arrepentido, se arrepentido
replying: Contestar
reposes: reposos
reprimand: reprimenda, reprender
reproach: reproche, censurar, reprender, reprobar, desaprobar,

reprochar
reproached: Reprochado
reproaching: Reprochar
repugnance: repugnancia
repulse: repulsión, repulsar
repulsed: Repeló
repulses: repulsiones
repulsing: Repelando
repulsion: repulsión
reread: releer
resembled: Parecido
resembling: parecido a, Parecer, pareciendo
resin: resina
resolutely: determinadamente, resueltamente
resonant: resonante
resound: resonar, resuene, resuena, resueno, resuenen, resuenan, resonamos, resonáis, resonad, resuenas
resounded: Resonado
resounding: resonando
respectability: respetabilidad
respectful: respetuoso
respectfully: respetuosamente
respiration: respiración
resplendent: resplandeciente
restitution: restitución, devolución
restraining: conteniendo, refrenando, reprimiendo
restrains: refrena, contiene, reprime
resuming: reanudando
reverberated: reverberado
reverberates: reverbera
reverberating: reverberando
reverberation: reverberación
revered: reverenciado, acatado, venerado
reverie: ensueño
reviving: reavivando
revolted: rebelado, rebelde
revolutionises: revoluciona
revolving: rotativo, girando
rheumatism: reumatismo, reuma
rhine: Rin
rhododendron: rododendro
rhyme: rima, rimar
rhythmical: rítmico
rickety: raquítico, decrépito, desvencijado
ridicule: ridiculizar, ridículo
rift: hendidura
rigidity: rigidez
rigorously: rigurosamente
rime: escarcha, rima
rinsed: enjuagado
ripples: ondulaciones
riveted: remachado
roadside: orilla del camino
roadway: calzada
roast: asar, asado, tostar, carne asada

robbing: robando, despojando, hurtando
rocked: Mecido
rods: bastones
romanticism: romanticismo
roofing: cobertizo, material para techado, techador, techumbre
rosettes: rosetones
rosewood: palisandro, palosanto, palo de rosa
rosy: rosado
rotted: pudrido, descompuesto, envanecido, podrido, se macado, corrompido
rotting: pudrir, podrido, podriendo, corrompiendo, pudriendo, envaneciendo, descomponiendo, macándose
rotunda: rotonda
rouge: colorete
roughen: poner áspero
roused: espoleado, instigado, animado
rowed: remado
rubicund: rubicundo, rubicunda, rubeo
rudder: timón, volante
ruddy: rojo
rudely: grosero, groseramente, bastamente, rudamente
rudeness: rudeza
rue: ruda, amargura
ruff: combatiente
ruffle: faralá, fruncir, agitar, agitarse, arruga, arrugar, arrugarse, chorrera, confundir, enmarañar, erizar
ruffled: erizado
ruffling: erizar
ruining: arruinar
ruinous: ruinoso
rum: ron, el ron
rumbled: retumbado
rumbling: retumbar
rummaged: registró
rummaging: registrando
runaway: fugitivo
rupture: ruptura, rotura, quebradura
rushes: copiones
russet: bermejo
rust: óxido, herrumbre, moho, oxidación, el moho, aherrumbrar
rustic: rústico
rustics: rústico
rustle: susurro
rustled: susurrado
rustling: crujido, crujiente, frufrú, susurrar, susurro, abigeato
ruts: carriles
rye: centeno
sable: marta cebellina, negro, marta
sabre: sable
sacerdotal: sacerdotal

sacrament: sacramento
sacraments: sacramentos
sacrificed: sacrificado
sacrifices: dewayne
sacrificing: sacrificar
sacrilege: sacrilegio
sacristan: sacristán
sacristy: sacristía
saddened: entristecido
saddles: monturas para equitación
saffron: azafrán
saliva: saliva
sallow: pálido, sauce
salons: salones
saltpetre: salitre
salutary: saludable
saluted: saludado
sameness: identidad, igualdad, monótono, monotonía, similaridad, uniformidad
sanding: lijado, smerigliatura
sanguineous: sanguinario, sanguíneo, sangriento, de color rojo sangre
sans: sin
sap: savia, jugo, zumo
sapped: agotó
sash: faja, banda, marco de ventana
satiated: harto, saciada
satiety: saciedad
saucepans: cacerolas
saucer: platillo, el platillo
saviour: salvador, redentor
savoy: Saboya, berza, col rizada
savoyard: saboyano
scabbard: vaina
scaffold: andamio
scaled: escalado, escamoso
scaling: escala, escalada
scalpel: escalpelo, bisturí
scandalised: escandalizado
scandalized: escandalizado
scarified: escarificada
scarred: marcar con cicatriz, cicatrizado, con cicatrices, marcado, que tiene cicatrices, rasguño, cicatriz
scarves: cáscara
schoolboys: colegiales
schoolmaster: maestro de escuela
scintillate: chispear, centellear, chispee, chispead, chispeáis, chispeamos, chispea, chispeas, chispeen, chispeo, chispean
scissor: cortar con tijeras, tijeras, tijera
scoffer: mofador
scolded: regañado
sconces: fortines
scornfully: desdeñosamente
scoundrel: bribón, sinvergüenza, canalla
scoured: fregado, batido, purgado, restregado, desgrasado,

desengrasado
scraps: chicharrones, recortes, residuos
scratching: arañar, arañazo, improvisado, rasguño, rasguñar, raspamiento, rayadura, rascadura, rascar
screams: carcajadas
screws: tornillos
scrofula: escrófula
scrofulous: escrofuloso
scroll: desplazar, voluta, desfilar, rollo de papel, pergamino
scrupulous: escrupuloso, meticuloso
scythes: guadañas
sealskin: piel de foca
seasoning: condimento, secado, sazonar, sazón
secondhand: de segunda mano
seduce: seducir, seduzca, seduzco, seduzcan, seducen, seducís, seduces, seduce, seducid, seducimos
seduced: seducido
seduces: seduce
seduction: seducción
seine: Sena
seizes: agarra, ase
seizing: agarrando, asiendo
seizure: toma, embargo, apoplejía, captura, incautación, ataque, convulsión, gripado, secuestro
self-command: dominio de sí mismo
self-possessed: dueño de sí mismo
semicircle: semicírculo
semicircular: semicircular
sensibility: sensibilidad
sensual: sensual
sensuality: sensualidad
sentinel: centinela
seraphic: seráfico
serene: sereno
serenity: serenidad
sermon: sermón
serpent: serpiente
serpents: serpientes
servility: servilismo
servitude: servidumbre
seventy-five: setenta y cinco
seventy-two: setenta y dos
sew: coser, cosa, cosemos, coso, coses, cosen, cosed, cosan, coséis, cose, pegar
sewed: pret de sew, cosido
sewing: cosiendo, pegando, costura
sewn: cosido, pegado
sextet: sexteto
shabbily: andrajosamente
shaded: matizado, obscurecido, matiz, matizar, obscurecer, Sombread, sombreado, sombrear, degradado, tono, sombra
shading: sombreado

shady: umbrío, sombreado
shafts: ejes
shakes: sacude
shako: chacó
shallop: chalupa
shamed: avergonzado
shameless: desvergonzado
sharpened: afilado, aguzado
shave: afeitar, afeitado, afeitarse, rapar
shaved: afeitado, rasurado
shawl: chal
sheathed: envainado
shedding: derramamiento
sheen: brillo, lustre
sheepfold: aprisco, majada, redil
shepherds: los pastores
shimmer: luz trémula, vibración
shimmered: brilló
shines: brilla
shingle: tablilla
shipwrecked: náufrago
shiver: tiritar, temblar, escalofrío
shivering: tiritar
shoemaker: zapatero
shone: brillado, pret y pp de shine
shopkeeper: tendero
shopkeepers: tenderos
shorten: abreviar, abrevias, abreviad, abrevio, abrevien, abrevie, abrevia, abreviáis, abreviamos, abrevian, acortar
shouldn't: contracción de should not
shovel: pala
shrank: pret de shrink
shreds: desbrizna, despedaza
shriek: chillido, chillar
shrill: chillón
shrilly: chillonamente
shrink: encoger, mermar
shrinking: contracción, encoger, encogimiento
shriveled: aborrajado, quemado, encogido, arrugado, secado
shrivelled: marchito, consumido, apergaminado, arrugado, secado
shroud: mortaja, obenque, protector, protector de contacto
shudder: estremecerse
shuddered: estremecido
shuddering: estremecer
shun: rehuir, rehuyo, rehuid, rehuimos, rehuís, rehuyan, rehuye, rehuyen, rehuyes, rehuya
shutter: obturador, contraventana, postigo, persiana
shutters: obturadores, obturador
shutting: cerrar
shyly: tímidamente
shyness: timidez
sickle: hoz
sickliness: palidez, mala salud, lo

empalagoso
sideboard: armario, aparador
siesta: sesteo
sighing: suspirar
signboard: letrero
signified: significado
silken: de seda, sedoso
sill: umbral, solera
simmering: estofando, fermentando, hirviendo
singular: original, excepcional, único, individual, raro, singularísimo, solo, extraño
singularly: particularmente, singularmente
sinner: pecador
sipping: beborrotear
siren: sirena
sixty-three: sesenta y tres
sketched: trazado
skimming: desnatando
skipping: saltar, salto a la comba
skittish: caprichoso, frívolo, nervioso, asustadizo
skullcap: solideo, casquete, gorro
sky-blue: azul celeste
slackening: aflojando
slandering: calumnia, calumniar, difamación, difamar, maledicencia
slang: jerga, argot
slanting: inclinado, sesgo
slapping: rápido, abofeteamiento, abofetear, batiente
slates: pizarra
slaughtered: matado
slaving: esclavizar
sleepiness: somnolencia, sueño
slipper: zapatilla, pantufla
slippers: zapatillas
slips: comprobantes de pago
sloped: atravesado, inclinado
sloping: costanero, inclinado, desarrollo de una curva gráfica, sesgo, inclinación, en pendiente
smacking: paliza, azotaina, abofetear
smallness: pequeñez
smashing: aplastante
smelling: oler
smelt: eperlano
smelts: amalgama, funde
smoothed: suavizado
smote: pret de smite
sneak: chivato
snore: roncar, ronquido
snored: roncado
snoring: ronquidos
snowball: bola de nieve
snuff: rapé
snug: acogedor, cómodo
sob: sollozar, sollozo
sobbed: sollozado
sobbing: sollozar

sobs: solloza
sock: calcetín
socrates: Sócrates
softened: ablandado
softness: blandura, suavidad
soiled: sucio
solace: solaz, consolar, consuelo
soldered: soldó
solemnity: solemnidad
solitude: soledad
solitudes: soledades
sonnet: soneto
sonorous: sonoro
soot: hollín
soothed: calmado
soothing: calmando, consolador, calmante, tranquilizador
sordidness: suciedad, sordidez, lo miserable, lo asqueroso, vileza
sorrel: alazán, acedera
sorrowful: afligido, pesaroso
so-so: así así, regular
soundly: sanamente, solventemente, sólidamente, razonablemente, profundamente, firmemente, vigorosamente
soups: sopas
soured: agrió
south-eastern: del sudeste
sowing: siembra
spaced: espació
spade: cavar, pala, laya
spadeful: pala
sparkled: chispeado
spartan: espartano
spasm: espasmo
spat: reñir
specifies: especifica, detalla
speculations: especulaciones
spelt: espelta
spendthrift: derrochador
spiders: hilar
spilt: pret y pp de spill
spinach: espinaca, espinacas, la espinaca
spiritless: exánime
spite: rencor
spitted: escupió
spitting: escupiendo
splashboard: alero, guardabarros
splashing: chapoteo, riego, salpicar, salpicaduras
splendour: fausto, pomposidad, fulgor, esplendor, lujo
splints: tablillas
spoiling: estropear
spoilt: nulo, pret y pp de spoil, mimado, estropeado, dañado, consentido
spoonful: cucharada
sprawling: yaciendo, desmadejado, extender

springing: saltar
sprinkle: salpicar, espolvorear, rociar
sprinkled: rociado
sprinkler: rociador, regadera, aspersor
sprinkling: rociadura
sprouting: brotante, brotar, brote
spruce: abeto, pulcro, picea
sprung: pp de spring, de muelles, brotado, saltado
spurred: espoleado
spurt: borbotón
spurted: chorreado
sputtering: chisporroteo, farfullando, pulverización en vacío
squandered: malgastado, derrochado
squatted: agachado
squeaking: chirriar, rechinamiento
squeamish: delicado, aprensivo
squire: escudero
squirrel: ardilla, la ardilla
squirt: chorro, jeringa
sta: algoritmo de árbol de extensión
stableman: mozo de cuadra
staggering: asombroso
stains: manchas
stair: escalón, escalera
stalk: tallo, pedúnculo
stammered: tartamudeó
stammering: balbuceo, tartamudo, estropajoso, balbuciente, tartamudear, tartamudeo, tartamudez, tartamudeando
stamping: timbrado, estampación
starch: almidón, fécula, almidonar
starched: acartonado, almidonado, almidonar, duro, plastificado, rígido, tieso, tirante
stationed: estacionado
statuette: estatuilla
staves: estrofas
stead: lugar
steeped: remojado, empapado
steeple: campanario, torre, aguja
steeps: remoja, empapa, escarpado
steppe: estepa
sterile: estéril
sternutation: el estornudo
stewed: estofado
stiffened: atiesado, endurecido, se agarrotado, anquilosado
stiffening: endureciendo, agarrotándose, atiesando, agarrotamiento, espesar, engomado, endurecimiento, endurecerse, endurecer, atiesarse, atiesar
stifle: babilla
stifled: se ahogado, sofocado, reprimido, callado, suprimido
stifling: sofocante, ahogante
stillness: quietud
stinking: hediondo

stirrup: estribo
stitched: cosido
stocking: media, la media
stodgy: aburrido, pesado
stoical: estoico
stoicism: estoicismo
stomach-ache: dolor de barriga
stoop: inclinar, rebajarse, rebajamiento, pequeña veranda, humillarse, inclinado, pórtico, inclinarse, agachado, agachar, agacharse
stooped: rebajado
stooping: inclinar, inclinarse, rebajamiento, rebajar, rebajarse, cargado de espaldas, agachado, agacharse, inclinación, humillarse, encorvado
stoppered: tapado
storey: piso
stormy: tempestuoso, tormentoso
stoutly: corpulentamente, fuerte, reciamente, resueltamente, robustamente
stoves: estufas
strabismus: estrabismo
straggling: vagando, disperso, retraso, extendido, fluctuación de trayecto
straighten: enderezarse, enderezar, enderece, enderezas, enderezan, enderezo, enderezamos, enderezáis, enderezad, endereza, enderecen
strainer: colador, filtro, cedazo
strapped: fajó
strapping: correaje, tira, robusto, fuerte, fornido, fajando, afilar, encintado, encintar, correa, atar
straying: extravío, desviar
streaks: mechones
streamed: corrido
streaming: flujo, difusión de video digital en tiempo real, efecto de canalización, correr, transferencia de datos desde el disco duro
strewing: esparciendo
strewn: regado, pp de strew
strident: estridente
strides: zancadas
striving: luchando, forcejeando, esforzándose, desviviéndose, afanando, pugnando, esforzar, esfuerzos
strove: pret de strive
strutting: pavoneo, pavoneándose
stucco: estuco
studs: columnas, tacos
stumbling: tropezar
stump: tocón, muñón, esfumino
stung: picado, pret y pp de sting
stupefaction: estupefacción
stupefied: aturdido, entorpecido

stupefy: aturdir, aturdid, aturda, aturdan, aturde, aturdes, aturdimos, aturdís, aturdo, aturden, entorpecer
stupefying: aturdiendo, entorpeciendo
stupendous: estupendo
stupidity: estupidez
stupidly: estúpidamente, estupidez, necedad, torpeza
stupor: estupor
suave: zalamero, fino, cortés, amable, afable
subjugated: subyugado
subjugation: dominación
sublime: sublimas, sublima, sublimen, sublimo, sublime, sublimamos, sublimad, sublimáis, subliman, admirable, bello
subscribed: se suscrito, subscrito
subsided: menguado, bajado
subtly: disimuladamente, sutilmente
subversive: subversivo
succeeding: consiguiendo
successively: sucesivamente
succour: prestar ayuda, socorrer, asistir, acudir, socorro
succulent: zumoso, carnoso, suculento, jugoso, planta carnosa, sabroso, suculenta
suck: chupar, mamar, libar, chupas
sucking: succión, lechal, mamar, mamada, chupadura, chupante, chupar, chupada, chupón, absorber
suckling: amamantando, lactando, lactancia
sufficed: bastado
suffocating: sofocando, sofocante, ahogándose, asfixiar
suffused: difundido
sugar-candy: azúcar cande
sugary: azucarado
sulkiness: capricho, resentimiento
sulky: malhumorado
sully: tachar a, manchar, mancharse, mancillar, mancille
sulphuric: sulfúrico
sultanas: pasas de Esmirna
sultans: sultanes
summer-house: glorieta
summonses: citaciones
sumptuous: suntuoso, rumboso
sunbeam: rayo de sol
sunburnt: tostado por el sol
sundered: partió
sundial: reloj de sol
sunken: hundido
sunshade: quitasol, sombrilla
superintend: vigilas, supervisas, supervisen, superviso, vigila, vigilad, vigiláis, vigilan, vigilen, vigile, supervisan
superintending: dirigiendo,

supervisando, vigilando, supervisar
supple: suave
suppliant: suplicante
supplication: súplica, ruego, oración
sups: cena, sorbos
sureness: confianza, seguridad, firmeza, certidumbre, certeza, lo certero
surfeited: sació
surmises: supone
surmounted: vencido, superado
surpassed: aventajado, sobrepujado
surrounds: rodea, circunda
susceptibility: susceptibilidad
suspecting: Sospechar
sustains: sostiene
sustenance: sustento
swallows: traga
swarm: enjambre, pulular, hormiguear
swarming: hormigueo, hormiguilla, enjambrando, ataque de enjambre, piquiña
swarthy: moreno
swayed: Oscilado
swaying: oscilación, oscilar, ladearse, tambalear, vaivén, que balancea, oscilante, mimbrear, influir en, inclinarse, inclinación lateral
swearing: jurando
sweated: Sudado
sweating: sudar
sweeps: barre
sweetness: dulzura
sweet-smelling: fragante, perfumado
swelled: hinchado
swelling: hinchazón, chichón, tumefacción, protuberancia, bulto
swivel: eslabón giratorio, giratorio, pieza giratoria, pivote
swum: pp de swim
symmetrically: simétricamente
syncope: síncope
tabernacle: tabernáculo
taciturn: taciturno, taciturna
taffeta: tafetán, tafeta
tailors: sastres
talisman: talismán
talkative: hablador, locuaz
talker: hablador
tallow: sebo
tanned: bronceado, curtido, moreno
taper: manipulador, taladro cónico, conicidad
tar: alquitrán, alquitranar, brea, pez
tarnish: manchar, deslustrar, empañadura, deslustre
tarnished: deslustrado, empañado, manchado
tartar: tártaro, sarro
tarts: tartas
tassel: borla

tasting: cata, degustación, gustando
tasty: sabroso, rico, gustoso
tavern: taberna
tax-collector: exactor
teapot: tetera, la tetera
tempered: templado
tempest: tormenta, tempestad
temptations: tentaciones
tenantless: sin arrendatario
tenderest: ofrezca
tender-hearted: tierno de corazón, bondadoso
tenderly: con ternura, tiernamente, endeblemente, delicado
tenderness: ternura
tending: cuidando, tendiendo
tendon: tendón
tendons: tendones
tenor: vencimiento de un efecto, curso, de tenor, para tenor, rumbo, tenor, camino, tendencia
tepid: tibio
terrify: aterrar, aterre, aterrad, aterráis, aterramos, aterro, aterran, aterras, aterren, aterra, terroriza
testily: malhumoradamente, irritadamente, irritablemente
tethered: atado
thatched: techar con paja, paja, de paja
thaw: deshielo, deshelar, deshelas, deshelo, deshela, deshelad, desheláis, deshelan, deshele, deshelen, deshelamos
thence: desde allí
theodore: Teodoro
therapeutics: terapéutica, terapéutico
therefrom: de eso, ahí dentro
thereto: a eso
thereupon: luego, por eso, por tanto, en eso
theriac: tríaca
thermometer: termómetro
thicket: matorral
thimble: dedal
thine: tuyo, tuyos, tuyas, tuya, tus
thinker: pensador
thinner: escaso, fino, flaco, ligero, ralo, enrarecerse, tenue, diluyente, aguarrás, débil, solvente
thins: afina
thirst: sed, la sed
thirsty: sediento
thirty-four: treinta y cuatro
thither: allá
thong: correa
thorax: tórax
thorns: espinas
thoroughbred: animal de casta
thoughtlessness: irreflexión, inconsideración, inconsciencia, desconsideración

threads: hilos
thrice: tres veces
thrilled: estremecido
thrilling: emocionante
thriven: pp de thrive
throbbed: Latido
throbbing: palpitante
throbs: latidos
thrusting: empujar
thud: porrazo
thunderclap: tronido
thundered: Tronado
thwarts: dificulta, frustra
ticking: terliz, tictac
tidying: Ordenar
tigers: tigres
tiled: alicatado, enlozado
tilled: embaldosado
tilt: inclinación, inclinar
timbered: enmaderó
timely: oportuno, a tiempo
timepiece: reloj
timid: tímido, encogido, miedo
timidity: timidez
timidly: temerosamente, temeroso,
    tímidamente, encogidamente,
    apocadamente
tingling: zumbido, estremecimiento,
    hormiguear, hormigueo, picar,
    picazón, zumbar
tinkling: tilín, retintín, que hace tilín,
    cencerreo, cascabeleo, campanilleo
tint: teñir, tinte
tiptoe: de puntillas, punta del pie
tire: neumático, llanta, cansar,
    cansarse, la llanta, fatigar
tiring: fatigoso
tithe: diezmar
to-day: hoy
togs: vestidos
toilette: wáter, de tocador, inodoro,
    lavabo, retrete, sanitario, servicios,
    tocado, vestido, atavío, baño
toleration: tolerancia
tolled: Tocado
tolling: tañido, gravamen, Tocar
tombs: tumbas
to-morrow: mañana
tongs: tenazas
tongues: lenguas
topaz: topacio
torches: antorchas
toreador: torero
torment: tormento
tormented: atormentado
torpid: torpe
torpor: estupor
torrent: torrente
torrents: torrentes
torsion: torsión
tortoise: tortuga, jicotea
tortoise-shell: carey

tortured: torturado
tortures: torturas
tossing: tirar
tottering: tambaleante, tambalear,
    tambaleando
toxicological: toxicológico
tradesman: comerciante
tradesmen: trabajadores
    especializados
tragedies: tragedias
trailed: Arrastrado
trampled: pisoteado
tranquilly: tranquilamente
transfigured: Transfigurado
transfixed: traspasado
transitions: transiciones
transparency: transparencia
traveler: viajero, viajante
travelers: viajantes
traverse: travesaño
traversed: Atravesado
traversing: Atravesar
trays: bandejas
treachery: traición
trefoil: trébol
trellis: caballete, espaldera, enrejado
tremble: temblar, temblor
trembled: Temblado, tembló
tremulous: trémulo
tress: trenza
tricolour: tricolor
trifle: bagatela, friolera, nadería
trifles: zarandajas
trifling: fútil
trills: gorjea, trina
trimmed: recortado
trimming: adorno, adornos
trimmings: recortes, arrequives,
    poda, guarnición, recorte, adorno,
    accesorios, adornos
triumphed: Triunfado
triumphing: Triunfar
trodden: pisado, pp de tread
trot: trote, trotar
trotted: Trotado
trotting: trote, hacer trotar, trotón,
    trotador, trotar
troubadour: trovador
troubling: molestar, atormentador,
    preocupante
troupe: compañía teatral
trousseau: ajuar
truncated: truncado
trunks: traje de baño, bañador,
    mampara encerradora de la
    escotilla, pantaloneta, pantalón de
    baño
trusses: bragueros
tub: bañera
tuft: manojo de vasos sanguíneos,
    cresta, mata, mechón, penacho,
    copete, copo

tufts: copetes
tulle: tul
tumbled: Derribado
tumbling: pérdida de estabilidad,
    pérdida de referencia, volteador,
    volteo, acrobacia, movimiento de
    rotación, derribar
tumefaction: tumefacción
tumid: protuberante, túmido
tumult: tumulto, ruido
tunic: túnica
turbid: turbio
turned-down: deterioro
turnings: torneaduras
turpentine: trementina
twilight: crepúsculo, anochecer
twitched: Retorcido
typhoid: tifoidea
tyrannical: tiránico
ugliness: fealdad
unappreciated: no apreciado
unattainable: inasequible
unbearable: insufrible, insoportable
unbecoming: impropio
unbound: pret y pp de unbind, no
    unido
unbounded: ilimitado
unconcerned: indiferente
unconnected: desconecto
unconsciously: inconscientemente
uncorking: descorchando
uncover: descubrir, descubre,
    descubrís, descubrimos, descubrid,
    descubro, descubren, descubran,
    descubra, descubres, destapar
unction: unción
uncut: sin tallar, no cortado, integral,
    en bruto, sin abrir, sin cortés, sin
    cortar, no tallado, sin labrar
undecided: indeciso
undefinable: indefinible
underdone: poco hecho
undertone: voz baja
undid: Deshizo, pret de undo
undone: deshecho
undress: bata, desnudarse, desnudar,
    desvestir
undressed: sin curtir
undressing: desnudar, desnudando,
    desvistiendo
undulated: ondulado
undulating: Ondular, ondeo
undulation: ondulación
uneasiness: malestar
unevenly: irregularmente,
    disparejamente, desigualmente,
    accidentadamente,
    desniveladamente
unfavourable: desfavorable
unfinished: inacabado
unfolded: desplegado
unfolding: desplegando

unharness: desenjaezar, desguarnezca
unheard: inaudito
unintelligible: ininteligible, incomprensible
unites: reúne, une
uniting: reuniendo, uniendo
unlace: desenlace, desenlazar
unlacing: desenlazar
unnatural: innatural, antinatural
unpicking: descoser
unpleasantly: desagradablemente, ingratamente, molestamente
unproductive: improductivo
unravelled: desenredado, descifrado, desenlazado, desenmarañado, deshilachado, deshilado
unrolled: devanado
unrolling: devanando
unsaddled: desazonado, desensillado
unsatisfied: insatisfecho
unseen: no visto
untied: desatado
untimely: inoportuno, intempestivo
unto: hacia
untoward: indócil
unwell: enfermo
uplifted: inspiró
uprights: vertical
ups: ARRIBA, altos
upturned: levantado, volcador
utensils: los utensilios, utensilios
uttering: Pronunciar
vacation: vacaciones, vacación
vaccination: vacuna, vacunación
vagabondage: bordoneria, vagabundeo, vagabundaje
vain: vano, hueco, vanidoso
valerian: valeriana
valiant: bravo, valiente
valise: maleta, maleta de mano
vanilla: vainilla, la vainilla
vanish: desaparecer, desaparezca, desaparezcan, desapareces, desaparecen, desaparecemos, desaparecéis, desapareced, desaparece, desaparezco
vanity: vanidad
vanquished: vencido, derrotado, rendido, logrado
vapour: vapor, vaho
vapourish: vaporoso
varnish: barniz, barnizado, barnizar, charol
varnished: barnizado
vastness: vastedad, inmensidad
vault: bóveda, sótano, cámara acorazada, caja fuerte
veal: ternera, carne de ternera, la ternera
vehement: vehemente
venal: corruptible, venal

veneer: chapa
venerable: venerado
veneration: veneración
venetian: veneciano
vengeance: venganza
venison: venado
ventured: Aventurado
venturing: Aventurar
verbena: verbena
verbose: verboso
verdure: verdura
veritable: verdadero
vermilion: bermellón
versed: versado
vertiginous: vertiginoso
vertigo: vértigo
verve: brío
vespers: vísperas
vest: chaleco, el chaleco, camiseta
vesta: cerilla
vestibule: vestíbulo
vestige: vestigio
vestments: vestiduras
vestry: sacristía
vesuvius: Vesubio
vex: vejar
vexation: vejación, zaherimiento, molestia, sinsabor, disgusto, atufamiento, animosidad, mal trato
vexed: enfadado
viands: vituallas
viaticum: viático
vibrate: vibrar, vibre, vibrad, vibro, vibren, vibras, vibran, vibráis, vibra, vibramos
vibrating: vibrando
vibrations: vibraciones, vibración
vine: parra, viña, vid
vinegar: vinagre, el vinagre
violet: violeta, morado
violets: huevas de mar
vipers: víboras
virile: viril
virtuous: virtuoso
viscount: vizconde
viscous: viscoso
visor: visera
vitriol: vitriolo
vocation: vocación
volubility: volubilidad
voluptuous: voluptuoso
voluptuousness: voluptuosidad
vomit: vomitar, vómito
vomiting: vomitar
vomitings: vómitos
vow: voto
vows: promesas solemnes
voyaged: navegado, viajado
vulgar: chabacano, cursi, grosero, cutre, corriente, vulgo, vulgar, ramplón, ordinario, ordinaria, común

vulgarly: vulgarmente
wadded: apretado, guata de relleno
waddling: zanqueamiento, Anadear
wafer: oblea, galleta, oblea de silicio, barquillo, el barquillo, hostia
wafers: los barquillos, galletas
wag: menear, meneo, mover
wainscot: panel, zócalo
waistcoat: chaleco, el chaleco
waistcoats: poniente
wallowed: se encenagado
wall-paper: papel pintado
waltz: vals
waning: menguando
warbling: Trinando
warlike: belicoso
warmed: entibiado
warranted: justificado, garantizado
washstand: lavabo, lavamanos
water-bottle: jarra
watercress: berro
watered: regado, inflado
waterfall: cascada, la cascada, la catarata
watering: riego
waterside: ribera
water-side: ribera
wavy: ondulado
waxed: encerado, parafinado
waxen: ceroso
weakens: debilita
weariness: cansancio, aburrimiento, fatiga
wearisome: fatigoso
weasel: comadreja
wedded: se casado
weep: llorar, llore, lloren, llora, lloro, lloras, lloran, lloramos, lloráis, llorad
weeps: llora
we'll: Haremos
well-bred: cortés, bien educado
well-dressed: acicalado, bien entrazado, bien vestido
well-rounded: polifacético, rotundo
well-to-do: acomodado
wept: Llorado
whalebone: ballena
whatnot: estante, cualquier cosa
wheedling: engatusando
wheeled: de ruedas, rodado
wheeling: rodar, transporte, ruedas, ruedo, rueden, ruede, rueda, rodamos, rodáis, rodad, ruedan
whence: de dónde
wherein: en qué
whetted: Afilado
whiffs: huele
whim: capricho, antojo
whims: caprichos
whimsical: caprichoso, antojadizo
whining: gimoteando

whipping: paliza, vapuleo, miembro de una Cámara, latigazo, látigo, fustigar, fustigación, fusta, flagelación, dar una paliza a, dar latigazos a
whips: zurriagar
whirl: giro rápido, torbellino, dar vueltas
whirling: turbulencia
whirlwind: torbellino
whiskers: patillas, bigotes
whispering: chismes, chismografía, con eco, cuchicheo, de difamación, rumores, susurro, de rumores
whistled: Silbado
whistling: silbido
whiten: blanquear, blanqueo, blanqueáis, blanqueen, blanquee, blanqueas, blanqueamos, blanquead, blanquea, blanquean
whitened: blanqueado
whiteness: albura
whither: adónde, adonde
whitish: blanquecino
whitsuntide: Pentecostés, Pascua de Pentecostés
wholesome: sano
wick: mecha
wicker: mimbre
widen: ensanchar, ensanche, ensanchen, ensanchas, ensanchan, ensancho, ensanchamos, ensancháis, ensanchad, ensancha, ensancharse
widowhood: viudez
wig: peluca
wildness: locura, furia, turbulencia, rusticidad, páramo, lo salvaje, lo estrafalario, lo disparatado, lo difícil, lo alborotado, lo fantástico
wilfulness: intención, testarudez, voluntariedad
willed: Hizo
willow: sauce
windings: bobinado
windmill: molino de viento
wisp: agudeza, fragmento, ingenio, jirón, manojito, rastro
withdrawing: retirando
withered: marchito, marchitado
witnessing: presenciar
woe: ay, penas
woes: dolencia
wonderingly: preguntar
wonderment: maravilla, admiración
wondrous: maravilloso
wonted: acostumbrado
woof: trama
wools: lana
workhouse: asilo de pobres
workman: obrero, trabajador
work-table: mesa de trabajo
worldly: mundano

worm-eaten: picado por los gusanos, carcomido, apolillado
wrapper: envoltorio, envoltura
wrapping: envoltura, envoltorio
wreath: guirnalda, corona
wretch: desgraciado
wring: arrancar, retorcer, arrancáis, arrancas, arranquen, arranco, arrancan, arrancamos, arranca, arrancad, arranque
wringing: arrancando, retorciendo
wrinkled: arrugado
wrinkles: arugas
writhe: retorcerse
writhing: retorcer, retorcimiento, retorciendo
yawn: bostezo, bostezar, el bostezo
yawned: Bostezó
yawning: bostezante, bostezando
year's: año
yell: grito, gritar, aullar, chillar
yellowed: amarillo
yelping: gañir, gañido, gañendo, gritar
yielding: cediendo, rindiendo, rentando
yoked: Unió
yonder: allí, ahí, aquel
yore: antaño, de antaño, hace tiempo, tiempos pasados
zeal: celo, ahínco

959319

Made in the USA